W9-CAA-025

The Memory System of the Brain

The Memory System of the Brain

BY

J. Z. Young

UNIVERSITY OF CALIFORNIA PRESS
BERKELEY AND LOS ANGELES
1966

University of California Press
Berkeley and Los Angeles
California

Library of Congress Catalog Card Number: 66-12649

Printed in the United States of America

Preface

These Hitchcock Lectures, delivered at the University of California, Berkeley, California, in November, 1964, are now published approximately in the form in which they were given. This has the disadvantage that the somewhat personal style may seem out of place in print, but perhaps there are compensating advantages. The view of nervous activities presented here is a personal one. It has been arrived at with the assistance of the work of many colleagues, but they do not by any means always agree with my conclusions. To all of them I should like to express my warmest thanks. Brian Boycott devised and carried out many of the early experiments with the octopus. Mrs. Marion Nixon helped with the more recent ones and Vernon Barber and George Savage assisted in the preparation of this book. Mrs. Jane Astafiev prepared many of the illustrations. Mr. G. Sommerhoff helped at many points with criticism of my ideas, as have others with whom I have been lucky enough to work, including N. S. Sutherland, E. G. Gray, W. R. A. Muntz, N. J. Mackintosh, J. Mackintosh, M. J. Wells and J. Wells. I am most grateful to all of them.

It is a pleasure also to thank the various individuals and organisations who have given their co-operation.

First, Dr. P. Dohrn and the staff of the Zoological Station at Naples, without whom the work on the octopus could not have been done. Mr. A. Packard has been especially helpful in many ways. Mr. J. Armstrong supervised much of the work in London on the structure of the brain, and Miss P. Stephens carried out the extensive histological preparations. The work has been aided financially by the Nuffield Foundation, and more recently by the European Office of the United States Office of Aerospace Research, to whom we are most grateful.

The structures in the octopus brain and the phenomena of learning shown by the animal have stimulated me to develop a system of ideas about cerebral coding and memory, which are incorporated in the recent book, *A Model of the Brain*. The present work is in the main a summary of this, but such systems develop with each reformulation. There is much here that has not been published elsewhere, especially on the touch learning system and the origin of memory.

Finally, it is a great pleasure to thank the University of California and all those in Berkeley and Los Angeles who welcomed me for the delivery of the lectures. Professor W. J. Asling, Professor T. H. Bullock, and many others combined to give me some idea of the greatness of the University of California.

J. Z. YOUNG, M.A., D.SC., F.R.S.

Department of Anatomy
University College, London
February, 1965

Contents

CHAPTER ONE

The Brain as the Computer of a Homeostat

Explanation in Biology

Probably we should all agree that the question "How do brains work?" is important and that it would be a good thing to know the answer, but would there be agreement on the form the answer might take? The brain is an exceedingly complicated system and our language and powers of understanding are but weak. In what sense therefore can we expect to be able to say, "I understand the brain"?

In the last analysis, the most severe criterion by which we judge our understanding of a system is our ability to take it to pieces and then put it together again, or make one like it. This might seem to be an absurdly ambitious criterion to apply to the brain, though it can be argued that in some respects we are already moving toward this end. We are beginning to come within sight of the power to make simple living things. It will be a long step from that to making a complex brain, but who is to say that this goal will not be achieved? In the meantime perhaps we should be more humble. We are so far from a complete understanding of the brain that we must not yet expect to be able to see a complete picture, but must be content for the present with what I shall call a model of the brain. We shall try to build this model from various sources. The present chapter presents various facts about the basic components of the nervous system. These are necessary before we can attack the much more interesting and difficult question of how to think about the way in which these components are assembled to make a whole brain.

For that synthesis, when we come to it, we may rely mainly on two sources. First, the facts of the organisation of the relatively simple brain and memory system of the octopus provide us with a model with which to approach the complex human brain. Second, to organise this information we shall explore how far it is possible to use the terminology of computer science. Computers are machines that perform some of the actions of brains. Apart from their great practical value they equip us with a language with which we can describe and discuss brains.

Throughout human history there have been repeated cycles of discovery. A substitute is invented to assist an activity previously performed only by human beings or animals, for example engines that assist the labour of man's hands. The basic sciences evolve alongside the development of such artifacts, studying the principles of operation of the tools and providing a language by which better machines can be produced. These are, in turn, applied to produce further new knowledge. To make a machine work properly it is necessary to understand its principles thoroughly. Every engineer knows this and every biologist should learn it from him. With the aid of the more exact language, biology is much better able than before to "explain" the living process for which the substitute was invented. This cycle has been repeated over and over again. For example, "energy," a concept originally applied only to living things, has been greatly refined and can now be used to give a vastly better understanding of biology.

Thus one group of meanings given to the word "explanation" as applied to living activities is certainly connected with the capacity to devise machines that assist in these activities. One of the most exciting advances of our age is the development of machines that help with some functions previously performed only by brains. But computers and automatic control systems do more than this. They actually imitate some of the features of living things as a whole. To some extent they are self-maintaining systems or homeostats, the name invented by W. B. Cannon of Harvard, the Hitchcock Lecturer in 1941 (Cannon, 1932). No man-made system is yet able to maintain itself over a prolonged period, nevertheless, from the humble gas oven or icebox to the guided missile or automatic factory, we now have many examples of machines in which *control* is exercised. These have become possible because of the development in this century, especially over the last twenty years, of a scientific study of the function that we call "control," previously a property attributed only to living systems. In particular there has been a great advance in understanding the principles of control through feedback systems, giving rise to what have been called directive correlations, for example servomechanisms (Sommerhoff, 1950). The language and the mathematics developed for the study of artifacts are available to biologists in their investigations of the organs that exercise control in the living body, especially the deoxyribosenucleotides of the nuclei, and the networks of nerve-cell fibres in the brain.

I propose to try to show to what extent we may be said to understand the brain in the terms that are used by engineers in their studies of communication, of computation, and of control. But my point of view throughout is that of a biologist, indicating the connections with these other methods of description rather than pursuing them in detail. I shall be using examples from machines to form a model that may help in understanding the brain.

To simplify, I shall, for the most part, deal not with the human brain but with that of the octopus, which is complicated enough to be interesting but not too complicated for us to begin to understand it. Moreover, the very unfamiliarity of the animal, in its behaviour and in the parts of its brain, forces us to think hard about such matters as motivation and memory. I shall also use the word "model" in yet another sense, saying that the brain contains a model of the animal's world, that indeed each species of animal or plant in a sense "models" or represents the world around it. Of course each species has receptors that detect changes only in a limited number of features that are relevant to its life. It can be said to represent the outside world only in respect of these features.

The Maintenance of Homeostasis by Selection of Responses

One of the first questions to ask if we are to understand any machine is "What is it for?" As regards the brain, the answer may be phrased as follows. Brains are the computers of homeostats and the essence of homeostats is that they maintain a steady state. Put in another way, the most important fact about living things is that they remain alive. Curiously enough, this is not always the central theme in discussions of living processes, though perhaps it should be. It may immediately be objected that a principal characteristic of organisms is that they die, and although the point is irrelevant we must deal with it. Living things maintain an astonishing stability. The mammals are older than the Rocky Mountains. But this survival is made possible only by a special device, which in a sense evades the problem. Permanent self-maintenance seems to be a logical impossibility. Every sort of machine has defects and these can be repaired only by other special repair machines and so on ad infinitum. "What repairs the repairer that repairs the repairer . . . ?" Living things escape this regress by the subtle means that we ordinarily call reproduction. They do not attempt indefinite repair. At intervals they discard the whole machine, *keeping only the instructions by means of which it is rebuilt.* These instructions are then combined (in sexual organisms) with the set that built a slightly different machine, and with the combined instructions a new model that is slightly different from either of the old ones is produced.

Thus living systems do not avoid the paradox. They are not truly self-maintaining systems; they maintain an approximately constant organisation only by repeatedly changing into something slightly different. This change is, of course, evolution, which thus appears as the long-term aspect of homeostasis. This shows the significance of the life cycle of birth, growth, and death. The entity that is preserved is not the individual but something greater, which goes on when each individual dies. The processes of reproduction and of evolution are direct continuations of the processes of control of bodily functions that we ordinarily deal with as the physiology of homeostasis.

All control consists in selection of the right response from a repertoire of possible actions of the system. Organisms remain alive by selecting at each moment of time the appropriate response. In the processes that we ordinarily call "physiological" we see how the animal selects the right values, say of its heart rate, to suit the circumstances. In evolution there is similarly selection of the right instructions to allow survival. The changes of evolution are in effect long-term physiological adjustments, long-term homeostasis.

The continuance of life for short term or long is thus dependent on selection of the response that is appropriate to whatever circumstances occur. We may define "information," at least for our present purposes, as the feature of any change in the communication channels of a homeostat that allows selection of an appropriate response. For adequate selection the basic instructions (or construction) of the homeostat must obviously correspond to the events that are likely to occur in the environment. It may be said to *represent* the environment, in the literal sense that it re-presents to it the actions that are needed for survival.

The wide capacity to perform efficient actions is one of the most striking characteristics of living things. Even the simple system of bacteria has a range of adaptability that seems almost miraculous. These capacities are the end product of a storage of information about the environment that has been going on for a long time, perhaps 3,000 million years. We are beginning to be able to speculate about how the capacity to form large sets of possible actions arose. It may well be connected with the power of the carbon atom to form series of homologous compounds. However this may be, the capacity to remain alive clearly depends upon the presence of a variety of possible responses and their suitability for the environment.

The Nervous System as Selector of Responses

This rapid examination of some principles of biology has, I hope, brought us nearer to a view of some of the aspects of homeostats that are relevant to an understanding of the brain. The brain, as the computer, plays a key part in selecting the responses that are made by the animal. Recognition of this factor of choice between alternatives is the central feature that makes it possible for us to understand the function of the brain.

The body has a large set of effectors by which to act upon the environment in order to ensure survival. For example, all the muscles are arranged in pairs, flexors and extensors, across the joints. By enumeration of the pairs it should be possible to estimate the number of actions that might be undertaken, bearing in mind that not all combinations are equally probable. In this way an exact and quantitative study of behaviour might be attempted. It is essential to appreciate the implications of the fact that actions are produced by repeated selection between pairs of alternatives. The information that implements this selection is embodied in the brain in a form not entirely different from that of a digital computer, which also deals in selection between alternatives. But at this stage we must beware of oversimplification. The choices between alternatives are not usually made in a strictly logical or even sequential manner. The processes in the organism reflect the changes in the environment and in turn influence these. The question, therefore, whether the brain functions more like a digital machine or an analogue machine is not easily answered.

Nerve Fibres as Communication Channels

Certainly, the nerve impulses, the signals conducted in peripheral nerves, are of an all-or-nothing digital nature. The researches of many investigators from Keith Lucas and Adrian to Gasser, Joseph Erlanger (also a former Hitchcock Professor), and a host of others throughout the world have established that the operation of the appropriate effector organ, say a muscle or gland, depends upon passage along the correct channel of trains of signals, the nerve impulses, which are all essentially alike. The frequency in the channel determines the degree of action, but usually carries no other information. The code is not one with several items in each channel, like a Morse code. Codification consists in selecting the right ones among a large number of channels, and the sensory or receptor channels function similarly.

These are very crude statements and much more could be written on the subject, but it is clear that in a multichannel system the number of channels is one of the most important variables and some figures may be useful. The numbers of fibres leading to the effector organs are moderate. Eccles and Sherrington found 233 to the soleus muscle of the cat. There are about 120,000 somatic motor fibres all together in a cat. They are more numerous in the nerves that control delicate movements, for instance of the eyes, than in those that regulate powerful actions of the limbs. An octopus has about 110,000 motor fibres leaving its brain (excluding those to the blood vessels and chromatophores).

The receptor channels are more numerous. In man there are unknown numbers of peripheral receptors (more than 100×10^6 in each eye) and about 3×10^6 afferent channels on each side leading to the brain. One million of them come from the eye, but only 30,000 from the ear. The octopus has a total of 8×10^6 peripheral receptors (other than in the eyes), but they transmit to the brain by only some 40,000 channels. Each eye of the octopus has 20×10^6 receptors and the same number of channels to the optic lobe.

If we had more facts about the numbers and sizes of cells and fibres we might understand the nervous system better. The numbers are often large, sometimes very large. But this is not simply a matter of ensuring redundancy, for some parts operate with far fewer channels. Each of the stellar nerves of the mantle of a squid has only one enormous fibre (up to a millimetre in diameter) though there are other smaller fibres with it.

Speed of conduction is one of the variables of the fibres; the larger fibres conduct faster. Diameter increase alone is a very inefficient way of obtaining fast conduction, since the velocity increases only with the square root of diameter, as theory predicts.[1] Fast conduction in the channels of the homeostat is obviously an advantage in a fast-moving world, and special means of obtaining it are found in the interrupted myelin sheaths that allow a saltatory conduction in vertebrates and probably in prawns and shrimps. Only these special devices for increasing velocity make it possible for a fast moving animal to have numerous channels. The nerves of the human arm contain hundreds of thousands of fibres, which would obviously be impossible if each had to be half a millimetre in diameter.

The small fibres are as interesting as the large. Why are there so many of them? Sometimes it must be a matter of economy. Each of the 20,000,000 fibres in the optic nerves of the octopus is about 1μ in diam-

---

[1] We have recently confirmed this by a study of conduction velocities in fibres of the octopus, cuttlefish, and squid. Fibres of similar diameters in the three species conduct at similar rates and dimensional factors seem to preponderate. The smallest fibres studied were about 2μ and conducted at <1 m/sec; the largest 500μ, at 23 m/sec. The best estimate over the whole range is that the velocity follows $D^{0.57}$ (Burrows *et al.*, 1965).

eter. If they were only ten times larger they would occupy an area greater than that of the entire surface of the animal. But economy can hardly be the only factor, for often there are numerous small fibres, although the functions to be performed seem to require little resolution. Thus, although the whole musculature of the head and eyes of an octopus is controlled by a mere 3,000 fibres, the nerves that control the salivary glands contain nearly a million fibres. This large number surely cannot mean an equally large power of differential response by the gland cells.

Nerve Cells and Synapses as Computers

The great difference between the nervous system and digital machines is in the large number of points at which computation is made. As von Neumann (1958), among others, has pointed out, the artificial computer makes its decisions in only a few organs and makes them very fast and in a highly regulated and logical order. The nervous system has many computing organs, for each nerve cell acts as such, and they are relatively slow and unreliable.

Computers work with localised memory stores, each point in which carries a single item of information, whose significance is determined by the fact that it has a precise "address." It is still an open question whether nervous systems contain any such highly addressed memory system. There must, in man at least, be a record of individual occurrences, and means for consulting that record. Yet much evidence shows that the neural memory system is distributed rather than localised.

There are dangers in using the language invented for computers, with their localised memories, for nervous systems, which are certainly rather different. Some scientists think that it would be wiser to avoid the computer language in neurology. Here we shall accept the risk of inappropriateness for the sake of the increased possibility of communication and indeed for the actual stimulus to investigation that the computer analogy provides. But the danger remains, and we should be continually aware that the analogy between brains and computers may be misleading.

And yet, the difference may not be so great as it might seem. It is true that the particular qualities of the digital computer are its speed and its generality. It can do anything if it is properly programmed to do it, whereas the nervous system is not a general computer; it can do only certain things, but it can take the data about these things direct from the environment. It is a special-purpose computer carrying its programme in the coded instructions of its DNA and the constructions to which they give rise. Yet, in spite of these differences, the operations that it controls are fundamentally those of selection from a code of possible alternative actions.

The numbers of nerve cells give us some measure of computing power. There are $1-2 \times 10^{10}$ of them in man and $1-2 \times 10^{8}$ in an octopus brain, but there are also 3×10^{8} in the octopus' arms. This animal really does "think with its hands." We say that the nerve cells act as computers because the nerve impulses must be initiated afresh in them. Each nerve fibre conducts in an all-or-nothing manner, probably without decrement to its very ends. But where these ends come into contact with the receptive dendrites of the next cell in the chain the individual impulses do *not* invariably pass on. Only if impulses arrive suitably distributed in time along one fibre or distributed in space over the endings on the dendrites does the cell emit a signal (or change its rate of signalling). The cell and the points at which it receives synaptic junctions from other fibres thus serve to add the effects of these presynaptic fibres. There is also subtraction, since some of them inhibit the setting up of impulses by the postsynaptic cell.

A great deal is known about the mode of operation of the synaptic junctions, where one nerve cell stimulates another, which, collectively, are thus the computers at which decisions are made whether a nerve cell shall send out a signal. Yet our knowledge has been limited by the difficulty of obtaining a view of the whole set of synapses on a cell with the microscope, or a record of their individual actions by microelectrodes. The terminal buttons that constitute the synapse were not even known for certain to exist throughout the cerebral cortex until nine years ago, when we found that they can be revealed by a method that stains their mitochondria (Wyckoff and Young, 1956). They do not show up readily with the classical silver methods that reveal these "boutons" in the spinal cord and elsewhere. The failure of cortical boutons to stain is probably due to the fact that they do not contain neurofibrils (though these may appear during degeneration). The density of boutons on motor cells of the spinal cord reaches 20 per $100\mu^2$; according to estimates of the area of these cells, there are some 30,000 boutons per cell (Wyckoff and Young, 1956; Aitken and Bridger, 1961). In the cerebral cortex they are much smaller than the boutons on spinal cord cells, and there may be 10,000 of them on a large pyramidal cell, but the surface areas of these are not known accurately, and the number of boutons per cell may be much greater.

Electron microscopy has told us a great deal about the detailed structure of synapses, including those of the cerebral cortex. They always show vesicles on the presynaptic side and differentiations of various sorts in the region of contact (Gray, 1964). Unfortunately we do not understand the molecular biology of these thickenings and therefore cannot assess their significance. We do not know whether the "truly synaptic" or transmitting portions of the boutons are the thickenings where vesicles are aggregated. Further, we have little secure evidence about the differences between boutons that are excitatory and those that are inhibitory. Some of the latter may be placed in positions where they can block the arrival of impulses along the presynaptic fibres. Endings that could do this have been seen by electron microscopy in the retina, spinal cord, and some centres in *Octopus* (Kidd, 1962; Gray, 1962).

The electron microscope has shown us much detail of synapses, but so far we cannot fully interpret it. It has not been possible to add much to our quantitative knowledge of synapses by electron microscopy. We do not know how much of the surface of cells and dendrites is covered by the transmitter regions. The space between the presynaptic and the postsynaptic membranes is still a controversial subject, and there are few data about the proportions of surface that are covered by the glia (the supporting and filling tissue of the nervous system; Kuffler and Potter, 1964). Even worse, for most parts of the system we have no idea whether one incoming fibre sends boutons to one or to many cells, nor whether all the boutons from one presynaptic source are grouped together or whether they are mixed with boutons from other fibres.

I mention these enormous gaps in knowledge not out of pessimism but in the hope of stimulating the development of methods that will enable us to answer these quantitative anatomical questions. We must know the answers if we are to understand the nervous system, yet most investigators prefer to follow the current vogue of placing electrodes within cell bodies that can be entered, or identifying the chemical molecules that are extractable from centrifugates. I do not wish to decry neurological studies of these or any other sorts, but to urge that perhaps *they should be guided more by what logic tells us we need to know, and less by the techniques found suitable in other disciplines.* The nervous system is a multichannel network. The first requirement for understanding it is to know its connectivity. Those who work out the connections have been the major pioneers of neurology. This appears very clearly from the work of C. S. Sherrington and Ramon y Cajal, who, together with many others, have established the model of the brain that we still use. Both men based their work on concepts of connectivity and Sherrington, the physiological experimenter par excellence, made his own anatomical and histological enquiries.

The study of cerebral connectivity is still in its infancy and demands the greatest powers that science can produce. To choose four fields as examples: (1) The development of machine methods for counting and measuring cells and fibres is obviously essential to supply the data relevant to a multichannel system. (2) The staining methods of Golgi and Cajal provide marvellously informative details of connectivity but we have no idea of the underlying physical and chemical principles of the stains. (3) The electron microscope provides resolution amply sufficient to see large molecules, but we have minimal information about what has been done to them by fixation. (4) We cannot even reconstruct whole neurons from electron micrographs.

The Organisation of the Nervous System

This survey of some aspects of knowledge about the nervous system may serve to introduce the means that we hope to use in building a model of the brain, which is perhaps the farthest we can go toward understanding it. We must know the nature of its units—neurons, nerve fibres, axons, dendrites, synapses—and have examples of how they function. Then we must know a good deal about the connectivity and especially the principles upon which it is based.

The sources of information with which the nervous system operates may be divided into three classes. First, there are receptors for signalling information from the outside world. Second, there are receptors that detect the departures from required levels of operation of the various systems within the body and send signals that indicate what is needed for self-maintenance. These two sorts of signals provide the information on which selection of appropriate responses is based. Third, the homeostat needs information about the results of its actions—whether these have been satisfactory for self-maintenance or destructive to the organism. Receptors that signal "pain" or "taste" are typical examples. In simpler nervous systems these receptors operate reflex actions, such as feeding or withdrawal, and in such systems the instructions as to which action is to be taken depend upon the inherited connectivity. But in higher nervous systems the instructions are supplemented by information stored in the memory about the results of previous actions of the animal. The signals of results thus acquire the further function of teaching the memory store.

The Memory of the Nervous System

At the present time we are especially interested in the nature of the neural memory, and it is important to try to see its place in the whole system. We shall not understand it by thinking of its chemistry alone, any more than we should learn how information is stored in a book by studying the chemistry of ink. We shall advance in our study of memory only when we recognise that the brain is the computer of a homeostat and that the memory provides part of the information by which the homeostat selects correct responses.

We must be careful about the use of the word "memory." It will here be limited, as by an engineer, to the unit within which a record is stored. The record itself will be called a representation within the memory. An early task is to try to find the code in which the record is stored. We must, as it were, learn the language that is used in the writing in the brain. Recently there have been very great advances in understanding the hereditary material since biochemists realised that they must search for codes. They looked for them and found them in the DNA. Moreover, some workers have found it desirable to pursue the analogy to great lengths, looking for words and punctuation of the genetic language, systems for reading-in to the record and reading-out from it and even for the turning of pages.

Curiously, there has been relatively little of the equivalent search in the study of memory in the brain. Many biologists still find such analogies distasteful, even whimsical. Yet there is nothing strange in using the terminology of artificial aids to communication and memory, such as writing, as a means for speaking about the brain. This process of making artifacts and then borrowing their terminology back into biology has been a recurring process through the ages. Physiologists have no hesitation in using the concepts of volts and amperes in talking about nerve impulses, yet some of them are reluctant to speak of the impulses as "signals in a code." There is much to be done to clear up misunderstanding about the status of analogies and other forms of words in science. The historian and the logician can both help us here.

In the investigation of memory in the brain a logical experimental program with a thoughtful strategy is especially necessary because the concepts of "language" and "representation" are not familiar to all scientists. We shall not find the memory change by probing with microelectrodes or by whirling bits of brain in centrifuges unless we have such a strategy.

We may begin with the proposition that each animal's memory, if it is to assist in selecting adequate responses, must contain some "representation" of the world in which it lives. This is a much stronger term than to say that the brain contains an engram, for we can use the analogy of "representation," for example by writing, to guide us as to what sort of entity to look for in the brain. Books are written with letters selected from a pre-established alphabet. The next chapter describes the search that we have made for the fount, as it were, from which letters are selected to print the writing in the brain of the octopus. Some progress has been made toward recognising them, in the forms of the dendritic trees of certain cells. If this is right, we can go farther and suggest how they are selected to make the representation or model, as we may call it, in the brain. By such a procedure we have been led to look in the appropriate places for the changes that constitute learning and have found there certain small cells and certain types of synapse.

We have not found the nature of learning, but have produced a rather coherent if somewhat childish picture of the whole process. This picture may seem so unsophisticated as to be laughable, but the truth is often simple, at least in its general outlines. It is surprising how many living processes have been found to have quite detailed similarity to simple mechanical processes. Life does involve many complications, but it is the general outlines that we need here. Given these, there will be many brains willing and able to fill in the complicated details.

We are sadly lacking in important data about the scheme of operation that will be suggested for the octopus brain, especially from microelectrodes and chemical procedures. The suggestions made here will almost certainly prove to be wrong in many respects, but I doubt whether we can be wholly wrong in our interpretation of how the various lobes of the octopus brain are used to write a record in the memory. As we have gradually traced the connectivity within this brain, it has revealed, with a curious inevitability, the basis of its logic, and perhaps the logic of all nervous systems (though they may not be all alike). The various lobes of the octopus brain are visible and distinct entities, arranged in a regular manner, and with a discernible order. They have differing types of neurons, which are readily stainable. The characteristics of the neurons and the fibre patterns of each lobe can, in some degree, be related to their places in the logical system. Moreover, the whole set of four lobes is repeated twice over. One set is associated with the visual memory; the other, with only minor differences, with the tactile memory. The approximate seats of the two actual records have been found and each can be removed separately without influencing the other.

The "centres" that we are talking about are undoubtedly really there and are distinct, although in life they may co-operate to some extent in ways that have not yet been revealed. The analysis can hardly be wholly wrong even if still some way from being right.

We may be wrong in holding that the representations are made by selection from an alphabet. It would be interesting to consider whether all representations are made with the use of pre-arranged codes. I should be inclined to say that they are. Like any agent in the process of information transfer, the representational nature of a physical event is defined by the fact that when this event occurs in the communication channels of an appropriate homeostat it elicits the selection of responses that are "correct" for homeostasis. This presupposes the existence of the type of pre-arranged correspondence that constitutes the definition of a code.

A further possibility is that we cannot usefully speak of the brain as containing a representation of the environment at all. Many who have been concerned with the problem of the adaptiveness of living activities have tried to deal with them without such language as I am using (Sommerhoff, 1950). It can even be argued that the brain does not have what can properly be called a memory in the computer sense, because it learns by changing its network and does not carry records of individual events. This objection surely falls because, in man at least, single particular events *can* be recalled and there must thus be a record of them. If it seems not to be so in other animals, this may be the result of our method of testing. Perhaps running animals in mazes is not the best way of finding out about the series of selections by which records are written in their brains. Of course it does not follow that the record of a "single event" is localised only at one place. In a multichannel system the record may be carried by changes at many points. Removal of some of them by injury or surgery may weaken the reliability with which the engram can control behaviour.

Whether the approach suggested here is invalidated by these or other criticisms will be shown by whether it leads toward the discovery of the nature of neural memory. I feel that it has led me further toward this end than did consideration of "adaptation" alone, although I have always been strongly interested in adaptation. But that concept is without much power until it is reinforced by consideration of sets of possibilities among which selection can be made.

The Octopus as an Experimental Animal

If we are to break the code of the brain it will be desirable to find a system that answers readily when we ask it such questions as whether object A is more similar to object B or to object C (e.g., Is a triangle more like a square or a circle?). From the responses of an animal that answers well we can discover what types of discrimination can be made and hence perhaps by what mechanism classification and discrimination are carried out. *Octopus vulgaris* is a very valuable subject in these respects. Much has been found out about the animal's visual powers by Boycott, Sutherland, Muntz, Mackintosh, Maldonado, and others. Its powers of discrimination by touch and chemical sense have been tested by Mr. and Mrs. Wells. The animal lives among the rocks, often hidden in a crevice, and comes out to attack objects moving in its visual field. The attack on an unfamiliar object is slow and cautious. If the object yields food, later attacks are much faster. If the object provides a painful result, the octopus rapidly learns not to attack it. Indeed, it retreats from it into the home, giving a definite response calculated to startle the attacker, which has been called the dymantic response (Boycott and Young, 1950).

This is an excellent situation for experimental purposes. The octopus sits in its home ready to come out, so far as we can tell, at any hour of day or night to attack a food object. We are not certain about its normal food in the sea and whether it has an inborn tendency to attack crabs, a common food object. It often eats mussels and other lamellibranchs, probably selecting them mainly by touch. *Octopus vulgaris* at Naples becomes pelagic for a while after hatching, and the question of its inherited capacities is therefore complicated. *Octopus briareus* of the Caribbean coasts remains on the bottom after hatching and should be studied from this point of view (Messenger, 1963). The octopus will eat a variety of foods, including pieces of dead fish. It can be trained to attack figures cut out of plastic and to discriminate between several pairs of figures. We give a subject up to sixteen positive and sixteen negative trials a day, usually in two sessions of sixteen trials each. To maintain this frequency of attack, an animal weighing 300 g must be given less than 0.5 g of fish per positive trial. But the octopus is a prodigious eater. One fed ad libitum went from 63 g to 220 g in 29 days. The intake of crab and fish meat was 284 g, a utilisation of 55 per cent for growth (Nixon, 1966). Octopuses are abundant, easy to catch, and easy to keep, except that they readily climb out of the tank.

The animal learns very rapidly. Responses may begin to be correct within a first session of sixteen trials and are sometimes quite good after the second session. Retention is excellent for the time it has been tested, up to five weeks. Learning can be reversed, if necessary repeatedly. In fact the animal answers well to the questions we wish to ask.

The octopus provides suitable material for experiments on both visual and tactile memory. The sites of the two distinct memory stores have been localised. Each is accompanied by a set of four auxiliary lobes, which are composed of neurons with differences that are characteristic of their functions in the system.

Summary

The experimental study of the memory will advance more rapidly if we recognize the part it plays in preserving the homeostasis or self-maintenance of the organism of which it is a part. The memory does this by providing evidence, more up to date than that of the hereditary memory, concerning the most likely result that will follow from the adoption of any one of a repertoire of actions in a given situation. To provide this evidence the memory must contain a representation of events that have occurred in the outside world and must also receive signals, such as those of pleasure and pain, that indicate the results of its actions. To make its representations the brain must have access to a pre-established code or alphabet, constituting, as it were, a fount of type from which by selection the appropriate record is printed. To understand how the record is written we must first search for the code set and then for the method of selection from it by the effects of pleasure and pain signals.

To obtain an understanding of the alphabet we must investigate the animal's capacity to learn to discriminate between formed stimuli. The octopus is a suitable animal for such experiments. It can learn to discriminate forms by sight or by touch. The memory stores for the two types of receptor are in separate parts of the brain. Each store is accompanied by four auxiliary lobes.

CHAPTER TWO

Breaking the Code of the Brain

The Visual Code of the Octopus

The position we have arrived at is that brains are special-purpose computers designed to operate each in its own environment. If this is correct we should expect to find that each type has receptors and computing equipment appropriate only to its needs. This clue is so commonplace that we tend not to recognise its value, especially for studies of the brain. During the processes of evolution a large range of variants of brain design has appeared, constituting, as it were, a series of experiments whose results we can study and make use of in our attempts to understand the brain.

This type of approach is particularly helpful if we are looking for the language or alphabet of the brain. One of the classical procedures of cryptographers is to guess what the signals may be about, and thus to "break the code." Indeed, concealment of the subject matter is the intractable problem in military encoding. The matters that are likely to be under discussion by soldiers, sailors, or airmen can be guessed rather easily, however they may try to disguise them. Similarly it is not very difficult, by simple observation of the needs and actions of animals, to make hypotheses in regard to the features of the world that are of greatest interest to them. This step must be taken if we are to use studies with microscope and microelectrode to break the code of the brain.

Some progress has been made in analysis of the attributes of visual situations that can be distinguished by the octopus. Unfortunately, these studies are not based upon the behaviour of the animals in the sea, for of this almost nothing is known. In laboratory experiments Sutherland (1957) found that the animals are able to distinguish vertical from horizontal rectangles but not between oblique rectangles set at right angles. He suggested that their system of shape recognition depends at least in part on estimating the extent of outline in vertical and horizontal directions and taking a ratio between them. The animals discriminate poorly between figures that do not differ in vertical and horizontal extent, (e.g., square and circle). Conversely they make what seem to us erroneous decisions when they are presented with some figures. Thus animals trained to attack a square but not a horizontal rectangle, when shown a vertical rectangle treat it like the square. For the octopus system this is not the error that it seems to us. The ratio of horizontal extent to the area is 1.0 for the square and 2.2 for the horizontal rectangle, but only 0.4 for the vertical rectangle, which is, so to speak, more square than a square by this system.

Vertical and horizontal extents are not the only

aspects that are measured. Other suggestions have been made by Deutsch (1960, *a* and *b*) and by Dodwell (1957, 1961) to explain the experimental findings. Sutherland and Mackintosh (1964) have put forward evidence that in rats various parameters may be measured and that there is an initial process of "switching in" by which the system selects the parameter that it has learned will allow discrimination in a given situation.

Classifying by Orientated Dendrite Fields

The evidence that horizontal and vertical extents are of special importance agrees with some striking facts about the arrangement of the visual system. In the retina the sensitive elements are arranged in a rectangular array with the axes horizontal and vertical, as the head of the animal is normally held under the influence of the statocyst. The pupil is a horizontal slit. Projection from the retina to the optic lobe is through a remarkable nerve-fibre chiasma, which inverts the pattern of distribution in the dorsal-ventral plane alone (fig. 3). Whatever this may mean, it shows that the system demands the maintenance of particular spatial relations between the visual field and the optic lobe elements. Other visual systems also show this feature: the projections from the eye to the tectum opticum of fishes or amphibia, or to the thalamus and cerebral cortex of mammals, maintain the retinal topology. The optic chiasms in the mid-line of vertebrates may have a function of re-inverting the retinal image as does the "unilateral" chiasma of cephalopods (see Young, 1962 *c*). In the bee and other arthropods there is also a system ensuring re-inversion of the retinal information on each side of the body.

Within the optic lobe of an octopus the fibres end in a plexiform zone that has remarkable similarities to the nervous part of the retina of vertebrates (figs. 1 and 2). There are outer and inner layers of amacrine cells. These are neurons with no single axon, but a bush of short processes ending within the plexiform zone, where they spread to varying extents (fig. 3). The retinal cells have connections with these amacrine cells, whose significance is obscure. Perhaps they are concerned with lateral inhibition and hence with increasing the contrast of contours. This may also be the function of the efferent fibres, many of which proceed from the plexiform zone to end in the retina (fig. 3).

The retinal fibres pass on, ending in the deeper part of the plexiform zone, where layers of fibres spread in the tangential plane. These are the dendrites of cells lying deeper in the lobes, the next link in the neuronal chain (fig. 3). Many of these dendrite fields are ovals, with their axes often in the horizontal plane. The fibres of many cells together thus form a grid, orientated in the vertical and horizontal planes (figs. 4 and 5). It was suggested, following Sutherland's experiments, that these fields may detect contours, especially in the horizontal direction (Sutherland, 1963; Young, 1960 *a*). There was no microelectrode evidence on this point in the octopus, nor is there yet. But Hubel and Wiesel (1959, 1962, 1963, 1965), in their observations on the visual fields of cells of the visual cortex of the cat, have found that each cell "looks at" an oval visual field, of-

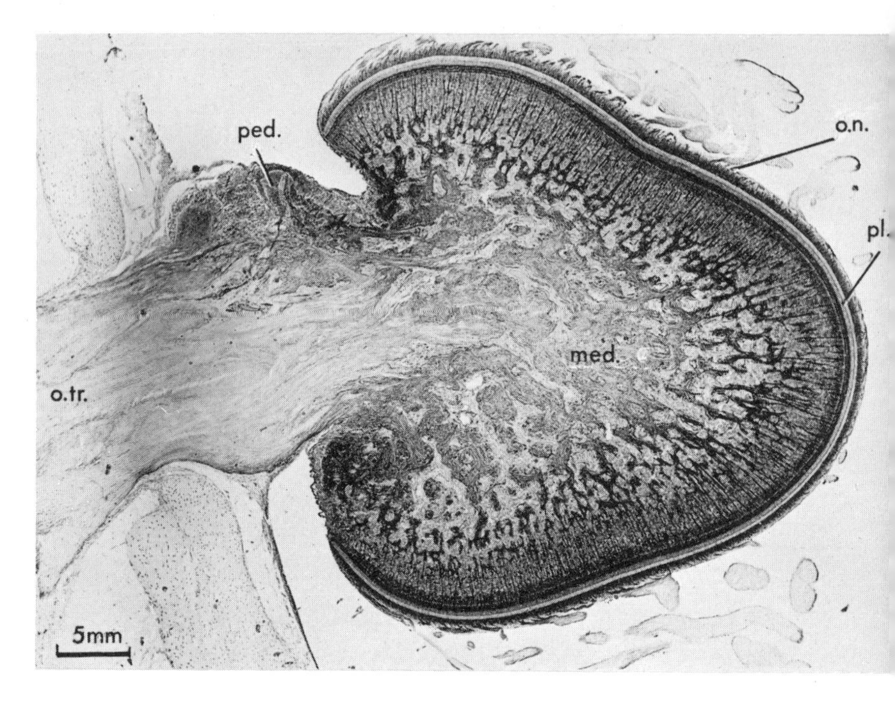

FIG. 1. Sagittal section of optic lobe of *Octopus*. med., medulla of optic lobe; o.n., optic nerve fibres (from retina); o.tr., optic tract (fibres to and from rest of brain); ped., peduncle lobe; pl., plexiform layer. (Young, 1962*b*)

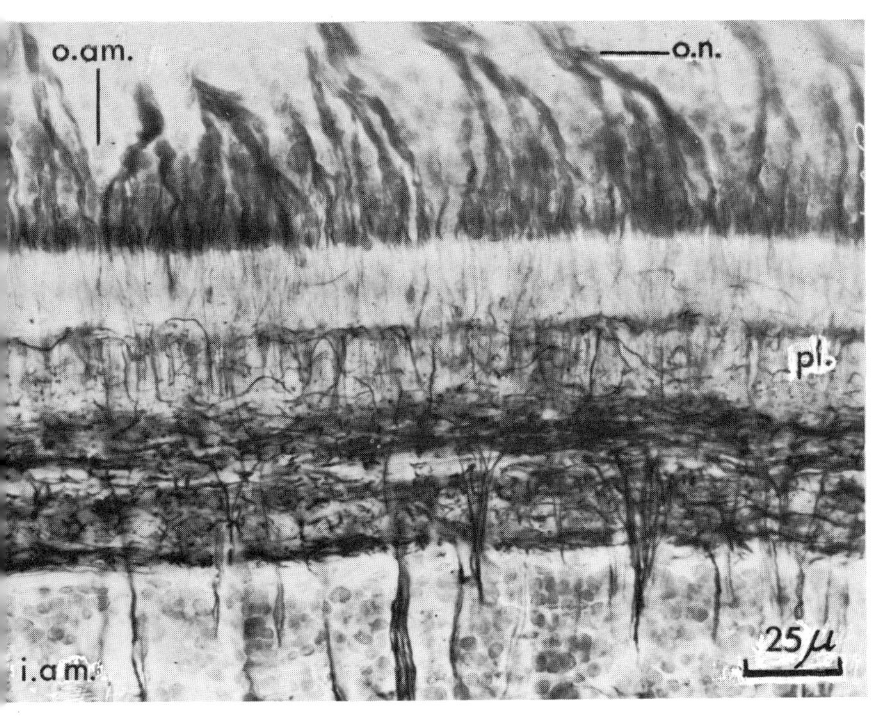

Fig. 2. Sagittal section of optic lobe of *Octopus*. i.am., inner layer of amacrine cells; o.am., outer layer of amacrine cells; o.n., optic nerve fibres (from retina); pl., plexiform layer. (Young, 1962*b*)

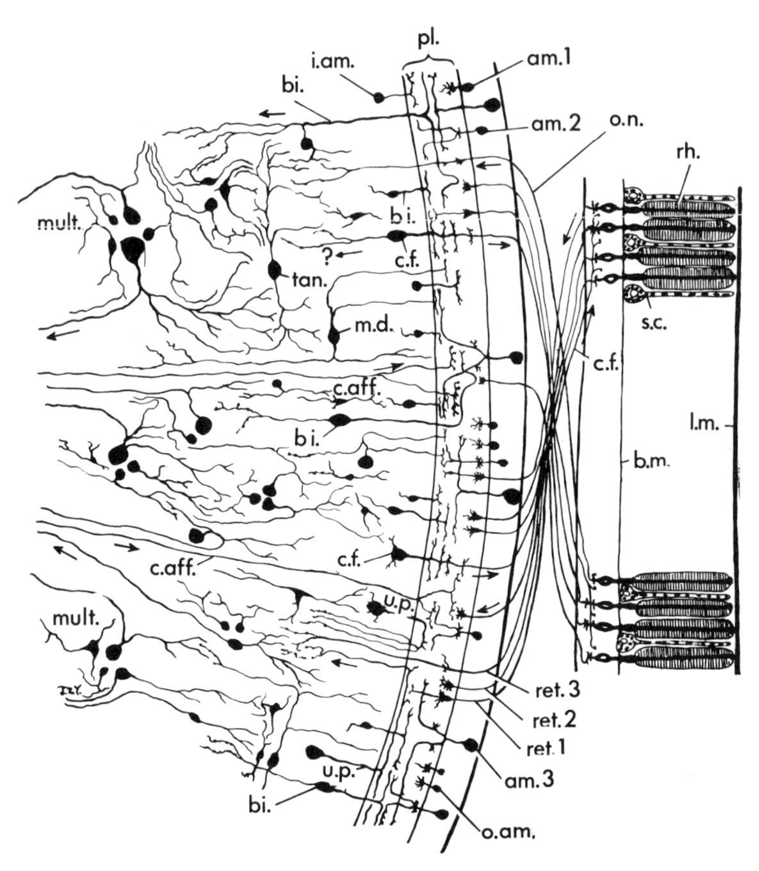

FIG. 3. Composite diagram of connections of neurons of optic lobe of *Octopus* as revealed by Golgi stain. am. 1–3, amacrine cells of outer granule cell layer; b.m., basal membrane; bi., bipolar cell; c.f., centrifugal fibre; c.aff., afferent fibre to plexiform layer from central regions; i.am., amacrine cell of inner granule cell layer; l.m., limiting membrane; m.d., cell with many dendrites proceeding outward; mult., small multipolar cell; o.am., amacrine cell of outer granule cell layer; o.n., optic nerves; pl., plexiform zone; ret. 1–3, retinal nerve fibres of three types; rh., rhabdome; s.c., supporting cell; tan., tangential cell of outer medulla; u.p., unipolar cell with a fibre running to plexiform zone and axons returning from this. (Young, 1962,*b*)

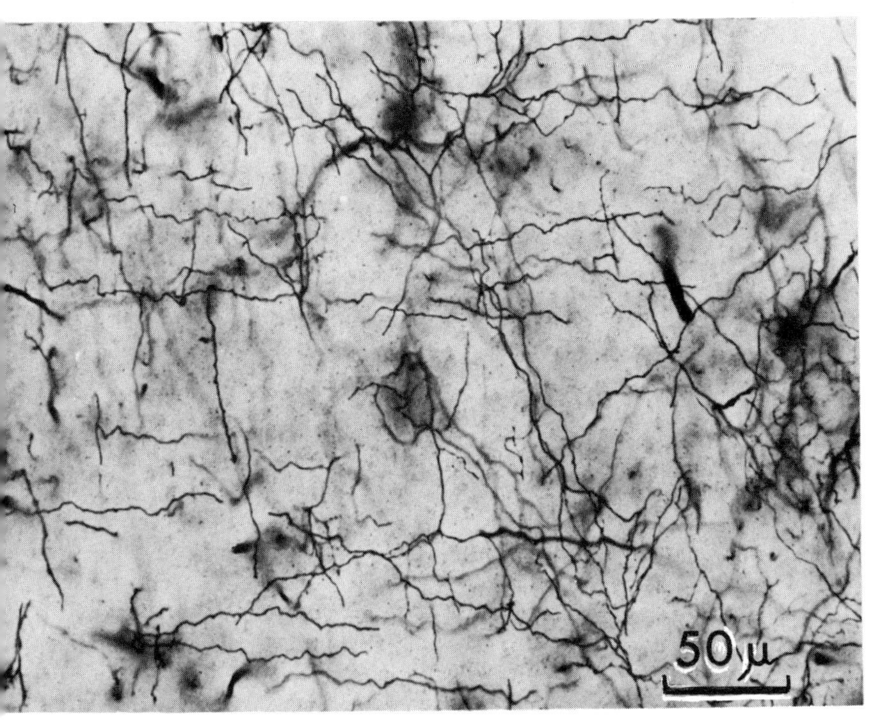

FIG. 4. Plexiform zone of optic lobe of *Octopus* seen in a section tangential to surface, showing dendrites running mainly in two directions, at right angles. Golgi stain.

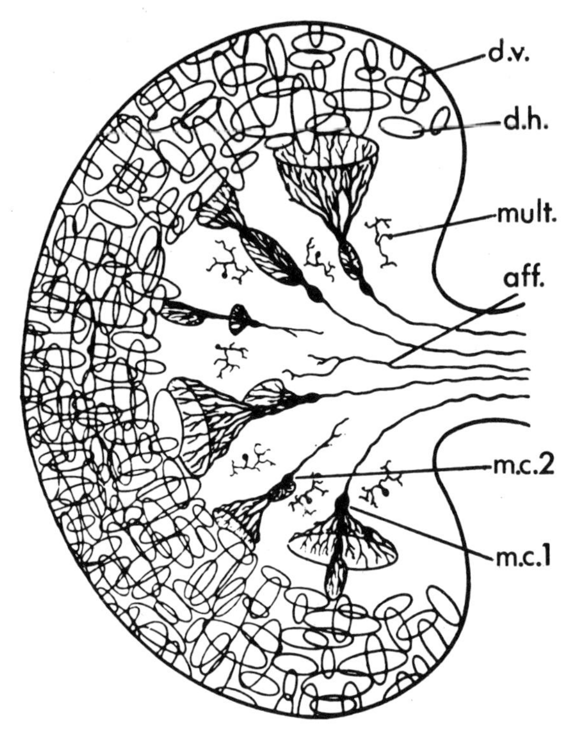

FIG. 5. Schematic diagram of arrangement of orientated dendrite fields of bipolar cells in optic lobe of *Octopus*. Some fields run vertically (d.v.), others horizontally (d.h.) Cells of medulla (m.c.1, m.c.2) with dendrites at different levels and in different orientations. aff., afferent fibres; mult., small multipolar cell. (Young, 1960*a*)

ten with an inhibitory centre and an excitatory surround or the reverse. Indeed, each such cell may operate as a detector of contour with a particular orientation, exactly as postulated above for the optic lobe. There are "simple" cells stimulated by illumination only of a highly specific field and "complex" ones that respond when illuminated by an area or edge with a particular orientation lying anywhere within their field. Thus some cells act as detectors for edges, dark bars, or illuminated slits. In the octopus there is certainly a preferential dendritic orientation of the fields, as the appearance of the grid shows. Unfortunately, whole single fields can be picked out only occasionally with the microscope, and the details of their shapes remain to be studied. Some fields are very large, more than half a millimetre across, corresponding to a large angle in the visual field. In many fields the long axis is horizontal, with several branches at right angles.

Hubel and Wiesel have not been able to study enough cells with microelectrodes to decide whether preferred orientations exist. However, Colonnier (1964) has studied the organisation of the visual cortex as seen in Golgi preparations cut in the tangential plane (figs. 6 and 7). He found many oval fields, as well as round ones, belonging to both pyramidal and stellate cells. These may be the features that determine the visual fields found by Hubel and Wiesel. Colonnier found distinct signs of preferential organisation in the visual cortex of the cat, with especially large numbers of fibres in the directions that correspond to the vertical and horizontal planes of the visual field. Moreover, he found orientated fields also in the cortex of the rat and the monkey.

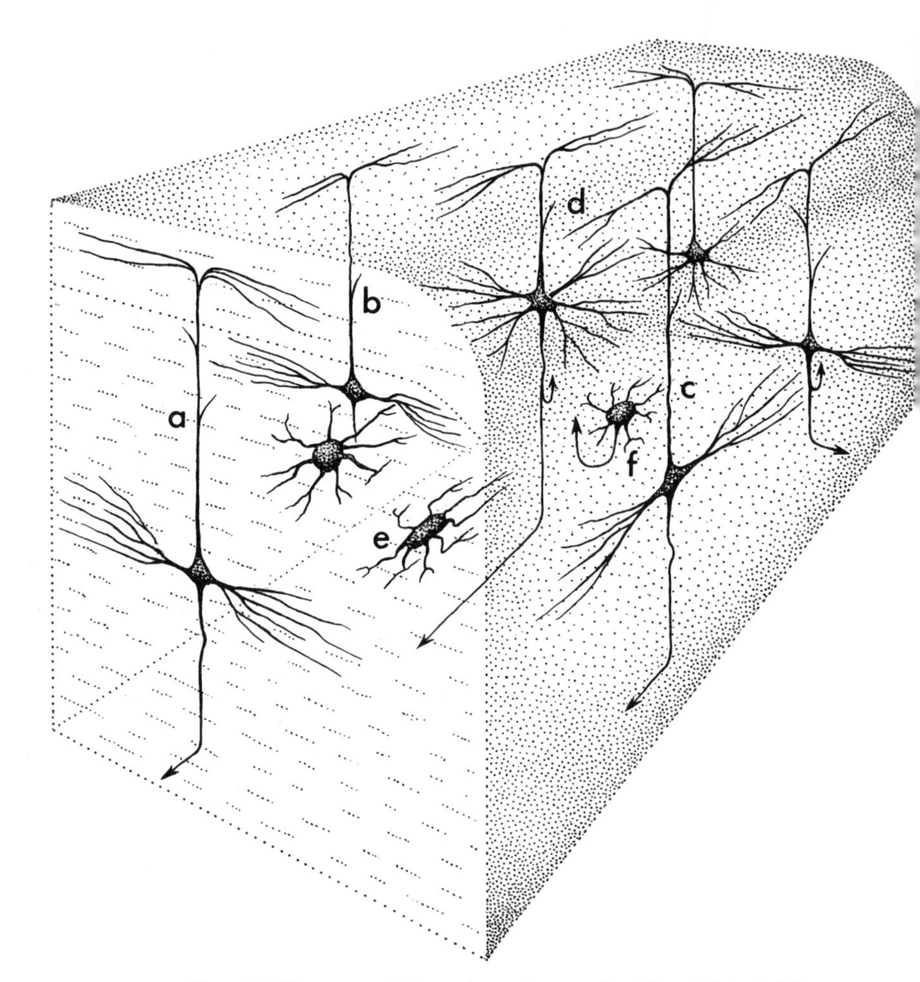

FIG. 6. Diagram of direction of spread of dendritic fields in visual cortex of cat (after Colonnier, 1964). Pyramidal cell *a* has apical and basal dendrite fields orientated in same (transverse) direction; *b* has its basal field transverse, apical longitudinal (anteroposterior). In *c* both are longitudinal. In *d*, basal field is cruciform; *e* is a stellate cell with an elongated field; *f* has a spherical field. Only some of the axons and their collaterals are shown.

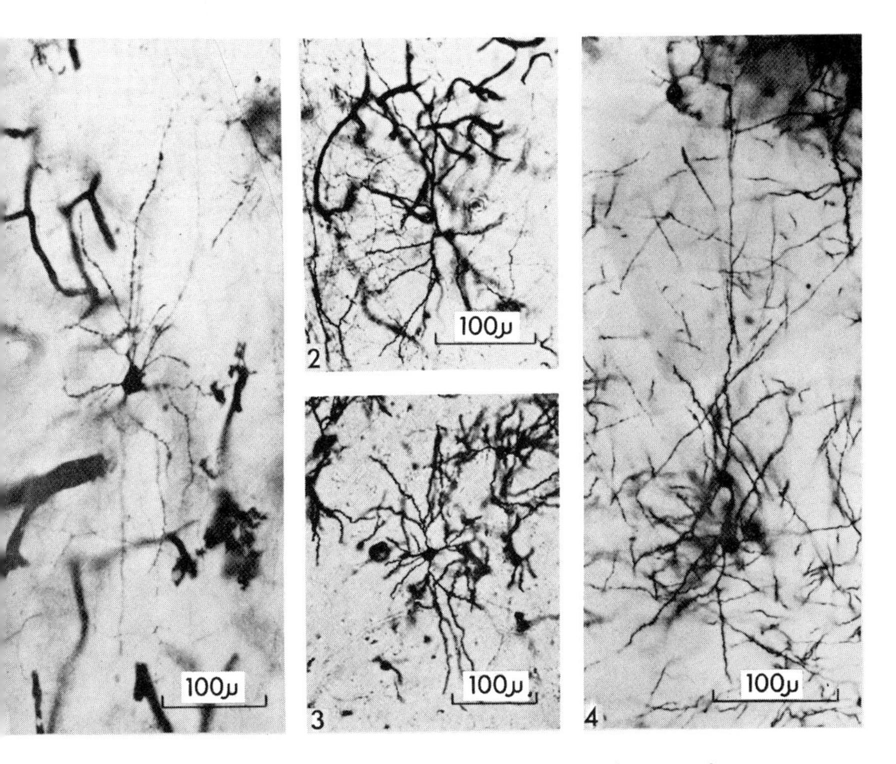

FIG. 7. Cells from visual cortex of cat seen in a section cut tangential to surface and showing elongated dendrite fields. 1. Basal dendrites and a pyramidal cell in layer VI. 2. Apical dendrites in layer I. 3. Basal dendrites of pyramidal cells in layers II and III. 4. Basal dendrites of pyramidal cell in layer IV. (Colonnier, 1964)

A striking result of these studies of the organisation of dendrites has been the discovery that individual dendrites run approximately straight for very long distances. We have heard much about the brain as a "random" system, but there is much that is not random about these dendrites; they must be highly determined at some stage in their growth. Hubel and Wiesel find that the fields have a similar orientation throughout each column of cells in the cortex. Other parts of the cerebral cortex have a similar organisation. In the somatic sensory cortex of the cat and the monkey the cells of a given vertical column respond to stimulation either of a particular area of skin or of deeper tissues such as a joint (Mountcastle, 1957; Powell and Mountcastle, 1959).

Sholl (1956) showed that there is an immense overlap between dendrite fields; each large pyramidal cell may share its field with up to 4,000 others. Any incoming fibre may connect with some among 5,000 cortical cells, spread through a volume of 0.1 mm^3. The possibilities of interaction between columns of cells responding to different orientations are therefore very large. Moreover, for pyramidal cells there is the possibility of different orientations of the apical and the basal dendrites. These features, together with the orientations of the dendrites of the short-axon stellate cells, would allow for a variety of combinations sufficient to explain even the subtle discriminations of shapes by man.

Learning as the Inhibition of Unwanted Pathways

To make the suggestion more explicit, we need a hypothesis that shows specifically how such cells could operate to provide the alphabet of the nervous system. The requirement seems to be that each classificatory cell shall be able to produce two (or more) outputs, leading to alternative actions. When the situation for which the cell encodes occurs in the visual field, one of these outputs is given and an action follows, say an attack on the object in the field. The detector systems for signalling results record the beneficial or prejudicial consequences of this action and these signals must then so alter the channels that the appropriate one is more likely to be used when the same situation occurs again.

Such a system has been postulated for the optic lobe of the octopus in figure 8. The classifying cells communicate each with two cells that may be called "memory cells," leading to channels for attack or retreat. The signals of results (e.g., taste or pain) arrive at the appropriate memory cells and, through collaterals of these, they pass to the opposite channel, which they inhibit. Learning consists in making this inhibition long-lasting, by changes (to be discussed later) which probably involve the small cells that are abundant in such centres (p. 93).

It should be made clear that only some of the components of this scheme of connections have been actually identified in the optic lobes. Cells that could act as classifying cells are there and they have axons with several branches among the cell islands nearer the cen-

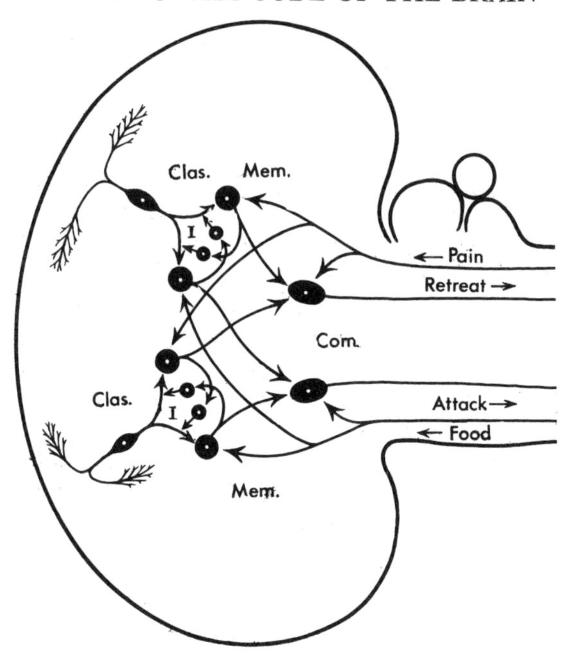

FIG. 8. A possible mode of functioning of the memory system in the optic lobes of *Octopus*. The shape of the object seen by the eye is analysed by dendritic fields of classifying cells (Clas.) in terms of horizontal and vertical extents. The information is passed to memory cells (Mem.), which, in the naïve state, pass on to command or motor cells (Com.) the signal to attack.

If the attack succeeds in securing food, fibres signalling this result activate the memory cells, increasing the excitability of those promoting attack in that situation. This may be achieved by the activation of small inhibitory cells (I), which, in this case, will prevent firing of memory cells whose output is to the motor cells governing retreat.

If the attack is punished, the memory cells receive a pain input; those cells governing retreat are activated, and in turn activate the inhibitory cells that suppress the tendency of the other memory cells to promote attack. (Young, 1964*a*) tre of the lobe. Here are cells with spreading dendritic branches, which may correspond to memory cells. These are accompanied by small multipolar cells, which may be the agents of inhibition, but the details of how all are connected have not yet been discerned in the complex tangle of fibres. In the islands nearest the optic tract are very large neurons that almost certainly initiate movements, since these can be elicited by electrical stimulation of this region, but not from other parts of the lobe.

The position is therefore that the components can be identified but their connections only in part. We can say only that the system *may* function approximately as suggested. The module of figure 8 has been made to include the two alternative possibilities, because an octopus can be trained to give either of two responses when a particular figure appears. Some experiments suggest, however, that in the initial situation the two outputs are not equally probable, that the tendency to attack is greater. Indeed, it is possible that the simplest learning systems had only a single outlet, the alternative being whether it should be open or closed.

The essence of the module is a group of cells specialised to alter the probability of the use of the channel (s) leading from a classifying cell. The alteration could be an increase or a decrease in any particular channel. If the change is complete it constitutes the storage of a single bit or item of information. It records whether stimulation of the given classifying cell was followed by results good or bad for the organism. This system for storing a single bit of information may perhaps be the unit we are looking for. Since the

Hitchcock Lectures were delivered, it has been suggested that it be called a mnemon (Young, 1965 *a*).[1]

If the system functions approximately as indicated, then, on any one occasion of seeing, only a limited number of the classifying cells will be stimulated, though the number may be extended to allow for generalisation (e.g., to the opposite eye; see p. 44). It is assumed that the inappropriate channels from the cells stimulated are fully closed by the signals of results arriving at the learning system, and that they do not reopen. Learning is thus complete for the cells stimulated on each presentation. The familiar slow development of the evidence of learning consists in the accumulation of enough trained cells to ensure a consistent response. Animals in their natural life may learn more rapidly than under the artificial conditions with which we test them in the laboratory. That human beings remember single occasions is obvious enough. The apparent slowness of learning in childhood may indicate that considerable time is required for the accumulation of a sufficient number of trained cells, appropriately interconnected to perform certain tasks.

The Model in the Brain

The various mnemons record which responses to each type of circumstance are likely to be good for the organism. The classifying cells at many levels are pre-

[1] Dr. A. Cherkin has kindly shown me his manuscript, suggesting that memory consists of units called mnemons (*Proc. Nat. Acad. Sci.* 55, Jan. 1966). He postulated these to account for gradations in the memory of chickens anaesthetised at various times after learning. The present hypothesis attempts to give a physical realisation of Cherkin's mnemons.

sumably able to record information in this way. Hubel and Wiesel have shown that there are cells able to respond to what they have called simple, complex, and hypercomplex features of the visual world.

So we can imagine a hierarchy of mnemons, constituting what may be called a model in the brain. This formulation or analogy was first used, I think, by Kenneth Craik of Cambridge in 1943, who was one of the earliest to develop ideas of the applications of control theory in biology and psychology. It is now possible to make the conception much more specific. A model is a representation. It is often made by selection and assembly of pieces from a set. What the brain learns must represent features of the world. Now it seems likely that this representation is made by selection among a set of cells, specified by their dendritic field systems.

The conception of a model often implies that the model works, and can be used to test possibilities by simulation, as a toy that is yet a tool. This is obviously true of the working model in our brains. Its value is primarily in enabling us to test out the probable consequences of various lines of action "in our heads" and then to decide what is likely to be the best course of action.

Representations in codes are used in homeostats for transmitting, storing, or manipulating the information by which self-maintenance is ensured, and this is exactly what the model in the brain does. Included in the concept of a model is that of the abstraction of the essentials of a situation, giving the expectation that perfectly forecastable and desirable results will follow from the use of a given model. This is the sense embodied in the use of the word "model" for a dress by a fashion designer, or for her mannequins by their admirers.

Without insisting too much on what is after all only one among many possible ways of speaking, we may thus find it reasonably helpful to say that as learning proceeds a model is built in the brain. Such a formulation stimulates us to look further for the elements of which the model is composed, for the method by which it is assembled, and how it is used. These are aspects of the anatomy and physiology of the nervous system that have not been sufficiently studied. The terminology of representation of the outside world by building a model in the brain will be justified if it leads to fruitful investigations and discoveries.

Transfer of Representations

If the dendritic fields of the cells of the optic lobes function as has been suggested, various problems of learning must be faced. If the change during learning consists in modification of the output from the cells that are stimulated, how do we account for transfer and generalisation of learning? There are very good opportunities for the study of transfer across the midline, since an octopus ordinarily uses one eye at a time and can be trained by figures shown exclusively in one visual field. Muntz (1961) has done this very successfully, showing that there is transfer and that it survives after removal of the optic lobe of the trained side. He investigated the commissures by which transfer takes place. For this transfer to occur the commissural system must include specific connections between classifying cells with similar field orientations on the two sides. This may seem to require a rather high degree of specificity in embryological development. However, since the discoveries by Sperry (see review by Gaze, 1960) and others of the high degree of specific connection in the vertebrate visual system, we should not be surprised to find that this is present to a relatively modest degree in the octopus. Interest in specific connections within the nervous system has revived in recent years, but there are still only a few who investigate the development of specificity.

The basic learning system suggested above requires a fairly high degree of specific built-in connections. The taste fibres must make connection with the pathways for attack and the pain fibres for retreat, but we are so used to seeing animals and men making the correct response (eating what is good and avoiding what is dangerous) that we have ceased to wonder at it. Animals do not commonly perform biologically absurd actions such as damaging their own tissues or starving to death in the midst of plenty. The systems of motivation and reward have become so subtle in man that they do sometimes produce deviations from behaviour that tend to preserve the individual (or even the race). These aberrations are part of the price that we pay for the advantages conferred in other ways by our elaborate and largely self-taught system of instructions. But most of us have enough specifically connected detectors of results to provide a reasonably high probability of survival (though pathological exceptions occur).

The classifying cells with two possible outputs in our scheme (fig. 8) obviously require specific connections to ensure opposite results from their two outputs. The collateral branches of the cells that have been called memory cells must have specific connections with small cells associated with the opposite pathway. To produce the learning system a fairly elaborate hereditary mechanism is required. But a memory can be a very valuable acquisition for a species, and under suitable circumstances there would be strong selection pressure to develop even a highly detailed morphogenetic mechanism for it. As we shall see in the last chapter, specific reciprocal connections are common in so-called reflex organisations that do not learn. To use a fashionable phrase, such systems are pre-adapted to evolve a memory mechanism.

Generalisation

The capacity for generalisation in the memory has also been studied in the octopus. When an animal has learned a specific discrimination it usually continues to perform correctly even when the situation is changed. For example, after learning to discriminate between white horizontal and vertical rectangles an animal may discriminate more or less correctly between black horizontal and vertical ovals. Many aspects of generalisation can be treated within our hypotheses by supposing that the dendritic fields that we have postulated as detectors are not rigidly restricted in their sensitivity and can be activated by situations that approximately resemble those that have been learned. If this is so, there must be limits to generalisation, and common sense tells us that this is true. We have investigated the limits for size generalisation in *Octopus* (Parriss and Young, 1962). As in other species, an octopus that has learned a discrimination between objects of one size can usually perform it also for larger sizes and to a lesser extent for smaller sizes. To investigate the capacity for generalisation more closely, we must avoid the obvious difficulty that an animal in moving about normally sees objects at a variety of retinal sizes. Octopuses are very convenient for such study because they can be made to remain in their homes. We accordingly trained them by giving rewards or shocks as soon as they began to move toward the figures, before they left the home, thus ensuring that they saw each figure only at one retinal size.

The capacity of these octopuses with limited movement to identify correctly the orientation of figures of other sizes was found to be much less than that of octopuses that were allowed to move toward the shapes and hence saw the figures at a range of retinal sizes (fig. 9). The capacity for generalisation in the animals with the smaller visual experience was more limited.

This suggests that no true process of generalisation really exists. What we call by that name may be the result only of the great variety of experience that active learning homeostats such as ourselves acquire over the years. The selecting of the responses that are likely to be most appropriate to the stimulation of the classifying cells of a given type proceeds continually—presumably until the whole fount of them is used up, if that stage is ever reached.

Reversal

Another problem is to show that the system suggested will account for reversal of the direction of learning.

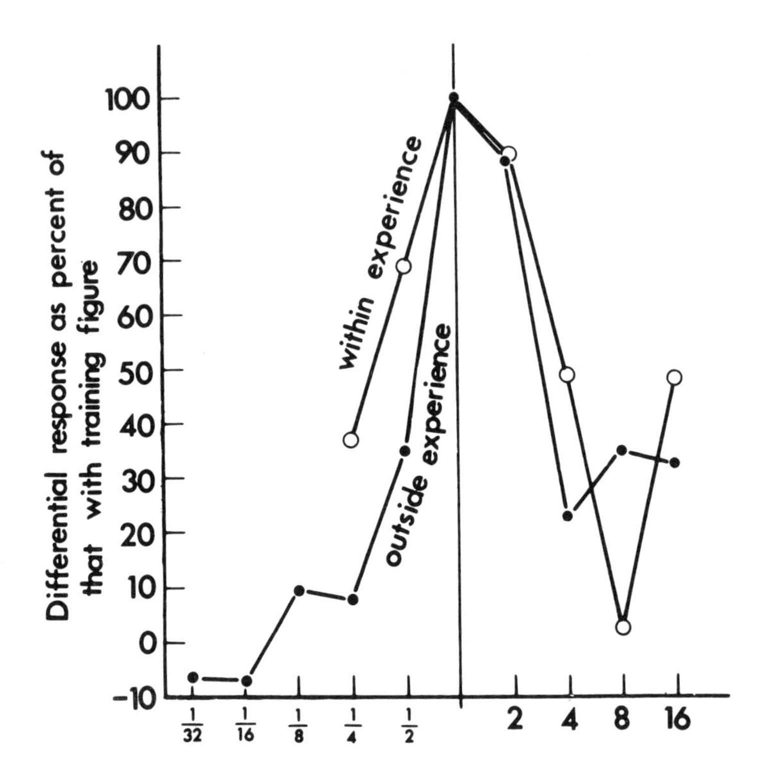

FIG. 9. Limits of size generalisation by *Octopus*. Accuracy of recognition during testing with vertical and horizontal rectangles of various sizes is expressed as a percentage of the accuracy with the figures used in training. Open circles, results for figures within the animal's experience during training. Solid circles, results with figures of sizes never seen during training; with these there is much less transfer, especially to smaller figures. (Parriss and Young, 1962)

After reversal the octopus continues for a considerable time to show signs of the original direction of training. The new representation in the memory is additional to the old one and not a substitute for it. Experiments with repeated reversal of the same discrimination showed an approach to a random level of attacks. Presumably equal and opposite representations are set up. However, although the total number of attacks declined, the proportion of all attacks that were correct increased. This was probably a result of the plan of the experiment; the food given on each showing of the positive figure served to weight the tendency to attack in favour of that figure. Various interesting phenomena appear with repeated reversal (Mackintosh, 1962; Mackintosh and Mackintosh, 1964 *a* and *b*), but these experiments show no evidence of a specific learning to reverse such as has been found by Harlow and others for birds and mammals. This capacity has not been found in lower vertebrates either (Bitterman, 1965). Reversal is probably one of the special functions that have been added to higher memory systems in the course of evolution.

Errors with Wrong Orientation of the Eyes

A further expectation from our hypothesis would be that alteration of the orientation of the eye or visual field in space should lead to errors of response. This was tested in an ingenious experiment by Wells (1960). After removal of the statocysts from an octopus, when the animal sits on a vertical surface the eye is not held in its normal horizontal position. Wells trained animals to react positively to a horizontal and negatively to a vertical rectangle and then removed the statocysts. When the animal sat on a horizontal surface it continued to perform correctly, but on a vertical surface its responses were erratic or actually reversed.

Conclusion

The hypothesis put forward thus accounts for at least some of the phenomena seen in the learning system of the octopus. No doubt it seems absurdly simplified and "static" to those who are familiar with the subtle learning systems of higher animals. So far as the octopus system is truly simple, it has the advantage of presenting a more easily understandable example, from which we can learn about more complex systems. I have an uneasy feeling, however, that the simplification grossly distorts the picture of the octopus itself. When other aspects of the classifying system are studied it is necessary to postulate additional mechanisms. Sutherland and Mackintosh (1964) postulate that an animal can use one of several classifying systems. It first learns to switch-in whichever system enables it to make a clear discrimination in a new situation. However, the touch memory system can operate when the central nervous system has been so greatly reduced that it is difficult to believe that any elaborate "switching-in" mechanism remains (p. 94).

The code of the nervous system must record many features of the visual world even in an animal as relatively simple as the octopus. This chapter has not tried to deal with all of them, but to show some of the principles upon which they may operate.

CHAPTER THREE

The Requirements of an Exploratory Computer

Signals of Need and Motivation

We have discussed some of the similarities and differences between brains and man-made computers, but we have not yet faced the problems of the design of a computer that explores. Living organisms acquire their own information about the world. More than this, they acquire, over the long process of evolution, their own instructions on how to build and operate an exploratory computer.

By study of the octopus over a number of years some progress has been made toward understanding how its learning system meets the requirements of such a device. Fortunately for the research worker, the octopus brain contains two anatomically distinct and localisable memory stores: one records the results of actions following visual events; the other, the results of actions following the touching of objects with the suckers. Moreover, in each system the actual memory store is accompanied by four lobes of auxiliary equipment. These have been investigated anatomically and experimentally; they seem to be concerned with activities that may be called reading-in to and reading-out from the memory. In particular they serve to send signals of the results of actions to the right addresses in the memory.

These phrases for characterising the functions of the parts must be used with the qualifications that have already been discussed. The nervous memory certainly differs greatly from a magnetic tape. It is by no means certain that we can usefully speak of reading-in to or out from given addresses in it.

Any exploratory learning computer obviously must have a certain bias to take actions. If it does nothing it will learn nothing. We commonly express this by saying that an animal must be motivated. Moreover, it will need detectors that signal when the system lacks essential raw materials, oxygen, food, or water, and these signals must initiate actions that are likely to relieve the need. For example, experiments with implanted electrodes in mammals have shown that feeding behaviour is controlled by paired centres in the hypothalamus. After excision of the lateral centre, a rat starves to death, but after injury of the medial centre he gorges almost literally to the bursting point. The details of the modes of action of such need-centres are only partly understood. Probably they contain the detectors that respond to a lack; this is almost certainly so in the hypothalamic centres that respond to lack of water, and glucoreceptors for sugar are also known.

The presence of such centres in the hypothalamus has been familiar now for some years. It is known that some of the hypothalamic circuits are involved also in recording in the memory. Yet there is little understanding of the principles of the neural mechanisms by which these systems operate. Besides the receptors that indicate the internal state (and hence the "need"), other receptors signal when the appropriate materials arrive (i.e., food or water). These signals must be able to influence the level of motivation and there must be means of adjusting any conflict of requirements. In particular, actions directed to obtaining needed materials must stop if danger threatens, as indicated by signals of pain.

Three Functions of the Signals of the Results of Action

In the octopus the four centres that are connected with each of the two memory systems seem to be concerned, among other things, with signals of taste and of pain (figs. 10 and 11). In these centres, fibres from the lips and mouth interweave with those from the specific receptors (eyes or suckers). Other fibres that probably carry impulses when tissues are damaged (pain) then join in. The two pairs of centres enable these impulses of taste and pain to have their proper effects.

It may be useful to consider what these effects should be to ensure survival of the homeostat. Signals of "reward," indicating to the system the results of its actions, have a series of functions. First, they must operate the appropriate consummatory reactions. When an animal reaches food it must eat; when it touches a very hot object it must withdraw.

Second, the level of exploratory action by the animal must be adjusted. In an unfamiliar situation an animal

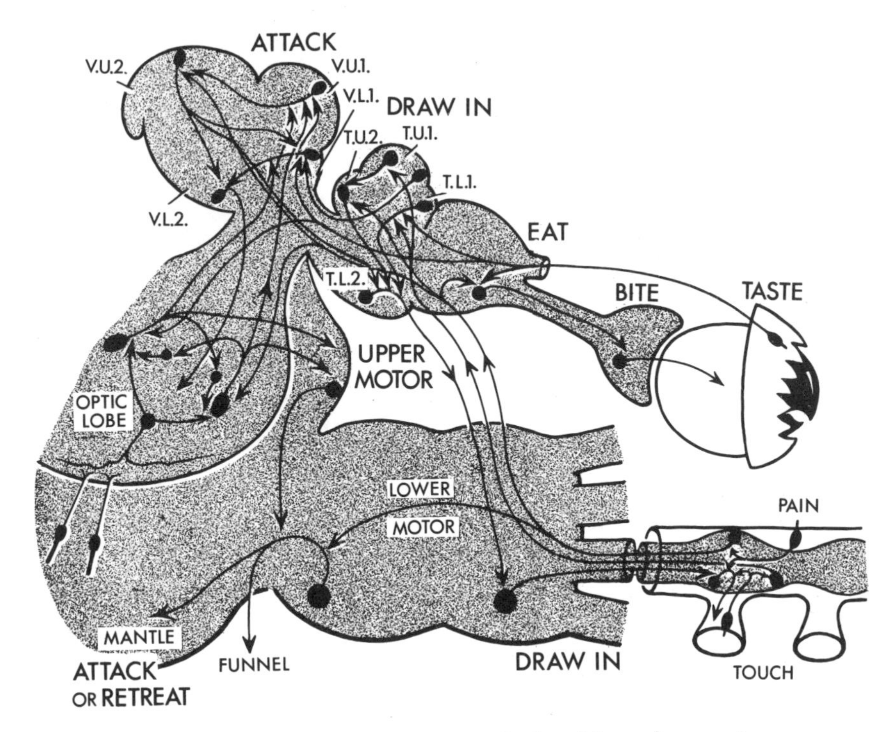

FIG. 10. Diagram of touch and visual learning centres and their connections in *Octopus*. The suggestion is that these "higher" centres have developed from "lower" eating centres, and serve to maintain the address of classifying cells between the moment when distance receptors react and actual contact with the object attacked. Receptors signalling results then deliver signals to the appropriate address. V.L.1, V.L.2, lower visual centres (lateral superior frontal and subvertical). V.U.1, V.U.2, upper visual centres (median superior frontal and vertical). T.L.1, T.L.2, lower tactile centres (lateral inferior frontal and posterior buccal). T.U.1, T.U.2, upper tactile centres (median inferior frontal and subfrontal).

The pathway from V.U. 2 to T.L. 2 is that by which the vertical lobe influences touch learning. This is the only connection between the two systems (except that they both receive taste and pain fibres). (Modified from Young, 1963*b*)

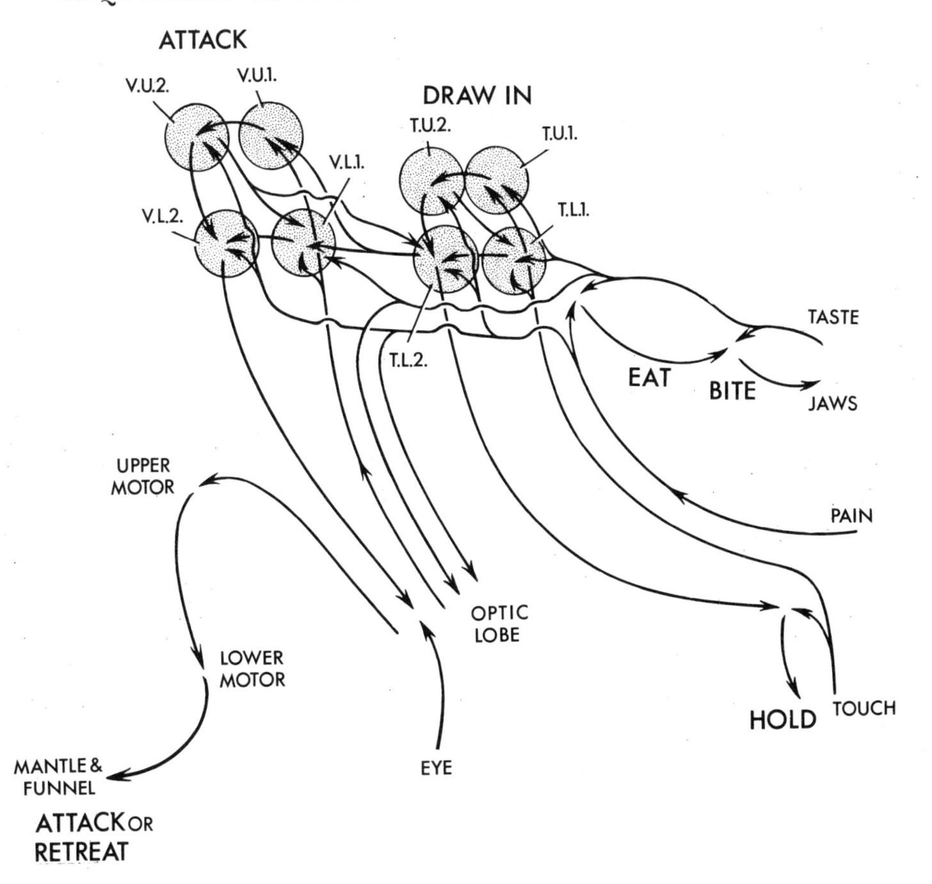

FIG. 11. A more diagrammatic version of figure 10, emphasising similarity of organisation in the touch and visual learning systems. Note mixing of taste and visual information in V.L.1 and V.U.1, and presence of pain fibres entering T.U.2 and V.U.2. (Modified from Young, 1964*a*)

should proceed cautiously. The octopus does not dash out at full speed to attack a new object. It emerges slowly, with every sign of caution. If the object yields food, the tendency to attack is unspecifically increased and conversely if the object proves painful. But most interesting for us is a third function of these signals of results. They serve to teach the memory specifically that the results of attacking a particular object were good or bad. To do this the signals must reach to the appropriate cells in the memory. One of the chief functions of the two pairs of auxiliary lobes of each memory system seems to be to spread these signals of results and mix them with those of the specific receptors so that they may reach to the appropriate parts of the classifying and memory systems.

It seems obvious that what are here called the signals of the results of action (pleasure, taste or pain) have these various functions to perform. Yet we do not usually find them so described or taught. There are too few situations in which we know how the fibres that carry the signals are routed. One of the chief values of such an analysis is that it directs our attention to the need for investigation of similar pathways and connections in mammals.

The Paired Centres of the Octopus Brain

This analysis has been arrived at, historically, not from first principles but by study of the brain and behaviour of *Octopus*. In this animal two sets of four lobes are connected with the visual and tactile systems respectively. Both sets contain complicated interweaving bundles of fibres. Both sets also include lobes with minute nerve cells—amacrine cells having no axon that leaves the lobe. These centres are so different in appearance from others in the brain that even to look at them suggests that they have special "higher" nervous functions (fig. 12). It was this appearance that led us some years ago to investigate the possibility that they might reveal something about the requirements of neural memory systems. Boycott and I soon found that interruption of the upper visual circuit produces serious defects in the animal's memory for things previously learned and also produces difficulty in further learning. At first we thought that the vertical lobe (second upper visual) was the actual seat of the memory. Then it gradually became clear that animals without that lobe *can* learn, under suitable conditions. Evidently the actual memory record lies elsewhere (in the optic lobe) and the four accessory lobes fulfil special functions, essential for the proper operations of the memory under normal circumstances.

It is not easy to define the functions of these lobes in a few words (perhaps because we have no machines with precisely similar parts). We might list their activities as (1) maintaining the addresses of classifying and memory cells until (2) they deliver to those cells the signals of the results of action (e.g., taste or pain). The paired centres produce these effects by suitable arrangements to mix and circulate signals from specific receptors (vision or touch) with those for taste and pain. They thus acquire as further functions (3) to regulate the level of the tendency to explore and to attack and (4) to transfer representations, especially

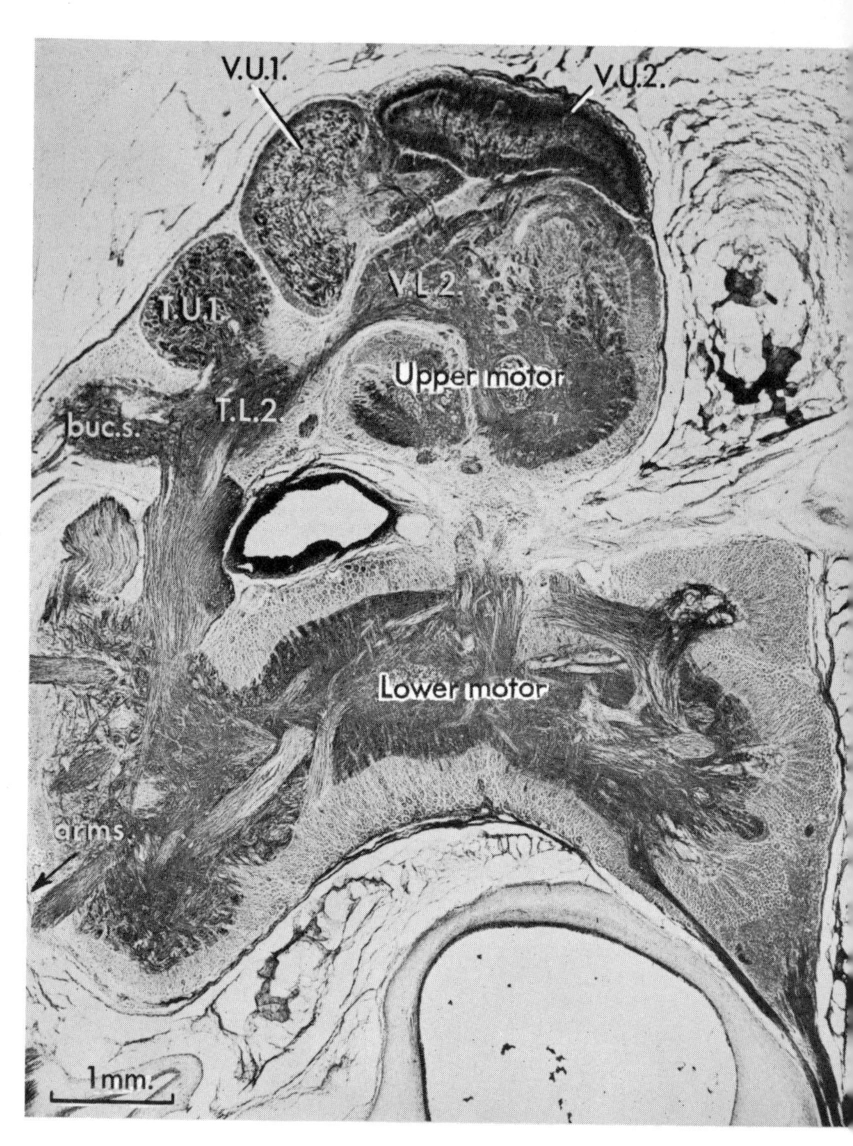

FIG. 12. A vertical longitudinal section cut through whole brain of *Octopus*. Above the gut lie centres for learning and other complex activities. Below it lie centres mediating mainly motor and visceral functions. Optic lobes lie more laterally. buc.s., superior buccal lobe.

from one side of the brain to the other, and to generalise them within each receptor field.[1]

This list is only an attempt to summarise the results of numerous experiments and studies of the connections of the lobes of the octopus brain. It is a measure of our ignorance of nervous systems that we still cannot easily find words to discuss even these relatively simple and clearly arranged nerve centres. It is not surprising that we find it so difficult to talk about our own brains.

To perform their various functions the lobes of both visual and touch systems are arranged as re-exciting circuits. They take input from the classifying and memory systems, combine it with signals of taste and (or) of pain, and return an output to the memory centres. Each system has two pairs of centres arranged in parallel one above the other (fig. 11).

Effects of Lesions to the Lower Visual Circuit

In the visual system we have much experimental evidence about the activities of both the upper and the lower pairs and are beginning to understand how their pattern of connections is related to their functions (fig. 13). After interference with the lower visual circuit the octopus is not blind (fig. 14, operations 6 and 7), and will still put out an arm to take a crab moving in the visual field near the animal. The lowest level of visual function, the seizing of the food, therefore, takes

---

[1] Apparently in *Octopus* there is no generalisation between vision and touch (see Wells, 1961).

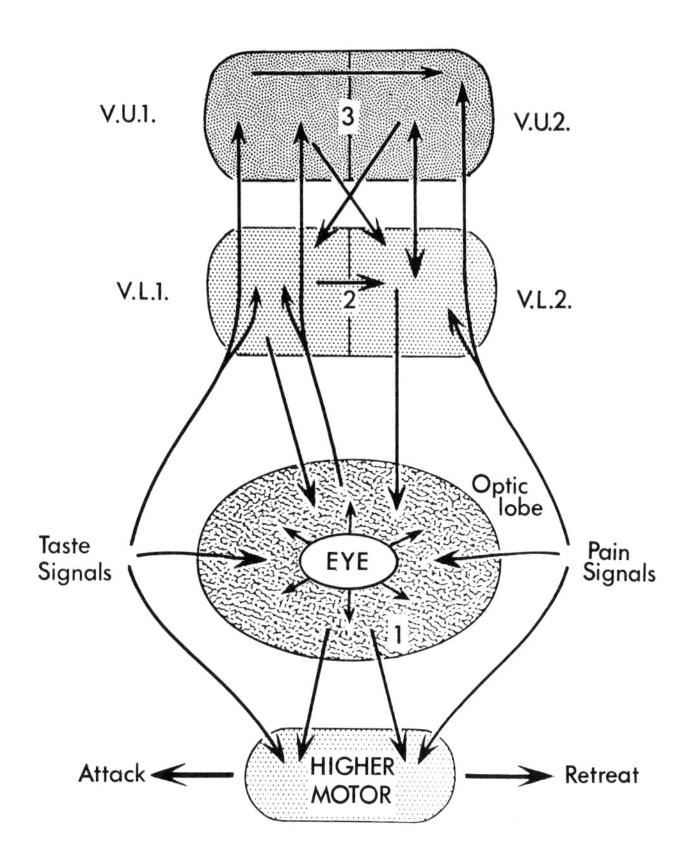

FIG. 13. Diagram of possible functional relationships in visual system. Visual information passes from eye to optic lobe (1). Here it may cause an arm to be put out by activating higher motor centres (basal lobes). Signals of taste and pain reach to the optic lobe, but this system (1) cannot by itself produce a full attack.

Attack requires lower visual circuit (2), which runs through lateral superior frontal and subvertical. Taste and pain fibres also enter these lobes and presumably increase or decrease the probability of attack. Upper visual circuit (3) allows further mixing of visual signals with those of taste, increasing the tendency to attack unless pain intervenes. The pathways shown are mostly well substantiated (though not their functions). Pathway from V.U.1 to V.L.2 is doubtful. (Young, 1964*b*)

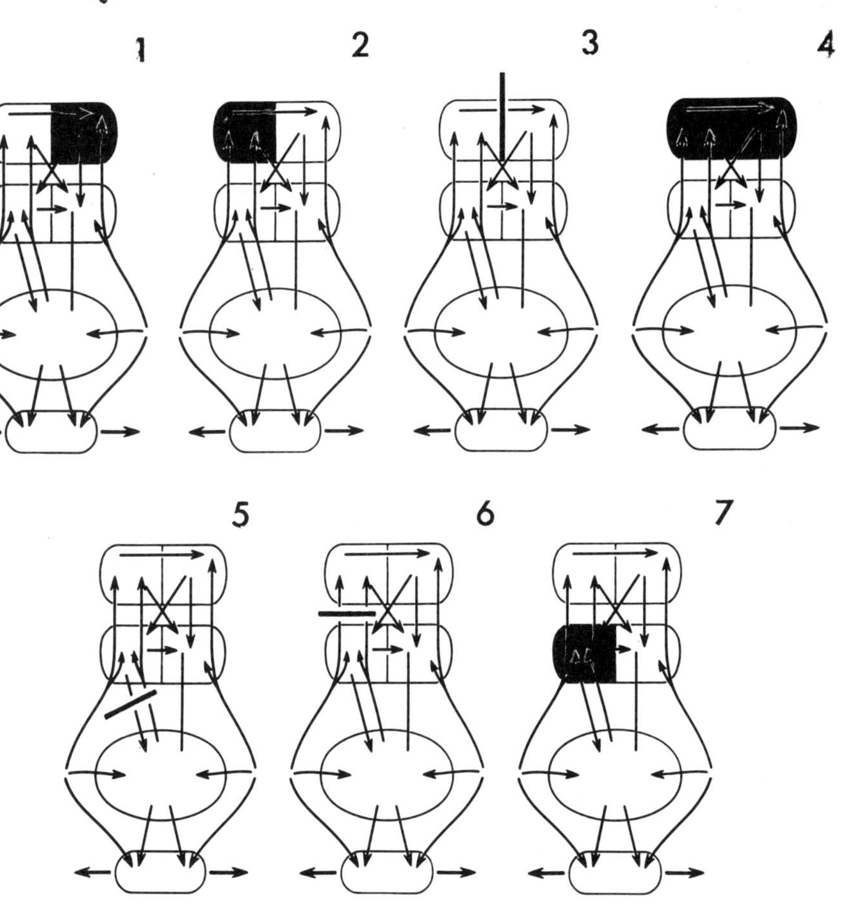

FIG. 14. Diagram showing types of operations performed on *Octopus*. 1. Removal of vertical lobe. 2. Removal of median superior frontal. 3. Cutting of fibre tracts between lateral superior frontal and vertical. 4. Removal of vertical and median superior frontal. 5. Cutting of fibre tracts between optic lobe and median superior frontal. 6. Cutting of fibre tracts between lateral and median superior frontals. 7. Removal of lateral superior frontal. (Young, 1964*b*)

place through the optic lobes alone, in the absence of the paired centres. But such animals never launch out to attack a crab moving at a distance from them. The function of the lower loop thus seems to be to increase the effect of the firing of a few cells of the visual system until it is adequate to produce an attack. This is achieved because each fibre of the input to the visual lower first centre (the lateral superior frontal lobe) runs across the dendritic fields of many cells of the lobe (figs. 14 and 23). There is also an input to the same cells from fibres coming from the region in and around the mouth, presumably taste fibres. Under appropriate circumstances these further increase the tendency to attack.

The axons of the first lower lobe in passing to the visual second lower lobe (subvertical lobe) probably also allow further amplification, since each cell of the first may stimulate many cells of the second. The cells of the lower second visual centre in turn send their axons back to the optic lobes. It is not known clearly what further operations are performed in the second lower lobe. It is the centre of the system in the sense that it receives the output of both the lower and the upper circuits. Its large cells serve to elaborate the "command" that is the final product of the whole system, to be sent back to the optic lobe (see Maldonado, 1963 *a, b, c*, and *d*). Fibres presumed to carry pain from all parts of the body also enter the second lower lobe. They may act here to prevent the system from formulating the command to attack if the situation is dangerous.

Because of the central position of the subvertical

lobe in the system, it is impossible to make a separate study of the effects of its removal. Any injury here reduces the tendency of the animal to attack. This must be due mainly to the removal of the effects of the lower pair of centres, because removal of the upper pair produces an animal that in general attacks too much, even in spite of pain (see later).

Connections of the Upper Visual Circuit

The most interesting part of the system is the upper tier of lobes, the median superior frontal and vertical. The mixed bundles of optic and taste fibres proceed through the lateral superior frontal to an astonishing system of interweaving bundles in the median superior frontal (fig. 15). This lobe has a greater proportion of neuropil to its cell layers than any other part of the brain. The incoming fibres run across the dendrite fields of the million small cells of the lobe (fig. 23). This system seems to be designed to allow the setting up of a range of combinations of visual inputs with signals from the chemotactile and taste systems. Any learning system beyond the simplest presumably requires a mechanism to allow for such combinations, and it is striking to see this logical requirement so clearly expressed in the connection pattern, not only here but in almost identical form in the tactile memory system (see later).

The axons of the cells of the first upper lobe pass mainly (probably exclusively) to the second upper lobe (vertical lobe), making as they do so a further elaborate plexus. This plexus ensures that axons of neighbour-

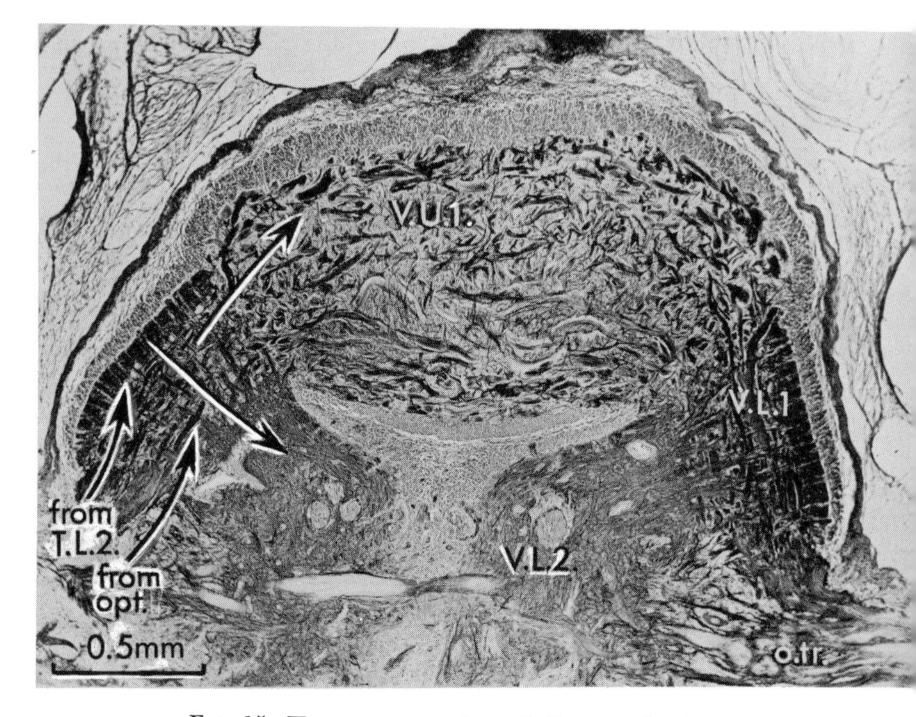

FIG. 15. Transverse section of *Octopus* brain to show lateral and median superior frontal (V.L.1, V.U.1), and subvertical lobes (V.L.2). Note fibre tracts bearing visual information to lateral superior frontal from eye, and fibres from median inferior frontal to lateral superior frontal bearing touch information. In the median superior frontal, the tangled neuropil serves to mix information from these sources. o. tr., optic tract; opt., optic lobe.

ing cells of the first lobe may or may not end near each other in the second lobe and conversely. This is obviously a further system for setting up combinations of activity, perhaps allowing representation of events in the surroundings. A second input to the second upper lobe enters from the subvertical lobe below (fig. 16). It is assumed that these bundles include pain fibres from various parts of the body (see above). The vertical lobe has a very characteristic structure, utterly different from that of the first upper lobe (fig. 23). It contains a vast number of minute amacrine cells (25×10^6) whose fibres do not extend beyond its own neuropil. The output is from a relatively small number of larger cells, with large dendritic fields. They end partly in the second lobe of the lower tier (subvertical), which is thus the output centre for both tiers, transmitting back to the optic lobes. Many other fibres from the second upper lobe pass back to the first lower lobe, providing a feedback, perhaps positive. This may serve to produce the amplification of signals that is necessary to promote or to reduce action.

Failures of Learning after Lesions in the Upper Visual Circuit

Any octopus in which the upper circuit has been interrupted tends to attack more readily than normal, even if the objects that it attacks prove unrewarding or painful (fig. 14, operations 2–5) Boycott and I found that the octopus can be trained by means of shocks not to attack a crab when shown a white square. After the vertical lobe has been removed, however, it immediately

Fig. 16. High-power photograph to show fibres of sub-vertical-vertical tract. The vertical lobe (V.U.2) has been removed, and the ends of nerves leading into it from below are regenerating, as evidenced by swellings at their tips. These fibres are presumed to carry pain signals.

begins to attack again in this situation. If given further shocks for such attacks it will discontinue them, but the memory is effective for only a few minutes. If shocks are given again within that time the record can be maintained, but it lapses if the interval is longer.

The superior frontal to vertical lobe circuit is thus concerned especially in suppressing responses when these lead to painful consequences. The provisional interpretation has been that the actions of the first lobe (median superior frontal) increase the tendency to attack an object that has been seen *unless* pain supervenes, in which case the second (vertical) lobe inhibits the attack tendency. Since the lobes are in series, interference with either may produce similar effects, and there is no doubt that after any operation that interrupts the upper circuit the animal is "uninhibited," in the sense that it attacks more persistently than the normal animal, in spite of pain. However, removal of the median superior frontal and vertical lobes does not produce precisely the same effects. Maldonado (1965) has made a careful comparison of the attacks made at crabs before and after removal of one or other

MEAN TIMES TAKEN TO ATTACK A CRAB ($\frac{1}{100}$ sec)[a]

Lobe Removed	Time Before	Days After		
		1–2	3–4	5–6
Median superior frontal	550	2,252	1,667	1,557
Vertical	756	1,057	1,024	1,209

[a] Maldonado, 1965.

of these lobes (see the accompanying table). Animals that attacked crabs at 100 per cent of showings before operation invariably attacked somewhat less thereafter.

Irregularity of response is one symptom of damage to the upper circuit. The reduction in attacks was rather greater if the first lobe was removed than for the second lobe, but great variation occurred in both classes. Much more significant was the fact that the mean time taken for the attacks was much less without the second lobe than without the first.

Maldonado's methods of measurement enabled him to show that this difference was almost wholly in what he calls the "first time delay," that is, the latent period while the animal is still in its home, before the attack is launched. The actual time in transit from home to crab was not greatly different after the two operations.

We can see, therefore, that the upper circuit is concerned in the decision-making process, before the attack begins. The time taken for this process is increased after removing either lobe, but much more so after removing the first lobe than the second. This agrees with the conception that the first lobe is especially concerned with "amplification," or more exactly multiplication, of the signals promoting attack, and the second lobe with inhibiting them.

The structure of the first lobe seems suited to this function. The incoming fibres branch and pass across many of the dendrite fields of the cells of the lobe. Thus impulses in a few incoming fibres may produce many outgoing ones.

The structure of the second (vertical) lobe is so fundamentally different that it must perform some other operation on the circuit. There are strong indications from electron microscopy that the arrangement allows for presynaptic inhibition (figs. 17 and 18). The trunks of the numerous minute amacrine cells of the lobe are packed with synaptic vesicles. They make contact with profiles that also contain vesicles, and have been shown by their degeneration to be the axons of the superior frontal to vertical tract. But the amacrine cells also make conventional synaptic contact with clear profiles in the neuropil, and these are presumed to be the dendritic spines of the large output cells of the lobe.

The endings of the input fibres reaching the lobe from below have not been identified with certainty by means of the electron microscope. However, it is probable that they also make synapse with the amacrine cells. The suggestion is that the incoming fibres from the median superior frontal make excitatory synapses with dendritic spines of the large cells. These pass on the amplified signals *unless* the pain fibres activate the amacrines to release inhibitory transmitter that blocks the incoming impulses. There are possibilities also for postsynaptic inhibition. Indeed, the function of these amacrine cells may be not so much to transmit signals to a distance as to produce an inhibitory clamp (perhaps by depolarisation) upon the system that amplifies the signals to attack.

From the relation between the incoming fibres and the amacrine cells there is good reason to suppose that presynaptic inhibition is involved. Synapses with vesicles on both sides have been found in mammals to be associated with presynaptic inhibition (Wall, 1964; Eccles, 1964). It is very striking that amacrine cells

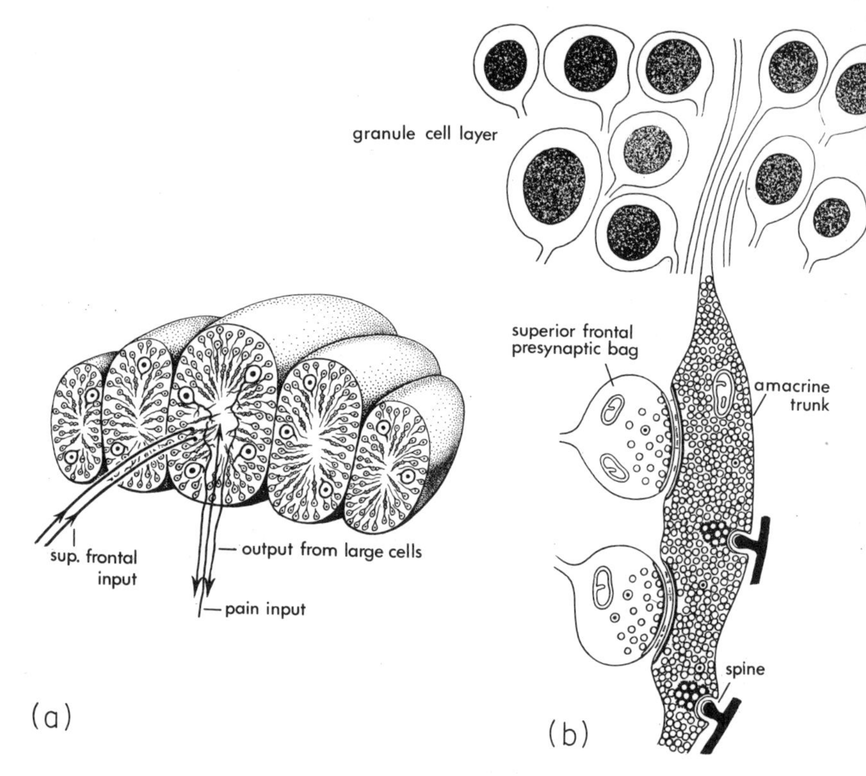

FIG. 17. Diagrams of vertical lobe of *Octopus*. *a*, arrangement of cells and fibres; note input of axons from median superior frontal lobe. *b*, connections in vertical lobe as revealed by electron microscopy. Median superior frontal fibres terminate in typical presynaptic bags, containing vesicles of presumed transmitter substance, which abut against processes of amacrine cells of vertical lobe. These processes are packed with transmitter vesicles, and would appear to pass on stimulation to clear spinous processes of unknown origin, perhaps dendrites of the large output cells. Synapses of the pain fibres not shown. (Gray and Young, 1964)

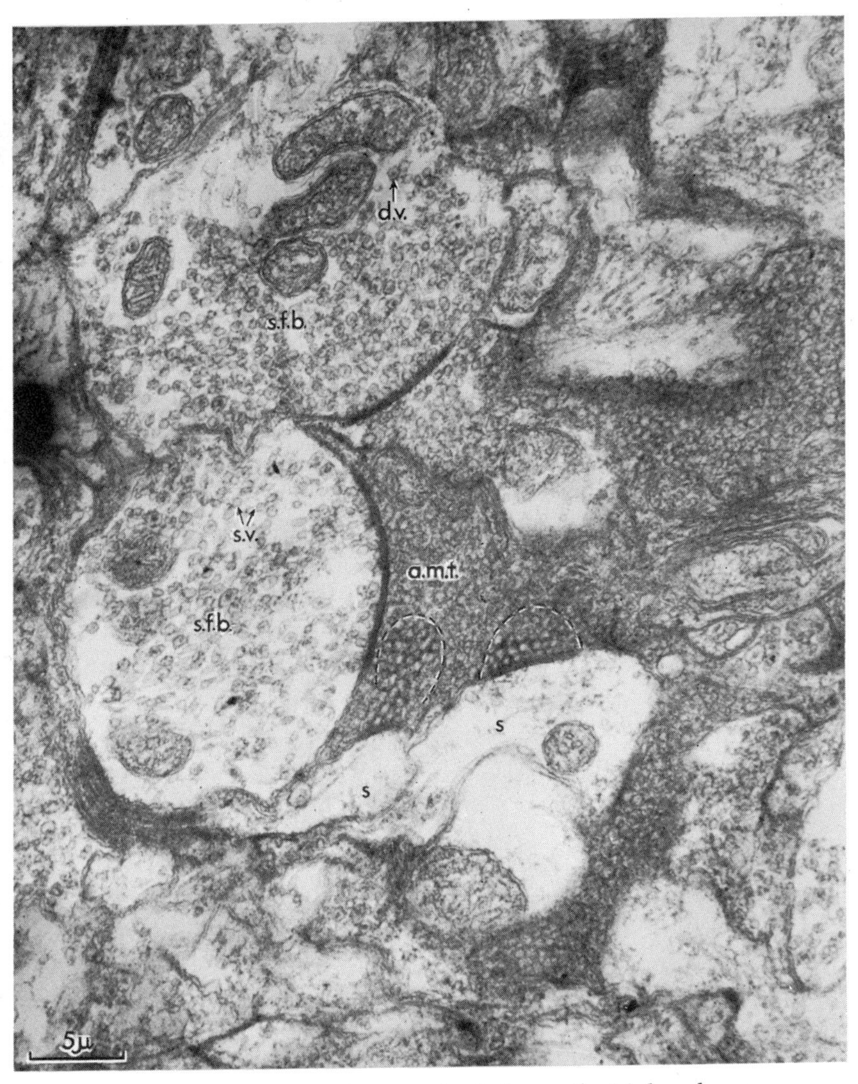

Fig. 18. Electron micrograph of the vertical lobe, showing superior frontal fibres, s.f.b., filled with vesicles, making contact with an amacrine cell; a.m.t. This is also filled with vesicles, and is in turn in contact with spines, s., which have no vesicles. d.v., dense-centred vesicle; s.v., synaptic vesicle. (Gray and Young, 1964)

and synapses with vesicles on both sides are totally absent from the median superior frontal lobe.

Although we do not fully understand the workings of the vertical lobe system, the experiments begin to show various clues to its place in the learning mechanism. Animals from which the vertical lobe is removed show at first no capacity to learn to attack one figure that yields food (say a horizontal rectangle), while not attacking another that gives a shock (say a vertical rectangle), *if these are shown successively* (fig. 19). Not uncommonly they continue to attack each figure at every presentation. This experiment does not show that the actual memory record lies in the vertical lobe system. If the animals are then tested by showing figures alone, without giving either rewards or shocks, they attack the "positive" figure more often than the "negative," although they had previously shown no sign of learning. The responses remain erratic, but are more often right than wrong, showing that something had been learned.

This result may be interpreted as indicating that a record can be written in the optic lobes, more or less correctly, even when they act by themselves, but that without the vertical lobes the record is not properly used or "read-out." When the animal takes food, the tendency to attack is unduly raised, and the record in the memory that prevents attack at the negative figure is not used. An attack occurs in spite of the record in the memory.

This is confirmed by training operated animals in a simultaneous discrimination situation. They now perform reasonably well, though less accurately than nor-

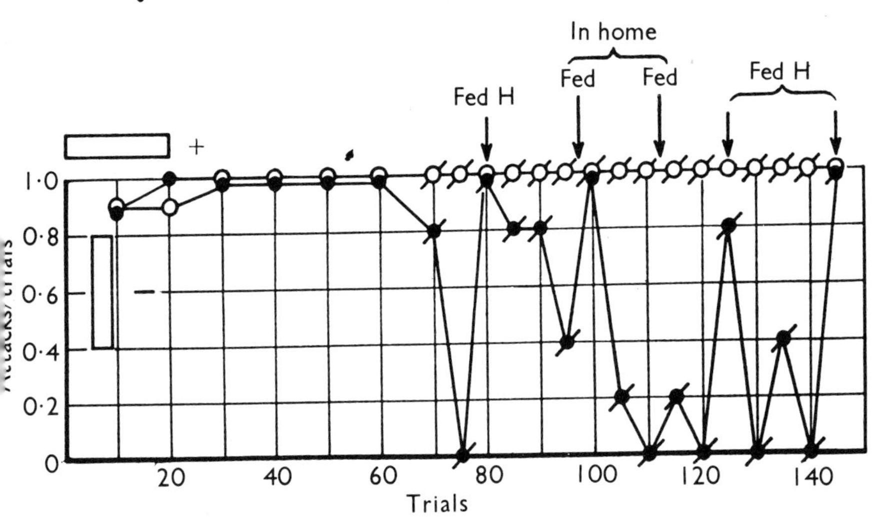

FIG. 19. Plot of responses of an octopus with 85% of the vertical lobe removed. Trained to attack a horizontal but to avoid a vertical rectangle (solid circles) it seemed to learn nothing in 60 trials, attacking nearly every time. In a series of tests without rewards (all barred circles) performance was correct, but again deteriorated when food was given (at the points shown with arrows). This happened whether the food was given in the home (Fed H) or with the horizontal rectangle. (After Young, 1958)

mal control animals (Muntz, Sutherland, and Young, 1962). In this situation the system must choose one of the two alternatives, whatever the attack level may be, and the information in the memory tips the balance in favour of the correct response.

Animals that had been trained before operation seem at first to have lost all capacity for correct response after removal of the vertical lobes (fig. 20). If they are then re-trained, however, they recover a degree of discrimination. This again shows that a record can be established outside the vertical lobe system. However, the performance was much more accurate when trials were given at intervals of five minutes than at hourly intervals. Much re-learning took place within each session (when trials were given at five-minute intervals) and was then forgotten before the next set of trials began six to twelve hours later. This again can be interpreted by supposing that the vertical lobe system is somehow concerned with maintaining the representation for a sufficient period for it to be "printed" in the more permanent memory.

The Upper Visual Circuit and Transfer of Representations

The demonstration that the actual record is not in the vertical lobe system makes the analysis of the functions of the vertical lobe all the more revealing. One striking result of interrupting its circuit is to prevent transfer to the other side of the body of a representation that is set up by training with only one eye. It was shown by Muntz (1961) that the octopus is particularly suitable

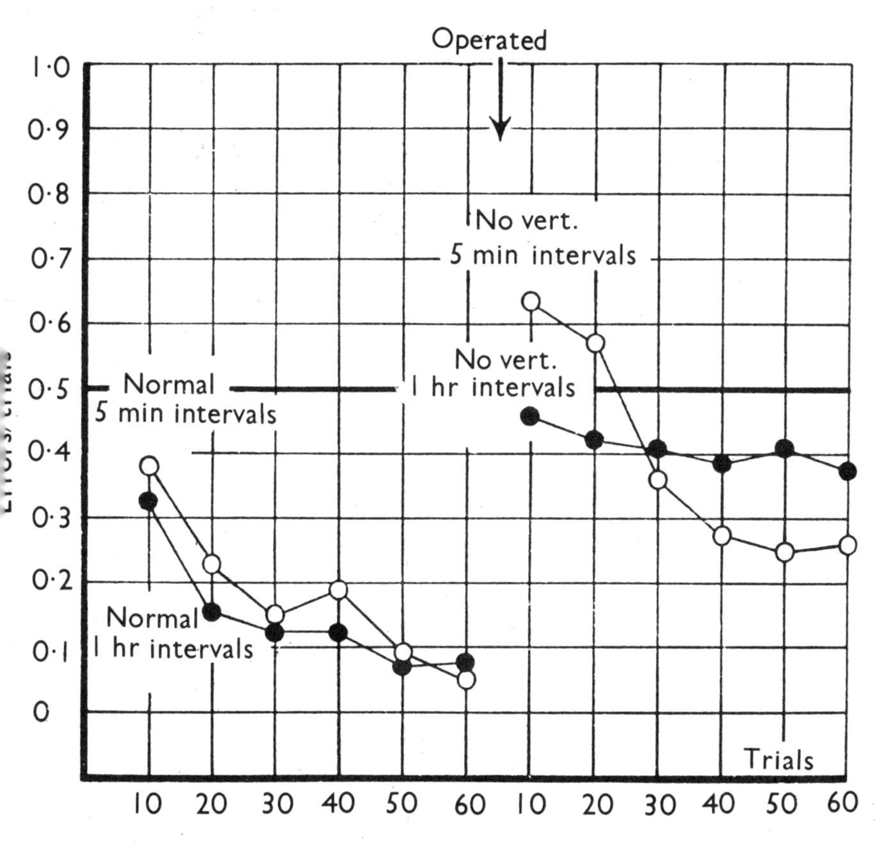

FIG. 20. Plot of the responses of 10 octopuses given trials at 5-minute intervals, and 10 at 60-minute intervals. Before and after removal of the vertical lobe (vert.). Food was given for attack at a horizontal rectangle (open circles), shock for attack at a vertical one (solid circles). Before operation the 5-minute group was slightly the more accurate. After operation it was initially less accurate, but finally more accurate than the 60-minute group. Thus the vertical lobe may serve to hold short-term memory before storage in the optic lobe. (After Young, 1960*b*)

for such experiments. The input can be given to one eye only and the optic lobe of that side then removed. The animal will perform correctly with the other eye, but only if the vertical lobe circuit had been intact during training. This is all the more interesting because the large optic commissure directly connecting the two optic lobes is left intact by the operation. The hypothesis is that the fibres of this commissure serve to connect similar classifying cells on the two sides. When cells classifying for horizontal are activated on one side, similar ones are made active on the other by the actions of the optic commissure. The function of the vertical lobe would then be to deliver to these cells the appropriate signals of taste or pain. The plexus of fibres of the tract that connects the first and second upper lobes allows many opportunities for fibres to cross from one side to the other.

Paired Centres in Sepia

The arrangement of the vertical lobe system, as a circuit re-exciting the optic lobes, suggests that it acts as a positive feedback, increasing the effect of the signals of taste on the memory cells. The internal feedback within the vertical lobe system may well further increase the effect. The significance of self re-exciting systems has been much debated. Many years ago, when a similar circuit was found in the vertical lobe system of *Sepia,* reverberation was suggested as the basis of the memory record (Young, 1938). The vertical lobe system of *Sepia* is simpler than that of *Octopus,* for it has no median superior frontal lobe. Fibres from a lobe with structure somewhat similar to that of the lateral superior frontal of *Octopus* proceed directly to the vertical lobe (fig. 21). From the latter, fibres run partly to the subvertical and thence to the optic lobe, and partly as a feedback to the superior frontal.

Little is known about learning in *Sepia,* but it was shown that the animals are capable of pursuing their prey (a prawn) when it disappears behind a rock (Sanders and Young, 1940). This simple form of memory would be valuable for a cuttlefish. After removal of the vertical lobe the animals were unable to hunt in this way. When a prawn disappeared from sight the cuttlefish without vertical lobe abandoned the search. The suggestion made at the time was that in a normal *Sepia* reverberation maintains what would now be called a "representation" of the prawn (Young, 1938). It is curious that this suggestion was made when, so far as I can remember, I had never heard about self re-exciting circuits in electrical engineering. I had of course read about them in the experiments and discussions of Lorente de Nó (1936) in relation to the control of eye movements.

Paired Centres and Addressing in the Memory

No one now considers that the permanent record in the brain is a continuous circulating memory, but probably even in mammals circulation plays an important part in maintaining the representation until it is printed. The significance of self re-excitation may be that it bridges the time gap, inevitable when any distance receptor is stimulated, between activation of

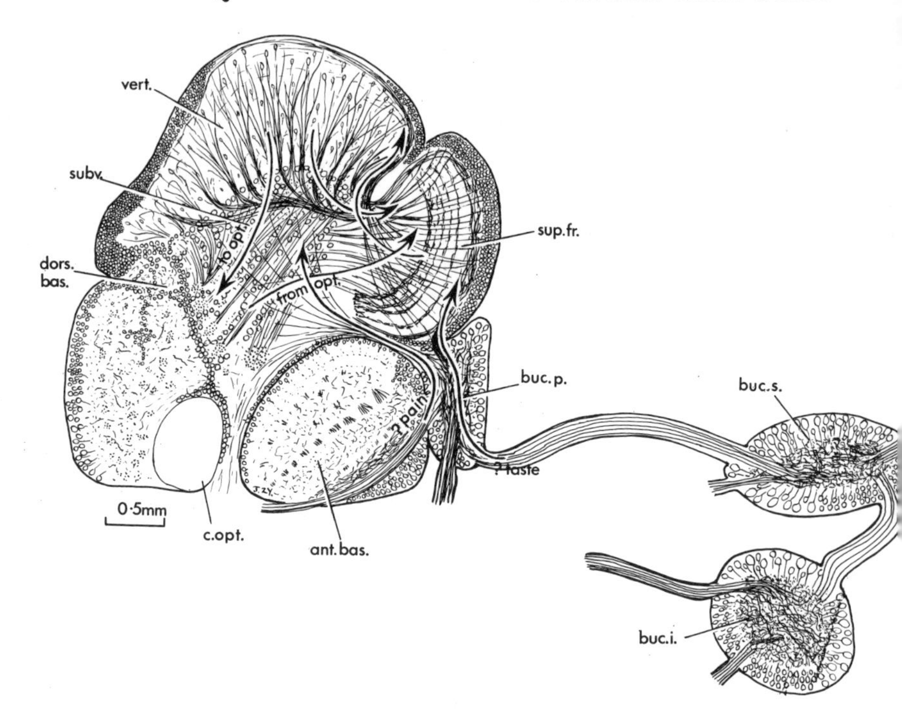

FIG. 21. Drawing of a vertical longitudinal section through the brain of *Sepia*, a decapod. Note that the visual learning system—superior frontal (sup. fr.), vertical (vert.), subvertical (subv.)—is as in *Octopus* but simpler. There is a simpler touch system since decapods rely less on touch than do octopods. The superior buccal is far forward, and there is no inferior frontal or subfrontal. ant. bas., anterior basal lobe; dors. bas., dorsal basal lobe; buc.s., superior buccal lobe; buc.i., inferior buccal lobe; buc.p., posterior buccal lobe; c.opt., optic commissure. (Young, 1963*b*)

the classifying cells and arrival of the signals indicating the result of the action taken. One function of the vertical lobe circuit is probably to maintain the addresses of the classifying cells that have been stimulated and then to deliver to them the appropriate signals when they arrive. In physiological terms this would consist in maintaining the relevant cells at a lowered threshold, perhaps by depolarisation.

A function of this sort is indicated by the fact that the octopus without a vertical lobe has especial difficulty in learning not to attack a figure that is unrewarding or painful (Boycott and Young, 1950). Under some circumstances the operated animal can do so only if trials are repeated at very short intervals. However, it is surprising that an octopus without a vertical lobe is still able to make delayed responses. If a crab is placed under one of two cups which the octopus is looking at from behind glass, when released it will choose the right one up to a minute later. This capacity is not lost after removal of the vertical lobe (Dilly, 1963).

Removal of the vertical lobe has shown that it is not the seat of the visual memory record, but is concerned with the establishment and use of that record, as we may say with reading-in and reading-out. How justifiable it is to use these terms remains to be seen. The nervous memory, it may be said, is not a detailed addressed record. But in conventional experiments on conditioning, maze learning, or discrimination we do not usually examine the system with the aims of discovering whether there are records of individual occasions of learning. We are so used to the concept of repeated "trials" as a part of the learning procedure that we forget that characteristic events must happen at each trial. This change at a single occasion of learning, rather than the study of results of repeated trials, should be the goal of physiological enquiry.

We know that the human brain is able to store a record of individual occasions and that this record lasts for many years. In man there is much to indicate that the first time of presentation of a situation is recorded with especial accuracy. Experiments with animals are seldom conducted with a view to discovering whether this is so for them also. To be useful in the wild state the memory must be able to establish records as a result of a relatively small number of occasions. Man and higher animals undergo a long period of learning to learn, during which the "model" is built up in the brain. Once a general representation of the world around is established, a record of the detailed results of fresh experiments can be added very rapidly. Perhaps one of the ways in which a simple memory like that of the octopus differs from our own is that it does not have to learn to learn. Heredity endows the octopus with the power to form quickly associations between relatively few features detected in the environment and the food value or pain that accompanies them. Incidentally, it is of great importance that not everything should be recorded in the memory, and that some items should be held for a short time and then erased. Indeed, "attention" ensures that only a part of the sensory input is filtered through for possible storage in the memory.

Addressing in the Memory and the Stream of Consciousness

The mechanism for reading-in to and reading-out from the memory throws light on the problem of the basis of individuality, including that of man. Although the brain is continuously bombarded with impulses from different receptors and along many channels, yet an animal or man pursues one more or less consistent line of action. Again, each human being follows one stream of consciousness. We "consult the memory" about one question at a time.

These are striking facts in spite of their familiarity, and they suggest that there must be a mechanism that ensures unity of action, and in particular performs an operation that could properly be called "consulting the memory." There is indeed some evidence that the appropriate mechanism is included in the reticular system, which lies at the centre of the gray matter throughout the brain and spinal cord. This system includes neurons that are activated from an exceptionally wide range of afferent sources (Jasper *et al.*, 1958). Efferent neurons from the system reach to many parts of the brain, including the thalamus and cortex. Stimulation of it influences the state of sleeping and produces "arousal responses" in the cortex.

Penfield has long held, as a result of his studies by stimulation of the human brain, that some "centrencephalic system" must exist at the centre of the human personality (see Penfield and Roberts, 1959). It is not possible at present to be very specific, although the problem is crucial for discussion of the nature of the memory system, at least in higher animals.

Systems for selective reading-in and reading-out are likely to be present as important and distinct mechanisms. As we have seen, they appear to be prominent in the octopus. We already possess a considerable amount of information about such systems in mammals. It is no accident that the centres in the hypothalamus that are concerned with establishing the level of need, as in food consumption, are also involved in consummatory acts such as feeding or defence. To initiate such actions is the primary function of the signals of results, taste and pain.

The same regions are involved also in circuits that are essential for recording in the memory. In man, defects of memory follow lesions in the hippocampus (if bilateral) or the mammillary bodies (e.g., Korsakoff's disease). The power affected is that of recording recent events; records already established are not impaired. In some respects the parallel with the vertical lobe system is striking; it suggests that the basal forebrain circuits are concerned with reading-in to the memory and, specifically, with maintaining the "addresses" of the classifying cells, presumably in the neocortex, and sending to them the signals of results. This hypothesis suggests that it would be worth while to look again at the pathways between the limbic system and the neocortex, which would be concerned with such addressing. These structures all form part of a complex system of circuits in which the hippocampus sends impulses down through the fornix to the mammillary bodies. From here fibres pass to the anterior nucleus of the thalamus and thence up again to the cingulate gyrus and so perhaps to other parts of the cortex and back to the hippocampus.

It has long been known that the limbic system somehow constitutes a "circuit of emotion" (Papez). We now begin to see how the involvement in "emotion" may be due to the fact that the system includes not only circuits of "needs" but also of "rewards." Rewards have the function of exciting not only consummation but also memory. Injuries in the hypothalamus or limbic system may thus disturb the whole or parts of the motivational and consummatory system as well as the memory records that go with them. We are only beginning the search for a clear language to speak and write about these centres, which so nearly affect our personality and well-being. It is curious that little attention has been given in the past to the question how nerve impulses in fibres signalling taste or pain can reach to all parts of the memory system of a mammal. They must somehow do so if they are to teach it. We have lacked a model that would suggest what questions may be asked about the connections of the memory. The octopus system, by its relative simplicity, reveals certain features that we may look for in higher nervous systems.

The Chemotactile Learning System of Octopus

Perhaps the strongest confirmation that our analysis of the functions of these circuits is on the right track is that the whole set of lobes is repeated in the part of

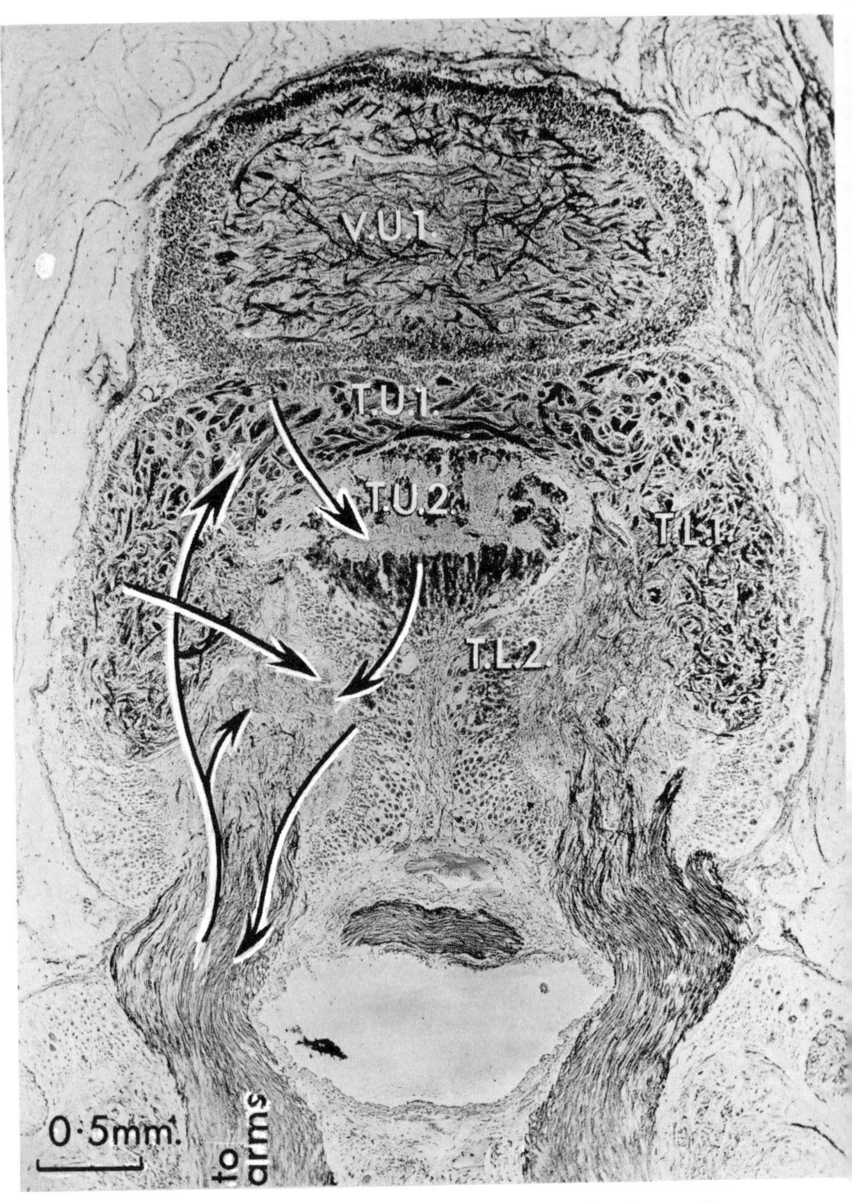

FIG. 22. Transverse section of octopus brain to show centres associated with touch learning. (Abbreviations as in fig. 10)

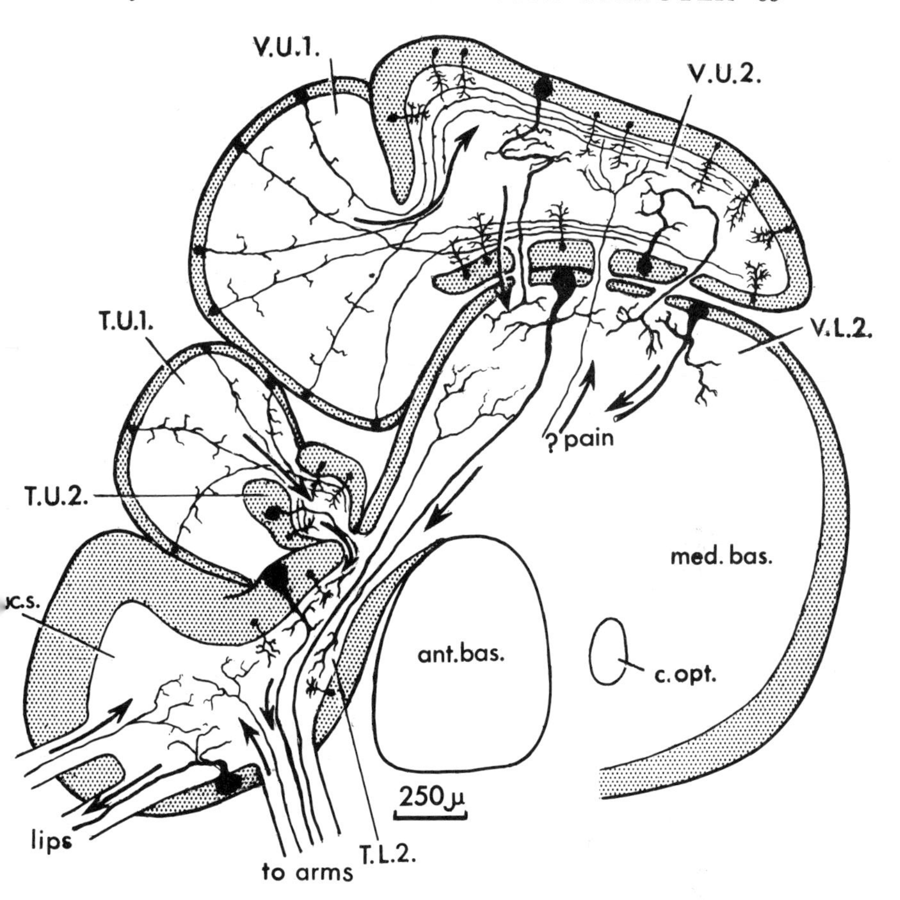

Fig. 23. Diagram of selected cells from various learning centres of octopus brain as revealed by Golgi stain. Compare with figs. 10 and 11. med. bas., median basal lobe. (Other abbreviations as in figs. 10 and 21) (Young, 1963*b*)

the octopus brain that is concerned with learning to discriminate between objects by touch (figs. 22 and 23). Mr. and Mrs. Wells have established (1957) that the animal readily learns to take a rough object but rejects a smooth one. Incidentally, the octopus was unable to distinguish objects by shape alone (i.e., square from cube) or by weight. As the Wellses point out, the amount of positional information coming from a flexible arm that lacks joints probably makes it intolerably difficult to compute its spatial distribution.

The part of the brain that is concerned with touch has four lobes closely similar to those of the visual system, though somewhat less sharply distinct from each other. There is no centre exactly corresponding to the optic lobe, but Wells showed that no learning is possible if the tactile lower second lobe (posterior buccal) is removed. This region of large and small cells apparently functions as the memory store itself. The system is less specialised than the visual one, and the posterior buccal lobe corresponds both to the second lower visual centre (subvertical) and to the optic lobe. This is perhaps a result of the fact that the touch memory is a relatively recent acquisition; hence no distinct tactile lobe comparable to the optic lobe has yet been evolved.

After interference with the upper circuit of the tactile system, simple discriminations can still be made. As in the visual system, these lobes are not the seat of the memory, but are needed for its proper use in more difficult discriminations. Moreover, they are concerned in transfer; after their removal a discrimination that had been learned by teaching only one arm or one side of the body is not performed by the others. Removal of these lobes does not in any way impair visual learning, and removal of the optic lobes does not influence the tactile memory. This is very striking when it is remembered that the optic lobes together weigh more than twice as much as all the rest of the brain. They contain 120,000,000 cells against 40,000,000 in the central ganglia. The entire section of the central system that pertains to touch learning contains 6,400,000 cells; 5,000,000 of these are the minute amacrine cells of the subfrontal lobes (Young, 1963 *a*). Of course the arms contain many cells concerned with touch, but the arm centres by themselves are incapable of learning.

In the octopus, then, visual and tactile memory functions are sharply localised. Yet the two systems are not wholly independent. Wells and Wells (1957) showed that touch learning is unduly slow after removal of the vertical lobe. This will no doubt prove to be another valuable clue to the vertical lobe functions.

We can be encouraged in our search for the principles of recording in the memory by finding these two sets of pairs of centres in the visual and tactile learning systems. Their plans of connection are exceptionally clear and precise. We do not yet fully understand them, even after years of work, but the basic design is beginning to appear. However wrong our interpretations may be in detail, they cannot be wholly so. The sets of pairs of centres are there. They have been proved to play a part in the learning of the octopus. They may provide hints as to the way to study some features of learning in higher animals.

CHAPTER FOUR

The Nature of the Memory Record and the Origin of Learning

Some Essential Features of Neural Memory Systems

A hypothesis that is likely to lead us toward discovery of the changes that occur in a neural memory is that learning consists in the limitation of choice between alternatives. The setting up of a representation in the memory of the nervous system is like the printing of a book in that it involves selecting appropriate items from a pre-established alphabet. We have evidence that such a repertoire exists. Each animal species has limited capacities to react to features of the external environment. Presumably it is similarly limited in the ability to make records in its memory. Brains are not general-purpose computers but specialised analogues. We must qualify this statement, because in the not unimportant case of our own brains we achieve a high degree of generality. In the evolution of the memory mechanisms of primates there has been a gradual release from dependence on the classifying systems built in by heredity. It is worth while to consider how this freedom has been achieved. It has apparently reached the point that the human brain at birth is almost a blank sheet ready to memorise anything. To do this is obviously the goal of the perfect learning homeostat, able to adapt to any environment. If we consider what a feat it would be to succeed in doing this we may be reminded that even our apparently powerful human brain is probably more specialised and limited than we realise. This may also remind us of the urgent need for further study of the human coding and classifying system and of its development, so that we may learn how to train it more efficiently. Until we know something of the principles of the operation of the memory, educational theory can only proceed empirically, with no real scientific basis.

It may be, however, that it is desirable to study first the methods of recording in simpler memory systems than our own. The fact that we are only just beginning to be able to recognise the nature of the problem shows the urgent need for a strategy that may proceed logically from well-understood simpler systems toward our own complicated one.

What essential features would be expected in a neural memory system? It is of little use to study chemical or electrical changes in the brain, or to look for synaptic alterations, unless we first decide what sort of system we are looking for and hence where the changes are likely to be. The need for a logical strategy is imposed on us by the fact that the brain is a multichannel system, with numerous parts of very small size. There are probably at least 10,000 synaptic points on one large cortical neuron (perhaps many more). How many of these would be altered when an animal has learned? Would they all change at once? Would some have been changed by previous learning? Worse still, there must be thousands of synaptic vesicles in a single presynaptic terminal. If learning consists in the production of a flood of inhibitory or excitatory transmitter, what changes, if any, should we expect to see in the vesicles? How many would be changed? The electron microscope is perhaps the one instrument with the resolution in space that is required to see changes, but we must know where to look. So far, we have no evidence on whether the changes are presynaptic (e.g., in the vesicles) or whether they occur in the transmitting or receiving properties of the synaptic membranes.

Some Hypotheses on the Mechanism of Learning

The microelectrode has about 1,000 times less resolution in space than the electron microscope, but its resolution in time is millions of times greater. It has already provided some interesting evidences of changes during learning, which it is not possible to summarise here (see Jasper and Smirnov, 1960). There is evidence of persistence of the effects of volleys of stimuli (post-tetanic potentiation or depression). When an animal is subjected to rhythmical stimuli the appropriate rhythm may appear in the brain, at least in some stages of learning, especially in the hippocampus (Adey *et al.*, 1960; Jasper *et al.*, 1958). Characteristic patterns of electrical activity can be transmitted across the brain to mirror foci and can be made to endure there (Morrell, 1960, 1961). Such results provide valuable clues, but they do not show how the changes serve the function of writing a particular record in the memory.

It is difficult to evaluate the work of Hydén (1960), who identifies the record as written by changes in the base ratios of ribosenucleotides in the nerve cells. The technique used, which makes possible the study of single cells, at least approaches the spatial resolution that is needed. To identify changes in base ratios in single cells is indeed a feat. The results suggest that some modification of the RNA is included in the learning changes. As Hydén has emphasised, these nucleotides are so abundant in nerve cells that it would be strange if they were not involved in the memory. It is not yet possible to see exactly how the changes that Hydén reports are connected with the actions that were learned, for example, by a rat balancing upon a wire. It would not be easy to specify exactly what alterations in motor pattern are concerned. Most serious of all, it is difficult to believe that the coding system includes the volleys of impulses of specifically timed frequency that Hydén's theory seems to require, or that these frequencies would be in the right range to control the synthesis of specific RNA's.

However, there seems to be evidence that changes in RNA base ratios do occur during learning, and this is to be expected. It does not necessarily follow that the changes in the RNA specifically embody the particular item to be recorded. A characteristic feature of brains as multichannel systems is that they achieve specificity by allowing particular channels for each item in the alphabet, rather than by passing coded signals along each channel. Similarly for the memory, our hypothesis here will be that each item is written in the memory by changing the state of a particular set of cells. The capacity for such change is almost certainly dependent upon the cell nucleotides and they themselves may well alter with the change. But the item recorded is not a function of the particular nucleotide change; it is a feature that the cell was pre-set to record. In this pre-setting, achieved during embryological development, the cell nucleotides provide the instructions by which a memory capable of recording certain items is built.

Learning by Closing Unneeded Channels

The thesis here advanced is that it may prove possible to make further progress by considering situations in which the record made in the memory during learning is the result of a choice between two specific alternatives. Most behaviour is compounded of a series of choices. For our purposes it is convenient to study situations in which the animal clearly does one of two things according to the record in its memory. In the octopus we have two such situations: the attack or retreat when some object moves in the visual field, and the taking or rejecting of an object by the arms. We know something of the cells and pathways that are involved and we can draw up a scheme for the process of recording in the memories. Moreover, we can form some idea how these memory systems have arisen from a state in which the brain was not capable of learning.

If the classifying cells of the visual system have been correctly identified we may suppose that they have outputs that can lead to either attack or retreat. The learning change consists, as suggested in the second chapter, in closing one of these channels (fig. 8). This may be brought about through collaterals of the cells, here labelled "memory cells" (because they provide the alternatives for choice). These collaterals may activate the small cells, of which there are many in the cell islands of the optic lobes, causing them to block the alternative pathway. There is little evidence, unfortunately, about the details of the anatomy or connections of the cells at the centre of the optic lobes—a vast tangle of fibres which has not been adequately described with the light microscope, let alone with the electron microscope. Small cells accompanying large are commonly found in this region, as in the parts of the brains that are thought to be responsible for learning in vertebrates and arthropods. They are found again in the touch learning centres of an octopus. It has been suggested for many years that some of the small cells in the spinal cord have the function of producing an inhibitory transmitter in a pathway (see Wall, 1964; Eccles, 1964). The present suggestion is that in centres that learn this process has been extended. These small cells have become specialised, with the result that upon receipt of appropriate signals they manufacture or release enough inhibitor to block the alternative path for a long time, perhaps permanently. There are many ways in which this could be achieved. In the vertical lobe, numerous small cells make serial synapses, at which there are vesicles on both sides of the membrane. These may well be sites of presynaptic inhibition. It is possible that the small cells of the optic lobes are similar and that they can produce a flood of inhibitor around the presynaptic junctions. Perhaps there is a suitably triggered enzyme system, itself held inhibited, to be released at the appropriate signal. The analogy of the mechanisms of genetic control is obvious and may suggest experimental approaches. The connection with the RNA metabolism may be found in the special mechanisms of synthesis of inhibitor that are needed.

It is not profitable to speculate further, but the hypothesis can in principle be tested at the chemical level, though little is yet known of synaptic transmitters in Cephalopods (see Welsh, 1961). Perhaps the touch learning system is even more suitable for study than the visual one. Wells showed originally, and he and I have recently confirmed, that learning to take a rough object and to reject a smooth one can take place with relatively few large cells, surrounded by a few tens of thousands of minute ones (figs. 24 and 25). Moreover, in animals functionally bisected we have been able to teach the two sides in opposite directions. There is here a wonderful material that has perhaps as much simplicity as can be expected in a learning system. When all the higher parts of the brain have been removed, the octopus lies as a postureless preparation, yet it is able, as soon as it touches an object, to draw it in or push it away. It is worth directing microelectrodes, electron microscopes, and microspec-

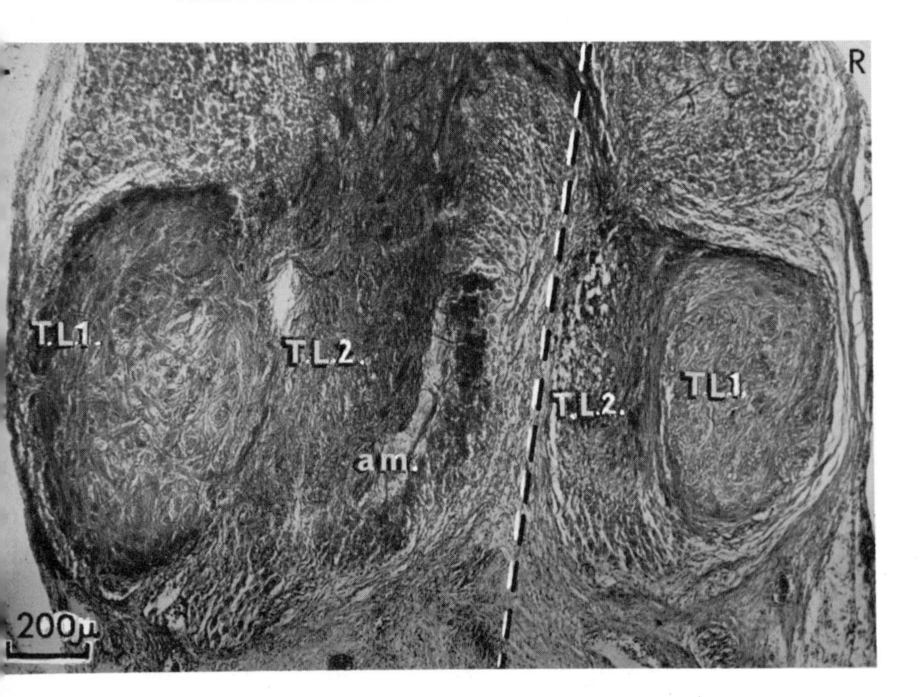

FIG. 24. Horizontal section of tactile learning centres of octopus after bisection. The cut has passed to the right of mid-line and has destroyed all small-celled tissue on that side. As a result, the left side was able to learn but not the right side (see fig. 25). am., amacrine cells. (Wells and Young, unpublished)

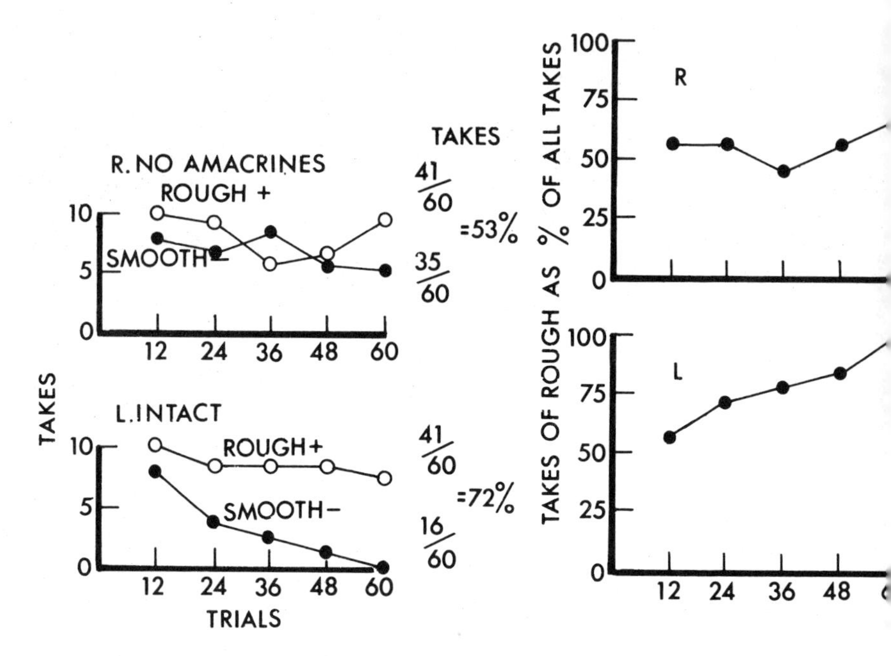

FIG. 25. Plot of sequence of learning by the preparation shown in fig. 24. Both sides were trained to take a rough cylinder (open circles) and reject a smooth one (solid circles). This was possible on left, but both cylinders continued to be drawn in on right. (Wells and Young, unpublished)

trometers on the relatively restricted regions that are concerned and to study whether the learning powers are affected by pharmacological agents, for example those that are are likely to inhibit protein synthesis.

There is certainly much work to be done. Even the gross details of the cells of this region are poorly known. A few of them have been seen stained with the Golgi method. Many of the large cells have two main trunks, and it is tempting to think of these as providing the two alternative pathways, for drawing in and for rejecting. But the sample available for study is small and imperfect. The small cells that send their axons into the neuropil alongside the large cells are packed with synaptic vesicles, like the similar cells of the vertical and subfrontal lobes (Graziadei, personal communication). They frequently show serial synapses, which provide the possible basis for presynaptic inhibition. If they have no long axon their function cannot be to transmit signals over a distance. It is much more likely that they serve to produce large amounts of a substance locally, perhaps the inhibitory transmitter. It is a problem why these cells are so small and numerous. It can hardly be to provide numerous specific channels. They must be highly redundant. Is it a matter of supplying large surface areas?

Unresolved Complications of the Hypothesis

In discussions of possible synaptic changes during learning it is usually assumed that the change is an increase in the ease of passage along a particular pathway, and that this increase occurs gradually, that is, partially on each occasion of learning (see, e.g., Taylor, 1964). The opposite hypotheses have been put forward here: that learning is by the inhibition of an unwanted pathway, and that this occurs suddenly and completely in each unit or module, the mnemon that is concerned. It would not fundamentally alter the character of the hypothesis to suppose that learning consists in lowering the threshold of the path that has been used. The circuits of figure 8 would be different in the sense that the collaterals would return to the pathway used, perhaps through small cells triggered to release material that increases excitability. There are various reasons for preferring the inhibitory hypothesis. The required negative feedback circuits are prominent in reflex systems and hence provide a ready-made system that with slight alteration could have evolved into a learning system. Positive feedback systems exist, but if they were used they would leave the alternative (unused) pathway still open (though unfacilitated) and in this sense the system would be inefficient. An even more serious difficulty is that the collateral system would have to increase the excitability of synapses in which they were not directly concerned (although made with the same cell). As Burns (1958) has pointed out, no such vicarious facilitation has ever been observed.[1] It is not impossible to imagine such a process,

[1] Heterosynaptic facilitation has however recently been recorded in a small proportion of neurons of the gastropod *Aplysia* (Kandel and Tauc, 1965).

for example by altering the level of polarisation of the whole cell, but the difficulty is less for the inhibitory hypothesis, especially if the clamp is placed by presynaptic inhibition.

However, the change may be in either direction or both. It is not even essential that there be more than one pathway. The alternative might be that the output from a given classifying cell be either used or not used. It is essential for the module to have classifying cells, each with one or more outputs, each provided with specialised systems capable of changing the probability of use of the channel after the arrival of impulses indicating the results of action.

The arrangement of the paired centres suggests that the signals of results are delivered in such a way as to compute the solution "attack—unless" for stimulation of each classifying cell. It is doubtful, however, whether this can be the complete solution. It does not allow for any direction of multiplied pain signals to the memory. No information is available as to types of combinations that are set up in the vertical lobe circuit. Are they all alike or are there various specific sorts? We are correspondingly ignorant in regard to the types of connection that are made in the feedback systems from the vertical (V.U.2) to the lateral superior frontal (V.L.1) and subvertical (V.L.2) to optic lobes. There may be much specificity, built-in or acquired, in these connections. If this is so, they may enter into the actual long-term storage functions of the memory in an even more intimate manner than has been suggested above.

It is assumed that the learning change is sudden and complete, for each cell concerned, on a single occasion of learning. This assumption is made because memory records of single occasions can be set up in men and animals, and rapid learning seems desirable for many situations in nature. However, there are obvious disadvantages as well as advantages in sudden changes in the probability of response. It is assumed here that changes in behaviour are not erratic because only some mnemons are switched at each occasion of learning. But it may well be that the learning cells are only partially switched at each "trial." This would again not fundamentally alter the hypothesis.

No provision is made here for erasure from the memory, since we have no evidence of this in the octopus. Human beings and animals certainly remember some things for a very long time. What we commonly call "forgetting" often seems to be more a matter of displacement by other "memories" or simply of failure to read-out from a record that is felt to be present though inaccessible. However, there might be a process of erasure, with re-use of units, although it is difficult to see how this would occur.

So many qualifications of the hypothesis must be made that in all honesty it must be admitted on examination to be little more than a rather vague guess. It is considered to be a guess worth making, however, not only to emphasise how little we know, but to direct attention to the nature of the information that we need.

The Evolution of the Learning Centres of Cephalopods

The touch learning system of the octopus has special attraction in that it has arisen relatively recently in the course of evolution. It has provided us with strong hints as to how a system regulated only by the hereditary memory became converted into a system with the capacity to store information during its lifetime. The octopods probably diverged from the squids and the cuttlefishes at least one hundred million years ago, in the Cretaceous Period, perhaps earlier (Donovan, 1964). Both derived from a previous stock resembling the living *Nautilus.* The squids and other decapods have no elabourate touch memory system (fig. 21). These animals manœuvre under visual guidance and then shoot out the long arms to seize their prey. There is little or no tactile exploration of the object seized, which is immediately bitten. In *Octopus,* in contrast, the arms reach for a considerable distance and are continually used in exploration of situations that are out of sight. The arms thus operate as distance receptors. Learning which of the objects touched are likely to yield food must be of great importance. In *Nautilus* the supra-oesophageal or cerebral cord shows none of the special centres found in modern forms (Young, 1965 *b*), (fig. 26). Yet equivalent structures can be vaguely discerned, as if they are still only partly differentiated. The entire front of the cord is concerned with regulating the buccal mass. The rest of

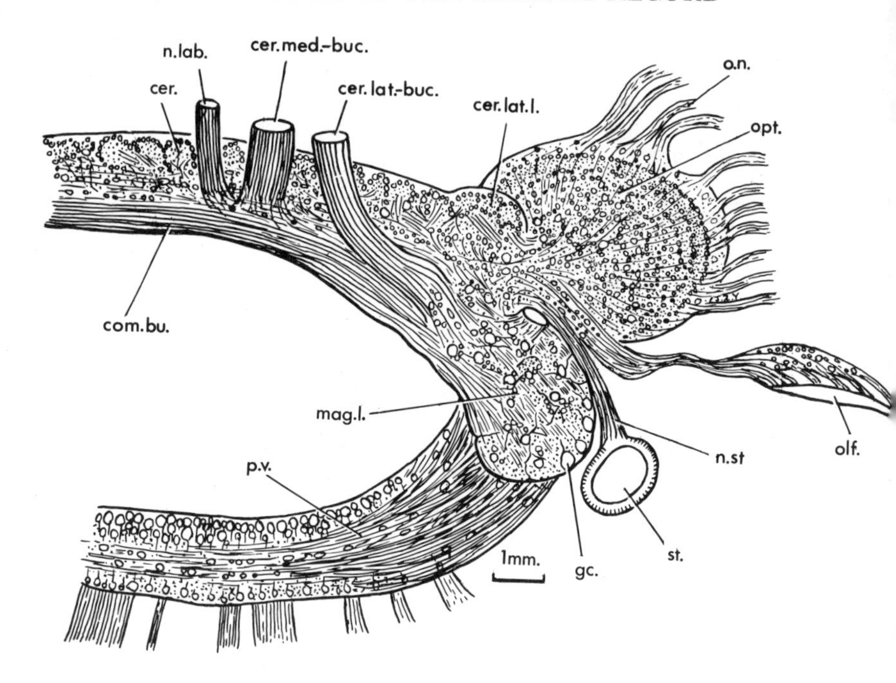

FIG. 26. Transverse section of circum-oesophageal nerve ring of primitive cephalopod, *Nautilus*. The simple eyes are presumably unable to report with accuracy on distant happenings. There is consequently relatively little development of the visual centres. The olfactory organ and its centres are large. The supra-oesophageal (cerebral) cord does not show the differentiated centres found in higher forms. It appears to be concerned mainly with control of eating and perhaps of bringing the animal to the situation where it can eat. cer., cerebral cord; cer. lat.-, cer. med.-buc., nerve trunks leading to ganglia that control the eating apparatus; cer.lat.l, lateral cerebral lobe; com. bu., commissural bundles; g. c., giant cell; mag.l., magnocellular lobe, a motor centre; n.lab., labial nerves; n.st., static nerves; olf., olfactory organ and nerve; opt., optic lobe; o.n., optic nerves; p.v., palliovisceral cord, a motor centre; st., statocyst, a gravity receptor. (Modified from Young, 1964*a*)

the cord provides systems that seem to allow opportunity for interaction between visual, tactile, and olfactory inputs. (The animal is macrosmatic and has a pinhole camera eye.) There is no information on whether the animal has a memory.

Perhaps the chief point to be learned from this *Nautilus* brain is that the higher cerebral centres have arisen within the system for the control of eating. Presumably a major part of the input from the special receptors is concerned with getting the animal into a situation where it can eat. In *Octopus* the touch memory system has developed out of the centre that at first was concerned only with the control of the eating apparatus of the buccal mass and the correlation of this control with that for arm movements.

Development of the Paired Centres of the Octopus

In an unhatched octopus the elaborate centres connected with the two memory systems have not yet developed (fig. 27). The tactile system is a single lobe in the position of the posterior buccal, hardly distinguishable from the superior buccal lobe. The median inferior frontal is a mere commissure in the mid-line and the subfrontals are hardly apparent, as groups of cells on the median wall (fig. 28). Thus the small-celled special lobes develop above the basal centres with large cells. The upper parts provide interweaving networks, and thus opportunities for interaction between inputs, and responses to particular sets of them. The small cells of the upper parts, somehow concerned with recording in the memory, are a devel-

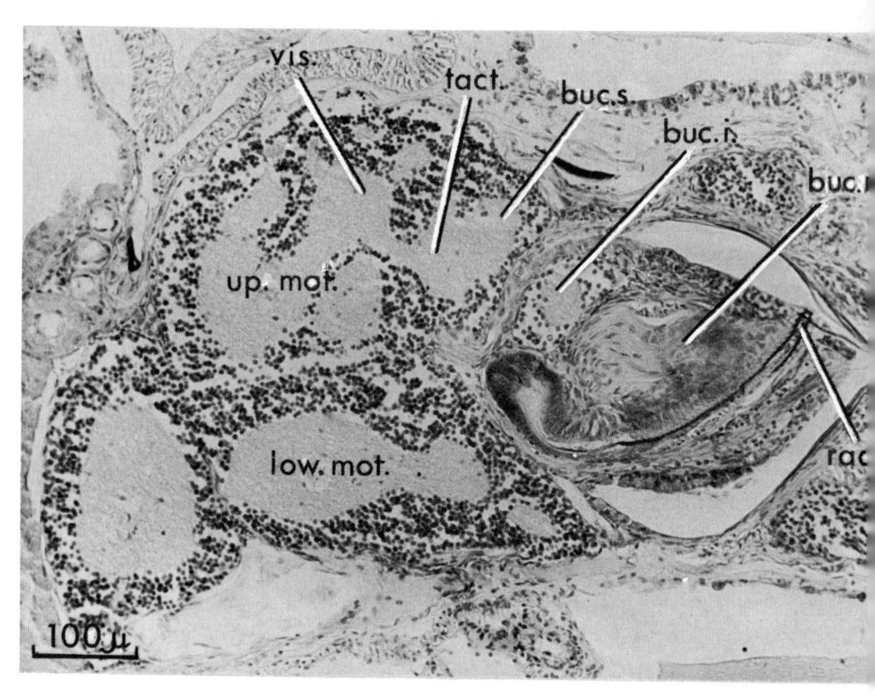

Fig. 27. Vertical longitudinal section through brain of a developing octopus. Note that lower centres are well developed before higher learning centres appear. buc.i., inferior buccal ganglion (centre for control of jaws and radula); buc.m., buccal mass, including muscles of jaws; buc.s., superior buccal ganglion, regulating all processes of killing and eating; low.mot., lower motor centres; rad., radula; tact., region where paired tactile centres will differentiate; at this stage they form a single lobe; up.mot., upper motor centres; vis., region where paired visual centres will differentiate; the median superior frontal and vertical lobes are just discernible at top. (Young, 1965*c*)

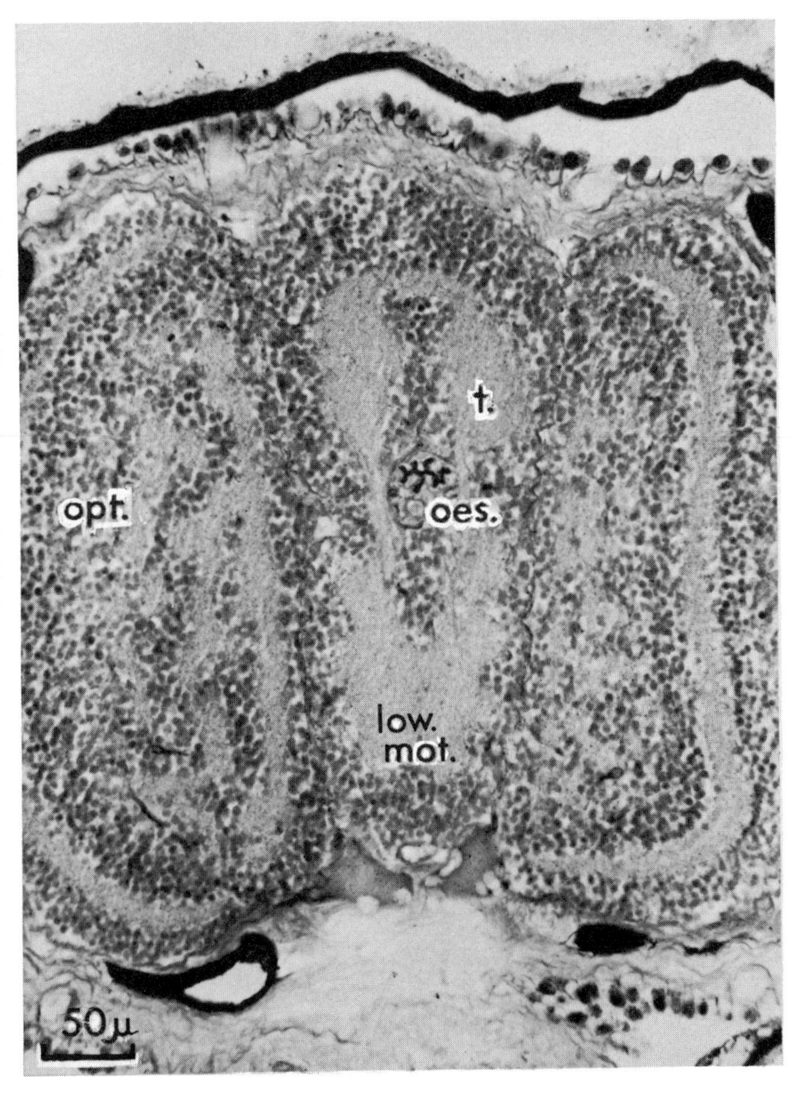

FIG. 28. Transverse section through unhatched octopus embryo at level of future paired tactile centres. At this stage they consist of a single pair of lobes (*t.*), joined by a commissure. The latter will develop into median inferior frontal lobe. low.mot., lower motor centres; oes., oesophagus; opt., optic lobe. (Young, 1965*c*)

opment of the small cells, mixed with the large, in the lower part of the system (fig. 29).

The visual memory centres also are hardly differentiated at the stage shown in figure 27. The subvertical lobe (second lower visual) is the centre out of which the others develop. It is broadly continuous with the second lower tactile centre (posterior buccal) (fig. 30). Thus the visual system, although much older than the tactile, probably developed originally by modification of the centres concerned with bringing the animal into a situation where it can eat.

These embryological facts may guide us in looking for the precursors of the memory systems. Learning cannot have appeared suddenly, but must have depended upon genetic changes that altered the previous synaptic arrangements, making them modifiable with use. Several workers have suggested that learning is based upon the alterations that take place in conduction through reflex arcs when they are either rested or strongly stimulated (see Eccles, 1964). The learning process must be a development of some such increase or decrease, with use, of conduction along pathways. The present hypothesis is that the chief factor is a decrease in the unwanted pathway, as by the continued release of an inhibitor.

The Origin of Learning

Even when the octopods were at a pre-memory stage, when seizure of food by the arms was the result of an inherited reflex mechanism, there must have been systems for inhibiting this seizure, for example at the

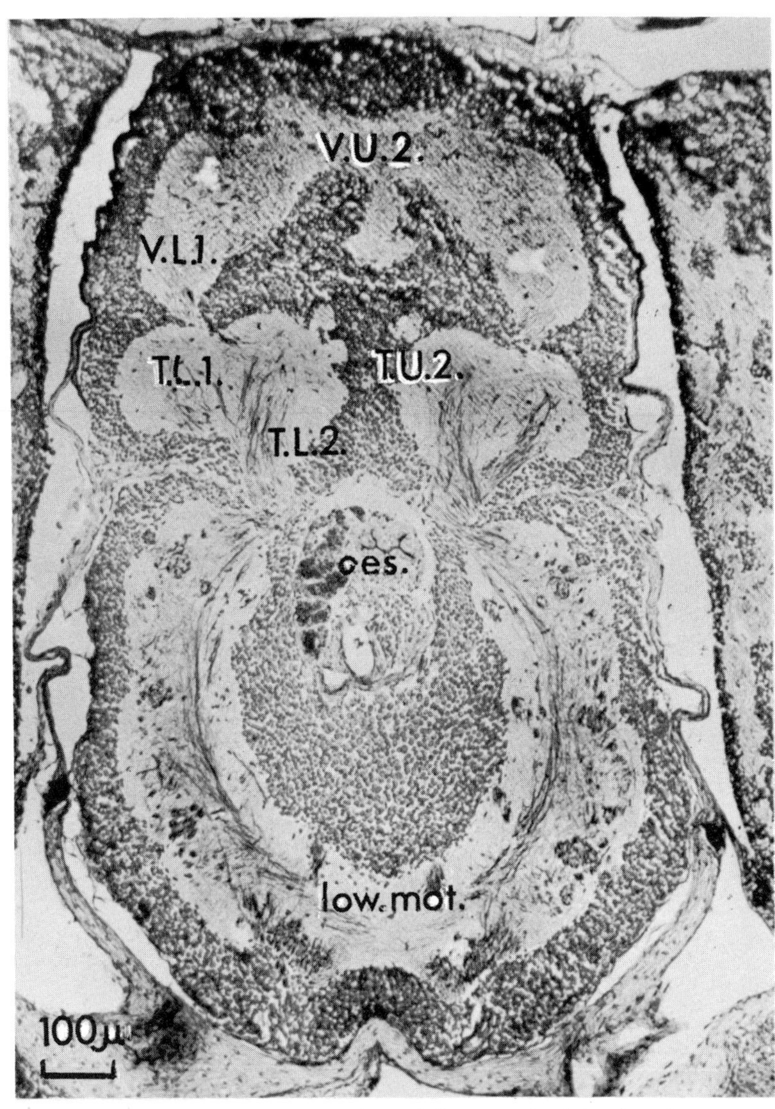

FIG. 29. Transverse section of front end of brain of an octopus at stage of hatching. The two lower tactile centres (T.L.1, T.L.2) are now differentiated. The second upper centre (T.U.2) is beginning to form as median wall of the original single lobe. The first upper centre does not show in this section. (Young, 1965*c*)

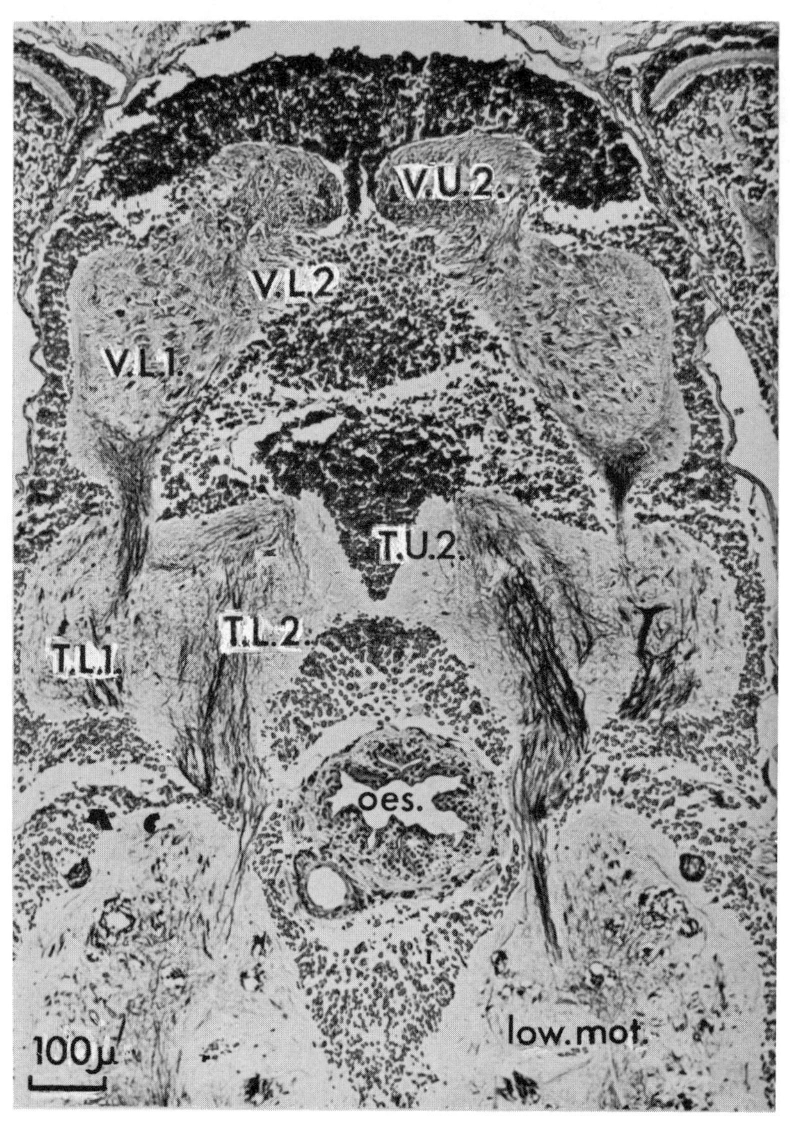

FIG. 30. Transverse section of front part of brain of a young octopus (2g). The tactile centres have further differentiated. Note that second upper centre (subfrontal) forms as median wall. The tactile first upper centre lies in another section. (Young, 1965*c*)

sudden onset of pain (figs. 31 and 32). In any animal organisation that permits a range of possible reflex actions there must be mechanisms for inhibiting the use of operations that are not required at the moment (Sherrington, 1947). This is an essential feature of the system of choices by which the homeostat operates. It is now suggested that the memory system has evolved by specialising the metabolism of the inhibitory cells so that they make long-lasting alterations in the probability of use of a given pathway. It has often been suspected that the basis of learning may be found in the changes that are known to occur during the use of reflex pathways, as in post-tetanic potentiation (Eccles and McIntyre, 1953). At first the change might have been simply a longer action of the inhibitory cells of certain reflex arcs, perhaps by eliminating responses that were consistently followed by pain. This would hardly be an efficient system to operate at the lowest motor levels if it led to the prolonged disuse of certain muscles. The development of alternative outputs at higher levels must have been an early stage in the evolution of the memory. The inhibitory systems, which already operated the hereditary mechanisms of choice, were then available with relatively little modification to close one channel and provide a long-lasting record. As evidence that something like this occurred, there are small cells in the superior buccal lobe, the reflex centre that controls eating in an octopus. Presumably they perform the function of inhibiting reflexes that are temporarily unwanted. The small cells lie mainly in the inner cell layers, near the neuropil. The centres for touch learning are directly continuous with this su-

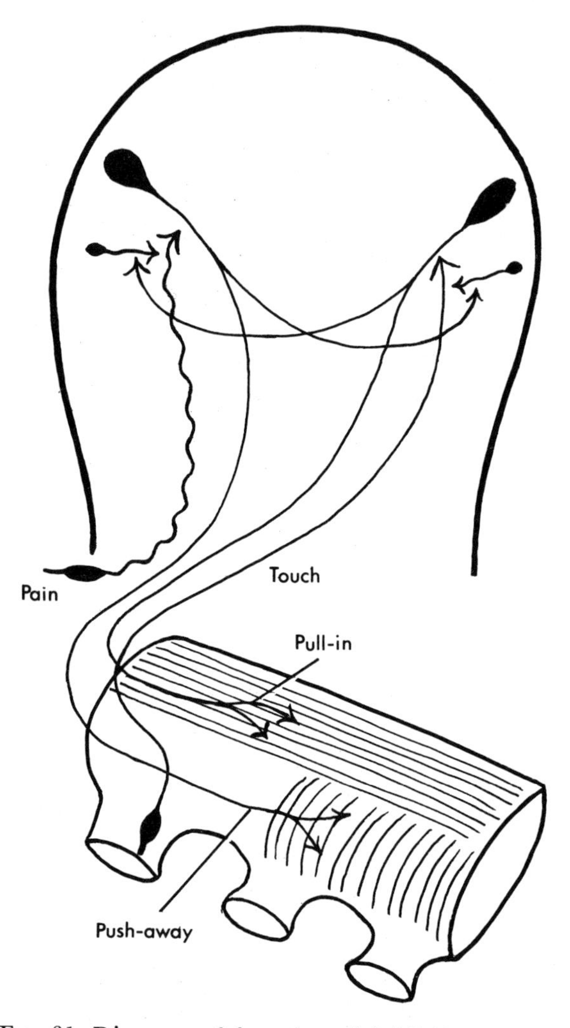

Fig. 31. Diagram of function of inhibitory small cells in a hypothetical purely reflex system. If sucker sense organ is stimulated alone, only one response, "pull-in," can occur. The opposite, "push-away," is inhibited by a collateral of the motor cell stimulating an inhibiting cell next to the cell controlling "push-away." Conversely, when pain receptors are stimulated, "push-away" is activated, "pull-in" inhibited.

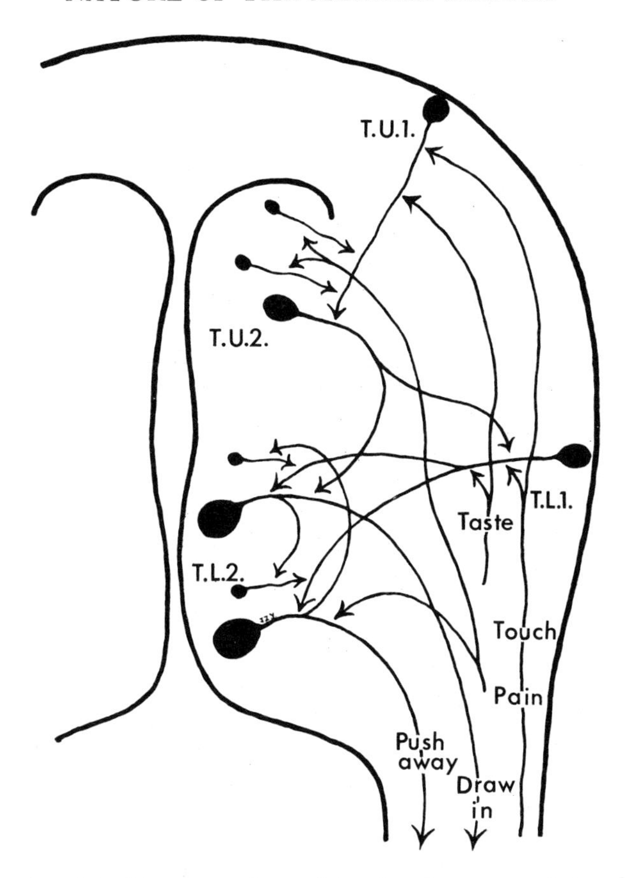

FIG. 32. Diagram of possible development of touch learning system from a reflex type as shown in fig. 31. The touch fibres have acquired two possible outputs through T.L.1. If, when a particular set of them is stimulated, "taste" results, the two sets of signals will combine in T.L.1 and activate the "draw in" neuron in T.L.2. This, through collaterals, will inhibit the "push-away" neuron in T.L.2. Inhibition can be set up by these two lobes acting alone, but is reinforced by the upper circuit through T.U.1 and T.U.2. The combination of touch and taste signals will reinforce the tendency to draw in (and inhibit the other) *unless* pain signals arrive, operating the "push-away" pathway.

perior buccal lobe, and their numerous minute cells are directly continuous with the inner layers of small cells in the reflex lobe (fig. 22).

Much is involved in making a useful learning system. If the classifying cells are not directly connected with fixed outputs it will obviously be advantageous to have a system for allowing representations of the actions of various sets of them to be set up in the memory. This is provided for in the octopus where the input fibres from the arms pass on to the upper part of the system, and there interweave and allow various combinations to be recorded. This is the origin of the upper circuits of the octopus systems. The significance of the fantastic nerve-fibre webs of the median inferior and superior frontal lobes is that they make possible many combinations of signals from the receptors and of those with signals of taste. The output from these combinations does not, however, leave the system at once, but passes to lobes consisting mainly of still smaller cells, whose axons do not even leave the lobe. While we do not fully understand the significance of these minute cells, the evidence is that they allow signals of pain to establish, when necessary, their effects in the memory. Both taste and pain signals were already entering the pre-memory system, serving to operate the appropriate reflexes. To produce a memory system, the specific afferents and the fibres carrying signals of results have continued into literally "higher" regions, above the reflex ones. These regions contain small and very small cells, which operate upon the combined inputs and then return signals to the more basal regions, where the actual memory cells lie. These may be relatively large cells with alternative possible outlets, one of which is then closed.

This sequence of changes has been discussed in relation to the touch learning system because this is a relatively recent acquisition and it has been possible to suggest how it may have arisen. The visual centres probably had a similar origin, much earlier. Their output is through the second lower centre, the subvertical lobe, which is a direct backward continuation of the posterior buccal lobe. The optic lobe can be regarded as an immense outgrowth of the subvertical. It appears clearly in *Nautilus* as a lateral extension of the supraoesophageal cord (fig. 26). The optic system, like the tactile, has grown out of the feeding system. All cephalopods, being carnivores, depend upon making correct predictions about the probability of obtaining food from objects attacked from a distance or touched. To make such predictions it has been an advantage to them to develop a neural memory system, which provides instructions that can be brought up to date more rapidly than is possible by the hereditary mechanism alone.

The touch learning system, acquired relatively recently by octopods, has been lost again in some members of that order. The Argonautidae are octopuses that have left the sea bottom and returned to live at the sea surface. In them the whole inferior frontal system has become greatly reduced, presumably because the information from the arms is of less value for life away from the bottom.

Control of the Collection of Information

The means for collecting information presumably change continually as organisms evolve. Nature thus develops a series of mechanisms, each suitable for dealing with a particular environment. To study the functioning of these variants of nervous organisation is the true comparative neurology. Such study requires that we understand the evolutionary history of the types of animal concerned. The variants that are revealed help to show the fundamental modes of functioning of the nervous system.

One of the most interesting variables among animal species is the length of life between generations. There is obviously some relation between the acquiring of information by shuffling the genetic determinants and the more direct means provided by the nervous system. There are enormous differences in length of life. A bacterium may live for ten minutes, a protozoan for some days (say 10^3 mins). Many animals live for a year (5×10^5 mins), larger ones for several years (up to 10^7 mins), and very few for 10^8, which is about a hundred years. What is the significance of these differences of one hundred million times in lengths of life? Surely it is that bacteria can live in only a limited range of habitats, in spite of their adaptability, whereas large organisms have more elaborate homeostatic equipment and take longer to unfold it. This is one of the distinctions we have in mind when we say that mammals are higher organisms than bacteria (Young, 1962 *a*).

The size of the brain and the length of life are

clearly related. Mammals with small brains breed often, and vice versa. The relationship is not precise, perhaps because we do not know how to measure the nervous system. To weigh it or even to count its cells is but a crude procedure. But clearly there is some relationship between brain and length of life and it is interesting that in a wide variety of animals the length of life is itself regulated by nerve centres that lie close to the learning mechanism, or are even a part of it. In mammals the rate of maturation is controlled by the hypothalamus, through the pituitary. The hypothalamo-hypophyseal tract is the only motor nerve leaving the forebrain and, incidentally, it works by neurosecretion.

Similar arrangements control the development of insects and crustacea and we have now found essentially the same arrangement in cephalopods. The optic gland controls the time of maturity of the female octopus and is itself controlled by a nerve arising from a centre immediately below the learning centres (Boycott and Young, 1955; Wells and Wells, 1959). It is not known that neurosecretion is involved here.

The Human Information-Collecting System

This similar situation in phyla so diverse is one of many instances in which similar problems evoke similar mechanisms. As animals evolved better powers of learning, it was necessary to find means of ensuring that they lived long enough to learn. As we come to see more precisely how such mechanisms play a part in the homeostasis of the species we shall know better what significant features of the control system to look for.

This may be of especial importance to Man, in whom the mechanism for acquiring information by the individual is greatly hypertrophied, and the time of development and maturation correspondingly lengthened. The acceleration of the rate of change in man's condition over the last few millennia has been the result of the development of codes by which information can be passed directly from one individual to another. This might be called "multiparental inheritance." We acquire information not just from two parents but from many. Indeed, we establish artificial information stores outside our bodies. We thus, as it were, construct models of the world outside our brains and outside our own genetic system. By proper use of these models we should be able to elaborate a system of homeostasis that overcomes all the risks posed by the environment.

But obviously there are dangers of misusing these powers. There must be co-operation between individuals and this means training during a prolonged pre-adult period. Only by delay in the development of fully adult characters do individuals become sufficiently tractable to operate the powerful systems that have developed. It has been said that man is a foetal ape. To paraphrase this—we are men because we never reach full apehood. To continue to develop our capacities for co-operation is perhaps the chief task confronting mankind. We must become even more like little children. The basis of this change may well be neurendocrine systems such as those we have been discussing. To find the principles upon which maturation is regulated in diverse animals may provide a modest contribution to man's survival.

References

Adey, W. R., C. W. Dunlop, and C. E. Hendrix
1960 Hippocampal slow waves. Distribution and phase relationships in the course of approach learning. *Arch. Neurol., 3*: 74-90.

Aitken, J. T., and J. E. Bridger
1961 Neuron size and neuron population density in the lumbosacral region of the cat's spinal cord. *J. Anat. (Lond.) 95*: 38-53.

Bitterman, M. E.
1965 The evolution of intelligence. *Sci. Amer., 212*: 92-100.

Boycott, B. B., and J. Z. Young
1950 The comparative study of learning. *Symp. Soc. Exp. Biol., 4*: 432-453.
1955 Memories controlling attacks on food objects by *Octopus vulgaris* Lamarck. *Pubbl. Staz. Zool. Napoli, 27*: 232-249.

Burns, B. D.
1958 *The Mammalian Cerebral Cortex.* London: Edward Arnold (Publishers) Ltd.

Burrows, T., I. Campbell, E. Howe, and J. Z. Young
1965 Conduction, velocity and diameter of nerve fibres of cephalopods. *J. Physiol. (Lond.), 179*: 39-40.

Cannon, W. B.
1932 *The Wisdom of the Body.* New York: W. W. Norton.

Cherkin, A.
1966 *Proc. Nat. Acad. Sci., 55,* January 1966.

Colonnier, M.
1964 The tangential organisation of the visual cortex. *J. Anat. (Lond.), 98*: 327-344.

Craik, K. J. W.
1943 *The Nature of Explanation*. Cambridge University Press.

Deutsch, J. A.
1960*a* The plexiform zone and shape recognition in the octopus. *Nature (Lond.), 185*: 443-446.
1960*b* Theories of shape discrimination in *Octopus*. *Nature (Lond.), 188*: 1090-1092.

Dilly, P. N.
1963 Delayed responses in *Octopus*. *J. Exp. Biol., 40*: 393-401.

Dodwell, P. C.
1957 Shape discrimination in the octopus and the rat. *Nature (Lond.), 179*: 1088.
1961 Facts and theories of shape discrimination. *Nature (Lond.), 191*: 578-581.

Donovan, D. J.
1964 Cephalopod phylogeny and classification. *Biol. Rev., 39*: 259-287.

Eccles, J. C.
1964 *The Physiology of the Synapse*. Berlin: Springer-Verlag.

Eccles, J. C., and A. K. McIntyre
1953 The effects of disuse and activity on mammalian spinal reflexes. *J. Physiol. (Lond.), 121*: 492-516.

Gaze, R. M.
1960 Regeneration of the optic nerve in Amphibia. *Int. Rev. Neurobiol., 2*: 1-40.

Gray, E. G.
1962 A morphological basis for pre-synaptic inhibition? *Nature (Lond.), 193*: 82-83.
1964 Tissue of the central nervous system. In *Electron Microscopic Anatomy*, ed. S. M. Kurtz. New York: Academic Press.

Gray, E. G., and J. Z. Young
1964 Electron microscopy of the synaptic structure of *Octopus* brain. *J. Cell. Biol., 21*: 87-103.

Hubel, D. H., and T. N. Wiesel
1959 Receptive fields of single neurons in the cat's striate cortex. *J. Physiol. (Lond.), 148*: 574-591.
1962 Receptive fields, binocular interaction and functional architecture in the cat's visual cortex. *J. Physiol. (Lond.), 160*: 106-154.
1963 Shape and arrangement of columns in cat's striate cortex. *J. Physiol. (Lond.), 165*: 559-568.
1965 Receptive fields and functional architecture in two nonstriate visual areas (18 and 19) of the cat. *J. Neurophysiol., 28*: 229-289.

Hydén, H.
1960 The neuron, in *The Cell,* vol. 4, eds. J. Brachet and A. E. Mirsky. New York and London: Academic Press, 216-308.

Jasper, H. H., C. F. Ricci, and B. Doane
1958 Patterns of cortical neuronal discharge during conditioned responses in monkeys. In *Ciba Foundation Symposium. Neurological Bases of Behaviour,* eds. G. E. W. Wolstenholme and C. M. O'Connor. London: Churchill.

Jasper, H. H., and G. D. Smirnov (eds.)
1960 Moscow colloquium in electroencephalography of higher nervous activity. *E.E.G. Journal (Montreal).*

Kandel, E. R., and L. Tauc
1965 Heterosynaptic facilitation in neurones of the abdominal ganglion of *Aplysia depilans. J. Physiol. (Lond.), 181*: 1-27.

Kidd, M.
1962 Electron microscopy of the inner plexiform layer of the retina in the cat and the pigeon. *J. Anat. (Lond.), 96*: 179-187.

Kuffler, S. W., and D. D. Potter
1964 Glia in the leech central nervous system—physio-

logical properties and neuron-glia relationships. *J. Neurophysiol., 27*: 290-320.

Lorente de Nó, R.

1936 Responses of oculomotor nucleus, facilitation and delay paths. *Amer. J. Physiol., 112*: 595-609.

Mackintosh, J.

1962 An investigation of reversal learning in *Octopus vulgaris* Lamarck. *Quart. J. Exp. Psychol., 14*: 15-22.

Mackintosh, N. J., and J. Mackintosh

1964*a* The effect of overtraining on a nonreversal shift in *Octopus. J. Gen. Psychol., 106*: 373-377.

1964*b* Performance of *Octopus* over a series of reversals of a simultaneous discrimination. *Anim. Behav., 12*: 321-324.

Maldonado, H.

1963*a* The positive learning process in *Octopus vulgaris. Z. vergl. Physiol., 47*: 191-214.

1963*b* The general amplification function of the vertical lobe in *Octopus vulgaris. Z. vergl. Physiol., 47*: 215-229.

1963*c* The control of attack by *Octopus. Z. vergl. Physiol., 47*: 656-674.

1963*d* The visual attack learning system in *Octopus vulgaris. J. Theoret. Biol., 5*: 470-488.

1965 Positive and negative learning processes in *Octopus vulgaris* and the effect of the removal of the vertical and median superior frontal lobes. *Z. vergl. Physiol.* (In press.)

Messenger, J. B.

1963 Behaviour of young *Octopus briareus* Robson. *Nature (Lond.), 197*: 1186-1187.

Morrell, F.

1960 Microelectrode and steady potential studies suggesting a dendritic locus of closure. In Moscow colloquium in electroencephalography of higher nervous activity, eds. H. H. Jasper and G. D. Smirnov. *E.E.G. Journal (Montreal).*

1961 Electrophysiological contributions to the neural basis of learning. *Physiol. Rev., 41*: 443-494.

Mountcastle, V. B.

1957 Modality and topographic properties of single neurons of cat's striate cortex. *J. Neurophysiol., 20*: 408-434.

Muntz, W. R. A.

1961 Interocular transfer in *Octopus vulgaris. J. Comp. Physiol. Psychol., 54*: 49-55.

Muntz, W. R. A., N. S. Sutherland, and J. Z. Young

1962 Simultaneous shape discrimination in *Octopus* after removal of the vertical lobe. *J. Exp. Biol., 39*: 557-566.

Neumann, J. von

1958 *The Computer and the Brain.* Silliman Memorial Lectures. New Haven: Yale University Press.

Nixon, M.

1966 Food intake and weight increase in *Octopus vulgaris.* (In preparation.)

Parriss, J. R., and J. Z. Young

1962 The limits of transfer of a learned discrimination to figures of larger and smaller sizes. *Z. vergl. Physiol., 45*: 618-635.

Penfield, W., and L. Roberts

1959 *Speech and Brain-mechanisms.* London: Oxford University Press.

Powell, T. P. S., and V. B. Mountcastle

1959 Some aspects of the functional organisation of the cortex of the postcentral gyrus of the monkey: a correlation of findings obtained in a single unit analysis with cytoarchitecture. *Johns Hopkins Hosp. Bull., 105*: 1333-162.

Sanders, F. K., and J. Z. Young

1940 Learning and other functions of the higher nervous centres of *Sepia. J. Neurophysiol., 3*: 501-526.

Sherrington, C. S.

1947 *The Integrative Action of the Nervous System,* rev. ed. New Haven: Yale University Press, 1961.

Sholl, D. A.
1956 *The Organisation of the Cerebral Cortex*. London: Methuen.

Sommerhoff, G.
1950 *Analytical Biology*. London: Oxford University Press.

Sutherland, N. S.
1957 Visual discrimination of orientation and shape by the octopus. *Nature* (*Lond.*), *179*: 11-13.
1963 Shape discrimination and receptive fields. *Nature* (*Lond.*), *197*: 118-122.

Sutherland, N. S., and J. Mackintosh
1964 Discrimination learning: Non-additivity of cues. *Nature* (*Lond.*), *201*: 528-530.

Taylor, W. K.
1964 Cortico-thalamic organisation and memory. *Proc. Roy. Soc. B*, *159*: 466-478.

Wall, P. D.
1964 Presynaptic control of impulses at the first central synapse in the cutaneous pathway. *Prog. in Brain Res.*, 12.

Wells, M. J.
1960 Proprioception and visual discrimination of orientation in *Octopus*. *J. Exp. Biol.*, *37*: 489-499.
1961 Centres for tactile and visual learning in the brain of *Octopus*. *J. Exp. Biol.*, *38*: 811-826.

Wells, M. J., and J. Wells
1957 The effect of lesions to the vertical and optic lobes on tactile discrimination in *Octopus*. *J. Exp. Biol.*, *34*: 378-393.
1959 Hormonal control of sexual maturity in *Octopus*. *J. Exp. Biol.*, *36*: 1-33.

Welsh, J. H.
1961 Neuro hormones of Mollusca. *Amer. Zool.*, *1*: 267-272.

Wyckoff, R. W. G., and J. Z. Young
1956 The motorneuron surface. *Proc. Roy. Soc. B*, *144*: 440-450.

Young, J. Z.

1938 The evolution of the nervous system and of the relationship of organism and environment. In *Evolution. Essays Presented to E. S. Goodrich*, ed. G. R. de Beer. Oxford: Clarendon Press.

1958 Effect of removal of various amounts of the vertical lobes on visual discrimination by *Octopus*. *Proc. Roy. Soc. B, 149*: 463-483.

1960*a* The visual system of *Octopus*. 1. Regularities in the retina and optic lobes of *Octopus* in relation to form discrimination. *Nature* (*Lond.*), *186*: 836-839.

1960*b* The failures of discrimination learning following removal of the vertical lobes in *Octopus*. *Proc. Roy. Soc. B, 153*: 18-46.

1962*a* *The Life of Vertebrates*, 2d ed. Oxford: Clarendon Press.

1962*b* The optic lobes of *Octopus vulgaris*. *Phil. Trans. Roy. Soc. B, 245*: 19-58.

1962*c* Why do we have two brains? Paper read at Conference on Cerebral Dominance, Johns Hopkins University School of Medicine, Baltimore, Md., April 23-25, 1961.

1963*a* The number and sizes of nerve cells in *Octopus*. *Proc. Zool. Soc. Lond., 140*: Pt 2, 229-254.

1963*b* Some essentials of neural memory systems. Paired centres that regulate and address the signals of the results of action. *Nature* (*Lond.*), *198*: 626-630.

1964*a* *A Model of the Brain*. Oxford: Clarendon Press.

1964*b* Paired centres for the control of attack by *Octopus*. *Proc. Roy. Soc. B, 159*: 565-588.

1965*a* The organisation of a memory system. Croonian Lecture of the Royal Society, delivered on May 6, 1965. *Proc. Roy. Soc. B, 163*: 285-320.

1965*b* The central nervous system of *Nautilus*. *Phil. Trans. Roy. Soc. B, 249*: 1-25.

1965*c* The centres for touch discrimination in *Octopus vulgaris*. *Phil. Trans. Roy. Soc. B, 249*: 45-67.

Index

MASTERPLOTS II

Drama Series

Revised Edition

MASTERPLOTS II

DRAMA SERIES

REVISED EDITION

3

Lie–Ser

Editor, Revised Edition

CHRISTIAN H. MOE

Southern Illinois University

Editor, First Edition

FRANK N. MAGILL

SALEM PRESS

Pasadena, California   Hackensack, New Jersey

Editor in Chief: Dawn P. Dawson

Managing Editor: Christina J. Moose
Project Editor: R. Kent Rasmussen
Production Editor: Joyce I. Buchea
Copy Editor: Sarah Hilbert

Assistant Editor: Andrea E. Miller
Research Supervisor: Jeffry Jensen
Acquisitions Editor: Mark Rehn
Layout: William Zimmerman

∞ The paper used in these volumes conforms to the American National Standard for Permanence of Paper for Printed Library Materials, Z39.48-1992 (R1997).

Library of Congress Cataloging-in-Publication Data

Masterplots II : drama series / editor Christian H. Moe. — Rev.
p. cm.
ISBN 1-58765-116-5 (set : alk. paper) — ISBN 1-58765-117-3 (vol. 1 : alk. paper) — ISBN 1-58765-118-1 (vol. 2 : alk. paper) — ISBN 1-58765-119-X (vol. 3 : alk. paper) — ISBN 1-58765-120-3 (vol. 4 : alk. paper)
1. Drama—20th century—Stories, plots, etc. I. Moe, Christian Hollis, 1929-
PN6112.5 .M37 2003
809.2′04—dc21

2003012651

Second Printing

PRINTED IN THE UNITED STATES OF AMERICA

TABLE OF CONTENTS

TABLE OF CONTENTS

COMPLETE LIST OF TITLES IN ALL VOLUMES

Volume 1

Volume 2

Volume 3

Volume 4

MASTERPLOTS II

Drama Series

Revised Edition

A LIE OF THE MIND

Author: Sam Shepard (Samuel Shepard Rogers, 1943-   )
Type of plot: Psychological
Time of plot: The 1970's or the 1980's
Locale: Oklahoma and Montana
First produced: 1985, at the Promenade Theater, New York City
First published: 1986

Principal characters:
JAKE, a man with a violent temper
BETH, his wife, who suffered brain damage when Jake beat her
FRANKIE, his brother
SALLY, his sister
LORRAINE, his mother
BAYLOR, Beth's father
MEG, Beth's mother
MIKE, Beth's brother

The Play

The first act of *A Lie of the Mind* consists of a series of short scenes, the first scene focusing on Jake, the second shifting to another locale and focusing on Beth, the third shifting back to Jake, the fourth to Beth again, and so on. The play begins with a phone conversation between Jake, a jealous man with an explosive temper, and Frankie, Jake's brother, in which Jake gradually reveals that he has badly beaten—perhaps killed—his wife, Beth. Although she has suffered brain damage and utters an inarticulate garble of sounds and words, Beth is in fact recovering from the beating in a hospital, where Mike, her brother, comforts her. In a motel room, Jake tells Frankie why he beat his wife. Beth, who had taken a part in a play, was preparing for her role by wearing provocative clothes and perfumes, but Jake does not believe in the line that separates acting from reality. Since actors "try to believe so hard they're the person that they actually think they become the person," Jake was certain that Beth had been unfaithful; therefore, he beat her. Still, Jake realizes that his whole life is lost with Beth gone, and he blacks out.

At the hospital, Beth resists Mike's insistence that she forget Jake, for the image of her husband-lover remains locked in her mind: Jake is a part of Beth's essential self. Having brought Jake back to his boyhood room, Frankie leaves him in the care of Sally, Jake's sister, and Lorraine, Jake's smotheringly protective mother, who imperiously decides to cure Jake by keeping him in his room for a year. Beth's parents, ranchers from Montana, arrive at the hospital. Baylor, the father, a gruff, aging cowboy, shows more concern for his mules than his daughter, and Meg, the mother, avoids facing her daughter's condition. In Jake's room, where Lorraine is baby-feeding him,

Jake violently revolts against her mothering, snatches his soup, and stomps it into his bed. Lorraine arouses Jake's jealousy by telling Jake that Frankie has gone to Montana to see Beth. Jake wants to follow Frankie, but Lorraine has hidden Jake's pants in order to confine him to his room. Finding his father's flight jacket, funeral flag, and ashes, Jake inquires about his father's death. Lorraine, confused, reveals that Jake was present at his father's death. The first act closes as Jake has a vision of Beth seductively oiling herself.

The second act of *A Lie of the Mind* opens with Beth and Meg overhearing Mike's argument with a man—Frankie—who wants to come up to the ranch house. Still suffering from the beating, Beth wants to see the man she thinks is Jake, but Mike prevents her. Then Baylor enters, supporting Frankie, whom Baylor has mistaken for a deer and shot in the leg. Mike objects to Frankie's presence, but Baylor decrees that Frankie will recover from his wound in the house. Beth's damaged mind identifies Frankie as Jake, the man she loves. Back in Jake's room, where Jake seeks Sally's help in escaping, Jake has a vision of Beth, shirtless, wrapping up Frankie's wounded leg. The vision proves true when Beth so ministers to Frankie. Beth's delusion has deepened; Frankie and Jake have inextricably coalesced in her mind. Obsessed with seeing Beth again, Jake—clothed in his underwear and his father's flight jacket, with the American flag used in his father's funeral around his neck—crawls out his window.

Act 3 of *A Lie of the Mind* begins with Sally recounting how she and Jake found their alcoholic father living in a ramshackle trailer in Mexico. Jake, always compelled to compete with his father, proposed a race—the first one to reach the United States, with a stop for a drink in each bar along the highway, would win. According to Sally, Jake challenged his father because he "had decided to kill him." The race ended when a truck splattered the father "all over the road like some lost piece of livestock." Sally and Lorraine finally realize that the men in their family will never return. In Montana, Meg suspects that Beth—like Meg's mother, and like her family in general—is cracking up. Beth enters in an outlandish costume, intending to marry Frankie, who because of his wound is a captive groom.

As Meg and Beth plan for the wedding, a shot rings out. Mike enters, boasting that he has captured Jake and will force him to apologize for beating Beth, but Beth is now totally submerged in her delusion and embraces Frankie. In the last scene of *A Lie of the Mind*, Sally sorts through the family mementos and Lorraine, travel brochure in hand, fantasizes about a trip to Ireland, where her family originated. When Sally wonders how they will clear out all their junk, Lorraine tells her not to worry: They will simply burn the house down. Calmly, she strikes a match and lights the pile of photographs, papers, and paraphernalia that Sally has been tossing into a metal bucket.

While the fire burns on one side of the stage, Mike enters the ranch house, driving Jake like a horse with the American flag between Jake's teeth. When Mike tries to force Beth to face Jake so that Jake can apologize, Beth refuses, and Mike and Beth struggle. Baylor, roused by the ruckus, objects to Mike's abuse of the flag and grabs it away from him. Mike breaks away from Baylor, grabs Beth, and forces her to confront Jake, who stammers out his apology: "I—I—I—I love you more than this earth."

Shaken and confused, Beth returns to Frankie; Mike, disgusted, exits into the darkness. Baylor and Meg begin folding the flag, heedless of the surrounding action. As Frankie watches, Jake crosses to Beth and confesses, "These things—in my head—lie to me. Everything lies. Tells me a story. Everything in me lies. But you. You stay. . . . You are true. I love you more than this life. You stay. You stay with him. He's my brother." Beth and Jake kiss, then Jake exits into the darkness. As Frankie screams for Jake to take Beth with him, Beth embraces Frankie. Baylor and Meg finish folding the flag and kiss. Beth continues to embrace Frankie as Meg catches sight of the burning mementos and describes the play's last tableau: "Looks like a fire in the snow. How could that be?"

Themes and Meanings

Sam Shepard's *A Lie of the Mind* explores the structure of the American family as well as the delusions, the "lies of the mind," that individuals construct both for each other and for themselves. Beth, who inhabits a world of self-created delusion and who is unable to communicate her ideas and needs to others, exemplifies the prevailing inadequacy of human nature. Unable to respond coherently to the world around her because of the brain damage she suffered when Jake beat her, Beth creates lies of the mind—fictions that permit her to survive. The play suggests that each character assembles a personal version of reality in his or her mind, and that those perceptions are locked in individual skulls. Lorraine blocks out the pain of being abandoned by her husband by pretending indifference; Baylor hides from his family by erecting a facade of the crusty frontier hunter; Jake erases all his memories of the race in Mexico that led to his father's death. The play suggests that the characters create solitary worlds of "pretend," that "reality" is a composite of discrete—and often contradictory—perceptions.

The significance of the action in *A Lie of the Mind* is conveyed by various examples of disjunction that emphasize the individual's isolation. As Beth's words indicate, one character's thoughts cannot be fully communicated to another: "You don't know this thought. How? How can you know this thought? In me." The union of man and woman in marriage inevitably decays into separation. Meg wonders when it was that Baylor moved out of the house and the family, and Lorraine's husband disappeared "like an apparition." Beth and Jake "never did see" each other; their relentless emotional dissolution culminates in Jake's final rejection of Beth at the end of the play.

Further, the "two opposite animals," the female and the male, even when yoked together by an irresistible and consuming passion, are torn apart by the violence of their fundamental incompatibility. The woman needs the man to be complete, and always expects him to return to her, but "the male one goes off by himself. Leaves. He needs something else. But he doesn't know what it is. He doesn't really know what he needs. So he ends up dead. By himself." *A Lie of the Mind* suggests that the male inevitably seeks isolation by attacking or abandoning the female, only to find that the pain of separation brings him back to her. These tensions ripple through every relationship between husband and wife, mother and son, and father and daughter in the play, but they are most clearly worked out in the relationship between Beth and Jake. Both Beth and Jake are trapped by their love—neither can be complete without the other. Their obsessive need to be reunited thrusts Beth into delusions of marriage and propels Jake to Montana to find Beth, but their drive for reunion at last proves futile. Jake exits into the darkness, and Beth turns to Frankie. *A Lie of the Mind* proposes that the American family, like Beth, is fundamentally crippled.

Dramatic Devices

Of the several dramatic devices in *A Lie of the Mind*, the most obvious, and perhaps the most important, is Shepard's use of the acting space. Although much of the action has an aura of realistic presentation, the stage directions are insistent reminders of the isolated and theatrical quality of the characters' actions and thoughts. The play occurs in a space which suggests that all of its actions are pageants that briefly reel through a void, then disappear. Only a few props appear on the stage to mark locales; the main effect "should be of infinite space, going off to nowhere." This impression of emptiness is underscored by the use of lighting as the opening stage directions suggest: "Impression of huge dark space and distance between the two characters with each one isolated in his own pool of light."

The line between acting and being is consistently blurred. Beth claims that the world of acting is "more real than the real world," that "ordinary is empty," and that "pretending fills." It was Beth's immersion in method acting that provoked Jake into beating her. The costuming also suggests that meaning in the play is primarily metaphoric. The costume Jake wears when he escapes from his room—boxer shorts, his father's flight jacket, and an American flag—signifies the mixture of roles directing his actions. The flag suggests that Jake is wrapped up in the myth of the American male—strong, independent, unable to deal with women, and violent. In donning the flight jacket, Jake has assumed his father's masculine preference for danger and solitude, yet Jake's lack of pants undercuts both his virility and sexuality. The outfit worn by Beth in act 3, a cross between the wardrobe of a cheap hooker and a 1950's bobby-soxer, represents her inability to reconcile society's conflicting demands that she be both wholesome and sensual.

Different levels of reality or meaning are suggested by Shepard's use of simultaneous action at critical points in the play. When Jake sees Beth seductively oiling her shoulders and breasts, the moment is clearly a manifestation of Jake's thoughts, since Beth is isolated from the rest of the action by a pool of light. When Jake's vision of Beth wrapping up Frankie's leg with her shirt is reenacted at the ranch house, however, the repetition of the gesture suggests that Jake builds a personal reality from his perceptions just as surely as Beth creates a wholly different reality from the fragmented images that surge through her mind. The fire that burns throughout the last scene punctuates the interpenetration of simultaneous action. Since Sally and Lorraine literally burn all of their ties to the past and to their men, the fire represents the violence that concludes all the relationships in the play. However, the fire also represents the passion that brings Beth and Jake together for the last time, and it signals a renewal of warmth and life in the frozen Montana wilderness. That a fire can burn in the snow is the critical paradox that informs *A Lie of the Mind*.

Critical Context

A Lie of the Mind belongs to the second phase of Shepard's career, in which he moved away from the expressionist style and episodic structure of his early works toward a linear (and ostensibly causal) dramatic structure. The influence of Samuel Beckett's absurdist plays on Shepard's early work is quite apparent in *Cowboys #2* (pr. 1967, pb. 1971). The heroes of *Cowboys #2*, Stu and Chet, have no past, no future, and no existence beyond the confines of the stage—they are characters, not realistic projections of human beings. Further, the play's action is a series of unlinked vignettes about acting: Chet and Stu begin as urban cowboys trapped in a modern metropolis, transform into a pair of old-timer cowboys who repel an attack by a Native American, and finally become observers who watch two unnamed actors enter and begin reading the script of *Cowboys #2*. *The Tooth of Crime* (pr. 1972, pb. 1974) uses the context of a verbal duel between Hoss, an aging rock star, and Crow, the usurper, to examine the interplay between the reality created inside the theater and the reality that exists outside the theater. In *Geography of a Horse Dreamer* (pr., pb. 1974) Shepard uses the play's central figure, Cody, a clairvoyant whose ability to predict winners in horse races is exploited by those around him, to explore the problems of artistic creation.

With *Curse of the Starving Class* (pb. 1976, pr. 1977), however, Shepard began to shift away from expressionism toward a more conventional realism in order to find a medium to explore the foundations, myths, delusions, failures, and triumphs of the American family. The action of *Curse of the Starving Class* issues from nominally realistic circumstances. Ella, the mother, wants to sell the house in order to escape from Weston, her alcoholic and abusive husband. Their children, Wesley and Emma, also fantasize about escaping the family. As Weston's spiritual return to the family suggests, however, none of them can escape the biological ties that entrap them. Even though *Curse of the Starving Class* has a verisimilar surface, expressionist techniques permeate the play. Dialogue often breaks down into monologue, and the play is centered on a metaphoric image system. The empty refrigerator symbolizes the family's spiritual and emotional dearth; the final image of the eagle and the tomcat tearing each other apart represents the family's destructive interdependence.

This combination of a realistic framework and a metaphoric or mythic center is refined in four more plays that constitute a distinct group of family dramas in the Shepard canon: Pulitzer Prize winner *Buried Child* (pr. 1978, pb. 1979), *True West* (pr. 1980, pb. 1981), *Fool for Love* (pr., pb. 1983), and finally *A Lie of the Mind*. This phase of Shepard's career was heralded as a major breakthrough in American drama as well as deplored as a reductive compromise that eliminates the freshness of the earlier plays. Either way, Shepard's plays are rarely met with indifference. Shepard's capacity to challenge both audience and critic keeps him at the forefront of the American theater.

Sources for Further Study

Bigsby, C. W. E. "Sam Shepard." In *Beyond Broadway*. Vol. 3 in *A Critical Introduction to Twentieth-Century American Drama*. New York: Cambridge University Press, 1985.

Bottoms, Stephen J. *The Theatre of Sam Shepard: States of Crisis*. Cambridge, England: Cambridge University Press, 1991.

DeRose, David J. *Sam Shepard.* New York: Twayne, 1992.

Graham, Laura J. *Sam Shepard: Theme, Image, and the Director.* New York: Lang, 1995.

King, Kimball. *Sam Shepard: A Casebook.* New York: Garland, 1988.

Marranca, Bonnie, ed. *American Dreams: The Imagination of Sam Shepard.* New York: Performing Arts Journal, 1981.

Mottram, Ron. *Inner Landscapes: The Theater of Sam Shepard.* Columbia: University of Missouri Press, 1984.

Sessums, Kevin. "Sam Shepard: *Geography of a Horse Dreamer.*" *Interview* 18 (September, 1988): 70-79.

Wilcox, Leonard. *Rereading Shepard.* Basingstoke, England: MacMillan, 1993.

Gregory W. Lanier

A LIFE

Author: Hugh Leonard (John Keyes Byrne, 1926-)
Type of plot: Psychological
Time of plot: The 1970's
Locale: A small town near Dublin, Ireland
First produced: 1979, at the Abbey Theatre, Dublin, Ireland
First published: 1980

Principal characters:
DRUMM, an aging civil servant
DESMOND "DEZZIE," young Drumm
DOLLY, Drumm's wife, age sixty
DOROTHY, young Dolly
LAR KEARNS, an unemployed salesman
MARY KEARNS, his wife
MIBS, young Mary

The Play

The stage lightens on Drumm consulting his notes. From a stone bandstand, he addresses an unseen audience on what amounts to a historical tour of local "Dalkey." Only his wife Dolly, who listens from afar, appreciates his talk. She both admires and is intimidated by Drumm, who never hesitates to insult her.

Drumm tells Dolly that the doctor has diagnosed his stomach problem as a duodenal ulcer. (The audience recalls that Drumm was a minor character in an earlier Leonard play who had "tummy" trouble.) Dolly, a simple, cheerful woman, feels immense relief at the news. She suggests that they buy a motorcar, since Drumm is scheduled to retire soon. Rather than humor her, Drumm grumbles that they have nowhere to go and no one to visit. He does not tell Dolly that he is in fact dying of stomach cancer.

Drumm later visits Mary Kearns in her newly decorated house. He has not spoken with her in nearly six years, and she is surprised to see him. It is gradually understood that Drumm has always been in love with Mary, although his pride has made him resist her. Mary, Dolly's age, has more intelligence, yet she too loves fun and spontaneity and finds Drumm a "bitter pill." Hinting that he has medical problems, Drumm confesses that he regrets the past six years. Mary knows and likes Drumm well enough to inform him that he has been a fool. Drumm contends that at least he is not hypocritical. He declares himself the most honest and reasonable man in town.

As Mary shows Drumm her new decor, which he cannot help but scorn, the stage lighting shifts to the same room forty years earlier. A young Drumm (Dezzie) and Mary (Mibs) study together. Drumm, serious and stiff, ignores Mibs's flirtatiousness, although he is clearly attracted to her. Mibs sees Drumm as a good catch, destined as he is for the civil service. Suddenly, young Lar Kearns, one of Mibs's suitors, comes for a visit—to the consternation of Drumm, who despises Lar's feckless good humor and laziness.

The scene switches to the present. Lar, now Mary's husband, greets Drumm congenially when he comes in. Drumm complains about his wife's silliness, but Lar chastises him for oppressing her. Although Drumm proves himself an insufferable grouch, Mary and Lar genuinely admire him and tolerate his acerbity. Indeed, his honesty and integrity seems unquestionable at this point.

The conversation turns to Mary's recent accident, which has left her limping slightly. Lar himself had backed over her in a borrowed car. The news incenses Drumm, and he launches into a tirade against Lar. Lar, stunned, leaves the room. Mary tells Drumm to leave at once and not come back. Drumm, longing for sympathy, says he has six months to live. The scene is juxtaposed to a scene from the past in which Drumm smashes the records on Lar's gramophone and threatens to kill him if he does not let Mibs alone. When, back in the present, Lar returns to the room, Drumm apologizes for his outburst. It is as if he is also apologizing for his past outburst.

In act 2, Dolly and Drumm visit Lar and Mary. Drumm is unaware that Dolly has visited them all along, despite his six-year ban on visits. The conversation turns to young Sean, Lar and Mary's son, but tension mounts and Lar changes the subject. Drumm reminisces about the speech he made years earlier, during which he was ridiculed and booed. The humiliation killed his dream of becoming an orator and soured him on life. He claims the masses cannot appreciate eloquence or intelligence. The scene reverts to the past, when Desmond discovers that Lar had written a love letter to Mibs and asked her to marry him. Hurt and incensed, Desmond tells Mibs that she should marry Lar since she will not do any better and he is her "sort." Mary realizes that Drumm has destroyed their own romantic prospects.

The present conversation turns to some forbidden subjects: the suicide of Drumm's father and, again, Sean, who abandoned his parents. Drumm bitterly faces the truth about these matters, whereas Lar tries both to evade them and to mollify Drumm. It also slips out that Dolly has visited Lar and Mary often, and Drumm becomes silently enraged. Mary attacks Drumm for daring to criticize Dolly. Drumm defends himself by saying that his wife's deceit has made a fool of him.

Shifting to the past, Drumm congratulates Lar and Mibs upon their engagement. However, he tries to sequester Mary in order to dissuade her from the marriage. Mary resists, realizing what a tyrant Drumm could become. Back in the present, Mary sustains her attack on Drumm for his self-proclaimed superiority, which she interprets as his revenge upon the town for jeering him at the debate. Drumm claims that indeed he may have too much pride, but that no one can accuse him of hypocrisy, laziness, or deceit. Mary does not accept his self-defense. She accuses him of trying to come between Lar and her and of turning her Sean against his father. Drumm had helped educate young Sean, and, in the process, the boy became ashamed of Lar's lack of education. Lar tries to stop Mary from talking, but it is too late.

Drumm is stunned that Lar could have remained his friend all this time. Lar says that Drumm got Sean but he got Mibs. By this point, Drumm is almost drowning in self-revelation. He realizes that his contempt is really cowardice, that his belief in principles has amounted to no more than vanity. "I've achieved nothing," he concludes.

The play ends with a reconciliation and recognition. Drumm realizes what he has been, and the four friends remain friends. Drumm also reconciles with Dolly, although, ironically, he will be dead in six months.

Themes and Meanings

Hugh Leonard once stated that most of his earlier dramatic work concentrated on the theme of betrayal. Betrayal is also a major theme of *A Life*. Drumm betrays Dolly by loving another woman. Dolly betrays Drumm by visiting Lar and Mary. Lar betrays Drumm by, in effect, stealing Mary (Mibs) away from him. Mibs, who prefers Drumm, marries Lar. Sean betrays his parents, and so on. Most important, Drumm betrays himself, which he learns at the end of the play. He has been uncompromising, highly principled, and perfectionistic for all the wrong reasons.

Through Drumm, Leonard also examines questions of universal import. Some other major themes which emerge as the play proceeds are the nature of wisdom and truth, the consequences of isolation, the contrast between success and failure, and the hazards of self-deceit.

Leonard implies that true wisdom has little to do with intelligence. In this sense, *A Life* conveys a typically modernist distrust of intellect. Drumm's intelligence, for example, has served only to isolate him from his fellowman and destroy his chances with Mibs. Leonard contrasts Drumm with the almost simpleminded Lar, whose life has been easy, happy, and grounded in ignorant faith. Truth, then, becomes tantamount to acceptance of reality as it comes. Lar not only accepts reality, he revels in it. The stern and idealistic Drumm, who rejects reality, only makes himself miserable. What he learns in the end is not the kindness of strangers, but the kindness of friends.

Leonard seems to equate pride with self-deceit. Drumm slowly recognizes that his lofty pride is really cowardice, his staunch defense of abstract principles, vanity. Man's most personal and self-defensive motives thus underlie his grandest illusions about himself.

Drumm's pride has also prompted him to a self-imposed isolation from his fellowman, as well as from his wife. This isolation is not constructive, as Leonard demonstrates. One of the salient messages of *A Life* is that one must learn to live with and even love others. Wisdom is, in fact, love.

The natures of success and failure can also be examined in Leonard's contrast of Lar and Drumm. All along Drumm had been regarded as the successful career man, while Lar lazed about and had no ambition whatsoever. However, in the end Drumm realizes that he has accomplished nothing. He has hated his work, lost the woman he loved, and failed to become an orator. Lar, on the other hand, wanted and expected little and got what Drumm wanted most, Mibs. Success, then, has little to do with career, money, or fame; it entails enjoyment of simple pleasures.

Dramatic Devices

A Life conforms to the tenets of dramatic realism in a most conventional manner. Indeed, the influences of Henrik Ibsen and Anton Chekhov saturate Leonard's play. The major device employed by the playwright, if, in fact, it can be called a device, is character study or delineation: Drumm comes to realize exactly what he is and what he has been. Everything that happens in the play serves to abet his self-revelation.

If realism is Leonard's mode, psychological insight is his method. The mere fact that Leonard explores a life, Drumm's life, focuses attention on those motives and dreams that mold Drumm. This is not to say that Leonard probes Drumm's mind with the meticulousness, persistence, or even ruthlessness of, say, a Henry James. The play does, however, contain little overt action; what happens proceeds dialectically, through conversation and revelation.

Leonard has earned his reputation as a master of technicality; tight structures and carefully plotted action characterize his work. *A Life* glows with such mastery. The play's two acts precisely parallel one another. In the present, for example, Dolly listens to Drumm make his historical speech at the beginning of the first act; at the beginning of the second, Dorothy (young Dolly) listens to Desmond (young Drumm) practice for his disastrous speech to the townsfolk. Both scenes are set in the same bandstand.

Leonard's constant temporal juxtapositions also parallel each other throughout the play. The playwright's purpose is to make the past present, to merge past and present, to show how one's past directly determines one's future. Through shifts in stage lighting, the audience can see the four characters simultaneously interact in both past and present. Such juxtapositions are perhaps the most "experimental" devices employed in the play, although they, too, became standard methodology in twentieth century drama.

A Life, grounded as it is in psychological realism, can also be described as a bitter comedy of manners. The play's action is largely recapitulated through conversation in the living room of Lar and Mibs. It could almost be said that Drumm is a character in search of a comedy of manners in which to insert himself. Lar, Mary, and Dolly are perhaps too "lowly" and unsophisticated to belong to the manners tradition, but the play itself assumes such form overall. In another sense, Drumm almost seems a parody of himself, a character designed to illustrate a humor, as in Molière or Ben Jonson. What saves Drumm in the end is his genuine self-revelation and turn of heart.

Finally, one of Leonard's most important dramatic devices is his electric use of language itself. The playwright has been accused of elevating style over content, but there is no denying the sparkling, living dialogue, which lifts an otherwise mediocre play into brilliance.

Critical Context

A Life, a healthy hybrid of several conventional genres, is at once a character sketch, a bittersweet domestic comedy, and a critique of social values as articulated by the protagonist, Drumm. The play's primary vehicle, psychological realism, has its roots in both the methods and tonalities of Ibsen and Chekhov. Leonard also draws heavily on his own Irish heritage of John Synge and Sean O'Casey, with emphasis on the antiheroic elements characterizing the latter work. Beyond these immediate influences, echoes of Molière's humors studies and August Strindberg's chamber plays can be discerned. *A Life*, then, assumes its direct place in the mainstream of modern European drama. What distinguishes it as a uniquely crafted work by Leonard is its further source in intimate autobiographical details from the playwright's life.

Leonard's work as a whole consists of innumerable theatrical and media adaptations of works by other writers, including James Joyce, Ibsen, Flann O'Brien, Keith Waterhouse, Seán O'Faoláin, and even Emily Brontë and Gustave Flaubert. His own original stage dramas, numbering in the dozens, display unusual consistency in craftsmanship and tone; a Leonard play is typically "perfect" with respect to technics and craft. Leonard's plays are also characterized by precocity of dialogue and sparkling, colorful language in general.

Leonard's modes include the mildly absurdist "exposure" plays popular in the 1960's (*The Poker Session*, pr., pb. 1963), dramatizations of material that is socially and historically Irish (*The Au Pair Man*, pr., pb. 1968, and *The Patrick Pearse Motel*, pr., pb. 1971), and intensely autobiographical revelations—the latter of which date from the early 1970's in Leonard's career as a playwright. The popular *Da* (pr., pb. 1973) and *A Life* belong squarely within this autobiographical category, both plays demonstrating a major shift from Leonard's earlier, more impersonal work. The autobiographical plays are richer and less pretentious than the earlier plays because they add a more human and compassionate dimension to Leonard's work.

Sources for Further Study

Chaillet, Ned. *Contemporary Dramatists*. 6th ed. Detroit: St. James, 1999.

Gallagher, S. F. "Q. and A. with Hugh Leonard." *Irish Literary Supplement: A Review of Irish Books* (Spring, 1990): 13-14.

Hogan, Robert. *After the Irish Renaissance: A Critical History of Irish Drama Since "The Plough and the Stars."* Minneapolis: University of Minnesota Press, 1967.

King, Kimball. *Ten Modern Irish Playwrights*. New York: Garland, 1979.

Leonard, Hugh. *Home Before Night: Memoirs of an Irish Time and Place by the Author of "Da."* London: André Deutsche, 1979.

Taylor, John Russell. "Plays in Performance: London." *Drama* 136 (April, 1980): 37-48.

Louis Gallo

THE LIFE OF MAN

Author: Leonid Andreyev (1871-1919)
Type of plot: Allegory
Time of plot: The early twentieth century
Locale: Russia
First produced: 1907, at the Kommissarzhevskaya Theater, St. Petersburg, Russia
First published: Zhizn cheloveka, 1907, in the journal *Shipovnik* (English translation, 1914)

Principal characters:
SOMEONE-IN-GRAY, the narrator and observer
MAN
WIFE
MAN'S RELATIVES,
MAN'S FRIENDS, and
MAN'S ENEMIES
THE OLD WOMEN
DRUNKARDS

The Play

The Life of Man begins with an empty gray room, feebly lit. Someone-in-Gray, so named for his hooded, shapeless gray robe, moves away from the wall and begins to speak. His tone is indifferent, dispassionate. He warns the audience that has come to the theater to "laugh and be amused" that it will see the whole of Man's life—from a dark beginning to a dark ending. He sketches the course of this life in the five scenes to come and the lights dim.

The first scene, "The Birth of Man," opens in utter darkness. Gradually, a group of women emerges, sitting in a large, dimly lit room. Though not midwives, they somehow obviously belong at the birth. In mocking, cynical tones they discuss the relative merits of boys versus girls, the husband's comical fear and distraction, and the wife's pain. They listen to her cries and muse on the ease with which animals deliver their young. As Man is finally born, Someone-in-Gray reappears and the candle in his hands lights. The room grows brighter and the Old Women scuttle away, to be replaced by the Relatives. Meanwhile, the Doctor and the Father trade remarks about the health of the child and the mother. The Relatives offer advice both moral and practical on what to name the boy and how to rear him. As the scene ends, the Relatives are discussing the merits of tobacco and the baby is crying.

In scene 2, "Love and Poverty," the Man is already grown. The room is once again large, nearly empty except for a few pieces of rickety furniture, but it is warmly and brightly lit. Someone-in-Gray is present, but stands in the darkest corner. His candle burns strongly and steadily. The Neighbors, who adore the Man and his Wife for their beauty and kindness, enter. The Neighbors scatter flowers and fragrant grasses; they decorate the poor young couple's room and leave them a fine cigar, a hair ribbon, a bottle of milk and some bread. They leave with hopes that Man will find work.

Man's Wife enters as soon as they leave. Her monologue explains their predicament: No one has yet recognized Man's talent as an architect; no one buys his designs. She has been in the city center seeking either luck or work, but has come home empty-handed. She prays for mercy and for a chance for her stubborn, independent husband to prove himself. Someone-in-Gray steps out to announce to the audience that indeed Man has been discovered, and that on the next day wealthy patrons will seek him out. Man comes home disillusioned and hungry; he has walked the city in search of work, stopping at every grocery window and raging at the well-fed, well-housed people he meets. Man and Wife console each other with fancies of Italian villas and Norwegian castles; she crowns him with a wreath of oak leaves and declares him her knight; the scene ends with their discovery of the Neighbors' gifts and their waltz to an imaginary orchestra.

The third scene is no imaginary waltz, but a full-scale ball at the Man's house. Some years have passed. The furnishings are sparse but rich and severe and somehow out of proportion. One group of Guests is dancing; another sits stiffly on gilt chairs along the walls. The latter group admires Man's wealth and good fortune, the size of his mansion, and the beauty of his young son, punctuating their remarks with exclamations of "how fine," "how rich," "how brilliant." The Man and his Wife enter, followed by his friends—all handsome, graceful, and slightly disdainful. The Friends are followed by Man's Enemies, who are as low and ugly as the Friends are noble and beautiful. This silent train slowly passes from one side of the stage to the other, accompanied by the Guests' obtuse and fawning remarks. They admire the Man's importance and fame, his Friends' loyalty; they gossip about his Enemies' cowardice. Once the procession passes, however, some of the Guests suspect they have been forgotten, and their talk takes a mean and spiteful turn. When they are invited to supper, though, they exit with all pomp, repeating their compliments of "how grand." The orchestra continues to play. The candle's yellow flame sharply outlines Someone-in-Gray.

Scene 4 is "Man's Misfortune." The candle is little more than a stump, and it flickers as it burns. The set is Man's study—large, gloomy, and dark. Man's only remaining servant, an old woman, tells the audience of his decline into poverty and obscurity. Styles have changed; his designs are no longer popular. His house is full of rats. He has lost his furniture, his car, his carriages. Worst of all, his son—now a young man—is dying from a chance blow to the head. The old servant directs yet another Doctor into the son's room and continues her soliloquy. Her constant refrain is "It's all the same to me. I don't care." The Doctor soon leaves, with cautious but reassuring words for the Man and his Wife. They are greatly aged. Man agonizes over the old broken-down toys in his study, and both pray: the Wife for compassion and mercy, the Man for justice. They reminisce and talk of his sketches and their old age. He falls asleep and she goes to tend their son, but soon returns with news of the boy's death. For the first time in the play, Man addresses Someone-in-Gray directly: He curses the day of his birth and the whole of his life, and then defiantly curses Someone-in-Gray and whatever indifferent power he represents. This very curse is his legacy, his immortality. The two figures confront each other silently and tensely as the lights go down.

"The Death of Man," the fifth scene, takes place in a tavern. Once again the room is large and barely lit, but now it is dirty and low-ceilinged. A shabbily dressed Man sits silently at a table in the center, surrounded by ragged, deformed Drunkards. Their voices are rough and coarse; their conversation is confused, alternately belligerent and tentative—they trade accounts of their hallucinations, fears, and complaints. One of their complaints is about the Man, who comes to sit and drink alone, taking no part in their feeble debauches. His Wife is dead, his mansion empty of everything save rats. The Drunkards taunt him with reminders of his fifteen rooms, his weak heart, his lost youth.

Gradually other voices are heard, and the Old Women from the first scene reappear, replacing the Drunkards entirely. They mockingly recall Man's life: One describes her visit to the empty house and abandoned nursery, while the others imitate the ball. They mimic the Guests' exclamations and caper around the silent Man. As the Old Women begin to sing, the Musicians from the ball reappear, and the Old Women slide into a dance, leaning toward Man and whispering that he will soon die. The dance becomes jerky and abrupt, but both they and the Musicians freeze when the Man suddenly stands up, calls for his wife-shieldbearer, then collapses and dies with a curse on his lips. After a moment of profound silence and darkness, the Old Women announce Man's death to the audience, then renew their dance. The music rises as the dance turns into a frenzy of screeching and whirling, which continues even as the stage goes entirely dark except for Man's face. Soon that light, too, is extinguished. The noise continues, reaching a nearly unbearable pitch, then abruptly dies away.

Themes and Meanings

Two forces—or sets of forces—are at work in Leonid Andreyev's *The Life of Man*. One set is human and social: Man's talent and innate nobility are ranged against the mediocrity and meanness of his natural inferiors. For all of its abstractions, the play does comment on the life and values of a particular milieu—the world of the successful professional. The portrayal of Man's early poverty and final ruin, unlike that of his prosperous middle years, has more to do with artistic symmetry than with social issues. Andreyev is rounding out the curve of beginning and ending. The conflict between Man and his fellows arises not because Man is an architect—a creator—and they are not. The conflict rather arises from their envy of the fortune his talent has accrued for him, and their tally includes not only Man's money, but his "luck" as well: his fame, his Wife, his beautiful Son. They envy what Man has, not what he is.

There are obvious autobiographical elements in the play, especially in the romance between Man and his Wife, in Man's love for grandness and gesture, and in the crowds of hangers-on. Andreyev almost seems to predict his own artistic decline and death, twelve years before the fact.

The confrontation between spiritual superiors and inferiors on this earth is secondary to Andreyev's chief obsession, which is the relationship between Man and the mysterious force shaping his life. Someone-in-Gray always seems to emerge from a wall, and critics have speculated on what the author meant by that gray, wall-like inevitability—God, fate, philosopher Arthur Schopenhauer's "will"? Whichever of these Someone-in-Gray may represent, if any, only one thing is certain. The enigmatic power controlling Man's destiny is huge, indifferent, inexorable and, if Someone-in-Gray is any indication, entirely humorless. There is cosmic irony here, on an immense and dramatic scale; moreover, it is deadly serious. No clowns or sardonic laughter lighten the tone, and even the Family, the Old Women, and the Drunkards are more ominous and horrific than they are comic. Man himself is self-consciously, pompously serious—a monumental figure even in his own eyes.

The solemnity of speech and tableau create an air of hopelessness and futility. Contemporary audiences largely missed what Andreyev considered to be Man's triumph—his rebellious spirit in the face of defeat. The exact source of the harpies, hypocrites, and madmen concerns Andreyev less than the vividness of the scenes they act out, and he is most interested in Man's defiance of them and what they represent. His attempts to dramatize metaphysics leave the nature of the universe a melodramatic given; it is human nature in conflict that attracts him.

Dramatic Devices

Andreyev's vision of the new theater, "neorealist theater," as he once called it, was more visual than verbal. He often declared his intention to present not life, but a reflection, a picture—and his later enthusiasm for film underscores how literally he spoke. An amateur painter, he conceived the idea for *The Life of Man* after seeing a work by Albrecht Dürer depicting the five stages of man's life, block by block. Like a mystery play or a narrative woodcut, *The Life of Man* seems two-dimensional, a series of animated tableaux or friezes, and Andreyev's text includes such detailed directions on sets, lighting, and blocking that he leaves the director and the actors little leeway in the matter.

The sets throughout are minimal, even at the scene of the lavish ball, where the furniture and windows appear out of proportion to the stage's dimensions. Walls and backdrops are gray, but within that grayness Andreyev demands stark contrast between light and dark. The main stage effects are to be created by lighting rather than by other means, and there are to be no offstage effects (sound or light) whatsoever. There is to be no superfluous, unchoreographed movement, especially in the group scenes. The groups of minor characters are all grotesques, from the sinister, haggish Old Women to the painted puppetlike Guests. Monstrous and comic at the same time, they appear as exaggerated as figures wearing masks.

The language of *The Life of Man* is equally ceremonial, and with the exception of a few dramatic moments, the lines are intoned rather than spoken naturally. Dialogue neither spurs action nor reacts to it; it merely comments on a course of events long since determined. The most formal commentator and observer is Someone-in-Gray, that mouthpiece of some mysterious force that is not precisely fate and not precisely God; the closest Andreyev himself came to defining it was to call it the "iron circle of predestination."

The play's construction is an attempt to depict that inexorable symmetry. It begins and ends in darkness; in the first scene Man merely cries, in the last scene he utters his final line and collapses. The Old Women dominate, supported by Relatives in the first scene and by Drunkards in the last. (Andreyev later rewrote scene 5 to make it even more of a match, replacing the Drunkards with Relatives and transferring the action back to Man's house.) In scene 3, the center of the play and the apogee of Man's earthly success, neither Man nor his Wife speaks a word, and the lines spoken by the Guests are mechanical and virtually interchangeable. Scenes 2 and 4, however, are given over to Man and his Wife. All of their dialogues and monologues are in these two scenes; in other words, these two scenes contain the most lyrical and dramatic moments in the play. Formal and stylized as they are, they lend a hint of psychological realism to an otherwise abstract piece.

Critical Context

Leonid Andreyev first came to fame as a fiction writer, and in the early years of the twentieth century he was ranked alongside Anton Chekhov and Maxim Gorky. His short stories dealt with controversial social issues, which placed him more or less in the camp of nineteenth century crusading realism—on its scandalous side, since he favored taboo subjects such as rape, venereal disease, and criminal insanity. He himself tended to associate with the realists and their concern for political and social improvement, but at the same time, Andreyev's fascination with the pathological side of human nature and with grandiose metaphysical schemes links him with the Decadents and the Symbolists.

These latter alliances were part of the general renaissance of Russian high culture known as the Silver Age, and their "reevaluation of values," for good or ill, embraced all the arts. What this meant for theater was, in part, a rejection of realist conventions and a return to conscious artifice and even ritual, be it *commedia dell'arte*, puppet theater, circus, or Greek tragedy.

Andreyev did write a number of plays in a realistic vein, including *K zvezdam* (pb. 1905, pr. 1906; *To the Stars*, 1907) and *Yekaterina Ivanovna* (pb. 1912; *Katerina*, 1923). Early in his career, he declared his intention to reform Russian drama, and *The Life of Man* was to be the introduction "both in form and content" to an entire cycle that would do just that. The form would guarantee that the playgoer never lost sight of the mask, the artifice, that he never forgot that he was in a theater, watching a representation. The content itself was obvious from the titles: "King Hunger" (the only one of the cycle ever finished), "War," "Revolution," and "God, Devil and Man." Death itself was to play a principal role; God would be the incarnation of movement, destruction, and struggle; the Devil, stillness and quiet; Man, bold thought and daring reason.

The Life of Man was a theatrical sensation in a way that more purely Symbolist plays could not be; although somewhat static, it was simply entertaining to watch. It combined the novel staging of the "new theater" with a dramatic and defiant hero who, although stylized, was no faceless Everyman. Produced and directed first by Russia's leading avant-garde director, Vsevolod Meyerhold, and then by famed director Konstantin Stanislavsky's Moscow Art Theatre, the play expressed both the philosophical and aesthetic preoccupations of its time perhaps better—or at least more obviously—than any other. However, like most of Andreyev's plays, it has not worn well and is rarely performed. Of all of his dramatic works, only *Tot, kto poluchayet poshchechiny* (pb. 1902, pr. 1915; *He Who Gets Slapped*, 1921)—an allegory disguised as conventional melodrama, set in a circus—has kept its appeal.

Sources for Further Study

Andreyev, Leonid. "Letters on the Theater." In *Russian Dramatic Theory from Pushkin to the Symbolists*. Translated by Laurence Senelick. Austin: University of Texas Press, 1981.

________. *Photographs by a Russian Writer: An Undiscovered Portrait of Pre-Revolutionary Russia*. Edited by Richard Davies. New York: Thames and Hudson, 1989.

Gorky, Maxim. *Reminiscences of Leonid Andreyev*. Translated by Katherine Mansfield and S. S. Koteliansky. New York: C. Gaige, 1922.

Kaun, Alexander. *Leonid Andreyev: A Critical Study*. 1924. Reprint. Freeport, N.Y.: Books for Libraries Press, 1969.

Newcombe, Josephine. *Leonid Andreyev*. New York: Ungar, 1972.

Woodward, James B. *Leonid Andreyev: A Study*. Oxford, England: Clarendon Press, 1969.

Jane Ann Miller

THE LION AND THE JEWEL

Author: Wole Soyinka (1934-)
Type of plot: Comedy
Time of plot: The 1950's
Locale: Ilujinle, a village in western Nigeria
First produced: 1959, in Ibadan, Nigeria
First published: 1963

Principal characters:
SIDI, the village belle
LAKUNLE, a schoolteacher
BAROKA, the "Bale" of Ilujinle
SADIKU, his head wife
THE FAVORITE, another of his wives
A WRESTLER
A SURVEYOR

The Play

The Lion and the Jewel takes place in Ilujinle, a small African village facing rapid change. As the play begins, it is morning, and the audience sees a marketplace, dominated by an immense odan tree. To the left of the stage is part of the village school, within which the students chant the "Arithmetic Times." Sidi enters the stage; she is a beautiful, slim girl with plaited hair—the true village belle. Balancing a pail on her head and wearing a broad cloth, Sidi attracts the attention of Lakunle, the young schoolteacher, who looks out the school windows to admire her beauty.

Lakunle, dressed in an old-style, threadbare, unironed English suit, scolds Sidi for carrying the pail on her head, telling her that the weight of the pail will hurt her spine and shorten her neck. He wants her to be a "modern" woman. Sidi, however, quickly reminds him of the times he has sworn that her looks do not affect his love for her. There is a comic exchange of charge and countercharge between the two, revealing Lakunle's uncomfortable attitude about Sidi's showing parts of her body: "How often must I tell you, Sidi, that a grown-up girl must cover up her. . . . Her shoulders."

This first scene also introduces Baroka, the Bale (the village chief): Sixty-two years old, wiry, goateed, he is also attracted by Sidi. The Bale, the opposite of Lakunle, is an artful, traditional man who resists the building of roads and railways, trying to keep his society insulated from "progress." The dialogue between these two men constitutes the crux of the play: the conservative, clear view of life represented by the Bale versus the progressive sloganeering of Lakunle. Beneath this sociopolitical theme is the other struggle—the war for Sidi's love.

The second scene of the play, "Noon," introduces Sadiku, for forty-one years the chief wife in the Bale's harem. Sadiku, acting as ambassador for the "Lion," the Bale, announces to Sidi that the Bale wants her for his latest wife; it has, after all, been five months since he last took a wife. In a comic exchange, Sidi, Sadiku, and Lakunle argue about whom shall have Sidi. Lakunle, in a rage more pretended than true, denounces the Bale: "What! The greedy dog! Insatiate camel of a foolish, doting race; Is he at his tricks again?"

Sidi reminds him that she can speak for herself, bolstered by her "fame" that has been spread throughout the region by the magazine pictures taken by a photographer. Sadiku, no novice at wooing wives for the Lion, appeals to Sidi by telling her that even the Lion has to die sometime, and Sidi will then have the honor of being the senior wife of a new Bale. Sidi, however, is not easily won. She slyly asks: "Baroka not request my hand. The stranger brought his book of images. Why did the Lion not bestow his gift before my face was lauded to the world?" Lakunle, always ready to insult the Bale, interjects: "I don't know what the women see in him. His eyes are small and always red with wine."

Lakunle contrasts his "dew-moistened" face with the Lion's "leather piece." Here and throughout the play, Lakunle's words result in his defeat. Soyinka's subtle use of linguistic register consistently highlights Lakunle's role of poorly prepared reformer. Lakunle espouses progress, success, civilization, and fame, but never supports his empty generalities.

The third and final scene, "Night," opens, much the same as the first scene, in the village center. The contest for Sidi's love continues with the Lion reminding everyone of his virility and touting his manliness. His attempts are again unsuccessful. In a conversation with Sadiku, the crafty Lion conceives a new ruse: He announces that his manhood is gone. The Bale's feigned impotence releases Sadiku's suppressed feelings, and she invites Sidi to celebrate the women's victory over the dominating male. Unfortunately for Sadiku and Sidi, the old Lion still has life in him.

Sidi cannot resist going to the Bale's house to tempt him; instead, the cunning Bale tempts her—to experience life instead of reading about it in books. Soon, Sidi reappears at the village center and reveals the Bale's deceit: "It was a trick." Lakunle's bombastic outrage is not convincing; neither is his speech about his ideal, platonic love for Sidi, which the audience now knows is a self-deception. Lakunle laments his loss of Sidi, who agrees to marry the Bale. As the play ends, however, Lakunle seems to be recovering: He is last seen chasing a young dancing girl.

Themes and Meanings

The Lion and the Jewel, on one level, is a comedy about love. Lakunle, the naïve, modernist schoolteacher, attempts to win Sidi's love by teaching her about the "new" woman's role, a role based largely on Western society. Opposing him is the shrewd Bale, striving to win Sidi's love by any means he can, including the ruse about his supposed impotence.

Lakunle's dress and speech indicate the shallowness of his role of reformer: His clothes show his rejection of the traditional dress of the villages, and his speech expresses his undigested ideas comically. He rejects a traditional element of the marriage ceremony, "the bride price." He addresses Sidi as an ignorant girl, demonstrating his impetuous lack of control; he alienates himself from the audience with his lack of valid ideas.

The Bale, who wins the sex war, presents himself more favorably. He impresses Sidi with his postage stamp machine, which does not work, and by allowing his servants to form a trade union and allowing them one day off. He is nevertheless, a conservative who plans to keep the village as it has always been. The Bale is a supreme protagonist: Lakunle is simply no match for him. Wole Soyinka's humorous caricature of Lakunle has the audience taking the Bale's side. Sidi and Sadiku also win the audience, with their sly understanding of the falseness of both men. Soyinka maintains the humor of the play through his characters—the self-parody of Lakunle, the coquettish behavior of Sidi, and the self-assured quality of the Bale.

The play also has an allegorical level. Sidi represents the Nigerian people, who are tempted to believe the impotence of the past, but eventually experience its power. The Bale represents the centuries of tradition that extend into the present. The mimes, which take place twice in the play, present flashbacks that give the play added historical depth. The play's energetic combination of dance, song, mime, and comic dialogue reinforces its themes. Soyinka shows a passionate concern for his society, seeking freedom for all. His ideas are not only African, however: His characters and mannerisms are African, but his people represent the whole race. Although many characters are potential victims of their own ingenuity, his heroes are marked ultimately by their ceaseless striving.

Dramatic Devices

The Lion and the Jewel describes the happenings of one day in the village. In the first scene, "Morning," the dramatist concentrates on the expectations of all three principal characters, the Bale, Lakunle, and Sidi, who are brought together by chance. The stage displays the new—the students chanting the "Arithmetic Times"—and the old: Sidi carrying the pail of water, the traditional work of Nigerian women. Lakunle's twenty-three-inch-bottom trousers attest his modern "civilized" tendencies. His chauvinistic remark to Sidi, "as a woman, you have a smaller brain than mine," immediately reveals his conceit to the audience.

Wole Soyinka introduces a metaphor for the modern world in the (unseen) person of the photographer who takes pictures of Sidi; the photographer is presented as a mirror for Lakunle. Four girls begin a chant, dancing around Lakunle; they are then joined by drummers. The girls construct a mime representing the four wheels of a motor car, in another parody of the civilized world. This subtle scene, without dialogue, reveals the true nature of Lakunle as he pinches the "tires," the girls' bottoms. The scene comes to an abrupt halt when the Bale enters and playfully accuses Lakunle of stealing the village maidenhead. As the girls chase Lakunle away, the scene ends with the Bale admiring Sidi's pictures in the magazine.

The second scene, "Noon," the longest in the play, introduces Sadiku, the Bale's head wife. She and Sidi now command the stage, and Sadiku begins her wooing of Sidi for the Bale. Another metaphor for progress appears onstage. The surveyor and his workers, who want to build a railroad, are bought off by the Bale, to Lakunle's disgust. The scene shifts to the Bale's house, where, attended by his harem, he conceives his plan to fool and subsequently win Sidi. The scene ends with the Bale's announcement of his loss of virility.

The last scene, "Night," begins with Sidi and Sadiku celebrating the Bale's loss of his manliness. Sidi enters his house, and the Bale begins his seduction in earnest. His outrageous sexual imagery goes unnoticed by Sidi, but not by the audience. The mummers enter and perform a dance of virility: the Bale's story.

The winning of Sidi by the Bale is logical and right. His concern is for life; Lakunle's is for rhetoric. Lakunle plans to "civilize" her by marrying her, without considering Sidi's own feelings and desires. The expectations of reformer Lakunle are stifled in the face of the Bale's cunning and expertise. Lakunle's own follies result in his loss of Sidi. The audience's last glimpse of him, however, portends a man losing his delusions and returning to his true self—a typical human being, fascinated by the physical attractions of the opposite sex.

Critical Context

The Lion and the Jewel, although an early play by Wole Soyinka, is perhaps his most widely known and performed drama. It was first produced along with *The Swamp Dwellers* (pr. 1958, pb. 1963); both plays are concerned with a society in flux and treat the issue with humor. *The Lion and the Jewel* differs in tone in that it conveys a sense of physical danger that is not apparent in the former. *The Lion and the Jewel* contains most of the dramatic themes and literary devices that Soyinka enlarges upon in later plays. Although it is lighthearted and contains music, dance, and mime, it also has a serious underlying theme—the possible dangers inherent in the clash between the old and the new.

Soyinka's continued concern with the theme of the battle between a traditional and an emerging society appears in later plays such as *A Dance of the Forests* (pr. 1960, pb. 1963) and *The Trials of Brother Jero* (pr. 1960, pb. 1963): The former views history as a cyclical movement; the latter unfolds a satire of undiscovered identities. Similar dramatic conventions appear in *Death and the King's Horseman* (pb. 1975, pr. 1976), in which traditional customs are challenged, and the age-old idea of self-sacrifice is shown to be no mere mechanical ritual. The protagonist, Elesin, is confronted with the same danger of change that confronts the Bale. When Elesin's son, Olunde, assumes the traditional responsibility that Elesin avoids, he embodies Soyinka's hope for the regeneration of a healthy community.

The canon of Soyinka's work—in drama, poetry, essay, and the novel—was justly acknowledged with his receiving of the Nobel Prize in Literature in 1986. Soyinka's dramas have a strong social impact; through his use of humor, satire, irony, and realism, he has created African drama that addresses universal concerns.

Sources for Further Study

Bossier, Gregory. "Writers and Their Work: Wole Soyinka." *Dramatist* 2 (January/February, 2000): 9.

Coger, Greta M. K. *Index of Subjects, Proverbs, and Themes in the Writings of Wole Soyinka*. New York: Greenwood Press, 1988.

Gibbs, James. *Wole Soyinka*. New York: Grove Press, 1986.

_______, ed. *Critical Perspectives on Wole Soyinka*. London: Heinemann, 1981.

Jones, Eldred Durosimi. *The Writing of Wole Soyinka*. 3d ed. Portsmouth, N.H.: Heinemann, 1988.

Soyinka, Wole. *Myth, Literature, and the African World*. Cambridge, England: Cambridge University Press, 1990.

Wright, Derek. *Wole Soyinka: A Life, Work, and Criticism*. Indianapolis: Macmillan, 1992.

Robert J. Willis

LOOT

Author: Joe Orton (1933-1967)
Type of plot: Absurdist; farce
Time of plot: The 1960's
Locale: England
First produced: 1965, at the Arts Theatre, Cambridge, England
First published: 1967

Principal characters:

McLeavy, a middle-aged, middle-class Briton whose wife has just died
Fay Jean McMahon, an alias for Phyllis Jean McMahon, the late Mrs. McLeavy's nurse
Harold "Hal," McLeavy's son
Dennis, Hal's friend, a mortician's assistant
Truscott, a police inspector who purports to be from the Metropolitan Water Board
The late Mrs. McLeavy, whose embalmed corpse, deprived of its coffin, plays a passive role onstage

The Play

Loot is, superficially, a play about the burial of Mrs. McLeavy, a middle-class British woman just deceased. The play opens immediately before her funeral. Her husband and her nurse, Fay, are onstage with the coffin, which stands on trestles. As the action develops, Mrs. McLeavy's son, Hal, is introduced. The audience by this time has learned that Fay, in her mid-twenties, has been widowed seven times. Accounts are soon given of what widowed her so regularly, including references to two husbands who disappeared and are presumed dead. Fay obviously hastened all of them to their reward.

Fay wears Mrs. McLeavy's slippers, and as the play progresses, she dons other articles of the dead woman's clothing. Fay wants to marry Mr. McLeavy, and she goes so far as to demand, before the funeral, that he propose marriage to her on bended knee. The club she holds over him is that on her deathbed, Mrs. McLeavy changed her will, leaving everything to Fay. McLeavy can share in his wife's bequest only if he marries Fay. Fay's reward is that, marrying McLeavy, she will stand to inherit everything he has, and it is clear that in Fay's capable hands, he will not reach a more advanced age than he has already achieved.

The McLeavy's son Hal, a ribald youth whom Fay, a devout Roman Catholic, scolds for making the priest work twenty-four hours a day simply to hear his confessions, does not plan to attend his mother's funeral. His friend and sometime lover,

Dennis, works with the mortician who will lay the woman to rest. Dennis soon arrives and provides the information that he has had sex with Fay beneath a picture of the Sacred Heart and that he and Hal have just robbed a bank and have to do something about hiding the money before Truscott, a police inspector masquerading as a Metropolitan Water Board inspector, comes nosing about close to the cupboard in the McLeavy house where the loot has been stashed.

The solution is simple: Dennis, who is in charge of sealing the coffin, will simply remove Mrs. McLeavy from it, put her remains in the cupboard, and put the loot in the coffin, in which it will receive the full rites of the Roman Catholic Church and a respectable Christian burial. Much of the remainder of the play is a parody of detective melodramas. The corpse, nicely embalmed, has been stripped of all of its organs, which are in a separate coffin to be buried with the first so that at the resurrection, Mrs. McLeavy will be complete and able to function well.

By the time Truscott arrives, the corpse has been stripped of its clothing and such other parts as can be removed—props such as a glass eye and false teeth, which become playthings thrown from person to person onstage as the play progresses. The telling evidence, Mrs. McLeavy's body, is to be weighted with ballast and dumped in a river inconveniently distant from the deceased's residence.

Truscott, with his Holmesian nose for crime, is on to two vicious felonies: a bank robbery and the murder of Mrs. McLeavy by Nurse McMahon. He sniffs around for evidence, usually missing by a split second the corpse's sequestration in the cupboard, in the coffin, or behind a screen. Orton keeps the audience on tenterhooks.

Meanwhile, on the way to the church, the hearse is broadsided by a vehicle run amok, killing the mortician. The coffin, however, is made of solid stuff and, even though set alight by the accident, protects its precious cargo. Finally, however, as in all good melodramas, truth will out. Fay, certainly nobody's fool, has already discovered Hal and Dennis's scheme, but they buy her silence. Then Truscott learns the truth, finding the corpse behind a screen, which gives him great negotiating powers. He strikes a deal for a portion of the loot, pins Mrs. McLeavy's murder on Mr. McLeavy—who is led away protesting—and, after assuring Hal that he can arrange to have his father dispatched to join his mother in paradise, tries to recruit Hal and Dennis as policemen.

Hal, now having the McLeavy house to himself, invites Dennis to move in with him. Fay reminds him that when she and Dennis marry, they will have to move out. Hal does not see the need, but Fay explains to him that people would talk and that they must keep up appearances. With that platitude reflecting conventional working-class, British morality, the final curtain is rung down.

Themes and Meanings

Joe Orton and his lover, Kenneth Halliwell (1927-1967), who on August 9, 1967, murdered Orton and then took his own life, were arrested in 1962 and sentenced to jail terms of six months each for willfully defacing seventy-two library books. They had skillfully and puckishly rewritten the blurbs on the flaps of the book jackets and had artfully altered them and some of the inside illustrations in ways that were judged obscene. Their motive was to engage in a spoof that would fluster and bewilder the stalwart library patrons who represent middle-class virtues. During his half-year in jail, Orton began to write in earnest, and his writing had consistently the same basic aim that had inspired his defacing of the library books. He wanted to hold up to ridicule what he considered the hypocrisy of British morality, and he wanted to do it in a brilliantly witty way. With *Loot*, he fulfilled this aim.

Loot is a farcical attack on authority and conventions of all sorts: parental, ecclesiastical, civil, judicial, sexual, even those of the mortuary. Much as Lewis Carroll (Charles Lutwidge Dodgson, 1832-1898) looked aslant at his world in *Alice in Wonderland* (1865) and *Through the Looking-Glass* (1872), so Orton viewed society with tongue in cheek but with rapier bared and in hand. The theme on which *Loot* centers is the hypocrisy of social institutions and of those who allow themselves to be manipulated by such institutions. Orton's technique is clever: What he is saying is so outrageous that it cannot be taken at face value; therefore, it offends less than it might. In all of his outrageous statements and observations, however, there is a glimmering of truth that makes audiences seeing the play go home and later reflect on its thematic impact.

Orton's play also leaves one with the impression that those who run society all have their price. When Fay castigates Truscott and tells him that the police used to be run by men of integrity, he makes no protest but merely assures her that such a mistake has been rectified. The play also whimsically suggests that the guilty always get off, often on the sort of technicality that makes it impossible for Truscott to build a case against Fay. He needs some cells from the dead woman's body to prove that it is indeed Mrs. McLeavy who is dead. He needs her stomach, which is in the small coffin containing the parts removed during embalming, but the stomach explodes, and Truscott is deprived of the evidence he requires.

No matter. He can still get a conviction and add another notch to his departmental belt. McLeavy is the perfect fall guy, and by felling him Truscott solves most of the drama's remaining logistical problems while sustaining Orton's theme.

Dramatic Devices

In its initial productions on the road in 1965, *Loot* was a failure because the cast acted it farcically yet formally rather than seriously. Joe Orton was insistent that the play could not succeed as the farce he intended unless the acting was totally serious. A director out only to exploit the play's humor and to get laughs does the play an injustice. Peter Wood, the play's original director, staged the production according to formal conventions reminiscent of eighteenth century drama. Orton accepted this approach until he realized that it was not succeeding. Wood's response to hostile reaction from audiences was to make the production even more formal, increasing audience hostility. Moreover, the original production employed an art nouveau set, and the characters were dressed largely in black and white. The set was visually pleasing but competed with the play for attention, and created significant problems. Orton knew instinctively that the play's chief aim had to be cerebral rather than humorous, although humor necessarily served as a vehicle. He knew that the set could not be permitted to upstage the dialogue.

Before the play reached London, its direction was transferred to Charles Marowitz. Orton had done considerable rewriting, heightening the humor of the glass eye scene by bringing it up again late in the play (when Truscott stumbles on the eye). He also added McLeavy's arrest after the out-of-town tryouts. Marowitz made the sets naturalistic. In the out-of-town productions, the coffin had been part of the furniture of the art nouveau set; in Marowitz's production, it was a coffin with a macabre, melodramatic horror attached to it, which was precisely what the play demanded.

A major problem involved getting audiences to accept the presence of a corpse onstage, particularly a corpse that was shifted from place to place. The problem was solved by swathing Mrs. McLeavy in bandages so that she resembled an Egyptian mummy, to which the dialogue frequently compares her. Audience acceptance is swift enough to permit the outrageous tossing about of her removable parts later in the play.

Critical Context

Although Joe Orton, one of the most inventive playwrights in twentieth century British drama, was far from derivative, the extremes to which he took his drama bring to mind some of the more puckish plays in Restoration drama, particularly William Wycherley's *The Country Wife* (pb. 1675). Among more modern writers, Orton can be compared to Evelyn Waugh, whose novels *A Handful of Dust* (1934) and, more particularly, *The Loved One* (1948), while not quite as outrageous as Orton's plays, move wittily toward that extreme of social criticism labeled outrageous.

The social criticism of Oscar Wilde, like Orton a homosexual rankling at Britain's narrow Victorian morality, was less sharp than Orton's although it aimed at achieving similar ends and, for its day, was almost as outrageous as Orton's work. Noël Coward used his acerbic wit subtly to eat through the thin veneer of middle-class British morality in such plays as *Private Lives* (pr., pb. 1930), *Blithe Spirit* (pr., pb. 1941), and even his patriotic play on the Victorian tradition, *Cavalcade* (pr. 1931).

Formally, Orton is indebted to the melodramatic writers of detective literature, whom he parodies in much of his work, as well as to such writers in the absurdist tradition as Samuel Beckett, Eugène Ionesco, Jean Genet, Arthur Kopit, Tom Stoppard, and Edward Albee. In the last analysis, however, Orton was a distinctive talent with a perversely witty view of life's most serious problems. The age in which he lived shaped him artistically, but he emerged as a playwright and social critic unique in twentieth century drama.

Sources for Further Study

Fraser, Keath. "Joe Orton's Brief Career." *Modern Drama* 14 (1971): 414-419.

King, J. Kimball. *Twenty Modern British Playwrights: A Bibliography, 1956-1976.* New York: Garland, 1977.

Lahr, John. Introduction to *Joe Orton, the Complete Plays*. London: Eyre Methuen, 1976.
_______. *Prick Up Your Ears: The Biography of Joe Orton*. New York: Knopf, 1978.
Orton, Joe. Interview by Giles Gordon. *Transatlantic Review* 24 (1967): 93-100.
_______. *The Orton Diaries*. Edited by John Lahr. London: Methuen, 1986.
Rusinko, Susan. *Joe Orton*. Boston: Twayne, 1995.
Taylor, John Russell. *The Second Wave: New British Drama for the Seventies*. London: Eyre Methuen, 1978.

R. Baird Shuman

THE LOST COLONY

Author: Paul Green (1894-1981)
Type of plot: History
Time of plot: July, 1584-Christmas, 1588
Locale: London and Roanoke Island, North Carolina
First produced: 1937, at the Waterside Theater on the grounds of the Fort Raleigh National Historic Site, near Manteo, North Carolina
First published: 1937

Principal characters:
JOHN BORDEN, farmer and leader of the Roanoke settlement
JOHN WHITE, governor of the settlement
ELEANOR DARE, his daughter
CAPTAIN ANANIAS DARE, Eleanor's husband
MANTEO, young Croatoan chief
OLD TOM, English beggar and drunkard
ELIZABETH I, queen of England, sanctions the Roanoke settlement
WALTER RALEIGH, English explorer

The Play

The Lost Colony eloquently recounts the story of the 117 men, women, and children of the doomed English settlement at Roanoke Island, North Carolina, who disappeared without a trace in 1588 after a yearlong struggle to settle the coastal wilds. Far from dwelling on the failure of the enterprise, the play offers an uplifting retelling that connects the daring of these first New World settlers (the Roanoke community predated Plymouth by more than thirty years) to the eventual success of the American experiment.

The prologue begins with a thundering organ solo followed by a sweeping choral rendering of "O God That Madest Earth and Sky." A minister in full vestment intones a prayer recalling the heroic Roanoke settlers and reminding the audience that this seaside amphitheater is, in fact, on the very site of that original settlement (the play was written to be performed at a specific site). The stage then comes alive with the vivid spectacle of the harvest dance of the native Roanokes, interrupted by the arrival of the initial English scouting cortege, who claim the land for the queen. An exchange of gifts and gestures of friendship promise cooperation.

The action shifts to London, specifically the happy confusion outside a tavern by the queen's gardens. Old Tom, a beggar and drunkard who, like the Shakespearean fool, is given to witty insights, anticipates the arrival of Sir Walter Raleigh. With great pomp, the queen herself arrives and, after listening to Raleigh and sampling the New World curiosity known as tobacco, sanctions a settlement. Amid the celebration, John

Borden, a dashing tenant farmer, exchanges tender words with Eleanor White, whose father owns the lands he farms. She is, however, already promised to Captain Ananias Dare, a union more appropriate to her social position.

The disastrous first attempt at settling the island by a military contingent dispatched in 1585 is rendered dramatically in scene 5. The English ambush the unsuspecting Indians during a dance ritual and kill their chief. After a period of escalating hostilities, the chorus explains, the settlement's leaders returned to England, leaving only fifteen soldiers behind to maintain the crude fort. Raleigh persisted in his dream, however, and outfitted a ship with more than one hundred men, women, and children, largely from the lower rural class, to start a permanent colony. John White is appointed governor. Act 1 closes at the Plymouth wharf on the day of their departure. Despite whisperings of the doomed nature of an enterprise designed only to make Raleigh richer, John Borden rallies the hesitant people. As the first act closes, the settlers, singing bravely, gather their meager belongings and head off.

Act 2 begins with the settlers' arrival in July, 1587. The fifteen men left behind have disappeared; the fort is in disrepair. The Roanokes are now implacably opposed to the English incursion. The settlers, nevertheless, vote to stay. Initially, the settlement bodes growth as the settlers are helped by the Croatoans, an indigenous tribe to the south. Indeed, in a comic subplot, Old Tom finds himself the object of the unrequited love of a squaw who follows him in exaggerated adoration. Scene 2 recounts the August, 1587, birth of Virginia Dare, the daughter of Ananias and Eleanor Dare, the first English child born in the New World. Yet even as the minister offers thanksgiving, the stage is rocked by a savage raid. The following Sunday, while the settlers celebrate the baby's baptism, a contingent headed by Governor White departs for England to secure provisions for the colony's survival, promising to return before Christmas. That promise gives the closing scenes their haunting poignancy. The audience watches as the imminent invasion of England by the Spanish Armada compels the queen to rescind her support for the New World empire and to marshal all ships for the defense of the English mainland, effectively dooming the settlement. The settlers themselves can only guess why the ships never return.

With Captain Dare's dramatic onstage death during a raid in scene 5, the play darkens. The action moves to the settlement's second Christmas. In tatters and walking feebly, the settlers, facing starvation, gather nevertheless to celebrate, the glad message of hope in their carols starkly ironic. Old Tom enters with his squaw, their comic relationship having matured into a marriage of mutual support. Amid the prayers, a child's plaint, "I'm hungry, mommee," underscores the reality of the slowly failing colony. Hysteria wells up (heightened by the chorus, singing of suffering) until John Borden, returning from a scouting expedition, fires his rifle to quiet the panic.

As the settlers disperse, Borden, now married to Eleanor, confides that they have been invited to follow the Croatoans south, where the game will be more plentiful. When a messenger arrives to announce that a marauding Spanish man-of-war has anchored with the intention of attacking, the settlers decide to abandon the fort, despite the discontented few who argue that surrender would ensure food. Encouraged by

Borden's brave words ("Let the wilderness drive us forth as wanderers across the earth, scatter our broken bones upon these sands, it shall not kill the purpose that brought us here"), they head into the Carolina wilderness, departing into the woods bordering the amphitheater, singing the hymn that began the play, "O God That Madest Earth and Sky." In opting for this conjecture about the settlers' fate, Green closes with an uplifting sense of affirmation.

Themes and Meanings

The Lost Colony resists elaborate intellectual analysis. Indeed, its fullest impact cannot be registered in being read: It is designed to be experienced as a multimedia event that elicits an emotional, rather than intellectual, response. However, if the drama has a thematic idea, it is undoubtedly community. Addressed initially to a nation dealing with the shattering trauma of the 1930's Great Depression, the play, drawn from one of American history's most compelling tragedies, affirms the heroic suffering, the unshakeable resolve, and earnest nobility of the United States' earliest settlers. The hero is no one character but rather the community of Roanoke itself, a collective realized onstage by a cast of more than one hundred players. The cast is less about individual characters and more about a single idea: the courage to realize dreams in a land of opportunity. The impoverished settlers are driven from an England entrenched in class divisions (underscored by the opulence of the queen's court contrasted to the settlers' bare belongings and by the forbidden romance between Eleanor Dare and the play's Everyman figure, John Borden). Under the difficult conditions in the settlement, however, they must act as a collective—together they pray, they celebrate, they build, they farm, they fight, and when the time comes, together they depart. The theme is underscored dramatically when, after the death of Captain Dare, Eleanor and Borden consecrate their love.

The theme of community is further rendered by Green's treatment of the American Indians. Over its long run, the play, responding to changes in American cultural temperament, has given dignity to the Roanoke and Coatoan characters, who were, in the original production, two-dimensional stereotypes. Although the initial encounter between the cultures is cordial, after the first party antagonizes the Roanokes, the play foregrounds violence in several staged raids. In heroic countermovement, Manteo, a young Croatoan chief who visits the court of Elizabeth, helps the struggling settlers and, before his death late in act 2, arranges for the remaining settlers to join in the southern migration. Amid the ongoing terrorism of the Roanokes, the subplot of the emerging love of Old Tom and his squaw introduces the potentially controversial subject of miscegenation, offered within Green's humane vision as a strategy for cooperation and community.

Less obviously than the large-scale heroics onstage, the play forges a subtler community by connecting the audience with its own history. *The Lost Colony*, as an outdoor drama, is designed for tourists, mostly families, who watch unfold the very history commemorated by the landmarks all around them. Such a populist drama encourages an emotional connection not only for the doomed men, women, and children of the Roanoke community but also for the America that their settlement would ultimately create. Thus, the audience feels a part of the very collective the drama celebrates: ordinary people dreaming of a better world.

Dramatic Devices

As the first and longest-running example of what Green termed a "symphonic drama," *The Lost Colony* represents a revolutionary genre that recalls the outdoor theatrical rituals of the ancient Greeks, the lavish medieval community pageants (notably the Oberammergau Passion Play), the staged spectacles of Wagnerian opera in Bayreuth, Germany, and the stylized pageants of seventeenth century Japanese kabuki theater. Begun as a local community effort to address what residents regarded as the long neglect of the historic events at Roanoke, the drama, planned for a single summer run, was commissioned in April, 1936, by the Roanoke Historical Association to commemorate the 350th anniversary of the birth of Virginia Dare. Yet, under Green's visionary direction, the production found a receptive audience and has run every summer six nights per week since 1937 (except during World War II).

While on a Guggenheim Fellowship to Europe in 1928-1929, Green was inspired by German playwright Bertolt Brecht's antirealism—with its unconventional strategies for involving the audience in a performance—and by Russian playwright Alexis Granowsky's experiments in introducing music into episodic drama. Green pioneered the return of drama to the outdoors, with its implicit invitation to enlarge the audience emotionally. *The Lost Colony*, with a chorus and pipe organ providing its sonic backdrop, deliberately aims for the impact of religious ritual. Many elements must work together to create this experience (hence the term "symphonic" to suggest how disparate elements must cooperate like the sections of an orchestra creating a symphony). Among its dramatic devices, the play coordinates poetic dialogue, choreography, lighting, costuming, sound effects, a score of period music (including hymns, carols, organ works, and dances), a cast of more than one hundred actors and a chorus of twenty voices, pyrotechnics, dramatically staged action sequences (including brutal raids), and lavish sets deployed across a main stage measuring more than two hundred feet across, as well as two smaller movable stages. Behind the scenes, teams of technicians maintain the spectacle, monitoring banks of computer equipment, state-of-the-art sound and lighting boards, and even Doppler weather radar.

Critical Context

When Green was first approached to work on a pageant based on Roanoke, he was already disillusioned with conventional theater. His first full-length drama, *In Abraham's Bosom* (pr. 1926, pb. 1927), a controversial play that boldly examined race relations, had won the 1927 Pulitzer Prize but had found little commercial success. Green, teaching philosophy at the University of North Carolina, then began to explore the folk stories and African American music of his rural east Carolina upbringing. As he evolved his interpretation of the Roanoke settlement and found broad support for his vision of a people's theater (the original staging was largely funded through President

Franklin D. Roosevelt's New Deal programs), Green wrote extensively of his conception of outdoor drama as an opportunity not only to mine regional history for its narrative appeal but also to bring theater to a new audience.

After the stunning success of this initial project, Green would spend the remainder of his considerable professional career (nearly thirty years) creating sixteen other outdoor dramas, staged largely in southern venues, where, Green argued, there runs a deep sense of regional history. Some, like *The Lost Colony*, recount the settling of the new continent by particular ethnic groups—including Scots, Spaniards, and British—while others re-create the struggles of settlers—in Texas, Florida, and Georgia, among other places—to create a community amid the wilderness. Green has been criticized for emphasizing spectacle and action, for rejecting the subtler, often pessimistic, thematic nuances of traditional theater, and for offering instead larger-than-life characters who are given to declaiming inspirational messages of faith in common humanity. Yet, Green's outdoor dramas, as well as the numerous productions inspired by their success, became one of the most successful original American dramatic genres of the twentieth century and have given Green an audience that often exceeds the more recognized playwrights of his era.

Sources for Further Study

Avery, Laurence G. *"The Lost Colony": A Symphonic Drama of American History.* Chapel Hill: University of North Carolina Press, 2001.

_______. *A Paul Green Reader.* Chapel Hill: University of North Carolina Press, 1998.

Free, William J., and Charles B. Lower. *History into Drama: A Source Book on Symphonic Drama, Including the Complete Text of Paul Green's "The Lost Colony."* New York: Odyssey Press, 1963.

Kenny, Vincent S. *Paul Green.* New York: Twayne, 1971.

Rabkin, Gerald. *Drama and Commitment: Politics in the American Theatre of the Thirties.* Bloomington: Indiana University Press, 1964.

Joseph Dewey

LOST IN YONKERS

Author: Neil Simon (1927-)
Type of plot: Comedy; realism
Time of plot: 1942
Locale: Grandma Kurnitz's living and dining rooms, Yonkers, New York
First produced: 1991, at Stevens Center for the Performing Arts, Winston-Salem, North Carolina
First published: 1991

Principal characters:

GRANDMA KURNITZ, the harsh, elderly German matron of the Kurnitz family
BELLA, her thirty-five-year-old mentally ill daughter who lives at home
LOUIE, Grandma Kurnitz's gangster son
GERT, Grandma Kurnitz's daughter who has left home
EDDIE, Grandma Kurnitz's son, and father of Jay and Arty
JAY, a grandson, fifteen years old
ARTY, a grandson, thirteen years old

The Play

The play takes place in the sparsely furnished living and dining rooms of Grandma Kurnitz's apartment above Kurnitz's Kandy Store in Yonkers, New York. A small kitchen is off to one side. Doors lead to two bedrooms, a bathroom, and a staircase going directly down to the store. Jay and Arty are waiting in the living room while their father talks to Grandma Kurnitz in her bedroom. The boys heartily dislike and fear their authoritarian grandmother. Jay remarks that there is something peculiar about each of Grandma's children. Their father, Eddie, trembles in fear of Grandma. Bella, their mentally ill aunt, is "a little . . . closed for repairs" upstairs. When Aunt Gert visits Grandma, she cannot finish a sentence without gasping for breath. Uncle Louie has become a bagman for gangsters.

Bella arrives in a state of confusion. She went to the movies but, unable to find the theater she was looking for, went to another one and wants the boys to go with her next week, if "I can find the wrong theater again." Eddie comes out of the bedroom and explains to his sons that he went in debt to a loan shark to pay hospital and doctor bills for their mother when she was dying of cancer. He owes the loan shark nine thousand dollars. Until the outbreak of World War II opened up new jobs, Eddie had no hope of repaying him. Now he can earn that much money in a year, traveling through the South and West and selling scrap iron, but only if Grandma takes care of the boys while he is away. As much as they hate the idea, the boys agree to stay with her. Grandma, however, rejects Eddie's request, telling him he is too weak and needs to grow up and solve his own problems. People, she says sternly, must be hard as steel to survive in the world. Grandma does not relent until Bella asserts herself by threatening to go away and leave her mother all alone if she does not take in the boys.

The passage of time is indicated by stage blackouts, during which the voice of Eddie is heard reading letters to his sons. In one scene, Aunt Bella confides to the boys that while at the movie theater she met an usher who wants to marry her. Although he is also mentally ill, the couple plans to open a restaurant if Grandma will loan them five thousand dollars. In another scene, Uncle Louie sneaks into the house carrying a black bag. He warns the boys not to touch it. When the boys mention that two men have been driving by looking for him, Louie bribes each boy with five dollars to say nothing if anyone calls asking about him. Act 1 ends with Eddie's voice-over: "Dear Boys. . . . The one thing that keeps me going is knowing you're with my family. Thank God you're in good hands. Love, Pop."

Act 2 opens with Arty in bed with a fever. Grandma cooks some horrible-tasting German mustard soup. After forcing him to eat it, she orders Arty out of bed. Uncle Louie tells him that as a child in Germany, Grandma suffered greatly and is convinced that children must be trained to endure a harsh world stoically. Badly injured during a political riot, when a horse fell and crushed her foot, Grandma has been in pain every day and needs to walk with a cane, yet she refuses to take even so much as an aspirin. When they were growing up, if Louie or his brother or sisters broke a dish or misbehaved in any way, they were locked in a closet for hours. When Grandma heard Gert talking in her sleep, Gert did not get supper for a week until she learned to sleep holding her breath. Now when Gert visits her mother, she gasps for air in the middle of every sentence.

After a dinner that Gert attends, Bella haltingly informs the family that she wants to marry her usher boyfriend and open a restaurant. When Louie finally understands that the usher is mentally ill, he asks if what her boyfriend really wants is her money. Bella insists that he wants more than her money. What could be more than money? Louie asks. "Me! He wants *me!* He wants to marry me!" she replies. Bella hopes to marry him and have his babies. She is certain they will live happier lives than she or her siblings. Bella pleads with her mother for help, but Grandma rises without a word, walks into her bedroom, and shuts the door behind her.

Bella leaves home for two days and returns crestfallen. In a powerful scene she tells her mother that she felt safe with her usher, knowing that because he was like her, he loved her and understood her. Although Louie gave her the five thousand dollars they needed from his black bag, her boyfriend was too timid to leave the protection of his parents, and Bella's plans fell through. Now she and her mother must learn to deal with what has occurred.

Simon provides an upbeat ending. In the play's closing scene, nine months have passed. Eddie has repaid his debts and returns to claim his children. Uncle Louie has enlisted in the army and is fighting the Japanese in the South Pacific. Bella informs her mother that she is going out with a new girlfriend; the girlfriend has a brother, and Bella will invite the two for dinner later in the week.

Themes and Meanings

The central focus of the play is Neil Simon's exploration of dysfunctional family dynamics. No one is inherently evil, and everyone is a victim. Each character, except for the two boys, has been disabled by childhood traumas. Simon insists that the play is not autobiographical. Although the two boys resemble Simon's depiction of himself and his brother in his semiautobiographical trilogy, *Brighton Beach Memoirs* (pr. 1982, pb. 1984), *Biloxi Blues* (pr. 1984, pb. 1986), and *Broadway Bound* (pr. 1986, pb. 1987), neither of Simon's grandmothers resembled Grandma Kurnitz. Nevertheless, Simon's own family was dysfunctional. His parents quarreled constantly. Relations between Simon and his mother were frequently tense. Several times his father abandoned the family for long stretches, forcing his mother to move in with relatives and work as a salesclerk at department stores. The scenes between Grandma and Bella are fictional, yet the intense emotional temperature of their exchanges, and Simon's understanding of Bella's desperate longing for warmth and affection, clearly reflect Simon's own childhood needs and experience.

Lost in Yonkers continues Simon's use of American Jewish themes begun in his *Brighton Beach* trilogy. His earlier successful comedies used characters whose attitudes and cadences were derived from New York Jewish humor, but no one was identified as Jewish. In this play everyone is explicitly Jewish. Simon uses comedy to soften his exploration of the darker aspects of immigrant Jewish experiences in America.

Specific reference to the Holocaust during the play would be anachronistic. In 1942 the Kurnitzes surely knew of the Nazi persecution of Jews, but they could not yet have been fully aware of the horrors occurring in Europe. Contemporary audiences do know of them, and that knowledge intensifies the effect of the play's German references. When Jay speculates about the possibility of recovering their father's inheritance from an uncle in Poland, Arty responds, "You think the Germans would let some Jew in Poland send nine thousand dollars to some Jew in Alabama?" The audience laughs, but their awareness of the Holocaust adds a darker edge to the humor. When Arty complains about his treatment by Grandma, she informs him that if he were a boy growing up in Germany he would already be dead. Grandma is presented as a victim of German oppression, but she is also a victimizer. Her German accent, and her harsh treatment of her family, make her Nazi-like.

Dramatic Devices

Simon wrote a well-made Broadway play nearly every year. In this play he uses a straightforward chronological narrative structure. Each scene flows from the preceding one and directly advances the action. At the start of the play, the exchanges between Jay and Arty introduce all the characters and establish their roles. When Bella and her mother appear onstage, they live up to the audience's expectations. Bella grows in emotional depth as the play develops, but Grandma does not deviate from the horrific figure the boys depicted. The personalities of Louie and Gert are similarly prefigured in the boys' conversation that opens the play.

Scene changes are well managed. The stage darkens and Eddie's voice is heard reading letters to his children. References to the cities he has visited help establish the passage of time as he travels across the South earning money. Hints of possible heart problems build suspense concerning his children's eventual fate. At the end of the first act, Eddie's voice-over provides an ironic contrast with the reality the audience has just observed.

Simon portrays Grandma's character more through what she fails to do than by her direct actions. Never does she supply parental warmth or provide emotional support for her children. In the play's most powerful scene she wastes not a syllable or breath refusing Bella's cry for help. She ignores her daughter completely. Rising slowly, she turns and silently limps to her room, quietly closing the door behind her.

Although some critics faulted Simon for depending on one-line gags, in fact most laughs are built on previously introduced material and enhance the central themes of the play. Arty's reference to Louie's information that, although Grandma is in constant pain, she will not even take an aspirin, provides a surefire laugh when he tells his brother, "I'm afraid of her Jay. A horse fell on her when she was a kid and she hasn't taken an aspirin yet."

Critical Context

Simon is famous for writing light domestic comedies that became major box-office hits. Of twenty-six plays produced in the thirty years before *Lost in Yonkers*, all but five attracted large audiences and earned Simon a multimillion-dollar fortune. Critics, less enthusiastic than his faithful fans, questioned his lack of interest in formal experimentation and often dismissed him as too prolific, mechanically creating gag-laden comedies. Although touring companies performed his plays to packed houses across the United States, and his plays were successfully produced in Great Britain and many foreign countries, Simon complained that his reputation as a lightweight kept many regional theaters from performing his work.

Critical attitudes began to change with the appearance of the *Brighton Beach* trilogy. The themes of the plays seemed more significant than critics expected, especially the presentation of a parent-child conflict in *Broadway Bound*. Some critics were even willing to concede that many earlier plays, previously written off as lighthearted comedies, actually portrayed the deeper dynamics and difficulties of personal relationships.

Lost in Yonkers received even more praise than the trilogy, winning Simon a Tony Award for best play and a Drama Desk Award. Although Simon predicted that he would never win a Pulitzer Prize, *Lost in Yonkers* won the 1991 award for drama. Many critics termed it Simon's best play—his least sentimental and most satisfying dark comedy, mining its humor out of very painful material. Not all reviews were completely positive, but most agreed that Simon had written an honest and compelling examination of family conflict, singling out the scenes between Bella and her mother for special praise. Some critics questioned the slow exposition of the family situation at the start of the play; others liked the plot up until its happy ending, calling it a forced and unconvincing conclusion for such a wrenching drama. Only Mimi Kramer in *The New Yorker* was wholly negative, finding nothing honest or authentic in the entire play. Despite Simon's fears, regional and collegiate theater groups have added *Lost in Yonkers* to their repertoire.

Sources for Further Study

Konas, Gary, ed. *Neil Simon: A Casebook*. New York: Garland, 1997.

Kramer, Mimi. "Ill Apportioned Parts." *The New Yorker* 67 (March 11, 1991): 75-77.

Lipton, James. "Neil Simon." In *Playwrights at Work: Paris Review*, edited by George Plimpton. New York: The Modern Library, 2000.

Richards, David. "The Last of the Red Hot Playwrights." *New York Times Magazine*, February 17, 1991, 30-36, 57, 64.

Simon, Neil. *The Play Goes On: A Memoir*. New York: Simon & Schuster, 1999.

Milton Berman

LU ANN HAMPTON LAVERTY OBERLANDER

Author: Preston Jones (1936-1979)
Type of plot: Naturalistic
Time of plot: 1953, 1963, and 1973
Locale: Bradleyville, West Texas
First produced: 1974, at the Dallas Theater Center, Dallas, Texas
First published: 1976, in *A Texas Trilogy*

Principal characters:
LU ANN HAMPTON, a small-town Texas girl
SKIP HAMPTON, her older brother
CLAUDINE HAMPTON, her mother
BILLY BOB WORTMAN, her high school boyfriend
DALE LAVERTY, her first husband
RED GROVER, the owner of Red's Place, a local bar
CORKY OBERLANDER, Lu Ann's second husband
RUFE PHELPS and
OLIN POTTS, bar patrons

The Play

Lu Ann Hampton Laverty Oberlander opens in the living room of the Hampton house in Bradleyville, Texas, in 1953. Teenage Lu Ann Hampton runs into the house dressed in her Bradleyville High School cheerleading uniform, followed by boyfriend Billy Bob Wortman. He is dressed in a white shirt, Levi's, boots, and a Bradleyville High School letter sweater. Billy Bob is a typical small-town boy of the 1950's, except that today his hair is green. The basketball players decided to startle the school at this morning's pep rally.

Lu Ann and Billy Bob argue about going to the senior picnic in a pickup truck instead of in his father's car. In a bit of foreshadowing, Lu Ann tells him that he sounds like a preacher. After he leaves, Claudine Hampton enters to ask about the pep rally. She expresses concern about her son, Skip Hampton, a Korean veteran who spends too much time in Red's Bar.

They discuss Lu Ann's plans, or lack of any, for life after graduation. Claudine says that she can get Lu Ann a job at the hospital where Claudine works. Lu Ann wants to get out of town, out of state. They are interrupted by Skip's entrance with Dale Laverty, an old army buddy. It is apparent that Skip is already an aimless drunk, full of war stories and hot air. As the buddies exit for Red's Bar, Dale asks Lu Ann if he may call her. Interested in his automobile and angry with Billy Bob, she says yes. At the curtain, she tells herself that Dale Laverty is a pretty name.

Act 2 opens in Red's Bar. Ten years have passed. Red Grover is watching Rufe Phelps and Olin Potts play checkers and argue, a nightly ritual. The audience learns from their small talk that Skip Hampton got drunk on Thunderbird wine in Red's the night before and cut his throat with a broken beer bottle. He is in the hospital. They also mention Lu Ann's divorce. Lu Ann enters, wearing a beautician's uniform. She says that she could have had her own beauty shop if "that worthless Dale Laverty" had not left her to bring up their daughter, Charmaine, by herself.

Corky Oberlander, a highway inspector, comes in and is introduced to Lu Ann. Their conversation gives the audience the highlights of Lu Ann's life since graduation. She asks him what kind of car he has. She tells him that she went to her senior picnic in her boyfriend's father's Hudson. He asks her for a dinner date. After he leaves, she says, at the curtain, that "Corky Oberlander is a right pretty name."

Act 3 opens in 1973, in the Hampton house. The radio has been replaced by a television set and the slipcovers are different. Charmaine, the "act 1 image of Lu Ann," is arguing with her uncle, Skip. She tells him that the whole town has called him "Crazy Skip Hampton" ever since he cut his throat and went to a mental hospital. She tells Skip that she went to San Angelo to see what her father looked like: "Old, fat, and kind of dumb-lookin', you know. God, what a letdown."

Lu Ann comes home with the groceries. She is wearing a Howdy Wagon uniform. She says "we said howdy to fifteen new families today." Skip tries to wheedle her out of a dollar for supper at the local restaurant. She refuses, reminding him that she arranged for a running tab at the restaurant, which she pays, and that the last time she gave him cash he wound up in a mental hospital.

Billy Bob Wortman appears at the front door. In the ensuing conversation, the audience learns that he was graduated from Texas Christian University and is a preacher in Kansas City, married, and the father of four boys. He and his family have traveled all over the world on his missionary work. Lu Ann tells him that she takes care of her mother, left paralyzed and mute by a stroke.

The two reminisce about the past, and Lu Ann refers to the day of the senior picnic, when she stood up Billy Bob and ran off to San Angelo with Dale Laverty. Billy Bob slips for a moment from his formal "preacher English" into his native West Texas dialect, but he catches himself up with "It's a waste of the Lord's time to dwell on the past." She replies:

> The Lord's got lots of time to waste. It's us the clock runs down on! You know, Billy Bob, it's a funny thing, but ah'm about the same age mah mama was when you and me was in high school. My God, ain't that somethin? It's like I was her and Charmaine was me and ever' body round us got old and different lookin'.

Lu Ann wheels in her mother, who sits in her wheelchair, mute and uncomprehending, while Billy Bob tries to make polite conversation with her. He tells Lu Ann he can help her put her mother in a nursing home. Lu Ann says that she cannot do that:

> . . . at least thisaway the burden is mostly on my body—if ah sent her off somewhere, the burden would be on my heart. You know, Billy Bob, them doctors told me that Mama would be a vegetable for the rest of her life—can you imagine that? A vegetable! Hell, my mama ain't no vegetable, she's a flower, a great old big pretty flower.

After Billy Bob leaves, Lu Ann says, "ah jest never could cotton to that boy's name. Billy Bob Wortman. Why it's jest plain silly-soundin'." The curtain falls.

Themes and Meanings

Lu Ann Hampton Laverty Oberlander is a play about the power of environment in determining one's life choices and the cumulative effect of seemingly small choices on the rest of one's life. Preston Jones wrote of his fascination with the meaning of time in human life: "But whatever the story is, for me it would always involve 'time' because time is not the sun going up and down every day. It is not a clock. It is not a calendar. Time is an eroding, infinite mystery. Time is, in fact, a son-of-a-bitch." By focusing on three days over twenty years in the life of Lu Ann, Jones demonstrates that the more things change, the more they stay the same.

In 1953, the time of act 1, Lu Ann's mother is supporting her son and daughter. Lu Ann is a perky cheerleader dating a basketball star and apparently has an open future ahead. However, she has no plans except vaguely negative ones. She does not want to live in Bradleyville, and she does not want to work where her mother works. She likes nice cars. Skip's entrance with his army buddy, Dale Laverty, right after her quarrel with Billy Bob sets her future. Because Dale has a car and a name she thinks is "cute," she leaves town with him instead of going to the senior picnic with Billy Bob. Lu Ann's brother Skip has already determined his future. He tells Dale that he turned down a chance to be co-owner of a Western Auto store because he has bigger, if vague, plans. He already drinks too much.

Act 2 shows the audience Lu Ann in 1963. "The years have hardened her prettiness into a tough, smooth gloss." Trapped back in her mother's house in Bradleyville by the early marriage, pregnancy, and divorce, she has one more opportunity. Again, it is less a free choice than a conditioned one. She likes Corky Oberlander's name and his new Chevrolet Impala.

In act 3, life has come full circle. If Lu Ann's second marriage could have made a difference in her destiny, fate prevented it when Corky was killed in an accident. Like her mother before her, Lu Ann works at an ordinary job and supports those dependent on her. In the last act she tells her brother Skip not to dwell on the "bad old days" and practices what she preaches when she puts thoughts of what might have been with Billy Bob behind her. Uneducated and not very articulate, she lives a life with which many people can identify and meets it with a kind of courage. Her mother is a flower, not a vegetable. And if for Skip, "all that stands between a man and the looney bin is his sister's tab down to the Dixie Dinette," she does stand between him and that fate. The author seems to suggest that, hemmed in by life and circumscribed by circumstance, Lu Ann has at least, like Samuel Beckett's protagonists in *En attendant Godot* (pb. 1952, pr. 1953; *Waiting for Godot*, 1954), kept her appointment. She has survived.

Dramatic Devices

Lu Ann Hampton Laverty Oberlander might be described as West Texas Chekhov. The big events happen not only offstage but also between the acts: Two marriages, pregnancy and birth, divorce, attempted suicide, a fatal accident, and a stroke occur between the times depicted in acts 1 and 2 and those in 2 and 3. Consequently, the characters primarily give the audience the necessary exposition of events and actions that have led to the present onstage moment. In addition, they reveal their habitual actions through their discussions and arguments about those actions.

Though the action is confined to only two sets, the Hampton living room in acts 1 and 3 and Red's Bar in act 2, references to people and places not depicted place the characters in the larger context of the town and region. Milo Crawford, the class nerd in 1953, is mentioned in acts 1 and 3 and makes a brief appearance in act 2. Another classmate is mentioned in acts 1 and 3 but never appears. Lu Ann's mother reminisces about her own dates with that classmate's father. These references function to bind the three acts together and to reinforce the sameness of the lives of the three generations.

Lu Ann wears a uniform in each act; these uniforms symbolize the stages in her life. In act 1, in her cheerleader's uniform, she sees her future without realizing it in her mother, who wears a hospital uniform. In act 2, she wears a beautician's outfit; in act 3, the Howdy Wagon uniform. The repetition of her fondness for "pretty names" and her interest in the kinds of cars her men drive reinforce the definition by labels: automobiles, uniforms, and finally the accretion of names. Lu Ann Hampton becomes Lu Ann Hampton Laverty becomes Lu Ann Hampton Laverty Oberlander. The living room set of acts 1 and 3, with the radio replaced by the television, as an automobile replaces another automobile, as one uniform replaces another, encloses both literally and dramatically the theme of the cumulative effects of the passing of time on a life without inner definition. In the final act, the house encloses all three generations, with the younger version of Lu Ann, her daughter, as uncomprehending of the future represented by her mother and her grandmother as Lu Ann once was of her own.

Critical Context

Lu Ann Hampton Laverty Oberlander is the middle play in *A Texas Trilogy*. The first play in the trilogy, *The Last Meeting of the Knights of the White Magnolia* (pr. 1973, pb. 1976), and the last, *The Oldest Living Graduate* (pr. 1974, pb. 1976), are also set in Bradleyville, in 1962. Characters overlap or are mentioned in more than one play in the trilogy. Jones's approach is essentially the same in all three plays: The characters talk about what has already happened. No decisions are made; no conflicts are revealed onstage. There is humor in the dialogue, and Jones has a good ear for small-town Texas speech.

Jones studied drama under Paul Baker at Baylor University and at Trinity University in San Antonio. Following Baker to Dallas, he worked as an actor at the Dallas Theater Center. After the success of the plays at the Center, where they were performed first on separate evenings, then in one marathon afternoon and evening, with a break for dinner, *A Texas Trilogy* had a successful limited engagement at the Kennedy Center, followed by an unsuccessful Broadway run. Jones returned to Dallas and in the brief time left to him wrote *A Place on the Magdalena Flats* (pr. 1976), *Santa Fe Sunshine* (pr., pb. 1977), *Juneteenth* (pr. 1979), and *Remember* (pr. 1979). Jones's sudden death on September 19, 1979, was called "particularly ironic . . . , for his continuing theme concerned the impermanence of life and the effect of time on human aspirations."

The individual plays in *A Texas Trilogy* continue to be performed in college theaters and summer stock, although Jones is remembered primarily as a regional writer with a gift for dialogue but a weakness in developing dramatic action.

Sources for Further Study

Bennett, Patrick. *Talking with Texas Writers: Twelve Interviews*. College Station: Texas A&M Press, 1980.

Busby, Mark. *Preston Jones*. Boise, Idaho: Boise State University Press, 1983.

Jones, Preston. "Author's Note." In *The Texas Trilogy*. New York: Hill & Wang, 1976.

_______. "Tales of a Pilgrim's Progress: From Bradleyville to Broadway." *Dramatists Guild*, Winter, 1977, 7-18.

Kerr, Walter. "The Buildup (and Letdown) of *Texas Trilogy*." *New York Times*, October 3, 1976, p. D3, D6.

Katherine Lederer

LUTHER

Author: John Osborne (1929-1994)
Type of plot: Biographical; psychological
Time of plot: The sixteenth century
Locale: Germany
First produced: 1961, at the Theatre Royal, Nottingham, England
First published: 1961

Principal characters:
MARTIN LUTHER, a Roman Catholic priest of the Augustinian Order
HANS, his father
KATHERINE VON BORA, Martin's wife
JOHANN VON STAUPITZ, Vicar General of the Augustinian Order
JOHN TETZEL, an indulgence vendor of the Dominican Order
THOMAS DE VIO "CAJETAN," General of the Dominican Order
JOHAN VON ECK, secretary to the Archbishop of Trier

The Play

Luther opens with a knight appearing on the stage, clutching a banner and announcing (as he will at the beginning of each of the play's three acts) the time and place of the following scene: the convent of the Augustinian Order of Eremites at Erfurt, Thuringia, 1506. The audience next sees a man in his early twenties kneeling in front of a prior, in the presence of an assembled convent, within a small chapel. He is Martin Luther, being received into the Augustinian Order. After being robed in habit, hood, and scapular, he vows to give up the world of men, to spurn his former self and live in obedience to God, the Sacred Virgin Mary, and "the Rule of our Venerable Father Augustine until death."

Martin's father, Hans, is in attendance, together with Lucas, Martin's former father-in-law, both of whom dominate the center of the stage briefly after Martin has spoken his vows and been escorted out of sight. A hard-talking coal miner, Hans expresses bitter cynicism about his son's decision to join the Order, just as he will a year later (in the third and final scene of act 1), when he attends the first Mass that Martin performs (act 1, scene 2). Hans laments over the loss of his son, as well as over Martin's choice to give up the career he could have had as a lawyer to an archbishop or a duke.

Beginning with the first scene, Martin is troubled throughout the play, not by his missed professional opportunities but by his overwhelming feelings of unworthiness before God, his ceaseless and self-abusive pursuit of perfection, and his inexhaustible striving after a life in total harmonious accord with the will of God. Only gradually, beginning in act 2, does he begin to expect of others (including the Roman Catholic Church and the papacy) the same selfless, servile attitude before God that he has striven to achieve. Whereas the play's tension in the first act derives primarily from Martin's struggle with himself, and secondarily from his father's bitterness over Martin's choice to reject the mundane world, by the opening of act 2, when the audience witnesses John Tetzel browbeating the citizens of Jüterbog into purchasing indulgences, does the play's focus widen beyond Martin's personal life.

Although his discussion with Johann von Staupitz in the second scene of act 2 (1517) indicates Martin is still grappling with the spiritual demands he believes his religion imposes upon him, the play now concerns his disapproval of the Church's practice of selling indulgences. He has recently begun to criticize the practice, asserting publicly that people cannot bargain with God or buy their way into heaven, and Staupitz informs him that his position against indulgences is upsetting powerful people. Martin refuses to stop his criticisms of the Church and of people who buy indulgences for entry into heaven; in the third scene of act 2 (1517), he preaches that "there's no security . . . either in indulgences, holy busywork, or anywhere in this world." He then steps down from the pulpit of the Castle Church in Wittenberg and nails to the church door his ninety-five theses for disputation against indulgences.

Less the result of the theses than of his sermon, in 1518 (act 2, scene 4) Martin is summoned to the Fugger Palace, Augsburg, to stand before Thomas de Vio (Cajetan). Pope Leo X has sent Cajetan to present to Martin three propositions: He must retract all sermons of his critical of the Church; he must promise to abstain from propagating his opinions in the future; and he must behave with greater moderation and avoid offending the Church in any way. "The Roman Church is the apex of the world, secular and temporal," Cajetan tells Martin, "and it may constrain with its secular arm any who have once received that faith and gone astray." Despite this threat, Martin refuses to retract his infamous sermon, and Cajetan informs him he will be released from the Augustinian Order. Although Martin later writes to Pope Leo X and pleads for an interview, in 1519 (act 2, scene 5) the pope views him as a "wild pig in our vinyard" that "must be hunted down and shot." Thus, in 1520 (act 2, scene 6), soon after receiving from Rome the papal bull of condemnation, Martin and his followers in Wittenberg burn the bull, books of canon law, papal decretals, and all documents relating to the Catholic Church and Pope Leo, who, according to Martin, is "a glittering worm in excrement."

Because much of the play's first two acts consists of dramatic reenactments of historical events germane to Martin Luther's religious career, the first two of three scenes in act 3 derive their substance from two such events: first, the Diet of Worms (April 18, 1521), during which Martin is brought before Emperor Charles V, and Ulrich von Hutten, the archbishop of Trier, and Johan von Eck; second, a scene in Wittenberg at the bitter end of the Peasants' War (1525). In the former scene, Martin is interrogated and told he must retract his numerous books—many of which supposedly contain heretical statements—or be officially excommunicated from the Catholic Church. Martin refuses to retract them. In the latter scene, Martin is accosted by a battle-weary knight who berates him for turning his back upon the German peasants after being the catalyst for their revolt against the ruling class and the Catholic Church. With his opposition to the now-ended war transformed into his expressed belief that the slaughtered peasants got what they deserved, Martin dismisses the knight and waits in a small chapel for his bride, Katherine von Bora.

Noticeably tired in the final act's third scene, and now the father of an infant son five years after his marriage to Katherine, Martin confesses to Staupitz that, instead of God's voice, in the past he has heard only his own. Moments before he slips into prideful reverie by recalling his rebellious stance in Worms, he prays: "Oh, Lord, I believe. I believe. I do believe. Only help my unbelief."

Themes and Meanings

More than a series of allusions to and reenactments of important historical events in the life of Martin Luther and the religion he founded, *Luther* is an incisive portrait of a self-divided man who—in pursuit of satisfying his own needs rather than those of his countrymen—shaped Germany's religious and cultural history.

When, in the final scene of *Luther*, Martin prays to his Lord that he believes, but nevertheless needs help with his unbelief or lack of religious faith, this seeming contradiction is consistent with John Osborne's portrait of him as a neurotic man who is, from beginning to end, a rebellious son used to being punished by his father yet in need of his father's love. "I beat you fairly often, and pretty hard sometimes I suppose," Martin's father Hans says, but he defends his past habit: "You were stubborn, you were always stubborn, you've always had to resist. . . ." From his acts of rebellion, therefore, Martin received a punitive expression of love sufficient for his need: "I loved you best," he admits to Hans. "It was always *you* I wanted. I wanted your love more than anyone's, and if anyone was to hold me, I wanted it to be you." Indeed, Martin equates punishment with love, and without the one he seems unable to believe he will be deserving of the other.

It is one thing to equate punishment and love in relation to a mortal father. In relation to a heavenly and physically absent Father, though, the reception of both punishment and love by the son depends upon his ability to perceive such by means of his faith. Thus Martin the son wants to believe in the Father but lacks the requisite faith to perceive his love; sensing that love's absence, and having been conditioned to expect love to be connected to punishment, Martin believes he needs punishment in order to make the absent love (and the absent Father) perceivable. By demanding of himself what Staupitz calls "impossible standards of perfection," Martin punishes himself with "mortifications," with "severe fasts," and he is obsessive about his constipation, gripes, insomnia, boils, indigestion—all of his maladies are to him his "meat and drink." He tells Weinand, "All I can feel . . . is God's hatred," and "He's like a glutton, the way he gorges me. . . . He gorges me, and then spits me out in lumps."

As a bitter son, intellectual priest, and independent, recalcitrant doctor of theology, Martin rebels against Hans, the pope, the Catholic Church and its spokesmen, the German people, and God himself. His single greatest weapon is his intellect; his place of greatest vulnerability, his malnourished heart. Indeed, he compensates for the latter by overemphasizing the importance of the former, and because of this the division between his head and heart, as well as between his need for God's love and his perception of it, widens into the creation of his own religion. "I smell," Martin says to a battle-weary knight near the end of the play, "because I never stop disputing with Him and because I expect Him to keep His Word."

Dramatic Devices

Through the use of a dark screen as backdrop, dim lights, and the seemingly cramped enclosure of a small chapel in the play's opening scene, Osborne establishes an intimate and private atmosphere for Martin's introduction. In the second scene, through the use of various dramatic devices, the playwright directs the audience's attention to the interior, psychological realm of Martin's life. By so doing he indicates that the play will not simply be a reenactment of historic events, expresses the internal battle Martin is fighting with himself, and primes the audience to consider Martin's psychology in the following scenes when such devices are absent.

The second scene is overshadowed by a huge knife, "like a butcher's," hanging several feet above the stage with its cutting edge turned upward; across the blade hangs a man's naked body, the head hanging down. Below the knife is an enormous cone, "like the inside of a vast barrel," and this object—surrounded by darkness—is filled with intense light. When Martin appears onstage, he walks slowly through the cone to its opening downstage. He is about to perform his first Mass, and it is clear by what he says to himself that he is racked with spiritual doubt. The central focus of his soliloquy is on his lost innocence, spoken of as a child: "I lost the body of a child; and I was afraid, and I went back to find it. But I'm still afraid. . . . The lost body of a child, hanging on a mother's tit, and close to the warm, big body of a man, and I can't find it."

Afraid that he cannot find the lost sense of belonging he once knew, he is also afraid, he says, of "the darkness." The cone from which he emerges into darkness, therefore, represents the mental tunnel back to his past, a tunnel narrow at one end (distant past) and wide at the other (recent past). Outside the tunnel, in Martin's present of self-doubt and insecurity, is bewildering darkness. The knife and body suspended over it clearly represent the torturous ordeal Martin is suffering and the requisite severance of his head and heart from his sexuality and mobility—a severance effected through living according to vows of celibacy and poverty. Although neither the butcher's knife nor the cone appears after this scene, the knife is alluded to in relation to God in act 3, wherein Martin asserts, "In the teeth of life we seem to die, but God says no—in the teeth of death we live. If He butchers us, He makes us live."

Instead of interior, symbolic imagery, in the remaining acts Osborne employs simply painted backdrops suggesting flatness rather than depth, caricature rather than portraiture, and "men in time rather than particular man in the unconscious." In other words, once Martin's unconscious matrix and related complexes have been exposed for the audience's consideration, all he says or does afterward finds its impetus in his pre-Augustinian psychological and emotional needs. Understanding history, Osborne suggests, demands that one delve below the surface of recorded historical events.

Critical Context

Of the four most important playwrights to emerge in the 1950's—Samuel Beckett, Harold Pinter, John Osborne, and John Arden—Osborne is generally noted for inspiring a postwar renaissance of the English theater; this he did with *Look Back in Anger* (pr. 1956, pb. 1957) and its verbally abusive hero, Jimmy Porter. Of the four, Osborne was the only one obsessed with portraying the rebellious fight of one individual against everything—his own emotional needs, his family and origins, his friends, his lovers, his country and its government, and his century.

Osborne was criticized for creating only one-man plays, insofar as his central heroes often grow too large for their plays and supporting characters are often merely foils, seldom permitted to exist as believably as the heroes. Nevertheless, in an era when such a character as Arthur Miller's Willy Loman seems the norm rather than the exception, Osborne's rebellious individuals garnered for him a worldwide audience. Whether it is Jimmy Porter railing against established order, or Archie Rice trying to convince himself and the audience he is immune to pain in *The Entertainer* (pr., pb. 1957); whether it is Martin Luther excoriating himself and the Catholic Church, or Bill Maitland stammering to defend his floundering existence in *Inadmissible Evidence* (pr. 1964, pb. 1965); or whether it is Alfred Redl's verbal denunciation of the Spaniards in *A Patriot for Me* (pr., pb. 1966), Laurie's contemptuous condemnation of K. L. in *The Hotel in Amsterdam* (pr., pb. 1968), or Jed's vitriolic warnings of doom in *West of Suez* (pr., pb. 1973), Osborne's recalcitrant heroes generally suffer loneliness as the normal condition of their lives, frequently resort to vituperative monologues, and are unable to accommodate infidelity between the actual world and their ideals.

"Am I the only one to see all this, and suffer?" Martin asks in a prayer in *Luther*, and with his words—as well as by his unyielding posture against the established group and order—he expresses John Osborne's characteristic theme.

Sources for Further Study

Banham, Martin. *Osborne*. Edinburgh: Oliver & Boyd, 1969.

Carter, Alan. *John Osborne*. Edinburgh: Oliver & Boyd, 1973.

Denison, Patricia O., ed. *John Osborne: A Casebook*. New York: Garland, 1996.

Ferrar, Harold. *John Osborne*. New York: Columbia University Press, 1973.

Gilleman, Lu. *The Hideous Honesty of John Osborne: The Politics of Vituperation*. New York: Garland, 2000.

Goldstone, Herbert. *Coping with Vulnerability: The Achievement of John Osborne*. Washington, D.C.: University Press of America, 1982.

Hayman, Ronald. *John Osborne*. London: Heinemann, 1972.

Page, Malcolm, and Simon Trussler. *File on Osborne*. London: Methuen, 1988.

Trussler, Simon. *The Plays of John Osborne: An Assessment*. London: Gollancz, 1969.

David A. Carpenter

LYDIE BREEZE

Author: John Guare (1938-   )
Type of plot: Dark comedy
Time of plot: 1895
Locale: Nantucket Island
First produced: 1982, at the American Place Theater, New York City
First published: 1982

Principal characters:
JOSHUA HICKMAN, the widower of Lydie Breeze
LYDIE HICKMAN, his daughter, age fifteen
BEATY, an Irish serving girl in her early thirties
GUSSIE HICKMAN, Lydie's twenty-two-year-old sister
JEREMIAH GRADY, the son of Joshua's deceased friend Dan Grady

The Play

Lydie Breeze opens at dawn at the Hickman house, on Nantucket. The "very sparsely furnished" parlor and stairs leading to a landing are visible; there is also a porch and a beach with an upended rowboat buried in the sand. Lydie enters, carrying a candle, and kneels in prayer, followed by Beaty, who leads her through a strange ritual that tells of the suicide of Lydie's mother, Lydie Breeze. The two invoke the dead woman's spirit to "keep her alive." It becomes clear that Beaty has been in charge of the girl's spotty education. She is attempting to inculcate in the girl a hatred of men and a fear of her own sexuality. Lydie has been injured in the eye, wears a pair of dark glasses, and frequently refers to herself as blind, though it is clear that the injury is minor.

Some references are made in this scene to Aipotu (Utopia backward), a tiny community founded by Lydie Breeze and three Civil War veterans: her husband, Joshua Hickman; Dan Grady; and Amos Mason. Young Lydie and Joshua are all that remain of Aipotu. Lydie Breeze and Dan Grady are dead, and Amos Mason is now a senator running for the presidency with the backing of William Randolph Hearst.

In scene 2, Lydie's older sister, Gussie, sweeps into the house, full of modern talk and attitudes. She is Amos's secretary—his "whore," as Beaty immediately surmises—and has persuaded Amos and Hearst to pay a visit to Joshua. Joshua reacts with typical sarcasm to her attempts to draw him into the spirit of Amos's visit: " 'The Senator from Wall Street' sails back to Old Nantucket to light up a corn cob pipe with an old scarecrow from the old, old past. 'Why, look at him! Amos Mason is a man of the people. He gets my vote!' " Gussie, hurt but undaunted, regales Lydie with stories of her new life, their father's killing of Dan Grady, his time in prison, and their mother's suicide "because she was still in love with the other man."

When a young bird-bander turns up with some eyedrops for Lydie, Joshua confuses them with Gussie's nose drops, which he puts into Lydie's eye instead, causing a considerable amount of pain and recrimination. The scene ends with the sudden, mysterious appearance of Jeremiah Grady, Dan's son, asking for Lydie Breeze.

Act 2 opens with Jeremiah first comforting, then passionately embracing young Lydie. Beaty, when she enters to protect Lydie, tells of having been seduced on this very beach and infected with syphilis. Scene 2 is a dramatic confrontation between Joshua and Jeremiah, who has had a great success on the London stage as the monster in *Frankenstein* and has returned to avenge his father and himself. Joshua tells the full story of his accidental killing of Dan, which evolved from a fight over Joshua's rough treatment of Jeremiah but which was also motivated by Joshua's jealousy of his wife's infidelity with Dan. Jeremiah tells how Lydie seduced him and infected him with syphilis, which she caught from his father, and Joshua realizes that Lydie's suicide note was an apology to Jeremiah, not to him. Jeremiah's attempt at forgiveness is met with searing anger and bitterness from Joshua: "I could kill you all over again." The stage goes black.

In act 3, the past violently invades the present, as Gussie and the young bird-bander tell Joshua of disaster on Hearst's yacht. Lydie has delivered an accusation against Amos from Beaty, who believes that Amos seduced, infected, and abandoned her. Hearst has read the account, Amos is ruined, and Gussie has been fired. In a haunting scene, Jeremiah reveals to Beaty that it was he, not Amos, who infected her, although Beaty is unable any longer to understand the difference. They disappear into the dark, to be discovered drowned the next morning, tied together at the wrists.

Act 4 begins with Jude comforting Lydie over Beaty's death, then shifts to Gussie and Joshua, who finally express their fondness for each other. At this moment Lucian Rock, an inventor traveling through town, arrives and announces in a long, comic speech that he is in love with and wishes to marry Lydie, whom he saw when she was injured in the eye. Gussie, thinking quickly, appears wearing a bandage over one eye and goes off with Lucian. The closing scene shows a misty, gray next day, with Joshua again treating Lydie's eye, this time successfully. Lydie tells her father, "I don't know anything about you," and Joshua wistfully answers, "I was a man who ached for a utopia." He then produces Walt Whitman's *Leaves of Grass* (1855) from an old trunk and starts to teach Lydie her mother's favorite poem, beginning "On the beach at night alone," as the lights fade into dark around them.

Themes and Meanings

Lydie Breeze is the first of four plays about this group of characters, although it concerns, chronologically, the last events. The others are *Gardenia* (pr., pb. 1982), *Women and Water* (pr. 1985, pb. 1990), and "Bullfinch's Mythology." Thus, *Lydie Breeze* is part of an epic exploration of failed idealism, which John Guare sees as the heart of American culture. Syphilis becomes the central metaphor for the corruption that eats from within at the American Dream. For Guare, ethics and ideals are destroyed not so much by the forces outside as by the rot inside people, which is the inescapable human tendency toward greed, ambition, lust, jealousy, and violent anger.

Each character in the play suggests a particular perspective on the theme of failed idealism; Joshua's bitterness, drunkenness, and self-pity are the manifestations of his sense of loss, not only of his wife and friends but also, more deeply, of his own innocence and optimism. He "ached for a utopia" but killed his best friend out of sexual jealousy and selfish greed, pettily symbolized by the bottle of Moxie he rips from Jeremiah's mouth. Gussie places her faith in the power and materialism represented by Hearst and Amos, only to see her dreams of the good life, and Amos's political ambitions, destroyed by the ghost of Aipotu. Jeremiah has achieved fame and wealth abroad, but just as he plays a monster on the stage, he is the monster of Lydie Breeze, forever haunted and finally destroyed by her.

People who are only mentioned in the play similarly suggest the pattern of the American dream and corruption. Mary Baker Eddy's insistence that disease is only in the mind is an eerily ironic commentary on the suicides of Jeremiah and Beaty. William Randolph Hearst's cynical attempt to wield power through Amos is ironically the only political consequence of Aipotu's ideals. Most important, Lydie Breeze herself, who named Aipotu, who taught the men, as Beaty says, and whose spirit haunts all the play's characters, in the end destroyed herself and the dreams through her passion for Dan, her seduction of Jeremiah, and finally her suicide, an act of despair and expiation.

In the fourth act, however, the play suggests the continuance of hope and optimism. As Beaty's and Jeremiah's bodies are symbolically washed clean of corruption by the sea, Lydie finds a reason to live through the naïve Christian Scientist Jude; Gussie runs off, full of new energy, with a quintessential American entrepreneur, Lucian Rock the inventor. Joshua, reconciled with his daughters, passes on their mother's legacy of love and idealism to Lydie, her namesake, as they read together the words of America's prophet, Walt Whitman: "A vast similitude interlocks all. . . . All souls All lives and deaths, all of the past, present, future, This vast similitude spans them, and always has spanned And shall forever span them and compactly hold and enclose them."

Dramatic Devices

Lydie Breeze employs an eclectic array of theatrical devices and dramatic modes. Visual symbols are given depth through verbal references. For example, the upended rowboat, symbolizing Aipotu's running aground, is given resonance by references to Hearst's yacht, culminating in Gussie's hilarious verbal slip in front of a campaign audience, "America is a yacht," and Joshua's characterizations of Gussie and himself as "a glorious battleship" and the *Marie-Celeste*, respectively.

John Guare strikingly underscores the way the past haunts the present through ritual reenactments of past events, as in the opening scene with Lydie and Beaty recreating Lydie Breeze's suicide, Joshua and Jeremiah's reliving of the day Dan died, and Jeremiah and Beaty's mysterious reunion in death.

The central metaphor of syphilis, however, is the most disturbing and most unifying of the play's devices. In Joshua's climactic diatribe against Jeremiah, the themes of corruption, of the far-reaching consequences of human carelessness and selfishness, and of the collapse of idealism through our "trust in the itch in the pocket" all converge in a shattering image: "After Lydie Breeze died, they cut her open and found all this rot. . . . Forgiveness from another human being? You'll never get it. Syphilis. That's all you'll ever get from another human being. Syphilis and suicide notes."

Still, for all the play's mythic and tragic qualities, it is penetrated throughout with ironic and sometimes almost farcical humor, as in Lucian's memorized courtship speech and Gussie's instant transformation into her fifteen-year-old sister with the addition of an eye bandage, or in the sudden shift from pseudo-Catholic liturgy to a baking recipe in the opening ritual scene. This continual use of humor not only keeps the audience off balance, never knowing what to expect, but also prevents the melodramatic plot from veering into sentimentality or triteness. Guare's sustained and controlled mingling of tragic and comic, mythic and realistic, melodramatic and ironic effects succeeds where more straightforward social criticism in contemporary drama does not.

Critical Context

Lydie Breeze was a turning point in John Guare's career. It was a departure from the mixture of farce and savage satire that characterized his most successful previous works, such as *Muzeeka* (pr. 1967, pb. 1969) and *The House of Blue Leaves* (pr., pb. 1971). While Guare had always been concerned with the corruption at the heart of American culture and with the related loss of ideals, he tended to attack these issues through farcical plots, bizarre characters, and fiercely ironic dialogue. *The House of Blue Leaves*, for example, which remains one of his greatest critical and popular successes, partly as a result of a revival in the 1980's, concerns a plot to blow up the pope and involves a weird collection of characters, including a zookeeper, three nuns, a film producer, and women named Bananas and Bunny. Guare acknowledges the influence of Georges Feydeau in his plotting of the play, which is a masterpiece of black comedy. *Marco Polo Sings a Solo* (pr. 1973, pb. 1977) and *Landscape of the Body* (pr. 1977, pb. 1978) make use of science fiction and the detective story, while many other plays (including *Muzeeka* and *The House of Blue Leaves*) make extensive use of song.

With his acclaimed screenplay for Louis Malle's film *Atlantic City* (1981), however, Guare began to move further toward realism (though he claims that *The House of Blue Leaves* is a realistic play) and a tone less sardonic and more elegiac, though no less deeply ironic. The *Lydie Breeze* tetralogy, beginning with *Lydie Breeze* itself, is on a larger scale than his earlier work, with something like the epic sweep of a nineteenth century novel (a comparison Guare himself makes). Guare's use of American history, particularly the Civil War (mentioned in *Lydie Breeze* but of greater importance in the other plays), gives greater scope to his themes.

Guare's style and concerns have not undergone abrupt reversals. He is an eclectic writer whose brilliance manifests itself in his audacious mixing of dramatic modes and in the ceaseless whirl of events and characters in his plays. The sad grandeur of *Lydie Breeze*, however, was a new note in his work for the stage, as was the positive ending of the play. While Guare is a harsh critic of American values, *Lydie Breeze* indicates that he remains optimistic at least about the human potential for love and hope.

In 2000, Guare revised *Lydie Breeze* and *Gardenia* and released the revision under the title *Lydie Breeze* (pr. 2000, pb. 2001). He gained critical and popular success in 1990 with his release of *Six Degrees of Separation*, a play which refers to the scientific claim that any given individual on earth is linked genetically with another individual by a mere six steps. The play served as a social commentary on the myriad isolation of contemporary people due to class, race, gender, and sexual orientation, among other factors. Other plays from the 1990's and early twenty-first century included *Four Baboons Adoring the Sun* (pr. 1992, pb. 1993), *The General of Hot Desire* (pr., pb. 1999), *Lake Hollywood* (pr. 1999, pb. 2000), and *Sweet Smell of Success* (pr. 2001). Most critics find that Guare has matured significantly in these plays; there is not much doubt that he has lived up to the promise of his early experimental work and is among the very best contemporary American playwrights.

Sources for Further Study

Bigsby, C. W. E. "John Guare." In *Beyond Broadway.* Vol. 3 in *A Critical Introduction to Twentieth-Century American Drama.* New York: Cambridge University Press, 1985.

DiGaetani, John. "John Guare." In *A Search for a Postmodern Theater: Interviews with Contemporary Playwrights.* Edited by John DiGaetani. Westport, Conn.: Greenwood Press, 1991.

Gross, Robert F. "Life Is a Silken Net: Mourning the Beloved Monstrous in *Lydie Breeze.*" *Journal of Dramatic Theory and Criticism*, Fall, 1994, 21-43.

Guare, John. "'Living in That Dark Room': The Playwright and His Audience." Interview by John Harrop. *New Theatre Quarterly* 3 (1987): 155-159.

Harrop, John. "'Ibsen Translated by Lewis Carroll': The Theatre of John Guare." *New Theatre Quarterly* 3 (1987): 150-154.

_______. "NTQ Checklist No. 3: John Guare." *New Theatre Quarterly* 3 (1987): 160-177.

Marranca, Bonnie, and Gautam Dasgupta, eds. *American Playwrights: A Critical Survey.* New York: Drama Book Specialists, 1981.

Savran, David. "John Guare." In *In Their Own Words: Contemporary American Playwrights.* New York: Theatre Communications Group, 1988.

Wetzsteon, R. "The Coming of Age of John Guare." *New York* 15 (February 22, 1982): 35-39.

David G. Brailow

M. BUTTERFLY

Author: David Henry Hwang (1957-)
Type of plot: Social realism
Time of plot: 1988, with flashbacks to Beijing, 1960-1970; Paris, 1966-1988; and Aix-en-Provence, 1947
Locale: Beijing, Paris, and Aix-en-Provence
First produced: 1988, at the National Theater, Washington, D.C.
First published: 1988

Principal characters:
René Gallimard, a French diplomat in Beijing
Song Liling, a Chinese opera singer
Marc, Gallimard's friend
Helga, Gallimard's wife
Renée Gallimarde, a businessman's daughter and, briefly, Gallimard's lover

The Play

From prison in Paris, René Gallimard looks back on his life, especially the love relationship and espionage trial that have made him the laughing stock of the world. Gallimard recalls his years of work in the French embassy in Beijing, where he developed an intimate relationship with Song Liling—a relationship made extraordinary by Gallimard's faulty perception of the Chinese opera star's sexual identity.

Gallimard recalls his first encounter with Song at the German ambassador's house in Beijing in 1960. Song's performance of the death scene from Giacomo Puccini's opera *Madama Butterfly* (1904; *Madame Butterfly*, 1905) enchants Gallimard, and when he and Song have the chance to talk after the performance, Song's strong statements about opera and Western misconceptions about the East stimulate Gallimard. Soon Gallimard regularly attends performances of Chinese opera, drawing attention from Song in return. Like Pinkerton, the American naval officer in Puccini's opera, Gallimard has a need to feel power in his relationship. To make Song need his love, Gallimard begins to avoid Song, disregarding several letters from her. When Gallimard returns to Song, the relationship becomes sexual, but Song insists on modesty, never appearing in the nude with Gallimard, even though they engage in intimacy. When Gallimard finally demands to see Song naked, Song consents, but Song's willingness to be naked makes Gallimard relent in his demand, leaving Song's sexual identity unverified. Song announces that she is pregnant, and Gallimard declares that he wants to marry Song. After Gallimard returns to Paris, Song joins him there, and their relationship continues until the French government arrests Gallimard and Song for espionage.

In the French foreign service, Gallimard at first was only a bureaucrat, but executive confidence in his knowledge of the Chinese grew, and eventually he became vice consul. During Gallimard's service in China, the United States was involved in the conflict in Vietnam, but it did not have full diplomatic relations with China. The French served as diplomatic intermediaries, and the United States relied upon the French to provide information about possible Chinese reactions to actions planned by the United States. Again thinking like Puccini's Pinkerton, who felt that the best policy toward people in the East was strong tactics, Gallimard recommends a strong approach in Vietnam, including the assassination of Ngo Dinh Diem, the first elected president of South Vietnam. When this policy proves ineffective for the United States, Gallimard falls from favor and is reassigned to Paris. In China, Song endured the hardships of the Cultural Revolution (1966-1976), including indoctrination and required service at a commune. Coerced by the Chinese government, Song travels to France and takes advantage of Gallimard's love to gather confidential information, which Song then passes to Chinese leaders. In the end, the French discover the espionage and convict both Gallimard and Song. In the process, Gallimard learns that Song is a man. In prison, Gallimard now suffers especially because the fantasy that was the basis of his love is destroyed, and he is humiliated and brokenhearted. He is driven to suicide.

To help the reader assess the development of Gallimard's sexual outlook, Hwang also provides Gallimard's recollections of his sexual experiences. For example, in 1947 Gallimard and his schoolmate, Marc, discussed plans for an adventurous weekend. Marc previously had gone to an apartment in Marseilles owned by Marc's father, and according to Marc, various women swam naked in the pool. With no moonlight, people could not see each other well, and the sexual contact was indiscriminate. Marc's plan to repeat the experience made Gallimard uncomfortable because he worried that the women would reject him. With Marc, Gallimard also remembers his first sexual intercourse, which Marc arranged: a woman named Isabelle climbed on top of Gallimard as he lay in the bushes near a cafeteria. The intercourse was rough and uncomfortable, and the woman dominated the experience. In marriage, Gallimard and Helga apparently based their relationship on social status rather than a loving sexual union. The couple was childless, and although Helga sought the help of a doctor, Gallimard rejected such help. After the affair with Song begins, Gallimard has another affair with a young woman named Gallimarde, the daughter of a businessman. Renée is shapely and unashamed about being naked; her frank discussion of Gallimard's penis seems inappropriate to Gallimard. Finally, in prison, Gallimard has a collection of magazines with pinup girls, and these photos stir Gallimard's fantasies. These sexual experiences are not fully satisfying, but the viewer of the drama must think of them when trying to understand how Gallimard could spend twenty years in a relationship with Song without ever determining that Song is a man.

Themes and Meanings

A central theme of *M. Butterfly* is love, the power of attraction between two people, and the descent into betrayal. If Gallimard's love for Song is perfect, surpassing any attraction or experience he has ever known, then the perfection depends on

Gallimard's imagination. As long as Gallimard can keep his "Butterfly" in mind and as long as Song sustains the fantasy, Gallimard can live his dream. However, Song betrays Gallimard and destroys the illusion. The spying is part of the betrayal, but without the arrest, the perfection of the Butterfly would endure. With the arrest, Song's male identity is revealed. Faced with this revelation, Song makes his betrayal worse by trying to convince Gallimard that the love relationship can continue, not as a relationship between Gallimard and his imaginary Butterfly, but as a relationship between two men. Gallimard rejects this suggestion. Having lost the Butterfly of his imagination, Gallimard turns to suicide.

Another central theme of the play is gender relations, reflected by the ongoing parallels between Hwang's drama and Puccini's *Madame Butterfly*. As the love relationship intensifies, Gallimard is like Puccini's Pinkerton, who abandons Cio-Cio-San and drives her to suicide. However, by the end of *M. Butterfly*, a role reversal occurs. When Gallimard is tried, convicted, humiliated, and stripped of his fantasy, he becomes the victim. Song compels Gallimard to face the fact that Song is a man. In response, Gallimard is ultimately like Puccini's Cio-Cio-San, choosing death with honor rather than life with dishonor. The correspondence between the opera and the play shows that, in Hwang's view, men prefer lovers who are submissive and obedient. The Eastern woman stereotypically fits this role. However, in the end, these stereotypical expectations make men susceptible to manipulation and betrayal.

Just as Pinkerton scorns his Japanese lover, the West scorns the East, insisting that Eastern nations be submissive to Western will, refusing to accept the worthiness of Eastern "manhood" or nationhood. Ironically, this Western attitude proves to be the downfall of the West. In the play, Song and the Chinese Communists exploit Gallimard's pattern of love to acquire confidential information. In international relations, the West's efforts to dominate Vietnam proved costly and ineffective.

Another main theme is Hwang's exploration of the contrast between reality and fantasy. The play is based on an actual case involving a real French diplomat and a real Chinese opera star, and in the playwright's notes that precede the text of the play, Hwang refers to an article in *The New York Times* about the case. The background involving the war in Vietnam and the Cultural Revolution in China is also real. However, Hwang's staging is unrealistic, with actors playing multiple roles, with minimal props suggesting complex scenes, and with a grown man not recognizing his lover's true sex for twenty years. By pitting historical reality against a nonrealistic production, Hwang compels his audience to review the contrast between reality and illusion.

Dramatic Devices

To stage the recollections of Gallimard, Hwang makes limited use of props, creates a dreamy connection between scenes, assigns multiple roles to actors, and heightens mood with music. For example, when Gallimard first appears in his jail cell, very few props are onstage, and Gallimard supplies the details of his cell with his lines. Simultaneously, Song appears onstage in a separate scene, performing a traditional Chinese opera and then drifting into a selection from *Madame Butterfly*. When Gallimard admits that he is the laughingstock of the world, a separate scene of a cocktail party appears onstage. Gallimard can hear scathing commentary, but the characters in the party scene are oblivious to Gallimard.

The surreal atmosphere in the play is intensified by actors who play multiple roles. One actor plays the role of the pinup girl, a woman at the cocktail party, and the businessman's daughter who briefly becomes Gallimard's lover. One actor plays Marc, a man at the cocktail party, and Consul Sharpless. One actor plays Song's servant Shu Fang, Cio-Cio-San's attendant Suzuki, and Comrade Chin. The same actor who plays one of the men at the cocktail party also plays Ambassador Toulon and the judge at the espionage trial. These multiple roles create a confusing, dreamlike impression, and the viewer of the drama connects this atmosphere with the workings of Gallimard's mind as he recollects his experiences.

The rendering of Gallimard's psyche is done suggestively through references to *Madame Butterfly*. As Gallimard recalls his relationship with Song, musical selections from Puccini's opera, including "Love Duet," "The Flower Duet," and the aria "One Fine Day" emphasize associations between *M. Butterfly* and *Madame Butterfly*. Lines in Italian from the opera (with immediate translations) are part of Hwang's script, reinforcing the comparison between Pinkerton's treachery and the treachery in the relationship between Gallimard and Song.

Critical Context

F.O.B. (pr. 1978, pb. 1983) marked the beginning of Hwang's rapid ascendance in the theatrical world. The play reveals Hwang's interest in ethnic origins and the struggle that occurs between a Chinese immigrant's cultural identity and the forces of assimilation. *The Dance and the Railroad* (pr. 1981, pb. 1983) and *Family Devotions* (pr. 1981, pb. 1983) explore similar issues, with the former play examining the struggle of Chinese railroad workers in the nineteenth century and the latter play analyzing a wealthy Chinese American family in the twentieth century. In these plays, Chinese individuals must learn to balance the traditions and values of Chinese and American societies. In *The House of Sleeping Beauties* (pb. 1983) and *The Sound of a Voice* (pb. 1984), Hwang departs from the issues surrounding Chinese immigrants in the United States and explores the sorrows of love, relying on Japanese sources.

Hwang's success as a dramatist resulted in his being awarded a Guggenheim Fellowship and a National Endowment for the Arts Fellowship. He continued to write and stage plays, including *Rich Relations* (pr. 1986, pb. 1990) and *As the Crow Flies* (pr. 1986), but Hwang's greatest recognition came for *M. Butterfly*, for which the playwright won various awards, including the Tony Award for best new play. After the major breakthrough of *M. Butterfly*, Hwang continued productively, bringing *One Thousand Airplanes on the Roof* (pr. 1988, pb. 1989), *Bondage* (pr. 1992, pb. 1996), *Face Value* (pr. 1993), and *The Voyage* (pr. 1992, pb. 2000) to the stage.

With its clear focus on ethnic identity, gender issues, and assimilation into American society, *M. Butterfly* fits neatly into the context of its era. One might compare Hwang's drama to Wendy Wasserstein's *The Heidi Chronicles* (pr., pb. 1988), which examines similar issues involving Jews, or to August Wilson's *Joe Turner's Come and Gone* (pr. 1986, pb. 1988) and *The Piano Lesson* (pr. 1987, pb. 1990), which interpret the African American experience. Plays of this era helped to advance acceptance and celebration of America's multicultural society.

Sources for Further Study

Eng, David L. "In the Shadows of a Diva: Committing Homosexuality in David Henry Hwang's *M. Butterfly*." *Amerasia Journal* 20, no. 1 (1994): 93-116.

Hwang, David Henry. Afterword of *M. Butterfly*. New York: New American Library, 1988.

_______. Introduction to *"F.O.B." and Other Plays*. New York: New American Library, 1990.

Kehde, Suzanne. "Engendering the Imperial Subject: The (De)Construction of (Western) Masculinity in David Henry Hwang's *M. Butterfly* and Graham Greene's *The Quiet American*." In *Fictions of Masculinity: Crossing Cultures, Crossing Sexualities*, edited by Peter F. Murphy. New York: New York University Press, 1994.

Lye, Colleen. "*M. Butterfly* and the Rhetoric of Antiessentialism: Minority Discourse in an International Frame." In *The Ethnic Canon: Histories, Institutions, and Interventions*, edited by David Palumbo-Liu. Minneapolis: University of Minnesota Press, 1995.

Morris, Rosalind. "*M. Butterfly:* Transvestism and Cultural Cross Dressing in the Critique of Empire." In *Gender and Culture in Literature and Film East and West: Issues of Perception and Interpretation*, edited by Nitaya Masavisut. Honolulu: University of Hawaii Press, 1994.

Remen, Kathryn. "The Theatre of Punishment: David Henry Hwang's *M. Butterfly* and Michel Foucault's *Discipline and Punish*." *Modern Drama* 37, no. 3 (Fall, 1994): 391-400.

Shimakawa, Karen. "'Who's to Say?' Or, Making Space for Gender and Ethnicity in *M. Butterfly*." *Theatre Journal* 45 (October, 1993): 349-361.

William T. Lawlor

MA RAINEY'S BLACK BOTTOM

Author: August Wilson (1945-)
Type of plot: Psychological
Time of plot: March, 1927
Locale: A recording studio in Chicago
First produced: 1984, at the Yale Repertory Theatre, New Haven, Connecticut
First published: 1985

Principal characters:
STURDYVANT, a recording studio owner
IRVIN, the personal manager to Ma Rainey
CUTLER, a fatherly trombonist and bandleader
TOLEDO, a philosophical and bookish pianist
SLOW DRAG, an easygoing bassist
LEVEE, an obsessively ambitious
MA RAINEY, a shrewd, proud, and temperamental blues diva
DUSSIE MAE, a gullible young woman

The Play

Ma Rainey's Black Bottom is set in late 1920's Chicago; the action originates in the bandroom and studio of a record company. Gertrude (Ma) Rainey is due to arrive momentarily to cut new sides of 78 RPM favorites which she has previously recorded; her recordings are released by the company's "race" division. Waiting for her are four black musicians, the white owner of the record company, and her white manager. The bandroom where the musicians are waiting is dingy and cluttered. There are a piano, a few chairs, boxes of paraphernalia, and a few old painted wooden benches. The upstairs recording studio has two levels, with another piano; on the lower level there are some high stools on a raised platform. A circular staircase leads up to the control booth. The studio and bandroom are connected by a backstage passageway.

The first act consists of monologues and small talk. The musicians engage in recalling past events in their lives. The chatter is topical, often reflective, sometimes humorous; in any case it helps to pass the time while they await Ma, lovingly referred to by her followers as the "mother of the blues." Such tributes provoke scorn from Sturdyvant, the studio owner; he simply wishes to record the songs and end the session.

Each musician's role provides enough material upon which to base a separate play. For example, the African nationalist among the group is the pianist, Toledo, in his late fifties, who informs the other musicians that "we done sold ourselves to the white man in order to be like him." Cutler, also in his late fifties, is the leader and trombonist of the group; he is weary of his profession and fatalistic about life in general. Slow Drag, the bassist, is in his forties; through surface humor he masks the injuries that he has suffered as a black musician in a racist society.

The final musician to arrive for the session is Levee, a trumpeter, in his middle thirties. He is a hyper-energized man, an obsessively ambitious player-composer bent on achieving his own goals while totally disregarding the wishes of his employer, Ma Rainey. Ridiculing Ma's style of blues singing as "jugband music," he embraces the new "jazz dance" style that has become a craze among African Americans in the urban North. He convinces management that his swinging version of "Ma Rainey's Black Bottom" should replace Ma's dated version. This conflict expands and eventually explodes after the final recording session, in which Ma accuses him of sabotaging her stylistic arrangements by adding extra musical notes and phrases.

A new energy and dynamic permeates the stage with the arrival of Ma Rainey. One of the first black singers to secure a recording contract within the "race" division of a white company, she is a star who understands the limits of the control which she briefly holds over her manager and record producer. Ma delays the recording session by insisting that someone buy her two bottles of Coca-Cola from the store. She will receive a mere two hundred dollars for the session while the producer, as she is well aware, will make much more money from the sales of her records.

The musicians, too, are well aware of their subservient situation, but, unlike Ma, they are totally vulnerable to the whims of management. Their joking and clowning around is reflected through Cutler as he relates the saga of Slow Drag and his exploits as a dancer and woman tamer. On a more serious note, he tells the story of a black minister who was stranded in a small Georgia town while awaiting a train north and was bullied into dancing for some vigilante "crackers" at gunpoint. In turn, Levee, the youngest musician, relates the childhood horror of witnessing his mother being gang-raped by white men. This atrocity led to the lynching of his father, who, forced to take justice into his own hands, had killed two of the rapists.

Act 2 begins on a humorous note with Ma and her band members waiting to do yet another take on the spoken introduction to the song "Black Bottom." Sylvester, Ma's nephew, is unable to say the words without stammering and stuttering, thus delaying a wrap-up of the session. Irvin informs Ma that the band will have to record Levee's version of the song because of Sylvester's inability to speak his part. She responds that her nephew knows his part, as she has promised; if time is not taken to do the song her way, she threatens, she will leave the session and Chicago to resume her tour.

The conflict between Ma and Levee is, in part, a result of his attention to the young woman Dussie Mae, in whom Ma has some interest herself. Ma cautions Cutler to "school" Levee because "he's got his eyes in the wrong place." (The nature of the relationship between Ma and Dussie Mae is not spelled out, though it is implied that the attraction is sexual.) Displeased with Levee's attitudes and his inability to take directions, Ma finally fires him during a heated argument.

The audience soon realizes how deeply Ma is affected by this environment in which she finds herself. In a conversation with Cutler, she reveals her understanding of Sturdyvant, Irvin, and the entire recording industry. Ma angrily complains about white people not caring for her as a human being, but only as a marketable commodity. "They don't care nothing about me. All they want is my voice down on them recording machines, then it's just like if I'd be some whore and they roll over and put their pants on." The overpowering presence of Ma Rainey, with a singing talent second to none and a sound mind for business, provides her with the elements necessary to succeed as a black entertainer in early twentieth century America. She finally completes the recording session but refuses to sign the release form until Sylvester is paid his own twenty-five dollars, separate from her personal fee. Sturdyvant and Irvin attempt and fail to extract Sylvester's pay from Ma's portion.

Levee, in contrast, is unable to name his own terms in an attempt to negotiate his original music with Sturdyvant. A broad smile, servile demeanor, and shining shoes are not enough to persuade Sturdyvant—who cons Levee into accepting five dollars for each of his songs—to revert to the terms of their original deal.

The final moments of act 2 focus on Levee. His world has collapsed, his pride, self-worth, and future dreams have vanished. The collective pressures that have distorted his life are suddenly too much to bear, and a physical confrontation with Cutler ensues, resulting from Levee's blasphemous tirade about God being created solely for the white man. In futility and rage, Levee challenges God to a knife duel. This psychotic behavior foreshadows the tragic end of the play. When Toledo accidentally steps on one of Levee's new shoes, Levee goes over the edge. Toledo's apology cannot stem the tide of hate and frustration that Levee feels. Toledo happens to be in the wrong place at the wrong time, and the play ends with his unpremeditated murder at the hands of Levee. The remaining musicians are left, as they arrived, in the position of having no control over their professional life. In another sense, their lives are as unfulfilled as that of Levee.

Themes and Meanings

Ma Rainey's Black Bottom examines the relationship between black artists and the world of mass communications in the early twentieth century. This relationship mirrors the position of black people in the society at large—a society dominated by white racism. August Wilson establishes these concerns early in the play through musical imagery and idiomatic language, using both the style and the lyrics of the blues as metaphors for African American life.

A bit of American history is indigenous to *Ma Rainey's Black Bottom*. In the 1920's Gertrude (Ma) Rainey was a force in the world of "race" recordings. Between 1927 and 1929, she recorded solely for the Paramount label, including the song that gives this play its title. The recording session dramatized in the script actually occurred in Chicago; most of the details and supporting characters have been invented.

The title of the play implies that all Ma has to do is appear and claim her rights as principal protagonist. In fact, however, Ma's testament of her struggles as an artist is overshadowed by the collective experiences of her musicians: From their dingy rehearsal space they dominate the play. There is a tragic dimension to the lives of these men that is lacking in Ma's experience. They are not faceless images of the masses—they are as distinct in their varying philosophies and sociopolitical viewpoints as they are in their dress and musical instruments—yet they represent the countless people who never attain celebrity and whose stories largely remain untold.

Dramatic Devices

Ma Rainey's Black Bottom invites the audience to share the experiences of these musicians through the devices of storytelling, poetry, and black music. The musicians' monologues reflect an African oral tradition through which black people have for centuries transmitted their culture. For example, the figurative and rhythmic language of the blues in the "jazz" talk of these musicians has been deftly captured by the playwright. Metaphoric and literal interpretation of the text is interwoven in dialogue that moves from farcical humor through sociopolitical propaganda to melodramatic insights.

This energized dialogue provides a forum through which the audience can share the hurts, the desires, and the frustrations which the characters express through their colorful yet haunting stories. The poetic imagery that is such a vital part of the language of the blues finds a parallel in the beauty and colorful verbal presence of black colloquial language. The play's social content overshadows the dramatic context at times, yet Wilson generally avoids broad stereotypical characters and situational clichés.

Ma Rainey's Black Bottom moves from the leisurely pace of act 1 to the melodramatic violence that concludes act 2. Act 1 depends primarily on dialogue to advance the action. At the same time, the sense of waiting for something to happen that pervades the first act creates tension in the audience, preparing viewers for the climax. As the second act winds down, Ma settles her recording business with management and takes her leave; Levee is observed begging Sturdyvant to purchase and record his compositions. These seemingly unrelated and fragmented actions connect in the play's violent climax. The tension existing between theme and action is finally objectified through the presentation of Levee as a powerless black artist and victim.

Critical Context

Ma Rainey's Black Bottom is the first in a cycle of plays by August Wilson that dramatize elements of black experience in each decade of the twentieth century. Other plays in the cycle are *Fences* (pr., pb. 1985), *Joe Turner's Come and Gone* (pr. 1986, pb. 1988), and *The Piano Lesson* (pr. 1988, pb. 1990), all of which were developed at the Eugene O'Neill Theater Center's National Playwrights Conference and given their premieres at the Yale Repertory Theatre.

Ma Rainey's Black Bottom opened on Broadway in October, 1984, to critical acclaim and won the New York Drama Critics Circle Award. *Fences*, subsequently produced at several regional theaters, opened on Broadway in the spring of 1987 and received the Pulitzer Prize, the New York Drama Critics Circle Award, and the Drama Desk and Outer Circle Awards, as well as Tony Awards for best play and for Lloyd Richards as best director. *Fences* is the story of a black family during the transitional years of the 1950's, preceding the civil rights upheaval which changed the face of history in the United States. Troy Maxson, the play's central character, is a trashman and a former athlete who, at various times, has been a lover, a bully, a liar, and a hypocrite. He is a man with his own system of values, to which he is strongly committed, but his responses are sometimes marred by irrationality and prejudice. His suppressed rage erupts in verbal outbursts that hurt and bruise his family.

Joe Turner's Come and Gone is based on the legendary story of Joe Turner, the brother of the governor of Tennessee, who would lure black men into crap games. He would fall upon them and force them into seven years of servitude on his plantation. This legend establishes the theme of enslavement, reinslavement, separation, and searching among a disparate group of individuals. Restlessness and disconnection permeate the lives that are dramatized in this play. What price freedom? Each character attempts to understand the nature and meaning of a newfound freedom.

The Piano Lesson (pr. 1988) is set in the 1930's; the play centers on a family dispute over what should be done with a hand-carved piano, the only significant heirloom in the family. The brother wants to sell it, but his sister cherishes it for its historical and personal significance. Thematically, *The Piano Lesson* dramatizes the perennial conflict of values that pits respect for the past against hope for the future.

First and foremost, August Wilson is a poet of the theater. He is a master of delineating strong and complex characters who doggedly hold to their beliefs and prejudices. What distinguishes *Ma Rainey's Black Bottom* from other plays in its genre, plays which echo similar voices against racism, self-hatred, and class exploitation, is the eclectic genius of its author. Wilson's concerns are primarily examined through a dramatic structure that encompasses social crises and renders them visible, and in a language that adds a vital new voice to the American stage.

Sources for Further Study

Elleins, Marilyn, ed. *August Wilson: A Casebook*. New York: Garland, 1994.

Kauffmann, Stanley. Review in *Saturday Review* 11 (January/February, 1985): 83-85.

Leiter, Robert. Review in *Hudson Review* 38 (Summer, 1985): 297-300.

Nadel, Alan, ed. *May All Your Fences Have Gates: Essays on the Drama of August Wilson*. Iowa City: University of Iowa Press, 1994.

Pereira, Kim. *August Wilson and the African-American Odyssey*. Champaign-Urbana: University of Illinois Press, 1995.

Rich, Frank. "Wilson's *Ma Rainey's* Opens." *New York Times*, October 12, 1984, sec. 2, p. 4.

Savran, David, ed. "August Wilson." In *In Their Own Words: Contemporary American Playwrights*. New York: Theatre Communications Group, 1988.

Shafer, Yvonne. *August Wilson: A Research and Production Sourcebook*. Westport, Conn.: Greenwood Press, 1998.

Shannon, Sandra Garrett. *The Dramatic Vision of August Wilson*. Washington, D.C.: Howard University Press, 1995.

Floyd Gaffney

MACHINAL

Author: Sophie Treadwell (1885-1970)
Type of plot: Expressionist
Time of plot: The late 1920's
Locale: A large American city like New York City
First produced: 1928, at the Plymouth Theatre, New York City
First published: 1928 (condensed), 1949 (complete)

Principal characters:
THE YOUNG WOMAN, Helen, an ordinary but sensitive working woman, later the Boss's wife
THE BOSS, a coarse, materialistic businessman
THE TELEPHONE GIRL, a cheap party girl
MOTHER, dependent on her daughter Helen
THE FIRST MAN, Richard Roe, an adventurer

The Play

Inspired by the notorious case of Ruth Snyder, an adulteress who died in the electric chair for the murder of her husband, *Machinal* is the personal tragedy of a gentle individual alien to a crowded, hard society. It is told in nine episodes in an expressionistic style, dramatized consistently from the viewpoint of the Young Woman. Each episode depicts a phase in the Young Woman's life, usually a situation in which a woman is supposed to be fulfilled. In only one phase does the Young Woman find companionship, peace, freedom, happiness, beauty, or meaning: That particular episode leads to her killing her husband and ultimately to her own death.

The play opens in a business office where typical office employees work to the incessant noise of their adding machines and typewriters, vocalize their working procedures, and in staccato, repeat themselves as well as office gossip. Through the gossip, the audience learns that the Young Woman lives with her mother and has no social life but that the Boss is "sweet" on her. The Young Woman distinguishes herself from the office regimentation by being late to work. She explains that she had to escape the airless crowd of the subway and walk in fresh air. The Boss proposes marriage, but the Young Woman is repelled by his touch. Although the other girls approve of marrying for security, the Telephone Girl tells the Young Woman to avoid that double bed. In soliloquy the Young Woman presents a hypothetical scenario that involves marriage, babies, exhaustion, and the search for real companionship with "somebody."

The Young Woman has no fulfillment in work or in her parental home. The second episode, accompanied by counterpointing offstage dialogue in other apartments, reveals the Young Woman's unsatisfying relationship with her mother, a nag who accepts the status quo of women even though she is a dependent widow whose chief entertainment is the daily garbage collection. The Young Woman agonizes over the convention that women must marry. She tells her mother of her revulsion for her boss and about her longing for love, but the two women cannot communicate well on this topic. In exchange for financial security, the mother is quite willing for the daughter to contract a loveless marriage with a decent man, and the Boss is a "Vice-President—of course he's decent."

Eventually the Young Woman marries the Boss. In the grim "Honeymoon" episode, the Young Woman is panicky. Although her new husband is not cruel, he is vulgar. Bragging about the hotel room that costs "twelve bucks a day" and repeating crude jokes, he is insensitive to her reticence about undressing but is prudish about keeping the curtains closed when his bride is trying to get a breath of fresh air. The scene darkens on the Young Woman's appearance in a nightgown, crying for her mother or "somebody." It is clear that this is not the happiest day of her life.

The Young Woman does not find fulfillment in motherhood either. The "Maternal" episode takes place to the machine sounds of construction on a new wing of a maternity hospital. The Young Woman find herself deeply afflicted with postpartum depression, a manifestation of her bound yet disconnected state of being. She gags on her husband's flowers and his self-satisfied paternity. The male obstetrician tells her how she should, or must, feel, and, unfeeling himself, prescribes insult for illness: If she cannot retain a liquid diet, she must be hand-fed solids. In her concluding, free-association soliloquy, she recalls memories of a pet dog whose pups were drowned and moves on to identify an unlovable God with her husband and the Virgin Mary with herself. She refuses to submit ever again—to her husband, to God, to future maternity, to this present child.

In the fifth episode, the Young Woman, in pursuit of pleasure, has come to a speakeasy with the Telephone Girl. Though the whole scene is permeated with male ascendency—an older homosexual enticing a mere boy, a man persuading a young woman into an abortion, the "free spirited" Telephone Girl servicing a married man for an hour or two before he goes home—the Young Woman and her blind date are not sullied. Her date, the First Man, a vagabond just returned from Mexico with a tale of having killed two bandits with a bottle of pebbles, proclaims the doctrine that a man must be free. For the first time the Young Woman is called by her name, Helen. For the first time, someone, concerned with her feelings, asks her "You like me—don't you, kid?"

There is no coarseness in the lover's room. For a moment, freed from submission to the duties of life, the woman gives herself freely. The First Man's honesty about his restless longing to be free ("I'll have to be moving on again, kid—someday, you know") makes the moment more precious. The lovers talk about childhood and travel in space. They know each other. Yet night ends their afternoon dream. A streetlight throws shadowy bars across the floor. Sophie Treadwell's stage directions indicate that Helen's departure is to be idealized. Voluptuous, protected, and nurturing, she is Woman, the Eternal Feminine. The First Man gives her a lily in a pot of pebbles.

The contrast of the fifth episode to the sixth is great. Helen has not settled into resignation or consolation in her nuclear family. At home on a typical evening, her overbearing husband still suffocates her. Her reading of an advertisement for precious stones and his reading of a revolution in Mexico trigger memories and inspire her with a means of escape: murdering her husband.

Prosecuted at her trial by both the prosecutor and the judge, Helen holds to her story of her husband's murder by intruders until the prosecutor introduces her lover's deposition, identifying the pebbles from the lily pot as part of her weapon. Helen confesses and begins "to moan—suddenly—as though the realization of the enormity of her isolation had just come upon her. It is a sound of desolation, of agony, of human woe."

As she goes to execution, Helen refuses the consolation of patriarchal pieties but understands a black prisoner's crying out toward God in a spiritual. She will not repent her moment of freedom and soaring with her lover but she does regret that she and her mother never really knew each other. She begs for more time to know her own daughter and to teach her about life but refuses to submit even to the barbers who must forcibly shave patches of her hair to place electrodes. Her last words "Somebody! Somebody" leave the audience wondering: Are the words a cry of self-pity or a cry for someone to teach her child?

Themes and Meanings

The title, *Machinal*, pronounced either as the French word meaning "mechanical" or to rhyme with "bacchanal" (suggesting an orgy of women otherwise repressed by their male-dominated society), implies the intertwined themes of the play: the modern commercial-industrial society's reinforcement of the stultifying effects of patriarchy on subjugated women. Inevitably, the play seems to say, the subordinated will seek freedom and significance by whatever means they can, even by violence.

The power of industrial and commercial mechanization to turn workers into robots (a newly minted term in the 1920's) was the subject of much of that era's social criticism. Like other expressionist dramas, Treadwell's *Machinal* uses mechanical devices to make her point: here, unnerving, vulgarizing, routinizing, isolating, and dehumanizing the characters of the play. Helen is unnerved by the great underground machine, the subway train, packing people into its breathless cars like sardines in a can. The clerks in her office become as numerical, alphabetical, and categorized as the materials with which they work: The Telephone Girl's responses are as routine as a phone's ringing, and the telephone becomes a factor in isolating the characters rather than in encouraging communication. Even the music in the speakeasy and outside the lovers' room is vulgarized by a mechanical player piano and hand organ. The final isolation and dehumanization by machine come with Helen's death in the electric chair.

However, behind the machines is always a human agent, and expressionists cast blame on capitalist society and its human cohorts in the established culture. Treadwell casts blame from a woman's perspective: She condemns women's subordinate social and economic position and women's collusion with the dominators. The working women in the play hold low-paying service jobs from which they consider escaping through the other acceptable servitude, marriage. Although men are the ostensible breadwinners, it is the responsibility of the unmarried daughter to provide for her widowed mother. Helen's mother, the acquiescent female, considers selling her daughter to the Boss—an honorable solution to her economic problem. The Boss is the master in his marriage: He sets the tone, prurient prudishness, to the wedding night, while in the "Home" episode, he assumes the role of self-congratulatory big shot and woman's teacher. The male doctor, aided by his sycophantic nurse, dominates the maternity scene, demonstrates no understanding of a woman's feelings, yet makes diagnoses and gives the prescriptions. An all-male court, not a jury of her peers, convicts Helen. The priest who accompanies her to the electric chair prays to a panoply of male saints for *Helen's* repentance and forgiveness. Even the lover who gave her "all [she] ever knew of Heaven" can roam free because he is a man.

Her bacchanals for freedom unsuccessful, Helen dies as she has lived—isolated—but her cry for "somebody" and her dying wish for "somebody" to tell her own daughter to live and enjoy life speaks to a generation of younger women who have the potential to free themselves and perhaps their society.

Dramatic Devices

Treadwell's play is characteristic of expressionist drama. For instance, her characters are types, not automata or caricatures. The dialogue, though repetitive and clichéd, typical of extreme expressionism, often catches the rhythm, even the brokenness, of common speech. The speech and the characters re-create the effect of regimentation that capitalism and mechanization have wrought upon them and thus also contribute to the dramatization of the protagonist's impressions of her society.

The one-box set (at times two-box), with minor adjustments from episode to episode, creates the claustrophobic feeling of Helen's world. Crucial scenes from six years are played fluidly, separated by darkness but linked by sounds that fill the darkness, contributing to Helen's feeling of unrelieved tension. Cacophony of machine noise is never raised to the wild roar that characterizes many expressionistic plays. It is instead intended to create a background atmosphere of mechanized life surrounding the heroine even as background dialogue in some scenes echoes or counterpoints her thoughts.

Helen as a heroine is a type, but as her unconscious is revealed through free-association soliloquies, as her commonplace experiences are dramatized from her viewpoint, and as her wishes and memories are revealed onstage, the audience sees in the type an individual struggling for rebirth.

Critical Context

In the decade of the 1920's, American theatergoers attended many good German and American social-protest expressionist plays but even more bad imitations. Most critics of the era recognized *Machinal* as a fine contribution to the genre, in theme and form acting as a companion piece to Elmer Rice's *The Adding Machine* (pr., pb. 1923). However, whereas Rice's Mr. Zero has a slave nature, which is eternally reborn through poor education, and his murder of his boss is a momentary aberration, Treadwell's Helen is always a rebel spirit, born of Treadwell's experiences as an international investigative reporter and feminist. She picketed for women's suffrage, wrote newspaper features on homeless women and a play about early feminist Mary Wollstonecraft, and accomplished such "masculine" feats as reporting on World War I and interviewing a hero of the Mexican Revolution, Pancho Villa. The themes of *Machinal* reflect the heart of her life's work.

Moreover, the themes of *Machinal* are central to expressionism and to the work of other female writers of Treadwell's time. Burns Mantle included *Machinal* in his *Best Plays* series because he found it a strong, original, stage-effective work, significant as a character study. Nevertheless, while *The Adding Machine* has been anthologized and eulogized, *Machinal*, though relatively successful on Broadway and in London and Moscow in the 1920's, was largely neglected except by the occasional theater scholar until feminist critics discovered it in the 1970's. Feminists have recognized the play for what it is: a forerunner to the plays of Harold Pinter, Wendy Wasserstein, and David Mamet, and in substance still acutely relevant to the concerns of women and others subjugated in twenty-first century society.

Sources for Further Study

Barlow, Judith E. Introduction to *Machinal*. London: Royal National Theatre and Nick Hern Books, 1993.

Bywaters, Barbara L. "Marriage, Madness, and Murder in Sophie Treadwell's *Machinal*." In *Modern American Drama: The Female Canon*, edited by June Schlueter. Rutherford, N.J.: Fairleigh Dickinson University Press, 1990.

Dickey, Jerry. "The 'Real Lives' of Sophie Treadwell: Expressionism and the Feminine Aesthetic in *Machinal* and *For Saxophone*." In *Speaking the Other Self: American Women Writers*, edited by Jeanne Campbell Reesman. Athens: University of Georgia Press, 1997.

_______. *Sophie Treadwell: A Research and Production Sourcebook*. Westport, Conn.: Greenwood Press, 1997.

Parent, Jennifer. "Arthur Hopkins' Production of Sophie Treadwell's *Machinal*." *Drama Review* 26 (Spring, 1982): 87-100.

Pat Ingle Gillis

THE MADMAN AND THE NUN
Or, There Is Nothing Bad Which Could Not Turn into Something Worse

Author: Stanisław Ignacy Witkiewicz (1885-1939)
Type of plot: Surrealist
Time of plot: The early twentieth century
Locale: Central Europe
First produced: 1924, at the Municipal Theatre, Toruń, Poland
First published: Wariat i zakonnica: Czyli, Nie ma złego, co by na jeszcze gorsze nie wyszło, 1925 (English translation, 1966)

Principal characters:
ALEXANDER WALPURG, a poet and madman
SISTER ANNA, a young nun
SISTER BARBARA, her Mother Superior
DR. JAN BIDELLO, a non-Freudian psychiatrist
DR. EPHRAIM GRÜN, a Freudian psychoanalyst

The Play

The Madman and the Nun is set entirely in a "cell for raving maniacs" in a lunatic asylum, furnished only with a bed, a chair and table, a window protected by thick metal bars, and a creaking door. The madman of the title is the poet Alexander Walpurg, who has been confined here with acute dementia praecox; as the play opens, he is sleeping, drugged and straitjacketed, on the bed. The consulting physician, Dr. Bidello, enters with Sister Anna, a young and beautiful nun. Since all else has failed, Sister Anna is to use her feminine intuition to circumvent the patient's defenses and shed light on the "complex" from which he is suffering. Bidello has agreed to this course of action only reluctantly, for to him it represents a tacit acknowledgment of the diagnosis of his rival, Dr. Grün, a psychoanalyst of the Freudian school. He leaves, admonishing Sister Anna not to gratify Walpurg's wishes.

As the madman awakens, he tells the nun, in tones ranging from lustful vehemence to great pathos, of his suffering, of the "infernal machine going in [his] head." When he introduces himself formally, Sister Anna recognizes him as a once-famous poet whose poems played a part in a romance that ended in the tragic suicide of her lover and precipitated her own retreat from the world. Walpurg, too, has lost a lover, whom he enigmatically accuses himself of having "tortured to death"—the ultimate reason for his madness. Sister Anna becomes more and more entranced with Walpurg in spite of herself, and he confesses his love for her after persuading her to undo his strait-jacket. Finally, the nun, "with no will of her own," according to the stage directions, yields to the poet's amorous advances.

Act 2 opens in the early morning of the next day. A storm is rapidly approaching. The two lovers are transformed by the night's experiences, Walpurg now vowing to seek "a perfectly ordinary life," and Sister Anna (whose worldly name is Alina) promising to remain faithful to him as she gives him a cross inherited from her mother. However, Walpurg admits, "There's some violent force in me that I can't control. . . . There's some higher power, above me or in me, whose orders I'm forced to follow." Sister Anna then fastens his straitjacket again to maintain appearances.

When the two psychiatrists, Bidello and Grün, enter with Sister Barbara, the Mother Superior, Walpurg seems controlled and restored, calmly asking for books and writing materials. Dr. Grün, elated that this presumed therapy has generated such good results—which fully affirm his theories—gives in to Walpurg's requests to remove the straitjacket, against Bidello's warnings. Walpurg commences writing a new poem as Grün expounds at length on the madman's supposed "twin sister complex" which he claims has been resolved by virtue of psychoanalysis. Suddenly, seeing Bidello privately conversing with Sister Anna, Walpurg flies into a jealous rage and strikes Bidello with his pencil, killing the psychiatrist. Sister Anna faints in horror, but Walpurg triumphantly declares himself fully cured, deftly twisting Grün's analysis to prove that he is not responsible for this murderous but liberating action. Sister Barbara ushers out the remorseful Sister Anna after she revives, while attendants bring Walpurg a hearty breakfast at Grün's behest and remove Bidello's corpse. Grün ecstatically contemplates writing a monograph about Walpurg's case, but the poet coldly and tauntingly rejects the doctor's familiarity. Grün leaves, satisfied that his "complex" theory has been vindicated, as Walpurg, straitjacketed again, jeers at this "game of make-believe."

Act 3 opens, presumably that evening, as Sister Anna, once again alone with Walpurg, undoes his straitjacket. He has slept soundly all day and now presents her with a newly composed poem, which she reads. They reaffirm their love, Sister Anna even admitting that Bidello's murder aroused in her a perverse excitement. Walpurg suggests that they go far away, to the tropics, declaring that "the universe demanded" their meeting. As they kiss passionately, they are surprised by Dr. Grün and Sister Barbara. While the Mother Superior covers her eyes, Grün utters his disappointment at Walpurg's betrayal, though he is confident that "psychoanalysis can cope even with this." As he commands the attendants to restrain the madman, Walpurg ("in a ghastly voice," as Witkiewicz specifies) commands everyone to stay where they are, in effect "freezing" them in mid-action. He then knocks out a window pane with Sister Anna's cross, ties a sleeve of his straitjacket to the bars, ties the other sleeve around his neck, and jumps from the table, "his arms spread out like a cross," as the curtain falls rapidly on the scene.

In his stage directions, Stanisław Ignacy Witkiewicz demands that the curtain be lowered only long enough to give the actor who is playing Walpurg an opportunity to exit, while stagehands replace him with a dummy. The action resumes again seconds later. Walpurg (the dummy) is cut down, and Sister Anna throws herself on the "corpse," Grün meanwhile comically lamenting the demise of his "guinea pig." The

Mother Superior, utterly indignant at this turn of events and at Sister Anna's perceived depravity, rejects the young nun's pleas for forgiveness. As they kneel in prayer and the attendants prepare to remove Walpurg's body for autopsy, the door opens and Walpurg enters, quite alive, clean-shaven, in a formal outfit and with "a yellow flower in his lapel." He is followed by Dr. Bidello in a frock coat, carrying a woman's dress and hat. Sister Anna falls into the resurrected poet's arms as Bidello declares that the dress is meant for her and that they will be "going into town." Walpurg announces: "I'm really completely sane now: sane and happy. I'll write something marvelous." They leave, and to confound matters more, the institute's director, Professor Walldorff, appears, blithely explaining to the bewildered Grün that he will henceforth give up psychiatry. He locks Grün, Sister Barbara, and the attendants into the cell, and they realize, to their horror, that they themselves are "the madmen now." With that, a chaotic brawl ensues, each violently thrashing the other. A "blinding blue light" comes from above as the curtain falls.

Themes and Meanings

The artist's position in society, his often anarchic and dangerous creativity, and the desire of the powers that be to harness and subdue the uncontrollable are the main concerns of *The Madman and the Nun*. Witkiewicz, however, chooses to approach the familiar subject of the enmity between the forces of conventionalism and the *bohème* with both a more tightly constructed governing metaphor and a more surprisingly idiosyncratic resolution than are to be found in most similar works.

The insane asylum, with its dank cell, represents the totality of a world devised purely to restrain and confine aberrant "madmen" such as Walpurg. The poet (whose name alludes to the German "Walpurgisnacht," the Witches' Sabbath, giving expression to his troubled and infernal, Romantic side) is a deliberate Witkacian self-portrait—like so many heroes in Witkiewicz's plays—but he also stands for the universally impetuous, unpredictable, even demoniac creative energies which the author believed were being systematically eradicated in the modern world.

Walpurg fears nothing more than to become a cog within the senselessly whirling machinery of the social order, but his paradox is that the uncontrollable and chaotic is the imperative of the artist: "Today the greatest art is found only in perversion and madness." The madness of Walpurg's (and, to a degree, also Witkiewicz's) avant-garde is a defense against the smooth functionalism of society at large, but it is finally self-defeating: Walpurg has himself become a demented, drug-ridden, poetry-producing machine.

The adversarial force is here a psychiatry which projects itself as benevolent and humane but in which dogmatic skirmishes (Freudianism versus non-Freudianism) have replaced effective therapy. The play abounds with satirical pinpricks against psychoanalysis; Dr. Grün is a caricature of the undeterrable proponent of a mechanistic, self-fulfilling Freudianism.

Sister Anna, too, is a prisoner: Stifled by an unforgiving religion embodied by the hypocritical Mother Superior, she like Walpurg is "beyond life," living but dead to the outside world. Her torrid affair with Walpurg is the first step toward her ultimate liberation, as is Walpurg's murderous attack on Bidello. Both acts are so antirational and in such flagrant violation of accepted codes of conduct that they become cathartic.

The Madman and the Nun is a parable of liberation through death and transcendence with manifest religious undertones. However, the moment of reversal, Walpurg's (and Bidello's) inexplicable resurrection, is played without gravity; it is rather a distinctly comical occurrence, an instance of unashamed wish-fulfillment (ironically, a Freudian principle) in which the author asserts the powers of imagination over the exigencies of reality. In *The Madman and the Nun*, Witkiewicz mirrors an ambiguous, disintegrating world, a world of chaos thinly veneered by civility, where nothing is so bad that it could not turn, as the play's subtitle indicates, into "something worse." Such was his vision of contemporary reality. Only in the theater, however, is the counteracting moment possible, which affirms that, in art at least, things can turn into something better as well.

Dramatic Devices

Like other Witkiewicz plays, *The Madman and the Nun* is remarkably short (requiring about ninety minutes in performance) and hence of an economy that serves its native theatricality well. By confining itself to a single setting, it creates an overall claustrophobic atmosphere which mirrors Walpurg's interior state and which can be enhanced (as in a 1967 production directed by Jan Kott) by utilizing expressionist scenic techniques and slide projections.

Startling contrasts in tone, from high seriousness to low comedy, from pathos to farce, are the most prominent hallmark of Witkiewicz's dramaturgy. Walpurg's first encounter with Sister Anna is by turns filled with touching passion and wry irony. The poet's violent and stunning attack on Bidello follows almost without warning upon a sequence in which Grün comically explicates his ridiculous psychoanalytic theories. Then, literally over the body of the slain psychiatrist, Grün nonchalantly orders breakfast. Professor Walldorff's sudden, unaccountable appearance deliberately thwarts the principle of character motivation of the well-made play. These ruptures of normality strengthen the impression that the viewer is not in an entirely rational environment—indeed, that in some way the theatrical representation reflects Walpurg's skewed subjective perception. Apart from Sister Anna and Walpurg, whom the author fleshes out sufficiently, the characters are largely mere caricatures of hypocrisy, incompetence, and narrow-mindedness.

The play's most radical departure from what could for the most part (in spite of its oddities) be called "realism" occurs with the suicide and subsequent resurrection of Walpurg. This scene is a veritable *coup de théâtre* in which a relatively credible reality is abruptly and jarringly confronted with a dreamlike vision. At this moment, the play becomes "surrealist" (or "absurdist" *avant la lettre*) with a vengeance, changing the rules of the game in mid-act. Thus, Walpurg is not only revived from the dead but also transformed into a suave character of the contemporary salon drama, spouting banalities. Grün, on the other hand, meets his fate in a grotesque, nightmarish cataclysm.

The author manages to keep the audience quite unprepared for this turn of events, which greatly enhances the effect.

Witkiewicz shows himself acutely aware of the theatrical tradition and utilizes its assorted devices parodically. The switching of the bodies at the climactic moment of suicide, as Daniel Gerould has observed, is a stage trick adapted from the turn-of-the-twentieth-century Grand Guignol theater. The brewing storm is a favorite contrivance of Romantic drama and its melodramatic derivatives. The blinding light from above is raided from the storehouse of expressionist devices. Even the color scheme of the play betrays Witkiewicz's eye for stage effect, as it progresses from the stark black-and-white of the beginning (nun's habit, straitjacket) to the yellow flower, the purple dress, and the blue light, underlining the otherworldly, transcendent quality of the ending. While Witkiewicz's self-conscious handling of the theater actively discourages "suspension of disbelief," it defines a newfound freedom of the stage to probe the realms of the subconscious and the metaphysical and to render them with supreme theatricality. In *The Madman and the Nun*, theme and form are interdependent: The liberation of the characters can be accomplished only through an unfettered theatrical imagination.

Critical Context

Stanisław Ignacy Witkiewicz (or Witkacy, as he liked to call himself) was trained as a painter but maintained truly universal interests. He wrote more than thirty plays, the greater part of these between 1918 and 1926. Few were published or even widely produced during his lifetime, and recognition of his importance as a playwright did not come until after World War II, when the rediscovery of his works fortuitously coincided with the vogue of the Theater of the Absurd. Within his oeuvre, *The Madman and the Nun* is perhaps the most accessible work, and it has therefore enjoyed far more performances outside Poland than any other Witkacian text.

The Madman and the Nun, with its surprising structural discontinuities, in many ways embodies the new type of drama that Witkiewicz had postulated in his 1919 essay, "Wstep do teorii czystej formy" ("An Introduction to the Theory of Pure Form"). Here, he posited a fantastic psychology and action unhampered by rational motivation or probability, a purity of dramatic plot that he had elsewhere called "non-Euclidian." The play is a highly successful exercise in stretching and ultimately breaking the conventions of realism and asserting the autonomy of the theater to formulate its own laws.

The Madman and the Nun must be described as a play of Witkiewicz's maturity as a playwright. It was preceded by largely experimental dramas such as *Tumor Mózgowicz* (pr., pb. 1921; *Tumor Brainiowicz*, 1980), a phantasmagoric exploration of science and imperialism the title character of which is a vitalistic counterpart to Walpurg, and *Kurka wodna* (pr. 1922; *The Water Hen*, 1968), a "spherical tragedy" in which conventional logic is suspended throughout in favor of "pure form." In *Matka* (pb. 1962; *The Mother*, 1968), written the year after *The Madman and the Nun*, Witkiewicz continues along the structural lines of the latter, contrasting Ibsenian domestic realism with the visionary frenzy of a cocaine dream.

Although he is utterly original in his dramatic voice, which was aptly characterized by the Polish critic Tadeusz "Boy" Żeleński as "metaphysical buffoonery" and "supercabaret," Witkiewicz partakes strongly of the theatrical enterprise of some of his better-known contemporaries—August Strindberg's destruction of naturalism from the inside; Antonin Artaud's search for an immediate, absolute theater; the surrealists' *épater le bourgeois*; Luigi Pirandello's metatheatricality; Vsevolod Meyerhold's satirical grotesquerie—and sets the tone for things to come, particularly the absurdism of Eugène Ionesco or of Witkiewicz's compatriot Witold Gombrowicz. While Witkiewicz is still ranked with the minor deities in the pantheon of modern drama, there is a growing awareness of his unique stature and original contribution to the theater.

Sources for Further Study

Dukore, Bernard F. "Spherical Tragedies and Comedies with Corpses: Witkacian Tragicomedy." *Modern Drama* 18 (September, 1975): 291-315.

Gerould, Daniel C. *Witkacy: Stanisław Ignacy Witkiewicz as an Imaginative Writer.* Seattle: University of Washington Press, 1981.

The Polish Review 17, nos. 1/2 (1973).

Weyhaupt, Angela Evonne. "Death and Resurrection in Witkiewicz's *The Madman and the Nun*." *Polish Review* 22, no. 4 (1977): 45-48.

White, Helena M. Review of *The Madman and the Nun*. *Theatre Journal* 48 (December, 4, 1996): 514-516.

Ralf Erik Remshardt

MADMEN AND SPECIALISTS

Author: Wole Soyinka (1934-)
Type of plot: Morality play
Time of plot: Unspecified
Locale: Unspecified, but suggestive of Nigeria after the 1967-1969 Civil War
First produced: 1970, at the Eugene O'Neill Theater Center, Waterford, Connecticut; first complete version, 1971, at the University of Ibadan, Nigeria
First published: 1971

Principal characters:
BLINDMAN, a mendicant and alms collector
GOYI, a mendicant and acrobat
CRIPPLE, a mendicant, drummer, and lead singer
AAFAA, the leader of the mendicants, St. Vitus Danser, and former military chaplain
DR. BERO, a specialist, formerly a physician, now an intelligence officer
SI BERO, his sister and assistant
IYA AGBA and
IYA MATE, two old women, earth mothers
PRIEST, a former patient of Dr. Bero
THE OLD MAN, Dr. Bero's father and prisoner

The Play

Part 1 of *Madmen and Specialists* opens with four mendicants at a roadside—Goyi, Cripple, Blindman, and Aafaa. Behind them is Dr. Bero's home with a basement office. To the side is a "semi-open hut" in which are visible two old women, Iya Agba and Iya Mate. The level space in front of Bero's home holds barks and herbs set out for drying. The mendicants, casualties of a recent war, wager parts of their bodies in a dice game and wonder if their former therapist, the Old Man, Dr. Bero's father, will ever fulfill his promise of taking them on a world tour, during which they would perform as a circus act, the "Creatures of As." When the doctor's sister, Si Bero, passes by them on her way home from gathering herbs, they put on their routine to beg for money. Being familiar with their act, she stops it, condemns them for not working for a living, tosses them a few coins nevertheless, and offers them the job of sorting herbs. They bless her for the contribution—all but Aafaa, who sarcastically blesses her brother instead. The others, in fun, follow suit, giving the first hint of Bero's inhumanity as they stage an arbitrary trial, execution, and burial of Goyi. After describing themselves as serviceable vultures, they reveal the reason they are begging before Bero's house. Still under orders as Bero's spies, they have Bero's father, who is a prisoner in the office, under surveillance.

When Si Bero chooses Blindman to enter the house to get the herbs, the mendicants' constant bickering escalates into resentment and sarcasm. Si Bero tries to restore order, but when she leaves for the old women's hut, a fight erupts between Aafaa and Blindman. Amid this uproar, Dr. Bero enters for the first time and must remind them of their orders. They are unhappy with their menial tasks and are distressed over their conflicting obligations to the three strong characters, Bero, Si Bero, and the Old Man. Blindman and Goyi are attracted by the atmosphere of love surrounding Si Bero. Aafaa, who had been a chaplain in the war and had never served under Bero, is the most defiant in his commentary on military intelligence as a cowardly activity; Bero strikes him in the face with his swagger stick.

Bero's reunion with Si Bero reveals how much Bero has changed since he left for the war. She wants to call all the neighbors to announce his return; he wants privacy. She pours palm wine in front of the threshold as a blessing to the earth; he calls it superstition and declares that he, in shedding blood, has spilled a more potent sacrifice. The scene exposes Si Bero's ignorance of Bero's real activities—that he rejected medicine for intelligence operations and thus participated actively in killing, and that he has had the mendicants sequester the Old Man in the basement. On the other hand, Bero is ignorant of her activities. She has engaged the services of the old women, has even installed them on the property so that they can aid her in discovering medical secrets.

The scene cuts away momentarily to the old women, who fear, as they observe Bero's behavior, that their spiritual energies have been misplaced. Si Bero had vouched for Bero to these "earth mothers," and now it appears that Bero is not to be trusted. When the scene cuts back to the brother and sister, Si Bero explains her activities as a balancing of cosmic forces, the healing power of the herbs against the destructive power of war. Now that Bero seems to have joined the other side, she fears for their father, who left for the war and has not returned. Bero does not yet announce their father's location but assures her that he has been able to keep track of him. He then explains his change of profession as a simple redirection of energies: His new function resembles the old—analysis, diagnosis, prescription—but now the prescription is death: "Power comes from bending Nature to your will."

The Priest makes only a brief appearance in the play. His entrance signals that of the ordinary person, uncomprehending, suddenly face-to-face with extraordinary events. According to his own simple values, he is evil because he has come directly to visit Bero without sharing the news of the return with others. He seeks treatment for an old ailment and will not trust even Si Bero with administering the medicine. He naïvely recalls conversations with the Old Man about cannibalism and reports on a letter the Old Man sent him from the war zone describing his work among the disabled and reiterating his cannibalism theory. While the Priest still regards the debate as purely academic and takes the Old Man's words at face value, Bero realizes the Old Man's true meaning—that cannibalism is only the logical extension of killing—but does not explain. Instead, he scares the Priest away with an invitation to have human testicles for dinner.

Bero thus admits to being serious about the virtues of cannibalism. Si Bero is horrified. Bero continues to amaze her as he recounts the crucial event in his life: eating human flesh that the Old Man had served him and his fellow officers. When he learned what he had eaten, Bero, unlike the other officers, recklessly asked, "Why not?" and tried it again. He thus discovered the means to power to be "the end of inhibitions," accepting this drastic condemnation of the war as a challenge instead of a warning and resenting anything that would stand in the way of his total authority. The Old Man remains, however, the main obstacle to Bero's total independence, both as father and as philosophical antagonist: Instead of simply rehabilitating the disabled, the Old Man taught "them to think, think, THINK!" No longer docile subordinates, Bero complains, the mendicants have become "choosy." As if in response to Bero's complaint, the spotlight shifts to the mendicants in Bero's office chanting to the god As and seating themselves around the Old Man. Bero finally confides to his sister where the Old Man is and hints that he must either keep him prisoner or kill him. Horrified once again, Si Bero refuses to follow Bero to the office; she moves instead toward the old women.

Most of the action in part 2 of *Madmen and Specialists* takes place in Bero's office. The mendicants are still chanting and are again, as at the beginning of the play, throwing dice. Aafaa goes down the alphabet searching for words that describe the god As, but the exercise turns into a blasphemous, vulgar game. The Old Man, silent, amused, and bored, refuses to aid him in his search. Cripple describes a recurring dream that depicts Bero as a Christ who operates on him and commands him to walk. The dream always ends before he can rise from the table. Goyi admits to having a similar dream, but Blindman and Aafaa object, the latter insisting that Bero, unlike Christ, does not use miracles to show off.

The Old Man begins to make demands—he wants his watch and glasses—as Bero enters with his meal. He then demands writing paper in order to send a complaint to Bero's superiors. Bero refuses, claiming that he has no superiors. After taunting the Old Man, Bero begins to interrogate him, without success. Meanwhile, as they speak, the mendicants are wolfing down the food that Bero brought for his father.

Bero goes out to argue with his sister: The old women must leave or he will kill them, since they have, he asserts ironically, no claim to the land on which they live. Bero proceeds to the hut to threaten them and demands to know the name of their "cult." "We move as the Earth moves," they say, and give him no satisfaction. Strongly drawn to the protest songs of the mendicants, Bero returns to his office to continue the interrogation; he wants to know how his father has captured the minds of the mendicants and calls him a Socrates who must be executed. They debate which one is living in illusion: the Old Man, who is committed to humanity, or Bero, who is committed to power.

As the climax approaches, the old women and the mendicants demand their due. For Bero's abuse of power, the old women will set fire to the herbs. The mendicants want their promised tour but realize that it may be too late. They hold a mock ceremony giving themselves medals for meritorious service, and Blindman gives a speech apparently defending the status quo against popular uprisings. At the conclusion of their performance, the Old Man, predicting the future, "freezes with his arm raised towards the next scene as if in benediction." While the old women approach the house to burn the herbs, Bero comes toward them with a revolver but is distracted by the Old Man's indictment of him as "the dog in dogma" and "the cyst in the system." When Cripple says he has "a question," the Old Man and the other mendicants shut him up, knock him out, and lay him on the operating table. Acting out Cripple's dream, the Old Man examines him and is about to make an incision to find out "what makes a heretic tick" when Bero enters and shoots his father. Si Bero runs to the office, Iya Agba sets fire to the herbs, Si Bero reappears in the doorway, and the two old women calmly walk away. The lights go out as the mendicants chant their Yoruba praise song to As.

Themes and Meanings

Madmen and Specialists presents a stark confrontation between good and evil forces. Good it defines as creative, beneficent, and humane; evil as destructive, sadistic, and reductionist. To make sure that the audience does not miss the point, Wole Soyinka provides two supernatural characters—the earth mothers Iya Agba and Iya Mate—to pronounce the law that governs the universe. Nature, they say, operates according to the principle of reciprocity: "We put back what we take, in one form or another. Or more than we take. It's the only law." Anyone who violates that principle is doomed, eventually, to fail. When Bero tries to "proscribe Earth itself" he attempts the impossible task of stepping outside the circle.

In addition, Soyinka gives another "elder" in the play, the Old Man, unusual intellectual powers and a moral sensibility that, in his case, borders on madness. His response to Bero's evil is a disturbing, ironic dialectic that proves even more elusive and provoking to Bero than the philosophical calm of the old women. Like them he strikes certain humanistic chords—"A part of me," he says, "identifies with every human being"—but his dealings with Bero are aggressive and extreme, a kind of psychological shock treatment. He lowered Bero and his fellow officers to the level of beasts when he told them, "All intelligent animals kill only for food . . . and you are intelligent animals." With the meal of human flesh, he "robbed them of salvation." While they are looking for him, they should instead "be looking for themselves."

Like Socrates, the Old Man insists on the importance of the examined life. He fails, however, to enlighten Bero any more than he has the mendicants. The best he can do is, like the blindman in the moral fable, shine his lantern on the thief to expose him. When Bero's cannibalism extends to patricide, he has made two fundamental denials of reciprocity: Man eats man instead of nourishing him, and cuts the generational link instead of continuing it. The ritual chant that the Old Man teaches his mendicants, but which they do not understand (as the audience may not), nevertheless suggests the continuum that Bero defies: "As—Was—Is—Now—As Ever Shall Be. . . ." By killing his father he tries to kill As. The continuum of the dead, the living, and the unborn is fundamental to Soyinka's Yoruba metaphysic.

The play deals, then, with the tragic fall of a particular man, Bero, who before the war had been a doctor, a specialist, engaged in uncovering the secrets of nature in order to heal the sick. His ability and his reputation are attested by the priest, whose dramatic purpose is partly to suggest what Bero used to be. By the time he returns from the war, however, he has become an intelligence officer, uncovering secrets to gain power over men. Soyinka thus incorporates a traditional tragic theme, the hero's defiance of the gods, the hubris that carries the hero beyond the bounds of safety. As the Old Man says to Bero, "Once you begin there is no stopping. . . . For those who want to step beyond, there is always one further step." Iya Agba's judgment is even more succinct: "Your mind has run farther than the truth."

The ultimate mystery cannot be known, cannot be named. What the audience sees in Bero is the frustrated operative of an intelligence agency, threatening the earth mothers with death if they will not reveal the "name" of their cult, threatening his father with death if he will not reveal the secrets of As that allow him to control the minds of the mendicants. He is obsessed with knowing the truth, but by reducing truth to a manageable thing that he can bring under his power, by reducing reality to a definition, he enters a world of illusion. The old women and the Old Man maneuver and frustrate him with riddles. Bero is caught hopelessly between the mysteries of nature and mind. The encouraging message of the play is that evil eventually defeats itself as the forces of good withdraw their support. The tragedy is that just when one seems on the verge of using the secrets of nature for good, when one seems, as Si Bero is, in perfect harmony with nature, the urge for power asserts itself and will not listen to reason or respond to humane impulses.

Dramatic Devices

Wole Soyinka creates a form of ritual drama, what, in one of his critical essays, he calls revolutionary drama. *Madmen and Specialists*, that is, takes place on a cosmic stage, giving it metaphysical dimension; it follows the paradigm of a Yoruba myth that is central to Soyinka's work, the voyage of Ogun. The two key events in Ogun's adventures are his initial challenging of the abyss (the chaos of transition between humankind and the gods) and his second confrontation with it, the drunken slaughter of human beings during a battle in which he cannot distinguish between friend and foe. The first is creative as Ogun builds a bridge of communication between humans and the supernatural; the second is destructive, the act of a madman. This mythic background is basic to themes, characters, and structure in *Madmen and Specialists*. The characters are, for the most part, larger than life; with the exception of the Priest, who exits in fear of the unknown, they have moved beyond the ordinary world onto a cosmic stage. It is a world of risk, horror, and madness. The goal: a "revolution" in the minds of the audience. The spectators must become celebrants; they must accompany Bero on his journey into the cosmic realm of transition.

Soyinka uses several dramatic devices to achieve communal empathy. Visually, the stage reflects the three realms: The hut of the old women is raised to suggest their supernatural being; the home and the herbs are on level ground; the doctor's office is in the cellar, death and the underworld, as it were, and it is here that part 2 mainly takes place, ending with the act of patricide, the ultimate challenge to nature's laws. In addition, Soyinka incorporates into the play a chorus of sorts: The mendicants function not only as casualties of war, bewildered pawns in the struggle for power, but also as worshipers who chant and dance to the songs of their god, disciples who eat the sacrificial food, "the favorite food of As," actors who perform their "circus" routine, politicians who conduct official ceremonies, and poets who tell a proverbial tale. They are both celebrants of the divine and, in William Butler Yeats's phrase, "mockers of man's enterprise." To add to the aura of mystery, one of their choral chants is in Yoruba. The ritual is enhanced by an occasional stop action, as characters freeze to allow characters on another part of the stage to act out their scene. In the final such action, the Old Man actually points to the next scene as if to indicate that he predicts the future consequences of Bero's actions.

The mythic dimension of the play is prevalent throughout, as the action is patently symbolic and the dialogue overtly raises philosophical questions. The characters are more representative than individual: Si Bero, the good woman aligned with the fruitfulness of mother earth; Bero, the embodiment of nihilism; the Old Man, the Socratic philosopher and dramatic artist who exposes falsehood; the Priest, conventional morality that cannot fathom the depths of cosmic forces; and finally the mendicants, victims, tools, and inadequate protégés of society's stronger wills. Aafaa proclaims Bero greater than Christ; Bero specifically calls his father a Socrates. The meal served to the Old Man but confiscated by the mendicant disciples is a parody of the Last Supper.

The Old Man's need for his glasses and watch suggests his alienation from space and time. Bero's offer of a "choice" to his father between his pipe and tobacco without a light and cigarettes with a light has a philosophical intent: The Old Man's refusal to smoke the cigarette, his refusal to be bought, sets him apart from both Bero and the mendicants, who no longer have the capacity for "self-disgust." The herbs, always in view during the play, are the constant symbol of nature's secrets, to which only the honorable have access. When the old women set fire to them at the end, Soyinka completes the symbol: In his universe, evil forces nature to withdraw its gift even from the good. The two cancel each other out. The play's ritual action imitates nature's laws.

Madmen and Specialists, then, from the set and the stylized action to the poetic imagery and the crazy protest songs of the mendicants, suggests a movement toward and a return from the realm of transition. The tragic hero's blasphemous defiance of cosmic law should send a shudder through the audience as it joins Bero on his cosmic journey.

Critical Context

Wole Soyinka's work, like most modern African literature, is closely tied to historical circumstance—the British colonization of Nigeria, the independence of Nigeria and other African countries in the early 1960's, the continued cultural and economic presence of Western capitalism, and the power struggles among ethnic groups within the independent nations. While to some extent Soyinka has dealt with the so-called conflict of cultures motif, including the tendency among some authors to blame the European incursion for Africa's current problems, Soyinka has focused primarily on more fundamentally human roots of social and political disturbances—roots that lie deeper than cultural differences. He also has insisted that Africans can draw upon their own cultural myths to understand themselves and their situation. Hence Soyinka frequently relies upon Yoruba mythology, in particular the tragic god Ogun, to explain the creative and destructive tendencies in human nature and the cosmic significance of human action. In this respect *Madmen and Specialists* is a typical Soyinka play; it is so little concerned with the effects of British colonialism that only the naïve Priest and parodies of its cultural heroes, Christ and Socrates, remind the audience of it. The core of the play is a confrontation of elemental forces. The language may be English, but the mythic and ideological basis is African.

While the mythic background is ahistorical, it gives meaning to particular historical events, and *Madmen and Specialists*, like other Soyinka plays, reflects a merger of myth and history. Soyinka wrote and produced it immediately after the mass genocides of the Nigerian Civil War (1967-1969), during which he was detained as a political prisoner. The play is a terrifyingly personal literary response to both the war and his own flirtation with death. As Soyinka recorded in his prison notes, *The Man Died* (1972), he spent much of his solitary confinement challenging the authorities with life-threatening fasts. His greatest fear, which became an obsession, was that he might die in dishonor, his public identity defamed by government lies. His physical survival depended upon his exposing, through secret prison contacts, the truth of his situation.

While *Madmen and Specialists* has no specific setting in place and time, and one speech is even designed to be changed to fit the political circumstances of the audience, there can be no doubt that the war and the two years in prison inspired everything about it, including its emotional and spiritual energy. Bero is surely based on General Yakubu Gowon and other officers responsible for the genocide, and the mendicants are not only the visible casualties but also the subordinate tools of terrorism, like the monstrous, though sometimes humane, warders (Polyphemus, Hogroth, Sow, and Caliban) who kept constant guard over Soyinka in prison. As Soyinka says in *The Man Died*, this was not a revolutionary war to change ideas, but a war to reinforce the old, inhumane ones. The specialists have lost everything but the will to kill, and the world has gone mad. The most interesting parallel between the historical events and the play is the resemblance of the Old Man's situation to Soyinka's solitary confinement.

Like Soyinka, the Old Man has become a public enemy because he has dared to expose evil and has thus been hidden from public view. For lengthy periods the public did not know where Soyinka was, or even whether he was still alive. He remained for two years an enigmatic figure. The Old Man, with his Socratic skepticism, is equally elusive. Fatigue, mental torture, and hunger finally drive the Old Man to insane behavior just before he dies. Soyinka experienced similar bouts with madness as his fasts carried him to the realm of "transition." Finally, the Old Man, as the manager of his circus of mendicants, is the dramatist whose main goal, as Bero complains, is to get people to "Think, Think, THINK."

This philosophical and mythic drama, then, has an intensely personal origin in concrete historical circumstances. The writer's function, as Soyinka argued in his 1986 Nobel Prize address, is to ensure that historical realities are put on the record. He must not allow governments to reinterpret history for their own self-serving ends. While autobiography itself is not new to Soyinka's work, *Madmen and Specialists* marks a change in his career to even greater political commitment and a deeper moral tone.

Sources for Further Study

Berry, Boyd. "On Looking at *Madmen and Specialists*." *Pan-African Journal* 5 (1972): 461-471.

Gates, Henry Louis, Jr., and Kwame Appral, eds. *Critical Perspectives, Past and Present.* New York: Harper Trade, 1994.

Gibbs, James, ed. *Critical Perspectives on Wole Soyinka.* London: Heinemann, 1981.

_______. *Wole Soyinka.* New York: Grove Press, 1986.

Jones, Eldred Durosimi. "*Madmen and Specialists*." In *The Writing of Wole Soyinka.* 3d ed. Portsmouth, N.H.: Heinemann, 1988.

Sekoni, Ropo. "Metaphor as Basis of Form in Soyinka's Drama." *Research in African Literatures* 14 (Spring, 1983): 45-57.

Soyinka, Wole. *The Open Sore of a Continent: A Personal Narrative of the Nigerian Crisis.* Oxford, England: Oxford University Press, 1997.

Wright, Derek. *Wole Soyinka: A Life, Work, and Criticism.* London: Macmillan, 1992.

Thomas Banks

THE MADNESS OF GEORGE III

Author: Alan Bennett (1934-)
Type of plot: History
Time of plot: 1788-1789
Locale: London and Windsor, England
First produced: 1991, at the Royal National Theatre, London
First published: 1992

Principal characters:
GEORGE III, king of England
CHARLOTTE, queen of England
PRINCE OF WALES, the heir to the throne
WILLIAM PITT, the prime minister
EDWARD THURLOW, the lord chancellor
CHARLES FOX, the Whig opposition leader in Parliament
RICHARD SHERIDAN, a Whig member of Parliament
EDMUND BURKE, a Whig member of Parliament
MARGARET NICHOLSON, petitioner to the king
LADY PEMBROKE, the queen's Mistress of the Robes
SIR GEORGE BAKER, the king's principal physician
DR. WILLIS, a specialist in mental illness
SIR BOOTHBY SKRYMSHIR, a member of Parliament
RAMSDEN, Sir Boothby's nephew

The Play

The Madness of George III opens in the autumn of 1788, approximately seven years after Great Britain's loss of the American colonies, a loss that continues to weigh heavily on the fragile mind of King George III. Surrounding the king are those who would supplant him and his Tory government, including his eldest son, the Prince of Wales, and the Whig leaders Fox, Sheridan, and Burke, who conspire to overturn the Tory government led by Prime Minister William Pitt.

It is not long before the king falls ill with what the playwright depicts, following a future diagnosis, as porphyria, a metabolic disorder, rather than the play's contemporary diagnosis of "madness." The king is unable to control his language, yielding to incessant and nonsensical talking as well as insulting and obscene statements. He falsely concludes that his wife is having incestuous sexual relations with the prince, and he himself becomes obsessed with Lady Pembroke, the queen's Mistress of the Robes.

The continuing illness prevents the king from providing the leadership that England requires, bringing the government to a virtual standstill. During the approximately six months of his illness, several political maneuverings are deployed simultaneously. Pitt attempts to keep the seriousness of the king's illness from members of Parliament, thus maintaining the Tory government in place while awaiting the hoped-for recovery. Charles Fox, a former prime minister, and his Whig allies work hard to forge a majority to bring a regency bill before Parliament, thus essentially replacing the king with the Prince of Wales, who in turn would dismiss Pitt and establish a Whig government led by Fox.

During the months of illness, doctors attempt to cure the king. One set of physicians (including Sir George Baker, the king's primary physician) employs traditional methods such as blistering the king's head and legs with extremely hot cups. Dr. Willis, who runs a mental asylum in Lincolnshire, is brought in by Pitt and increasingly becomes the king's primary doctor. Willis uses a number of unusual techniques, including binding and gagging the king when he acts or speaks inappropriately, and staring the king in the eye to force his patient to remember who he is and reassert control over his speech and behavior.

Just as Fox is close to forging his majority, the king recovers sufficiently to reassert his rule. His government, led by Pitt, survives, and the king and queen resume their domestic bliss as "Mr. King" and "Mrs. King," phrases that George III uses at both the beginning and end of the play. The final line, uttered by the king, states clearly the status of the leading character and the nation at the conclusion: "The King is himself again." The status quo has been restored.

Themes and Meanings

A historical play that ends where it begins seems to violate common expectations of plot and character development. That the play succeeds nonetheless is because the audience quickly develops a sympathy for George III that transcends the political reality that the king stands for a long-rejected primacy of monarch over Parliament. What is most important to the audience is that the king embodies basic values of sincerity, kindness, domestic felicity, and fondness for the masses much more than do the elected representatives who appear onstage.

Asked to choose between the father and the son, the audience immediately chooses King George, when, assaulted in the first scene by the crazed petitioner Margaret Nicholson, he commands that she not be hurt. The Prince of Wales, on the other hand, seems more disturbed by her tearing the king's waistcoat than by any potential harm to his father. In the following conversation with his son, the king asks whether he knows why the people call their ruler "Farmer George." The prince answers that they are impertinent, but the king corrects him, explaining that it is out of love and admiration. Historically, the appellation also reflects the king's great interest in agriculture.

The audience knows that a return to normality for the king will be a return to his commitment to his wife, to his country, and to his people. This sense of devotion is contrasted throughout with the Prince of Wales, who is self-absorbed, interested only in the superficial ("To me style is the thing," he says), repeatedly derided as fat (another sign of his self-indulgence), and impatient to shove his father aside.

As sincere as the king is, he also understands the importance of playing a role. The theme of performance is an important element in the play, as the king must play himself in order to reassure his nation. During his illness, however, he loses his identity. He informs Dr. Willis during his treatment that "I am the King. I tell. I am not told. I am the verb, sir. I am not the object." Unfortunately, he is describing who he was.

Edward Thurlow, who plays both sides to retain his position as lord chancellor regardless of which party triumphs, visits the king at Windsor and immediately is pulled into a dramatic reading of William Shakespeare's *King Lear*. Thurlow assures the king that he seems more himself, and he is. Playing a role that parallels his own life is both therapy and sign. The king has learned how to control his speech and behavior; he has learned how to play the king again. "I have remembered how to seem," he replies to his visitor.

Appearing with his wife and sons near the end of the play, George III reminds them that they "must be a model family for the nation to look to." The appearance may truly be the reality, or at least it may appear to be the reality. Either one works for the good of the nation, the play appears to assert, but the audience knows that the king *is* rather than merely *seems*, and that is why the audience is content with the way things were.

Dramatic Devices

In his goal to make restoration of the status quo the ultimate triumph of the play, Alan Bennett uses a variety of dramatic devices to highlight the king's changing health and his return to normality.

The opening scene includes two important uses of foreshadowing. When Margaret Nicholson strikes the king with a dessert knife, the king responds, "The poor creature's mad. Do not hurt her, she's not hurt me." Later in the play, the king, now a patient, makes similar pleas when he is subjected to such medical treatments as blistering and being strapped into a restraining chair. Also in the first scene, with his arms outstretched to assist with removal of his coat, the king describes the torture that a French citizen would undergo for an assault on the French king. Both the king's physical appearance and his words foretell the torture that he will later endure during his illness.

Throughout the play, word usage is a sign of the king's health status. Initially, he ends statements with such phrases as "Hey, hey" and "What, what," phrases that, however odd, are quite normal for him. As his illness strikes with full force, he speaks long rambling clusters of nonsense, including considerable punning along with insults and obscene allegations. His resumption of "What, what's" in the second part of the play signals his return to his original condition.

Bennett uses considerable irony in statements and visual images, including transitions from scene to scene, to invite comparisons between father and son. For example, Sheridan informs the Prince of Wales that Parliament will attempt to impose restraints on his rule as regent, while at nearly the same time the king is struggling against the physical restraints of the restraining chair. That scene with Sheridan and the prince opens with the prince's servant shoving a foot into the prince's back as he attempts to lace up a corset on the overweight son. The previous scene had concluded with a similar image of one of the king's pages pulling tight the straps on a waistcoat that is a type of strait jacket. Many more examples of irony appear throughout the play.

Music also appears as both an ironic and signifying element. George Frideric Handel's music can be heard in the opening scene. Later, during the king's illness, Handel's coronation anthem, "Zadok the Priest," plays while the king is being enthroned in his restraining chair. The same anthem, however, signals the king's recovery near the end as a portion proclaiming "God save the king, may the king live forever" resounds.

The device of a play-within-a-play parallels the theme of a king's rule as performance; to some extent, then, all that the king does is a royal play. However, there are more specific applications of this device. Playing the part of the suffering King Lear, torn into madness in part by misjudging his daughters, is therapeutic for George III. An earlier scene at the palace at Kew is designed to call to mind King Lear and his Fool by the placement of George and his page. The king's recollections of his dead son Octavius recall King Lear's lament for his wronged daughter, Cordelia. The Sophoclean presence also is felt strongly as the Prince of Wales seeks to replace his father, with echoes of Oedipus even more explicit when the ill king rants about his son sleeping with the queen.

Bennett also introduces touchstones to reflect the way that the political as well as medical winds are blowing. Before the extent of the king's illness is widely known, Sir Boothby Skrymshir appears before Pitt to request a position for his nephew, Ramsden. When the regency appears inevitable, he turns his attention to the Prince of Wales. A third solicitation occurs near the end of the play, as uncle and nephew appeal this time to the recovered George III.

In a play so psychologically heavy, comic interludes are welcome. The double-dealing Thurlow worries about his own health, badgering the doctors to check his pulse and stool. The king exacts revenge on his personal physician by dumping his chamber pot over Sir George Baker's head. Having recovered his senses, the king inquires of Lady Pembroke whether he behaved inappropriately toward her, half hoping that he had done so. "Did we ever forget ourselves utterly, because if we did forget ourselves I would so like to remember. What, what?"

Critical Context

The Madness of George III was widely hailed for its wit, energy, use of history (altered when necessary for dramatic purposes), occasional echoes of modern-day English politics, and ability to engage audiences in accepting a play that ultimately goes nowhere except back to the status quo.

Alan Bennett's stature in England already was high before the first production of the play in 1991, thanks to his long career, which began in the early 1960's, as actor, director, screenwriter for films and television, author, and playwright. He turned from a satirist to a versatile writer of considerable substance, attaining the position of England's finest living playwright in the judgment of some critics. His awards began with the London *Evening Standard* Drama Award in 1961 for *Beyond the Fringe* (pr. 1960), a comic revue in which he partnered with Peter Cook, Jonathan Miller, and Dudley Moore, and the awards have continued to accumulate.

The Madness of George III opened in New York City in 1993, introducing Alan Bennett as a dramatist to American audiences. Bennett gained even more fame in the United States when the film version, titled *The Madness of King George*, premiered in 1994 (its title changed so American viewers would not think it was a sequel). Bennett authored the screenplay, and the film, considered by some critics even more successful than the stage version, garnered four Academy Award nominations.

Sources for Further Study

Bennett, Alan. Introduction to *The Madness of George III*. Rev. ed. London: Faber and Faber, 1995.

_______. *Writing Home*. New York: Random House, 1995.

Lyons, Donald. "Theater: On the Superiority of European Methods." *New Criterion* (September 11, 1992): 59-63.

Schiff, Stephen. "Cultural Pursuits: The Poet of Embarrassment." *The New Yorker* (September 6, 1993): 92-101.

Turner, D. E. *Alan Bennett: In a Manner of Speaking*. London: Faber and Faber, 1997.

Wolfe, Peter. *Understanding Alan Bennett*. Columbia: University of South Carolina Press, 1999.

Edward J. Rielly

MARGARET FLEMING

Author: James A. Herne (1839-1901)
Type of plot: Domestic realism
Time of plot: 1890
Locale: Canton, Massachusetts
First produced: 1890, at the Lynn Theatre, Lynn, Massachusetts
First published: 1930

Principal characters:
PHILIP FLEMING, a mill owner
MARGARET FLEMING, his wife
JOE FLETCHER, a traveling salesman
DR. LARKIN, Margaret's doctor
MARIA BINDLEY, Margaret's German nursemaid
MRS. BURTON, the caretaker of Maria's dying sister Lena
MR. FOSTER, the manager of Philip's mill

The Play

Margaret Fleming opens in Philip Fleming's private office at his mill. Philip enters and goes through the morning's mail. He confers briefly with his manager and his foreman and then smiles when his office boy brings in a soiled calling card. It is from Joe Fletcher, who used to work at the mill for Philip's father. Joe is now a traveling salesman who sells medicines and household articles. Joe is tired and thirsty. He eagerly takes a drink from Philip's liquor cabinet and asks Philip if he still drinks as he used to do. Philip responds that he has now married and settled down. He proudly shows Joe the picture on his desk of Margaret, his wife, and their small child, Lucy. Joe's visit is interrupted by Dr. Larkin, who has come to see Philip. Dr. Larkin has just learned that Philip is the father of a baby born during the night to Lena Schmidt, a girl who used to work at the mill. He angrily reprimands Philip, who says he has done all he can for Lena, but Dr. Larkin insists that Philip go to see her because she should not have to die alone. Philip reluctantly calls Margaret to say he will be late coming home.

The second scene of the first act takes place in Margaret and Philip's living room. Margaret sits by the fireplace getting Lucy, the baby, ready for bed. Maria Bindley, the German nursemaid, is gathering up the baby's clothes and quietly crying. Margaret tells Maria not to cry. Maria says that she has had a hard life. Her second husband was Joe Fletcher, the man who came by the house that morning. He left her, she says, and now her younger sister, Lena, is dying. Margaret tells Maria to go to her sister.

Margaret finally gets the baby to sleep and puts her in the adjoining room. Philip comes in, tired and wet. Margaret scolds him for being so late, but then she sees how weary he looks. Philip presents Margaret with a bank book and some legal papers, including a deed to the house. Margaret asks Philip if he knew that the tramp who came by the house this morning was Maria's husband, who robbed her and left her. Maria swore at him in German and threw him down the stairs, Margaret says, laughing. Seeing how pale and tired Philip looks, Margaret insists he go to bed.

The second act takes place in the same room. It is the next morning, and the sun is shining. Dr. Larkin is putting out some medicines for Margaret, who has been having trouble with her eyes. When Margaret leaves the room, Dr. Larkin tells Philip that Margaret has a tendency toward an eye condition called glaucoma and that she must not undergo any great emotional strain. After the doctor leaves, Joe Fletcher comes in through the garden. He is trying to avoid Maria, but she comes into the room and sees him. He tries to escape but trips and sprawls on the floor. Maria throws him out the door. Margaret, hearing the commotion, enters and inquires about Maria's sister. Maria says that she is worse and asks Margaret if she will go to see her. Margaret agrees to do so.

The third act takes place in the sitting room of Mrs. Burton's cottage. Dr. Larkin knocks on the door and enters into the empty room. Mrs. Burton enters from the next room with a tiny baby. When the doctor asks about his patient, Mrs. Burton says that Lena died about one hour ago after writing a long note. There is a knock at the door. It is Margaret. She is surprised to see Dr. Larkin and he is shocked to see her. He tries to get her to leave, but she thinks she can be of some assistance. Dr. Larkin finally tells Margaret that there is contagion in the house. As Margaret starts to leave, Maria enters with a letter in her hand. She tells Margaret that she will have to leave with the baby and pulls a revolver out of her pocket. Margaret, in a calm voice, asks for the revolver and asks Maria to read the note because she cannot see it. It is addressed to Mr. Fleming. Margaret sinks into a chair. Dr. Larkin finally tells Margaret that she is in danger of losing her eyesight. Margaret writes a short note to Philip asking him to meet her at the Burton cottage. She asks the little Burton boy to take the note, and she sends the doctor away, saying she must see Philip alone. As the women wait, the baby begins to cry. Margaret tries to comfort him. As he continues to cry, Margaret picks him up and at last starts to unbutton her blouse just as Philip runs into the room. The lights fade.

The last act takes place in the Flemings' living room. Maria is sitting near the door to the garden where the babies are. Dr. Larkin comes in, and then Margaret comes in from the garden with her arms full of flowers. A few moments later the doorbell rings. It is Mr. Foster, the manager of the mill. He tells the doctor that Philip is outside. He does not dare tell Margaret, leaving that to the doctor. When the doctor tells Margaret, she asks why he does not come in. Philip enters looking very weary and broken. He is shocked to find that Margaret cannot see him, but Margaret says the doctor will operate to restore her sight. When Philip asks for forgiveness, Margaret says there is nothing to forgive, but when he calls her his wife, Margaret says that "the wife-heart" has gone out of her. What if she had been unfaithful to him, she asks. Philip is horrified at the idea. He asks Margaret if he should go away, and she responds that his place is here and since he is a man he will soon live down the disgrace. He has responsibilities to his second child, his son, who is out in the garden with little Lucy. Philip goes into the garden to see the babies. Margaret stands looking into the darkness, as a serene look of joy illuminates her face and the stage lights dim.

Themes and Meanings

Margaret Fleming is the first American play that seriously attempted to move away from sentimental theater and present domestic realism. The subject is the double standard between the sexes and the consequences of marital infidelity. Philip Fleming, though seemingly very happy with his marriage to Margaret and with his baby, Lucy, has had an affair with Lena Schmidt.

When Lena becomes pregnant he thinks he has averted trouble by paying her off. Yet Margaret finds out about the baby. She does forgive Philip but cannot accept him as her husband. She asks how he might have felt if she had been unfaithful to him. Philip is horrified at the idea. Margaret says "You see! You are a man and you have your ideals of—the—sanctity—of—the thing you love. Well, I am a woman—and perhaps—I, too, have the same ideals. I don't know. But, I, too, cry 'pollution.'"

Philip is amazed that Margaret has brought his baby boy to their home to care for him. "You brought that child here?" he asks. "What other thing was there for me to do?" Margaret says. "Surely if he was good enough to bring into the world, he is good enough to find shelter under your roof." She insists that Philip must give the boy a name and educate him in order to atone for the wrong he did to the child's mother. Philip seems almost helpless in trying to face the present situation. Margaret says there is no need to lament the past. They must face the living future. "We will fight this together," she says. Margaret has not only personal integrity but also a social conscience and great strength.

Dramatic Devices

Margaret Fleming was much too realistic for audiences and many of the critics of the 1890's. There were no big climactic scenes. Both the audiences and critics were shocked by the nursing scene. Most important, the general public did not like the ending. They expected a sentimental reunion of Margaret and Philip, a sudden revelation that Philip was innocent, or a noble death to atone for Philip's guilt. James A. Herne denied the audience such a melodramatic ending. He instead left Philip to acknowledge his guilt and live with the consequences. One critic called Margaret "a monster of morality" for not taking Philip back.

Margaret Fleming still has some touches of melodrama. Joe is the comic character. There are also several unexplained coincidences. The Flemings' maid is Joe's former wife, and she is Lena's sister. Dr. Larkin is called in as a consultant when Lena is about to deliver her child. It is melodramatic when Maria pulls a revolver out of her pocket and threatens to kill Philip. Margaret's failing eyesight and subsequent blindness are a sentimental touch to gain sympathy for her.

However, there are some very realistic scenes that had not been seen before in original American plays. The first scene, portraying the day-to-day routine in a work environment, Philip's office, is very realistic until the doctor arrives. The domestic scenes with Margaret and the baby in front of the fireplace are quiet and real. The quiet ending of the play was an innovation in American drama.

Critical Context

James A. Herne started as an actor in the prevalent melodramas of the 1850's. Even as a young man, he liked playing character roles. He was especially fond of some of the characters in the dramatic adaptations of Charles Dickens's novels. He shocked audiences with his fierce intensity as Bill Sykes in *Oliver Twist* (1837-1839) and charmed them with his characterization of Daniel Peggotty in *David Copperfield* (1849-1850). Herne later paid tribute to the influence Dickens had on his writing. When Herne started writing and adapting plays, he started with melodrama, but he gradually began to do away with some of the melodramatic devices and tried to make the characters and the plots more realistic. After he married a young Irish actress, Katherine Corcoran, he began writing believable characters for her roles as well as for his own work.

In 1889 the Hernes were acting in Herne's original temperance drama, *Drifting Apart* (pr. 1888), at a second-rate theater in Boston. Hamlin Garland, a young writer from the Midwest who had recently moved to Boston, was told by the literary editor of the *Boston Evening Transcript* to go see the Hernes in *Drifting Apart*. Garland was overwhelmed by the quiet realism in the play. William Dean Howells, the outstanding writer and advocate of literary realism at the time, also praised *Drifting Apart* as a play very simple and honest in method. At the time, Herne was writing *Margaret Fleming*. Encouraged by the praise of the realists, Herne proceeded with his even more realistic play, *Margaret Fleming*.

Margaret Fleming was given three "tryout" performances in Lynn, Massachusetts, in July, 1890. Hamlin Garland reviewed the play and gave a detailed summary of the plot in the *Boston Evening Transcript* in July, 1890. Herne rewrote the ending of the play several times. The plot summary in this essay describes an ending created later by Herne and shows how he worked to make the play more realistic. In this early ending, four years have elapsed since the third act. Maria, because of her hatred for Philip, has taken little Lucy, telling Joe Fletcher, who now is back as her husband, that the child is her sister's. Margaret and Philip have been searching for the child, but Maria will not tell them that this child is Lucy. The fifth act of the play takes place in the office of the inspector of police. The inspector leaves Margaret and Philip alone after asking them to work things out. Though Margaret tells Philip that she cannot take him back as her husband, when the inspector comes in and sees them together he thinks they have arrived at a reconciliation and calls in the next case. The audience can see how much simpler the later ending of the play is.

In spite of the praise from people like Garland and Howells, the Boston and New York theater managers would have nothing to do with such a realistic play. They knew that such a play could not be a box office success. Howells suggested that Herne produce the play himself, as some of the realists were doing in Europe. The Hernes found that they could rent a concert hall in Boston. The hall could seat about five hundred people, and Herne was given permission to make what alterations to the stage he wanted.

A distinguished audience attended the opening night. The play received some excellent reviews and ran for two weeks, but the general public did not come. Not until 1907, six years after Herne's death, with his daughter, Chrystal, playing Margaret, was *Margaret Fleming* both a popular and a financial success. The American audiences had at last caught up with the vision of realistic drama that James A. Herne had foreseen many years before.

Sources for Further Study

Edwards, Herbert J., and Julie A. Herne. *James A. Herne: The Rise of Realism in the American Drama*. Orono: University of Maine Press, 1964.

Matlaw, Myron. *Nineteenth Century American Plays*. New York: Applause Theatre Books, 1985.

Perry, John. *James A. Herne: The American Ibsen*. Chicago: Nelson-Hall, 1978.

Quinn, Arthur Hobson. *Representative American Plays from 1767 to the Present Day*. New York: Appleton-Century-Crofts, 1953.

Robinson, Alice M. "James A. Herne and His 'Theatre Libre' in Boston." *Players Magazine* 48, nos. 5/6 (Summer, 1973).

Wilson, Garff B. *Three Hundred Years of American Drama and Theatre*. Englewood Cliffs, N.J.: Prentice-Hall, 1973.

Alice McDonnell Robinson

THE MARRIAGE

Author: Witold Gombrowicz (1904-1969)
Type of plot: Absurdist
Time of plot: World War II and the interwar period
Locale: France and Poland
First produced: 1963, at the Jeune Compagnie Théâtre competition, Paris
First published: El casamiento, 1948; *Ślub*, 1953 (English translation, 1969)

Principal characters:
HENRY, the protagonist, a son and a prince
FRANK, his father, an innkeeper and a king
KATHERINE, his mother, an innkeeper's wife and a queen
JOHNNY, his friend and a courtier
MOLLY, a servant and Henry's betrothed
DRUNKARD, a troublemaker

The Play

The Marriage takes place in an oppressive, shadowy landscape; the ruins of a disfigured church can be discerned in the background. The notion that the scene is a dreamscape is suggested by Henry's first speech and is reinforced by subsequent scene shifts from the battle-torn landscape of northern France to the faintly emerging structure of walls and outlines of rooms from which a country manor house in Poland comes into view. This manor house is simultaneously a cheap roadside inn. The characters who appear in this dreamscape are also subject to Henry's dream and consequently respond to Henry's thoughts as if he were the internal director. Since the characters are dream projections, however, they often take on a grotesque, threatening existence of their own.

In act 1, Henry, a Polish soldier in France, sees his childhood home, his parents, and his betrothed in a dream. In the outer fringes of his dream, he is accompanied by Johnny, his childhood friend and companion at the French front. At first Johnny functions as Henry's guide to the dream-constructed interwar Poland; later, however, he joins the other characters as a courtier in the inner dream.

As Henry and Johnny come upon what appears to be a cheap dive, Henry, through Johnny's suggestions, recognizes the inn as his ancestral home in Poland and, in a travesty of recognition scenes, the slovenly innkeepers as his parents. A festive dinner of horse guts and cat urine is served with due ceremony, and Henry finds himself subject to old rituals and forms. The father reestablishes a semblance of authority by forbidding Henry to lift his spoon until he, as father, has commenced eating. As the shadowy inn acquires concreteness, Henry recognizes Molly, the servant, as his former betrothed. Thereupon, the Drunkard at the head of other drunkards enters and propositions Molly. The father tries to prevent him, and the Drunkard starts to harass and insult him. In terror, the father announces that he is as "untouchable as a king." Action freezes as Henry assumes the role of the son of a king and kneels to pay homage to his father, thereby transforming him into an "untouchable king" and making him invulnerable to the Drunkard's "touch," or pointing finger. The father, in turn, proposes that by his sovereign power he intends to grant his son a "respectable marriage" with Molly, whose purity will thus be restored. The act closes with the arrest of the jeering Drunkard, who continues to threaten to touch the "untouchable king."

The second act discloses a large room in semidarkness as dignitaries question the authenticity of the "respectable marriage." Preparations for Henry's marriage to Molly are in the meantime being made. Henry, caught in these dream events, decides that everything hinges on whether he is to regard the marriage "wisely" or "foolishly," and in his "wise" speech temporarily convinces himself as well as the skeptical dignitaries of Molly's purity and respectability. The Drunkard, however, has escaped from prison and soon dispels Henry's confidence as he renews his threats to touch the king with his finger. As a countermove, Henry invites the Drunkard to high tea. By virtue of the invitation, the Drunkard acquires the status of a dignitary; he tempts Henry to overthrow his father-king. The Drunkard also attempts to convince Henry that, having assumed the throne, he will have the power to grant himself an honorable marriage to Molly. Aghast at how easily he can become a traitor, Henry rejects the Drunkard's temptations. The king, however, terrified by rumors of treason, fears even Henry. Henry's attempts to calm his frantic father end in his touching him, and thus the form of treason has been enacted. Transformed into a traitor, Henry dethrones his father, has his parents arrested, and proclaims himself king with the right to grant himself a marriage.

A scene follows in which the Drunkard presents a flower to Molly and asks Johnny to hold it over Molly's head. Then suddenly the flower disappears, leaving Molly and Johnny in a highly suspect position. A ghastly conjecture forms in Henry's mind as he accuses the Drunkard of binding the two in a base and ignoble marriage. As the Drunkard and Henry resort to name-calling, the scene ends with the laughter of the dignitaries.

In act 3, Henry has become a dictator and has arrested the entire body politic, all institutions, ministries, and the police. Once again, as in act 2, a wedding is being prepared: Henry's marriage to Molly is to be the test of his absolute power. Doubts about Molly's purity, however, propel Henry to have his parents brought in "by the snout"; he hopes to terrorize them into a reaffirmation of Molly's respectability. Instead, the father reminds Henry that he retains the form of his authority as father, and both he and the mother tell tales of Molly's sluttish behavior with Johnny and others. Reeling with jealousy, Henry now believes that his power will have no validity as long as it is not confirmed by someone who will voluntarily sacrifice his life. He sends for Johnny and Molly to prove their innocence; unconvinced by their protests, he asks Johnny to kill himself because he, Henry, wills it.

As the ceremonies for the wedding proceed, Henry sees himself in a world of fiction, lies, and empty forms. The Drunkard's pointing finger, intended to disclose

Molly and Johnny behind a curtain, instead reveals Johnny's body. Henry recoils, horrified by the reality brought about through the imposition of his will, and he submits to his new role as prisoner. The act ends with a funeral procession.

Themes and Meanings

The Marriage is a play about a social construct that Witold Gombrowicz calls the Formal Imperative. Forms may start as embryos or dreams, as in the case of Henry's dream, but they insinuate themselves into life and gradually take on an existence of their own. Human beings use forms to dominate others while in turn being subjugated by forms imposed by others. Gombrowicz implies that forms may evolve imperceptibly and insidiously. Something is said, Henry adapts himself, and one word creates another. Since forms invalidate reality, Henry is forever imprisoned by doubts about the existence of reality, and the stage metaphor of a dream existence brings out this deformation, for in a realm of dreams there is no absolute even though the dreamer, dreaming, still lives in the real world.

In Henry's recognition of his father in the first act, he submits to the forms imposed by the father/son relationship. As a consequence of this submission, Henry also assumes the form of appropriate respect for his former betrothed, Molly, even though she is now a sluttish maid at the shabby inn his father owns. When the Drunkard challenges Molly's purity as well as the dignity of his father, Henry responds by kneeling before his father. One form creates the next one, and Henry's father is by this act elevated to the dignity of king. As king, he has the formal authority to declare Henry's respectable marriage to Molly.

In the second act, the question of how forms generate new forms is further explored when Henry goes through the form of touching his untouchable father/king and finds himself a traitor. Something that began as a mere symbol is transformed into a reality: Henry really does seize power. As Gombrowicz suggests, however, since the individual is also subject to forms created between others, Henry's will is inadequate when faced with doubts voiced by the Drunkard about Molly's relationship to Johnny. This doubt in turn necessitates Henry's formal act of will imposed upon Johnny, who is to commit suicide because Henry wills it. However, this act of will is subject to the constraints of the external world, and Henry finds himself once again a prisoner of form.

While some insist that *The Marriage* presents Gombrowicz's criticism of the social constraints and vapid social forms of interwar Poland, others suggest that the play represents Gombrowicz's analysis of the rise to power of a tyrant such as Adolf Hitler or Joseph Stalin. Historical interpretations aside, *The Marriage* is a play about Henry's imprisonment by and through form; it enacts a confrontation between form and humankind's freely exercised ability to give particular significance to events. As the action progresses, Henry deliberately tries to destroy form in order to gain control over it. However, no sooner does he discard one form than he assumes another. In the process, as Henry comes to recognize, he has been turned into something he is not. The inability to become a real self thus emerges as the real tragedy of Henry's submission to the Formal Imperative.

Dramatic Devices

The Marriage directs the spectator's attention to Henry's dream experience through a variety of devices that create an awareness of the illusory quality of the events represented. Even this dreamworld is put into question as Henry's opening words, "The curtain has risen . . .," remind the spectator of the theatricality of the events to follow. From then on, the theatrical and dream worlds merge, as an awareness of Henry's dream state is projected through both scenic metaphors and textual allusions. Henry is pulled into the dream as the initially shadowy forms of the Polish manor house become more concrete; although aware that he is dreaming, he accepts the dream as a form of reality.

Henry's oscillation between his desire to play out the form of the events he is dreaming and his desire to stop the dream at will is foregrounded as occasional artillery shooting is heard throughout the play from what the audience takes to be the reality of the wartime French landscape of the opening scene. The dreamworld and the real world collide as well when Henry compliments Johnny on the watch Johnny bought in Brussels, thereby merging Johnny his friend and companion in France with the dream Johnny. This confusion brings out the horror of the reality of Johnny's suicide as Henry, despite his dream state, assumes responsibility for his act of will.

To emphasize the dreamlike nature of the action, the actors are instructed to express themselves artificially, dramatically, and theatrically. Frequent repetitions, echoes, and exaggerated exclamations emphasize the artificial nature of Henry's constructed reality. Tonal differences in these utterances lend a musical element; as Gombrowicz instructs, the "various themes, crescendos and decrescendos, pauses, sforzandos, tuttis and soli should be executed in precisely the same manner as a symphonic score."

Since the external world presented onstage is subject to Henry's dream, sudden scene changes occur. When Henry kneels to pay tribute to his father, the inn changes to the reception room of a grand castle and dignitaries in opulent clothing merge with the leering drunkards. Like Henry's dreamworld, which lacks fixed dimensions, none of the characters has fixed traits; instead, they shift abruptly from role to role. Consequently, it is impossible to identify with any of them as they progress through all the changes taking place from battlefield to inn to court to high tea to a funeral procession.

Actions, too, take on a theatrical quality. The gesture of the Drunkard's pointing finger, for example, becomes more vulgar, more coarsely physical with each repetition. This finger takes on an ominous significance, as if it were a character in its own right, as everyone looks to it to touch the king, to reveal Johnny and Molly in the artificially constructed obscene pose, and then to reveal Johnny's body.

Intent on representing Henry's dream state, Gombrowicz pays no heed to Aristotelian concepts of time, space, logic, or action; he also refuses to surrender to the tyranny of probability or the psychological depiction of characters. The irrational world of artificial constraint is projected through the decor, costumes, and masks of the actors, creating a world of "eternal artifice, eternal imitation, falsity and mystification." This constant awareness of the theatrical nature of reality is present even when reality intrudes and Henry realizes that Johnny is dead: "It's only a dream. It's even extremely artificial. And yet he's lying here." Even this tragic realization is theatricalized through repetition. In the end, Henry submits to the artificial forms of this theatrically constructed world by joining the funeral procession.

Critical Context

The Marriage is one of Gombrowicz's three plays presenting characters caught between the force of form, on one hand, and the desire for freedom from form, on the other. In *Iwona, księżniczka Burgunda* (pr. 1938, rev. pb. 1958; *Ivona, Princess of Burgundia*, 1969) Gombrowicz presents the conflict of form with formlessness as Princess Ivona's pathological shyness in the most formal of all societies, the court, prevents her from giving in to the forms imposed on her. She immobilizes other characters' social selves through her formlessness, thus exposing inner selves normally guarded from others through formalized relationships. When their identities are exposed as masks, however, the characters feel panicky and cannot perform their social roles. The social game of form must continue, and Ivona must die in order to maintain the world of form wherein masks of maturity are worn for the sake of others while dependent, at the same time, on the perception of others.

Operetka (pb. 1966, pr. 1969; *Operetta*, 1971) parodies the genre which in itself is a parody of form and shares with *The Marriage* rapidly changing scenes encompassing a period of forty years from the era preceding World War I to the end of World War II. *Operetta*, like *The Marriage*, may be read as a commentary on history and on the bankruptcy of political ideology, projected through the pretenses of an "operetta" society which adheres to empty, insipid, yet rigorously structured forms. Like *The Marriage*, *Operetta* presents the disastrous consequences of escape into false ideology: The ideologue mistakes form for reality and attempts to impose that form on everyone else.

Sources for Further Study

Baraniecki, Maria. "Gombrowicz's Drama Within and Without the Absurd." *Canadian Slavonic Papers* 27 (September, 1985): 241-247.

Brodsky, David. "Gombrowicz and the Theatre." *Theatre in Poland* 23 (1981): 18-23.

Goldmann, Lucien. "The Theatre of Gombrowicz." *Tulane Drama Review* 14 (1970): 102-112.

Gombrowicz, Witold. *Diary, 1961-1966*. Edited by Jan Kott. Evanston: Northwestern University Press, 1994.

Kott, Jan. "On Gombrowicz." In *Theatre of Essence and Other Essays*. Evanston, Ill.: Northwestern University Press, 1984.

Thompson, Ewa M. *Witold Gombrowicz*. Boston: Twayne, 1979.

Christine Kiebuzinska

MASTER CLASS

Author: Terrence McNally (1939-   )
Type of plot: Biographical; musical
Time of plot: 1971
Locale: Juilliard School of Music, New York City
First produced: 1995, at the Plays and Players Theatre, Philadelphia
First published: 1995

Principal characters:
MANNY WEINSTOCK, the accompanist
MARIA CALLAS, the famous opera singer
SOPHIE DE PALMA,
SHARON GRAHAM, and
ANTHONY CANDOLINO, her students

The Play

Master Class is based on the master classes given by the renowned real-life opera singer Maria Callas at the Juilliard School of Music in New York City in 1971 and 1972. In the play's two acts, Maria's interactions with her students are interspersed with reminiscences of her stormy life.

After Maria enters, wearing expensive clothes, she tells the audience there must be no applause because this is a working session. Music, she says, is a demanding discipline. There are no short cuts to success. She tells of how, during World War II, she used to walk to the conservatory and back every day, even though she had no proper shoes. Then she subjects her accompanist to some withering remarks that reveal her abrupt and imperious manner, after which she turns her attention to her first student, a young soprano named Sophie de Palma. Maria criticizes her appearance and tells her to get over her nerves. Sophie manages only to sing the first word of her chosen aria, from *La Sonnambula* (1831) by the Italian composer Vicenzo Bellini, before Maria interrupts. It is not the only time she interrupts, as she tries to get Sophie to listen to the music and to feel the true emotions of the character, the passion behind the words. She berates the hapless student for not having a pencil handy to take notes and for not knowing the names of all the great sopranos.

As Sophie begins to sing, Maria reminisces about her own performance as a recording of Maria Callas is played. She recalls her relationship with the wealthy Greek businessman Aristotle Onassis. Imitating his crude manner of speaking, she has him say that it was because of his connection to her that people began to respect him in a way that they had not formerly done. He boasts of his wealth and wants her to end her singing career and have his child. Then Maria recalls with a feeling of triumph her great performances at La Scala in Milan, and how she had succeeded against all the odds.

In act 2, the next student, Sharon Graham, enters. She is a soprano who is to sing one of Lady Macbeth's arias from Giuseppe Verdi's opera *Macbeth* (1847). Maria tells her to go off the stage and reenter in character, and she also mentions that Sharon's gown is inappropriate for the occasion. Sharon exits but does not return, and Maria realizes she has hurt the student's feelings. Yet, she is unapologetic.

The next student is Anthony Candolino, a tenor. Like the other students, he receives his share of criticism from Maria, who tries to send him home. He persists, and when he finally sings an aria from Giacomo Puccini's opera *Tosca* (1900), Maria is enthralled.

After this, Sharon returns, claiming that she was sick. She tries once more to sing Lady Macbeth's aria, but again Maria stops her and gives her some coaching about how to sing with passion. She sends Sharon backstage and then summons her again to repeat the scene. This time the audience hears not Sharon but a recording of Maria Callas singing the same piece in a live performance from 1952. As she listens, Maria recalls some dramatic moments from her life, including her debut at La Scala, in which she had thirty-seven curtain calls; the moment she told her husband Battista Meneghini that she would be marrying Onassis; the time when Onassis bullied her into aborting their baby; and the day she was fired at La Scala.

When the recording of Callas ends, Maria tells Sharon she should work on music more appropriate to her limitations. Upset, Sharon lashes out at Maria, telling her she can no longer sing and is envious of anyone younger who can. She leaves.

The play ends with Maria's reflections. She says that she has tried to communicate her beliefs about what the artist and musician do. Her advice to the singer is to think of the expression of the words, practice good diction, and express deep feelings.

Themes and Meanings

Maria Callas was the greatest dramatic soprano of her generation, possessed of an electrifying stage presence and supremely able to communicate the intensity of emotion that opera requires. Her personal life was almost as dramatic as the operas in which she sang. Her fiery temperament led her into feuds with opera managements and rivalries with other singers, while her glamour and her love affair with Onassis made her a regular subject of newspaper society and gossip columns. Much of the drama of Callas's life is conveyed in *Master Class*, both in Maria's personal reminiscences and in her interactions with her students. She is presented as a contradictory figure. She is proud and egotistical, rude and supercilious, yet she is also vulnerable and self-pitying. She is highly dedicated to her art, which she regards as sacred.

However, the character of the diva, although it supplies much of the entertainment in the play, is not its primary focus. *Master Class* is, most important, an exploration of the nature of dramatic singing; it is the playwright's interpretation of the secret of Callas's extraordinary success.

Maria's instruction to her students falls into two categories that she emphasizes again and again in the play. First, opera singing is a demanding profession. It requires hard work, discipline, and commitment over a lifetime. There are no shortcuts to success. Second, the singer must be able to totally inhabit the role she or he is singing. Whatever the emotion the character is experiencing, whether it is love, hate, rage, jealousy, joy, or sadness, the singer must fully experience it too. In order to do this, she must dig down into her own experience of life. Maria asks Sophie, for example, whether she has ever had her heart broken, because this is what her character, Amina in *La Sonnambula*, is singing about. Similarly, Maria asks Sharon if there is anything she would kill for—a man, perhaps, or a career? The question is important because murder is what Lady Macbeth is contemplating in the aria that Sharon is about to sing. If Sharon has not felt a similar desire herself, how can she sing about it? "You have to listen to something in yourself to sing this difficult music," Maria tells Sharon. Otherwise, the singer will merely produce a sequence of notes, which, even if technically correct, will fall short of what the operatic genre requires.

Maria's instruction calls on a concept developed by acting coach Lee Strasberg, known as "emotional memory," a concept in turn based on the "method" system of acting of the renowned director Konstantin Stanislavsky. The technique of emotional memory requires the actor to recall with his or her senses the precise atmosphere of a past activity. With this recall comes the emotion associated with the occasion. The recovered emotion is used by the actor (or the dramatic singer) as the equivalent of the emotion being experienced by the character in the play.

Dramatic Devices

The two acts of *Master Class* have a similar structure. In act 1, Maria's session with her first student is followed by a monologue in which Maria recalls significant moments in her life, including the moment when her lover Onassis asked her to bear his child and that of her triumphs at La Scala. The reminiscence forms the climax of the act. It is sparked by the aria that her student has been attempting, and this is also the cue for a recording of Maria Callas to be played, singing the same aria. Act 2 follows in parallel fashion: Maria's sessions with her two students are followed by a monologue, which again features Onassis and La Scala, and which also serves as the climax of the act. As in act 1, a recording of Callas plays, prompted by the same circumstances. The similarity in structure between the two acts gives shape to a play which has no plot in the usual sense of the word.

Since Maria is the only character who is developed fully, the success of the production rests on the ability of the actress who plays Maria. It is a demanding role, which was ably performed by Zoë Caldwell in the original production. She fully captured the quirky, domineering yet fragile nature of the diva.

Another dramatic device, appropriately enough given the subject matter, is music. Two Callas recordings are played, and the students also sing arias onstage. A poignant theatrical moment that illustrates the centrality of singing comes when Maria (the character onstage, that is, not Maria Callas on the recordings) attempts to sing a single line of music. She fails dismally; the stage directions read, "What comes out is a cracked and broken thing. A voice in ruins. It is a terrible moment." It is a reminder to the audience of the tragedy of Callas's life. Although she was blessed with a wonderfully expressive voice, by the time she was giving her master classes in 1971, it was only a shadow of its former glory.

Critical Context

Terrence McNally, who has written many plays for the Broadway stage, is a lifelong fan of opera and of Maria Callas. He first heard Callas sing on a recording in 1953, when he was a high school student in Texas, and he later heard her sing in person many times before her retirement from opera in 1965. McNally believed that the secret of Callas's ability to move her audience was that she identified so completely with the emotions of her characters. Her deep emotional involvement communicated itself to the audience and awakened similar emotions, whether of sorrow or joy, that they experienced in their own lives.

Master Class is not the only play McNally has written with operatic themes. In *The Lisbon Traviata* (pr. 1985, pb. 1986), two opera fans are in search of a recording of one of Callas's performances as Violetta in Verdi's *La Traviata* (1853). A recording was not known then to be in existence, although one has since been discovered. *The Lisbon Traviata* had only limited appeal, and it was with *Master Class* that McNally found a wider audience. The play ran from November, 1995, to June, 1997, on Broadway and received three Tony Awards. By 1997, there had been about forty productions of the play abroad.

Master Class is important because it re-creates on the stage, for a modern audience, a singer-actress of almost legendary status. Although there were some complaints from critics that McNally's quarrelsome, egotistical Maria was not historically accurate—unlike her fictional version, Callas conducted her master classes in a professional, helpful manner—the play nonetheless provides a compelling exploration of how great dramatic art is created.

Sources for Further Study

Ardoin, John. *Callas at Juilliard: The Master Classes*. Portland, Oreg.: Amadeus Press, 1998.

Brustein, Robert. "Stars and Their Gasses." *The New Republic* 214 (February 5, 1996): 27-28.

Franklin, Nancy. "Goddesses." *The New Yorker* 71 (November 27, 1995): 109-111.

Gurewitsch, Matthew. "Maria, Not Callas." *Atlantic Monthly* 280 (October, 1997): 102-107.

Kroll, Jack. "Concerto for Diva: *Master Class*." *Newsweek* 126 (November 13, 1995): 85.

Zinman, Toby Silverman, ed. *Terrence McNally: A Casebook*. New York: Garland, 1997.

Bryan Aubrey

THE MATCHMAKER

Author: Thornton Wilder (1897-1975)
Type of plot: Comedy
Time of plot: The 1880's
Locale: Yonkers and New York City
First produced: 1954, at the Royal Lyceum Theatre, Edinburgh, Scotland
First published: 1956, in *Three Plays*

Principal characters:
HORACE VANDERGELDER, a merchant of Yonkers, New York
DOLLY LEVI, a friend of his late wife
CORNELIUS HACKL and
BARNABY TUCKER, clerks in Vandergelder's store
IRENE MOLLOY, a milliner

The Play

The Matchmaker tells the story of a rich widower, Horace Vandergelder, who employs the services of a matchmaker, Dolly Levi, to find him a wife. While he is in pursuit of his own happiness, Vandergelder does his best to thwart the happiness of others, including his two overworked clerks, Cornelius Hackl and Barnaby Tucker, and his niece Ermengarde, who wants to marry Ambrose Kemper, a penniless artist. Act 1 takes place in Vandergelder's living quarters above his general store in Yonkers. In the opening scene, Vandergelder informs Ambrose that he will never be allowed to marry Ermengarde. That done, Vandergelder proceeds to outline his plans for the day, plans that include a trip to New York City to visit Irene Molloy, a widowed milliner whom he is thinking of marrying. While he is getting ready to go out, he is visited by a shady character named Malachi Stack, who is looking for a job. On an impulse, Vandergelder hires the man and sends him ahead to New York to book a hotel room.

Meanwhile, Ambrose tries to persuade Ermengarde to elope with him, but she will not hear of it. Mrs. Levi interrupts the couple to counsel caution, reminding Ambrose that Ermengarde stands to inherit a fortune if she does not disobey her uncle. She also informs them that Vandergelder might soften toward their situation because he himself is planning to marry. She then reveals her philosophy of "profit and pleasure," explaining that by arranging things for people she ekes out a living, but that her real pleasure is in making life more interesting. She says that she is like an artist who finds that nature is never completely satisfactory and must be corrected.

In the next scene the audience gets its first glimpse of Mrs. Levi and Vandergelder together. Although ostensibly she is operating as a matchmaker to find him a suitable bride, it is clear to the audience that she herself has her cap set for him and will probably use every trick at her disposal to catch him. In fact, in order to cool his ardor for

Irene Molloy, Mrs. Levi invents a new love interest for him, "Ernestina Simple," and promises to introduce them that evening at the Harmonia Gardens in New York. Meanwhile, Cornelius and Barnaby decide that it is high time to get out of Yonkers and have an adventure, so they light a fire under some canned goods until the cans explode, creating such a mess that the two clerks have no choice but to close the store and head for New York.

Act 2 takes place in Irene Molloy's hat shop. As the curtain rises, Irene is lamenting to her assistant, Minnie Fay, that she longs for some excitement in her life. At that point Cornelius and Barnaby, who have been wandering around town, enter the shop to avoid being seen by Vandergelder, whom they have just seen with Mrs. Levi in the park. Pleased by the unexpected intrusion, Irene helps them hide when Vandergelder appears in the shop a few minutes later. From their hiding places, they overhear Irene boast to Vandergelder that she knows a certain Cornelius Hackl, a wealthy young man-about-town who dines regularly at the Harmonia Gardens—misinformation supplied by Cornelius in an effort to impress her. Even Mrs. Levi tries to protect the young men from discovery, but a sneeze betrays them; Vandergelder, suspecting the worst, storms out, vowing to turn his attentions to Ernestina Simple. Irene insists that Cornelius treat them all to an evening on the town, complete with a fancy meal at the Harmonia Gardens. Act 2 ends with the clerks agreeing that, although they have no idea how they are going to pay for the evening ahead, they are, indeed, in the middle of a real adventure.

Act 3 takes place at the Harmonia Gardens, where Vandergelder and Malachi Stack arrive together, followed by Mrs. Levi with Ermengarde and Ambrose in tow. The moment Mr. Vandergelder spots them, he orders Malachi to see to it that Ambrose and Ermengarde are taken to the home of a spinster friend, Miss Flora Van Huysen, with a note instructing her to detain them until he arrives. Meanwhile, Cornelius, Barnaby, Irene, and Minnie arrive and are seated within earshot but not within view of Vandergelder, because a screen separates the two parties. At one point Vandergelder is unaware that he has dropped a purse full of money, and Malachi retrieves it and gives it to Cornelius, who is then able to splurge. Mrs. Levi then tells Vandergelder that Ernestina Simple has run off with another man. Before he has a chance to protest, she lets him know that if he has any designs on herself instead, she has no intention of marrying him. While he blusters in bewilderment, she keeps insisting on her opposition to such an idea—an idea that she has now firmly planted in his mind.

Act 3 continues in a farcical mode with all opportunities for confusion and concealment exploited. Toward the end of the act, Cornelius and Barnaby try to disguise themselves with items of clothing borrowed from Irene and Minnie in an attempt to deceive Vandergelder, but Cornelius is found out and fired. The act ends with Vandergelder having lost or alienated nearly everyone of any importance to him—a sad situation that Mrs. Levi makes clear to him in no uncertain terms.

The conflicts of act 3 are resolved happily in act 4, which takes place in the living room of Flora Van Huysen. It is clear from the start that Miss Van Huysen is no ally of Vandergelder and is only waiting for the chance to compensate for her own lost hopes by helping young lovers find happiness together. The act begins in confusion when Cornelius arrives with Barnaby, who is still dressed as a girl, and the two are mistaken for Ambrose and Ermengarde. Moments later, the real Ambrose and Ermengarde arrive, and in spite of the confusion of identities, Miss Van Huysen rushes to befriend them. Shortly thereafter, Mrs. Levi and Vandergelder arrive. It is obvious that Mrs. Levi's candor at the Harmonia Gardens has had its effect on Vandergelder's attitude, for he forgives the young people, gives them his blessing, and then asks Mrs. Levi to marry him. She agrees, and the play ends with the promise of marriage not only between Vandergelder and Mrs. Levi but also between Ambrose and Ermengarde, Cornelius and Irene, and, one suspects, Barnaby and Minnie.

Themes and Meanings

The Matchmaker is a play about accepting life, about the choice one has to make between living apart from it or participating fully in it. As Mrs. Levi says at the end of act 4: "There comes a moment in everybody's life when he must decide whether he'll live among human beings or not—a fool among fools or a fool alone. As for me, I've decided to live among them." It is Dolly Levi's return to the world that is at the heart of the play. Although the origins of the play go back to the early nineteenth century, the character of Dolly Gallagher Levi did not appear until Thornton Wilder introduced her in *The Matchmaker*, a revision of his own comedy *The Merchant of Yonkers* (pr. 1938, pb. 1939). Wilder had based this play on a comedy by Austrian playwright Johann Nestroy, *Einen Jux will er sich machen* (pr. 1842), which was in turn based upon an English original, *A Day Well Spent* (pr. 1835) by John Oxenford. By adding the character of the matchmaking widow and shifting the focus of the play to her "return to life," Wilder transformed a hackneyed farce based on mistaken identities and improbable plot twists into an affirmation of life in an age of doubt and confusion.

At first Dolly Levi's part in the play seems almost incidental; she appears to be simply a comic character whose interfering is pleasantly annoying and whose pursuit of Vandergelder is fairly obvious. Later, in the hat shop scene, she reveals herself less as a manipulative businesswoman than as a woman with heart whose purpose is to nudge destiny toward happy resolutions. Only at the end of the play, when her schemes begin to work for the greater happiness of all concerned, does she emerge as a character with a statement to make. It is not until moments before the play ends that viewers learn of Dolly's deceased husband, Ephraim, and of her deep feeling for him. After his death, her grief had turned her into a recluse, emotionally impoverished and only passively involved in the world. Through a revealing monologue in which she "talks" to Ephraim, the audience learns that she would retreat to her room in the evenings, drink a rum toddy, thank God that she was independent, and fall asleep a "perfectly contented woman." After two years, she says, an oak leaf fell out of her Bible, a leaf she had placed there the day her husband asked her to marry him, "a perfectly good oak leaf—but without color and without life." Suddenly she saw herself as that oak leaf—dried up, tearless, with nothing to look forward to. At that moment, she decided to "rejoin the human race."

"Yes, we're all fools," she says, "and we're all in danger of destroying the world with our folly. But the surest way to keep us out of harm is to give us the four or five human pleasures that are our right in the world,—and that takes a little *money*!" Money is Wilder's other major theme in this play, and Mrs. Levi delivers his message this way: "The difference between a little money and no money at all is enormous—and can shatter the world. And the difference between a little money and an enormous amount of money is very slight—and that, also, can shatter the world."

It is not Mrs. Levi who has the last word but Barnaby; she urges him, as the youngest person present, to make explicit to the audience the moral of the play. Barnaby, whose part has been relatively minor, now steps forth as the play's spokesman and states in simple terms a truth and a blessing: that happiness resides in an equal balance between wishing one were at home when one is caught in the middle of an adventure and wishing one were having an adventure when one is stuck at home.

Dramatic Devices

The Matchmaker is at once a parody of nineteenth century Viennese farces and a tribute to them. Thornton Wilder understood the appealing comic irony of scenes in which characters divided by a screen are unaware of each other's presence or in which characters are unaware of others hiding in a nearby closet. The playwright used such familiar devices to make a fresh point. Stock devices—trap doors, concealed characters, mistaken identity—are used to advance the theme that it is only immersion in life, regardless of its foolishness, that brings joy. Those who sit back and watch—as most of the characters do at the beginning of the play—become cynical, detached, and unhappy.

Those who immerse themselves in life have little time to waste analyzing it, for they are too busy living it. Dolly Levi's return to life is symbolized by her return to the Harmonia Gardens, a place of enormous vitality and excitement. All sorts of people dine there, and there is music and gaiety and dancing—a scene of almost frenzied activity when compared with the hothouse solitude of Miss Van Huysen's house or Mrs. Levi's lonely room near Trinity Church.

Another convention Wilder puts to good use is that of introducing several couples who, after overcoming many obstacles or putting up much resistance, end up in each other's arms. In a play titled *The Matchmaker*, one expects the presence not only of a character eager to arrange matches but also of several couples either eager or reluctant to be matched. Wilder's matchmaker is able to satisfy the needs of heart, head, and purse and, in the end, to upset convention but surprise no one by reserving the best arrangement for herself.

Finally, Wilder uses scene changes effectively to give the play the momentum it needs to make its point. Vandergelder's feed and grain store in act 1 symbolizes the world of plod and profit, in contrast to the world of pleasure and abandon symbolized by the Harmonia Gardens of act 3. The millinery shop in act 2 is respectability in conflict with scandal, since it is assumed by the upright patrons that the proprietress is a fallen woman. In contrast to this is Miss Van Huysen's home in act 4, the lonely retreat of an unhappy spinster. Because her home is also in contrast to the chaos that invades it, however, it provides the right atmosphere for Mrs. Levi's magic to work. In this setting, all conflicts can be resolved, and Mrs. Levi can deliver her soliloquy about life and money free from the distractions of a crowd of diners.

Critical Context

During his lifetime, Thornton Wilder was the object of much critical controversy. While critics such as Edmund Wilson praised him for his optimism, seeing in it an affirmation of the invincible human spirit, others deplored what they considered a lack of social consciousness. Although some dismiss Wilder as a literary lightweight, the undiminished popularity of his works and the apparent timelessness of his themes have prompted a reappraisal that has been largely favorable. Revivals of *Our Town* (pr., pb. 1938) have demonstrated that play's continuing ability to capture something of the paradoxical American spirit, that curious combination of hope and melancholy.

Those who know little about Wilder often approach him expecting to find Walt Disney and are surprised to find that he is closer in spirit to Walt Whitman. The message that emerges from all of his works is that human happiness is a matter of cooperating with destiny. In his Pulitzer Prize-winning novel *The Bridge of San Luis Rey* (1927), Wilder first expressed his faith in the logic behind destiny, and his later novels such as *The Ides of March* (1948), *The Eighth Day* (1967), and *Theophilus North* (1973) all illustrate his belief that it is this faith that gives humankind the power to temper logic with humanity and thus create its own myths. *The Skin of Our Teeth* (pr., pb. 1942) is the most obvious example of Wilder's mythmaking in dramatic form, but the presence of myth also explains the continuing appeal of both *Our Town* and *The Matchmaker.*

Because he broke with stage convention by using a virtually empty set in *Our Town*, Wilder made the play's mythical qualities more apparent than they are in *The Matchmaker*, where they are obscured by the trappings of Viennese farce. Nevertheless, he manages to make it abundantly clear, through the use of soliloquies, that Mrs. Levi's skill as a matchmaker stems from her understanding of the need for compromise between the logic of viewing the world as foolish and the wisdom of accepting its foolishness. Because of his experimentation with staging and structure, not to mention the enduring popularity of his unfashionable optimism, Thornton Wilder has had a profound influence on the modern American theater.

Sources for Further Study

Blank, Martin. *Thornton Wilder: New Essays*. West Cornwall, Conn.: Locust Hill, 1999.

Burbank, Rex J. *Thornton Wilder.* New York: Twayne, 1978.

Castronovo, David. *Thornton Wilder.* New York: Ungar, 1986.

Dekoster, Katie, ed. *Thornton Wilder.* San Diego: Greenhaven, 1998.

Grebanier, Bernard. *Thornton Wilder.* Minneapolis: University of Minnesota Press, 1964.

Lifton, Paul. *Vast Encyclopedia: The Theatre of Thornton Wilder.* Westport, Conn.: Greenwood Press, 1995.

Schroeder, Patricia R. "Thornton Wilder: Disparate Moments and Repetitive Patterns." In *The Presence of the Past in Modern American Drama*. Teaneck, N.J.: Fairleigh Dickinson University Press, 1989.

Wilder, Thornton. *Conversations with Thornton Wilder.* Edited by Jackson Bryer. Jackson: University of Mississippi Press, 1992.

Thomas Whissen

THE MEMORANDUM

Author: Václav Havel (1936-)
Type of plot: Satire
Time of plot: The 1960's
Locale: Prague
First produced: 1965, at the Balustrade Theatre, Prague, Czechoslovakia
First published: *Vyrozumění*, 1966 (English translation, 1967)

Principal characters:
JOSEF GROSS, the director of an office
JAN BALÁŠ, his deputy
ZDENĚK MAŠÁT, the chief of a translation office
JAN KUNC, a Ptydepe linguist
HELENA, a bureaucratic official
MARIE, a secretary in the translation office
HANA, Gross's secretary
J. V. PERINA, the Ptydepe instructor
VÁCLAV KUBŠ, a silent man of unspecified importance
JIRKA, the office spy
IVO KALOUS, a small bureaucrat

The Play

The curtain rises on three similar offices placed side by side on the stage. They differ in the arrangement of furniture and so on, but, as Václav Havel says, the atmosphere in each is exactly the same. Gross, the director of one of the offices, enters and begins to sort his mail. He throws some away, then halts in surprise when he opens one letter. He begins to read aloud from the letter, which seems to be written in some nonsense language. Baláš and Kubš enter the office and Baláš explains to his boss that this letter is written in Ptydepe, a new experimental bureaucratic language which Baláš himself has ushered into use at Gross's office without the latter's knowledge. Gross, understandably, is taken aback at this effrontery, yet what surprises him most is that a language which so few bureaucrats can understand should be introduced into the bureaucracy as an efficiency measure. Gross is left with a document that may be very important, yet which he cannot read. Hana, his secretary, informs him that a translation office has been installed in order to deal with such problems.

After a short scene 2, in which the audience witnesses a Ptydepe class in progress, the action shifts to the translation office. Getting the translation proves to be no easy matter. Trying to explain his problem to Mašát, the head of the translation office, Gross is constantly interrupted by people coming in and going out. It seems that Mašát, and most of the other officials as well, have only one thing on their mind: lunch. Besides the fact that Gross simply cannot get Mašát to pay attention to him, it seems that he has stepped into another, totally incomprehensible world: A man of tradition and humanist culture, he is constantly addressed in the familiar by Helena, a total stranger, which is socially unacceptable in polite Czech speech.

Getting the text translated will be an impossible task. Mašát cannot allow the text to be translated for Gross until he has official permission from another bureau. Permission, on the other hand, cannot be granted until this latter bureau knows what is in the Ptydepe text, and they cannot read Ptydepe. Gross, it seems, is the only person who can hand over the text for translation, but he cannot do so without permission from this second bureau—and so it goes: a vicious circle.

Gross finally decides to go about the matter in an unofficial way. Playing up a bit to Marie, the translation secretary, he proposes that she translate the text for him on the sly. Jirka, the office spy (concealed in the wall), is privy to this exchange, unfortunately for Gross and Marie.

Gross, understandably, wants to do away with Ptydepe. Baláš, however, backed by the ominously ever-silent Kubš, overrides Gross's determination in scene 4 with a bit of three-penny blackmail. Gross now "realizes" how indispensable Baláš is to him, especially as far as Ptydepe is concerned, and proposes that they run the office on an equal footing. This short scene is not yet complete when Baláš subtly declares himself the new chief of the office, and Gross agrees to become his deputy.

In scene 5, the new deputy takes part in Ptydepe class and fails miserably to understand the basics of this incomprehensible tongue. Unable to learn Ptydepe, Gross resumes the sisyphean labor of trying to get his text translated. He returns to the translation office and finds the same confusion and party atmosphere as in scene 3. Again unable to get anyone's attention, inundated by the devolution of conversation into blabbering Ptydepe, Gross finally screams out "Quiet!" Everyone freezes. Gross, relieved that at last someone is listening to him, does not realize that Baláš has just entered from behind with Kubš. This is the reason for the sudden stillness. Gross continues his tirade against the vicious circle of Ptydepe, inveighing against the new language in no uncertain terms—still unaware of Baláš's presence. At the end of the scene, Gross dutifully confesses his "crime" of little faith and bureaucratic sabotage and is fired by Baláš. Jirka, the office spy, is named Baláš's new deputy.

The increased duties of office head, however, are beginning to weigh upon Baláš. Having to deal with Ptydepe himself now, he is beginning to see the difficulties that Gross originally faced. In the seventh scene, when Gross arrives to finalize the details of his expulsion, Baláš reconsiders and offers Gross the now-vacant post of office spy.

Now the fortunes of Gross begin to rise as those of Ptydepe continue to fall. The number of Ptydepe students has dwindled to one, as the audience learns in scene 8. In scene 9, there occurs a curious, intimate exchange between Gross and Marie. The secretary of the translation department, ever sympathetic to the director fallen from grace, tells him that she has found a position for him at the theater where she has a brother. Gross is moved, yet declines with thanks, as Baláš has made him his deputy once again. He does not particularly relish this, as the matter of blackmail, which Baláš holds over his head, still clouds his future. Marie, with naïve faith, is sure that all will come out right in the end. Gross gently scolds her naïveté, as his own humanistic leanings and intellectual, dreamy nature have only won him trouble in this practical world. At the end of the scene, Marie translates Gross's letter from Ptydepe. Ironically enough, it is a note from higher-ups expressing satisfaction with Gross and praising him for his fight against "anti-humanistic" Ptydepe.

Gross demands his position back. Baláš hands it over with melancholy, yet characteristic sangfroid, and Gross is once again director. However, nothing has really changed in this bureaucratic morass. In scene 11, by another bureaucratic edict, Ptydepe is replaced with a new artificial language called Chorukor, which, although based on completely different linguistic principles, promises to be just as incomprehensible and inefficient as the fake tongue it replaces.

At the conclusion of the play, Marie, fired from her post for her unauthorized translation of Gross's missive (which Jirka, renamed office spy, witnessed), asks her friend for some help. Gross, however, afer a long, moving speech, in which he cites *Hamlet*, refuses her petition and goes to lunch with the rest of the bureaucrats.

Themes and Meanings

The Memorandum is a satire on the bureaucratic system of the former socialist countries of Eastern and Central Europe. Despite the boasts of the planned economies of socialist countries during the Cold War era, it was no secret that they were far behind the capitalist West in production and economic vitality. As with all dogmatic systems, so in Marxism it is forbidden to acknowledge the failures of the system. Thus, socialist states covered up their basically inefficient structures with the complicated façade of bureaucracy in an attempt at least to look busy. The socialist paper mill is noted for the absurdities it grinds out, for finding "work" for people who must work, even when no real work is to be found. Such absurdity is the main theme of *The Memorandum*, which centers on a bureaucratic language that no one can understand, invented in the name of "efficiency," the invention of which in turn spawns the creation of a "translation office" which in practice is empowered to translate nothing.

The Memorandum is a comic play, yet its humor is the same as can be found in Prague native Franz Kafka's *Die Verwandlung* (1915; *Metamorphosis*). The comic quality of Gross's bureaucratic nightmare rapidly devolves into a very vicious circle indeed, when the humanistic hero, who throughout the play has struggled with a certain dignity against the dehumanizing situation, in the final moments accedes to the absurdity and sheds the last remnants of his self-respect in favor of the easy way out. *The Memorandum* is a play about incompetence—a chilling incompetence that destroys human beings.

Dramatic Devices

Ptydepe (pronounced "petty dip"), the language invented by the bureaucracy, is the play's chief dramatic device. It stands between people and their ability to fulfill themselves through labor, and creates a situation in which a person, the animal who talks, is no longer the master of language but rather its slave. Havel's bureaucratic tongue owes much to the governmental "Newspeak" in George Orwell's prophetic novel *Nineteen Eighty-Four* (pb. 1949), yet it is all the more threatening in that it is not made up of familiar, if truncated, words, but is a totally alien jumble that allows one no familiar entry point into its disturbing linguistic maze.

Havel built his satire on communist bureaucracy around the incomprehensible artificial tongue in order to emphasize as concretely as possible the inhuman, inefficient, and absurd nature of the bureaucratic system itself. Communication is the basic requirement of all human enterprise, and when the possibilities of communication are minimized or destroyed, cooperation and progress necessarily come to a standstill. All "business" in such a situation loses touch with reality and becomes nothing more than an empty ritual, a fake. When an institution or government is unable to order its own affairs, it cannot pretend to order the affairs of others. Thus *The Memorandum* is not only a satire that makes light of communist bureaucracy; indeed, it is a satire on the communist system itself, a system which subordinates all to ideology, including logic.

This point is further emphasized with the introduction of Chorukor, the new artificial language of bureaucracy which is to replace the "outmoded" Ptydepe. One might think that with the failure of Ptydepe, the bureaucracy would have learned its lesson and resigned from all such foolishness. The introduction of Chorukor shows that, on the contrary, the bureaucratic system of communism is already so soaked through with incompetence, absurdity, and corruption that it is unable to find a way out of a situation that it recognizes as unproductive.

This emphasis on the vicious circle of red tape about which Gross complains, and which cannot be escaped in a society such as the one described by Havel, is the main reason behind the introduction of the new language in scene 11, as it really plays no role in the denouement of the play. Also suggested by Chorukor is the ease with which a communist society dispenses with the "truths" of yesterday, replacing them with the new "truths" of today. (This process is excellently demonstrated by the workings of the "Ministry of Truth" in *Nineteen Eighty-Four.*) It is also possible to find a subtle pun suggesting the excessive docility and lack of independence of Gross's society (and, in the end, of Gross himself) in the name of the new language, as the word *chór* in Czech means "chorus."

Further adding to the atmosphere of threat is the unseen stage presence of the "office spy." The audience hears other characters converse with him time and again, yet he is seen onstage only rarely. He crawls out of the woodwork like an ominous cockroach from time to time, yet his (sometimes vocal) presence can be felt in all three identically arranged offices which make up the stage scenery. He is a comic figure, if threateningly so. His clownishness (he emerges from the wall backside first) is a jarring picture which thrusts the following question at the audience: If these people are so absurd and inefficient, so comical in their incapacities, what is it that is making the audience so afraid of them, so willing to put up with the boobish eye of Big Brother in the casement? This dramatic device, which can perhaps be seen as the cornerstone of absurdity in *The Memorandum*, suggests that the common people in such a society are downtrodden because they agree to be used as doormats by the laughable dolts who "govern" them. As in Polish poet Stanisław Barańczak's verse "Ci mężczyźni, tak potężni" ("Those men, so powerful"), *The Memorandum* makes the point that, if only "we" would for a moment cease to be so afraid of "them" at the top, we would see that it is really *they* who are most afraid.

Critical Context

The Memorandum must be understood in the context of the everyday situation of the citizens of the former socialist countries of Central and Eastern Europe during the Cold War era. As is clear from the numerous "stupid policeman" jokes which color the contemporary humor of these peoples, Czechs, Slovaks, Poles, and Hungarians were accustomed to looking on their governmental systems with a large dose of satire and irony. However, as mentioned above, as incompetent as the socialist bureaucracies of Eastern and Central Europe were, they were not to be taken lightly. In addition to the external threat of reprisal against nonconforming citizens (which saw Václav Havel imprisoned several times), there existed also a no less serious internal threat, that which destroys Gross: the danger of acquiescing to the system and renouncing one's own inner self for the external peace of an obedient, well-fed beast of burden.

Sources for Further Study

Goetz-Stankiewicz, Markéta. *The Silenced Theatre: Czech Playwrights Without a Stage*. Buffalo, N.Y.: University of Toronto Press, 1979.

_______. "Václav Havel: A Writer for Today's Season." *World Literature Today* 55 (Summer, 1981): 389-393.

Goetz-Stankiewicz, Markéta, and Phyllis Carey, eds. *Critical Essays on Václav Havel*. New York: G. K. Hall, 1999.

Kriseova, Eda. *Václav Havel: The Authorized Biography*. Collingdale, Pa.: Diane, 1993.

Schonberg, Michal. "A Biographical Note on Václav Havel." *Modern Drama* 23 (March, 1980): 1-5.

Schumschida, Walter. "Václav Havel: Between the Theatre of the Absurd and Engaged Theatre." In *Fiction and Drama in Eastern and Southeastern Europe: Evolution and Experiment in the Postwar Period*, edited by Henrik Birnbaum and Thomas Eckman. Columbus, Ohio: Slavica Publishers, 1980.

Trensky, Paul I. *Czech Drama Since World War II*. White Plains, N.Y.: M. E. Sharpe, 1978.

Charles S. Kraszewski

METAPHYSICS OF A TWO-HEADED CALF
A Tropical Australian Play in Three Acts

Author: Stanisław Ignacy Witkiewicz (1885-1939)
Type of plot: Surrealist
Time of plot: The 1920's
Locale: British New Guinea and Australia
First produced: 1928, at the Teatr Nowy, Poznan, Poland
First published: Metafizyka dwugłowego cielęcia, 1962 (*Metaphysics of a Two-Headed Calf*, 1972)

Principal characters:
SIR ROBERT CLAY, the governor of New Guinea
LADY LEOCADIA CLAY, his wife, forty-eight years old
PATRICIANELLO, the sixteen-year-old son of Lady Leocadia Clay
PROFESSOR EDWARD MIKULIN-PECHBAUER, a famous bacteriologist
LUDWIG, PRINCE VON UND ZU TURN UND PARVIS, thirty years old
MIRABELLA, his half-sister, eighteen years old
JACK RIVERS, the president of the Gold Stock Exchange of Kalgoorlie, Western Australia
HOODED FIGURE, a tall sinister character
KING, the chief of the Aparura clan
OLD HAG, a hunchbacked old wreck in rags

The Play

The first act of *Metaphysics of a Two-Headed Calf* opens in a room of Governor Clay's mansion in Port Moresby, the capital of British New Guinea. Open double doors reveal a thicket of tropical plants covered with gigantic pink, red, and blue flowers swaying in the late afternoon breeze. Lady Leocadia sits reading, dressed in an unfastened white dressing gown, while close to her, in a small chair, Patricianello, dressed in crimson tights, is gluing together cubes of cardboard. Lady Leocadia expresses annoyance that Patricianelo is playing with the cubes, or "thingamajigs," while Patricianello tells her about his dream of his "other" mother, the "real" one, young and beautiful, who held him on her lap kissing him. It is revealed that the governor, who has gone on an expedition to Fly River to add to his collection of exotic bugs, although supplied with Mikulin's serum against tropical fever, may be dead. As Patricianello keeps reading and muttering phrases from a book on empiricism, Professor Mikulin-Pechbauer, dressed in a black coat, enters and says that the report about Governor Clay has been confirmed. Patricianello thereupon accuses his mother of being Mikulin's mistress and Mikulin of killing his father. Prince Parvis enters, carrying a riding whip and dressed in expedition clothes and pith helmet; he is followed by King Aparura, who is naked except for his loincloth, headdress, and wild hair. Invited to make himself a drink, he stands by the sideboard, tossing them off one after another.

A struggle ensues among these curious characters for Patricianello's future as each envisions what Patricianello should become. Both Leocadia and Mikulin want him to be an extraordinary individual entirely their own, although it is totally irrelevant to them whether he is to be a criminal or cabinet minister. His cousin Parvis, however, reminds Patricianello of the potential of total freedom and independence of will and promises to whip Patricianello into shape. Patricianello is more concerned with his identity: It is revealed that he is Mikulin's son from an affair with Leocadia. At first horrified that the governor is not his father, Patricianello soon realizes that he must create his own reality; he asserts that truth is relative.

Meanwhile, all are aware that they must leave Port Moresby as soon as possible now that Mikulin's serum has been proven worthless by the governor's death. Patricianello, however, expresses a desire to end up as a bug in the governor's collection "stuck on a pin and chloroformed." At these suicidal thoughts, Parvis starts lashing at Leocadia and Mikulin with his whip, and he tempts Patricianello back to life by promising him his half-sister Mirabella as a new "thingamajig." Leocadia, jealous at this new complication, tells Patricianello that she will remain forever in his dreams. Mikulin produces a photograph of Leocadia as a young woman, and Patricianello recognizes the "real" mother from his dreams. Parvis, however, draws out another photograph, that of his sister Mirabella, and Patricianello sees an exact likeness of Leocadia as a young woman. At this Patricianello swoons, crying, "She's alive." King Aparura and Parvis make a pact to bring up Patricianello together.

In the last scene of the first act, six sailors bring in the governor's corpse while Leocadia goes into perfunctory hysterics. At the same time six Papuans come in and prostrate themselves before King Aparura. Parvis orders Patricianello to take off his red tights and change into more proper attire. Fear of being infected by the governor's corpse forces everyone to make a hasty retreat, and all including the king hasten to catch the boat to Sydney, while the six Papuans remove the governor's body. Thus the first act ends with the packing off of Patricianello.

Act 2 opens at dusk in a room of the Hotel Australia in Sydney. Leocadia, in a white nightcap and with a compress covering her face, lies dying while Patricianello, now dressed in a suit, sits in an armchair reading to her. Leocadia interrupts to assure him that she loved him the most, despite her husband the governor, her lover Mikulin, and her other lover, young Parvis. Patricianello regrets that he cannot believe in Parvis's philosophy and, bereft of all fathers, must now face growing up alone. Leocadia's death agony is long and tortured; she feels the bacteria with which she has been inoculated by Mikulin attacking her brain. Mikulin enters, and Patricianello threatens to kill him for killing his mother; Mikulin reveals that he has prepared a new serum, which, although too late to save Leocadia, may save the rest. Parvis enters with Mirabella, dressed in a tailored suit. Patricianello finds her pretty, but, despondent at his mother's imminent death, he says that love has no charm for him, adding that everything in life "comes either too early or too late." Parvis reassures him that Mirabella will take his mother's place, and since Mirabella seduced Jack Rivers, president of the Kalgoorlie Gold Exchange, who has been skimming the profits from the mines, their financial security is assured. At this, the king, now nattily dressed in a gray suit, enters with Jack Rivers, who suggests that they leave for the gold mines as soon as possible.

As Leocadia lies in her final death struggle, a hooded figure in a brown coat enters and announces that he is Kala-Azar; at this Leocadia dies, meowing like a cat. Mikulin then proceeds to give all present a shot of his new serum. All agree to leave for the desert, including the hooded figure, who will pack himself into a trunk. An uncertain Patricianello asks Rivers to help him learn how to love Mirabella, and he agrees to share Mirabella with him. Parvis, attempting to retain control of Patricianello, tells Mirabella to change her clothes so that they can look at her "from a different viewpoint," and she returns wearing a "devilishly fancy ball gown."

At this vision Mikulin begs Patricianello to give him Mirabella in order that he might relive his love for Leocadia. The figure, too, is bewitched and protests that he cannot pack himself in the trunk; as the sounds of Oriental music played on a piano emerge from the next room, the figure sweeps Mirabella into a wild dance. Captivated by Mirabella as the others are, Patricianello says that Mikulin must die so that he, Patricianello, will be free to start another life. At this, the figure, while gyrating wildly in the dance, grabs Mikulin and, still dancing, strangles him. Patricianello tells the figure that he feels as if he has committed a crime but nevertheless has a completely clear conscience. Now that he is an orphan, he asserts that Mirabella is the "real mother" he saw in his dream, and when Mirabella kisses him, he collapses in a dead faint. Parvis in the meantime drags in a trunk and orders the figure to pack himself in. Two porters take out Patricianello's unconscious body and the trunk; the king offers Mirabella his arm, and they and Rivers go out. The old hag who played the piano approaches Parvis, who pays her for "her niece."

Act 3 opens in the red plain of a desert extending to the horizon. A road cuts diagonally across, while in the distance the glow of a city can be detected. To the right stands a signpost with two signs pointing to "Kalgoorlie" and the "Desert," while to its left stands an open telephone booth. Patricianello enters, dressed in khaki, with pith-helmet and knapsack; in a Hamlet-like speech he debates whether "to wait or not to wait." Rivers, dressed in similar attire, also wanders in, and it appears that they must leave as soon as the others arrive for fear of the police since Rivers has forged the signatures of Mikulin, Leocadia, and Patricianello.

Patricianello calls Rivers an "ordinary scoundrel, not a metaphysical one," and asserts that his partnership with Rivers regarding Mirabella is finished. Soon Parvis and Mirabella enter as well, dressed in similar attire, and Parvis shoots Rivers, boasting that he has forged a passport for himself in Rivers's name so that all proceeds from the mines will become his property. Parvis also mentions that he saw Leocadia and Mikulin in town racing in a car at breakneck speed; they should arrive at any moment. Sir Robert Clay, the governor, wearing a top hat and tails, wanders in unnoticed and sits next to the hooded figure, who has emerged from the trunk and is sitting by the signpost. In the meantime Patricianello argues with Parvis over the meaning of life and rejects Parvis's pragmatic viewpoint, declaring that in his soul he is an artist, although he realizes that he will probably never be one. At this point Parvis notices the governor, who assures him that he is not a "ghost" but indeed quite alive. Patricianello expresses his confusion, but the governor assures him that he is indeed his father and encourages him to assert his independence. Patricianello at this expresses hope that he will start writing, painting, or composing, since "bored automatons have to be entertained."

As Parvis, Mirabella, and Patricianello lie on the ground discussing metaphysical questions, a car driven by the old hag, with Mikulin and Leocadia in the front seat and King Aparura in back, all wearing fur coats, pulls up to the road sign. A battle of the fathers and mothers for the domination of their putative children ensues. Patricianello expresses his despair by pulling out a revolver and pointing it to his head; Leocadia scolds him for constantly playing with "thingamajigs." Mikulin kills Parvis, his second putative son, thus resolving the question "of whether or not to shoot one's own son."

The battle for Patricianello continues; despite Patricianello's desperate pleas that all he wants is to live out his own life with Mirabella, Mikulin asserts that he will live through Patricianello to be "the greatest representation of mankind." Thereupon, Mikulin, Leocadia, and the now debased king grab Patricianello, gag him, and load him into the car and drive off. As Mirabella protests that she loves Patricianello, the hooded figure reminds her that he is still there; throwing off his robe he is revealed to be identical to Patricianello. He and Mirabella face each other wordlessly. In the meantime, the governor stalks them, shoots down Mirabella, and, calling the figure "Murphy," goes to the telephone and orders that his car be sent around to Crossroads Number Eight. To comfort the now shivering figure, he pours the contents of a flask down the figure's throat. "Gin cordial," he says. "Do you a world of good, Murphy, my boy." The play ends with this gesture held until the lights go out.

Themes and Meanings

In *Metaphysics of a Two-Headed Calf*, Stanisław Ignacy Witkiewicz explores the complex relationships of a family viewed against the context of an aboriginal culture represented by King Aparura. From his expedition to Australia and New Guinea with anthropologist Bronisław Malinowski, Witkiewicz draws on his visual memories of a tropical landscape to render what he refers to as "tropical madness," a condition used by such characters as Mikulin, Rivers, and Parvis to justify cruelty and rapaciousness. In the world of tropical madness, brutality serves as a powerful stimulus to sexual desire, represented by Mirabella, who along with his whip is used by Parvis to excite and tempt the other characters into even further excesses.

In the background of the brutality and rapaciousness lurks the dread of the plague. Terror of the plague, called Kala-Azar, known in Hindi as the black disease, becomes the driving force of the play and is embodied in the second act by the hooded figure dressed in black who introduces himself as the special envoy of the Golden Frog. Even in the face of terror of the plague, the Europeans are driven by their lust to possess, as when the governor sets out to the pestilential Fly River to capture a rare water bug "with green abdomen and rosy little wings" for his prized collection. When Mikulin, after his experiments on Leocadia with his worthless serum, introduces a serum that will contain the plague, the figure Kala-Azar packs himself into a trunk and is taken along by Rivers and Parvis on their journey to outback Australia. This packing in of Kala-Azar suggests that the plague itself has been contained and controlled and can now be unpacked at will.

In contrast to the acquisitive rapaciousness of the Europeans, King Aparura and his Papuans have a preconceptual understanding of the world. In the first act the king presents a contrast to the white man's system of authority as he is surrounded by the prostrate Papuans while the governor's body, propped up in a lounge chair, is ignored in the feverish attempts to flee the plague. Even in the first act, however, the debasement of the king has begun as he tosses off the white man's gin fizzes. This debasement progresses act-by-act as he abandons his nakedness (which suggested that he had nothing to hide) and his king's headdress for an elegant suit in the second act and for tails and fur coat in the third as he crawls out from the backseat of Mikulin and Leocadia's car. He is thus co-opted to serve a system which is based on power controlled by lust and greed, in contrast to the power he enjoyed at the beginning of the play, based on a shared acknowledgment of the mystery of existence.

Patricianello, the adolescent child-witness of the play's events, represents the attempt to create a self within the context of shifting, ambiguous relationships, instability, and uncertainty. Patricianello, the calf of this play, attempts to construct reality—an undertaking imaged by the constructions of cardboard cubes with which he plays in the first act. Unlike the cardboard constructions, however, his creation of a self is undermined by uncertainty about his parentage and consequently about his very identity. His bewilderment is manipulated by his putative "real" fathers, the governor and Mikulin, as well as his "spiritual" fathers, Parvis, the king, and Rivers.

The end of each act finds Patricianello's futile attempts to become a free individual thwarted by the battle of parents trying to coerce their children into becoming images of automated beings. Further, once Patricianello has been packed off, the hooded figure discloses an image identical to Patricianello, but this split-image figure, representing Patricianello's continuous spiritual struggle, is also reduced by the governor, who kills Mirabella and pours gin fizzes down the throat of his putative son "Murphy." The chances of Patricianello to become an independent creative being are thus twice negated in the two-headed image of two calves destroyed by the putative fathers of civilization.

Dramatic Devices

Metaphysics of a Two-Headed Calf takes the spectator from the tropical setting of the governor's mansion in Port Moresby, New Guinea, to the first-class chic of the Hotel Australia in Sydney, to the final dreamlike red desert of outback Australia. The tropical thicket with brilliant gigantic pink, red, and blue flowers which serves as the backdrop for the colonial parlor, with its shutters and mosquito netting, juxtaposes the natural setting of King Aparura with the corruption of his naked state by the gin fizzes of the parlor sideboard. The appropriation of the tropics is manifested in the second act as Aparura appears dressed in a stylish suit. The hotel-room setting also presents a world in transit and transformation as the characters pack themselves in or are, like Patricianello, packed in.

The first two acts, played within the walls of illusionistic rooms, confine the characters to a reality where only a hint of the mysterious world appears in the brilliant hues of tropical vegetation, King Aparura's nakedness, or the prostrate Papuans. The third act, however, shifts the perspective of confinement to the infinite space of the desert extending to the horizon. At this point Witkiewicz increases elements of the irrational by placing a signpost pointing to Kalgoorlie to the right and the Desert—with the number 8, suggesting infinity—to the left. The misplaced telephone booth brings another touch of the surreal and irrational to the scene.

The image of the ghost parents coming to haunt their children in the third act shows both family and societal values disintegrating as the power-thirsty parents destroy any semblance of European cultural integrity through betrayal, and murder. Violent, illogical murders occur throughout the play as Witkiewicz flouts causality and forestalls any attempt to understand the psychology of the characters. The third act in particular abandons any semblance of the plot machinery set in motion in the first act, and the characters themselves show their awareness of the theatricality of the action by stepping out of character to comment on the absurdity of the play's events. "Red desert or flower creepers or luxury hotel, the setting doesn't change anything," says Mirabella, underscoring the extent to which the setting has become a theatrical expression of the diminished hopes of Patricianello and Mirabella. Indeed, the brilliant tonalities of the flowers and Patricianello's red tights fade with each succeeding act until there is an almost total absence of color in both landscape and costumes as the tonalities of gray, black, and brown in the third act project the drabness overpowering the expectations of the young calf Patricianello.

Critical Context

Metaphysics of a Two-Headed Calf is one of several plays in which Witkiewicz makes use of imagery and impressions from his expedition to New Guinea and Australia with social anthropologist Bronisław Malinowski. In these plays, Witkiewicz explores the cultural polarities between East and West and what he considers to be the plague of civilization thrust upon the primitive paradise by Europeans. Unsated by their conquests, the Europeans succumb to tropical madness. In *Pragmatyści* (pb. 1920, pr. 1921; *The Pragmatists*, 1971) Witkiewicz presents the character Plasfodor, who has kidnapped Princess Tsui, seduced her, and, still unsated, drunk her blood "through a straw made of dried Wu grass."

The mummified princess returns from the dead to take Plasfodor and the other Europeans to the edge of existence. In *Mister Price: Czyli, Bzik tropikalny* (pr. 1926;

Mr. Price: Or, Tropical Madness, 1972) Witkiewicz constructs a dream about British colonial life peopled by demented characters who may well have fabricated their madness as they eagerly revert to the status of beasts of prey, succumbing to the laws of the jungle. In the second act of *Tumor Mózgowicz* (pr., pb. 1921; *Tumor Brainiowicz*, 1980), Witkiewicz presents the representative reactions of the members of a European expedition to a tropical island: Sir Alfred Green plants the British flag for the glory of the empire; Iza wishes to make love to the islanders, not out of passion but a lust for power; and Tumor expresses fantasies about becoming the prince and ruler of the island.

These plays are linked not only thematically but also structurally, with sudden plot shifts, disruption of causal relationships, illogical action, and fantastic characters. Witkiewicz's theoretical writings advocating "Pure Form" for the theater outlined his attempt to project simultaneously themes of humanity's loneliness in the cosmos, death, sexual insatiability, the conflict between the artist and family or society, social decay, and the increasing mechanization of life. To shock spectators out of their complacency, Witkiewicz used dramatic devices such as exaggerated claustrophobic space, retardation and acceleration of action, the viewing of corpses, anachronistic visitors out of historical time, the spotlight effect, split-images, and the violation of laws of psychology, physics, and biology. Death, like time and space, becomes relative, and the dead, as in *Metaphysics of a Two-Headed Calf*, are likely to reappear in the next scene. Witkiewicz's representation of chaotic and contradictory events expresses the uncertainty of his many artist protagonists in a world in which material reality has been radically redefined by non-Euclidian geometry and Einsteinian physics. These concerns, given dramatic form with brilliant originality, have drawn increasing attention to Witkiewicz both as a precursor of the Theater of the Absurd and other movements in contemporary drama and as a significant dramatist in his own right.

Sources for Further Study

Dukore, Bernard F. "Spherical Tragedies and Comedies with Corpses: Witkacian Tragicomedy." *Modern Drama* 18 (September, 1975): 291-315.

Gerould, Daniel C. *Witkacy: Stanisław Ignacy Witkiewicz As an Imaginative Writer.* Seattle: University of Washington Press, 1981.

Gombrowicz, Witold. *Diary, 1961-1966*. Edited by Jan Kott. Evanston: Northwestern University Press, 1994.

Kott, Jan. "Witkiewicz: Or, The Dialectics of Anachronism." In *The Theater of Essence and Other Essays*. Evanston, Ill.: Northwestern University Press, 1984.

Miłosz, Czesław. "Stanisław Ignacy Witkiewicz: A Polish Writer for Today?" *Tri-Quarterly* 9 (Spring, 1967): 143-154.

Tarn, Adam. "Witkiewicz, Artaud, and the Theatre of Cruelty." *Comparative Drama* 3 (Fall, 1969): 162-168.

Thompson, Ewa M. *Witold Gombrowicz*. Boston: Twayne, 1979.

Christine Kiebuzinska

MISS LULU BETT
An American Comedy of Manners

Author: Zona Gale (1874-1938)
Type of plot: Comedy of manners
Time of plot: 1920
Locale: A middle-class home in a small American town
First produced: 1920, at the Belmont Theatre, New York City
First published: 1921

Principal characters:
LULU BETT, a thirty-three-year-old spinster who cooks and cleans for her sister's family
DWIGHT HERBERT DEACON, her brother-in-law, a dentist and justice of the peace
INA DEACON, her sister, Dwight's wife
MRS. BETT, mother of Lulu and Ina
NINIAN DEACON, Dwight's brother, an adventurer
MONONA, Dwight's younger daughter
DI, Dwight's older daughter
MR. CORNISH, a family friend of the Deacons

The Play

Dwight Deacon looks forward to capping his day as a dentist and justice of the peace by sitting down to a family meal cooked by his wife's sister Lulu, a spinster who drudges for his family to earn her keep. However, his spoiled younger daughter Monona has been snitching cookies and refuses the creamed salmon. Lulu is asked to prepare milk toast for Monona, is reprimanded for buying a pink tulip in a pot for the center of the table, and is squelched when she tries to answer Dwight's question about the price of canned salmon. The crotchety Mrs. Bett, mother of Lulu and Dwight's wife Ina, has to be coaxed to the table. Elder daughter Di finally arrives, accompanied by Mr. Cornish, with whom she is flirting at the expense of her infatuated schoolmate Bobby. The tongue-tied Cornish clumsily tries to express his respect for Lulu, but every compliment misfires. Dwight announces that next week will bring a visit from Ninian, a brother he has not seen in twenty years.

A week later, Lulu is making apple pies and Ninian engages her in conversation. He sees how shabbily the others treat her. Lulu's responses show both a quick wit and feelings of inferiority. Ninian invites her out to dinner and a show that evening. Dwight and Ina agree to come along. As the family gathers, Ninian jokingly passes the time by reciting marriage vows and Lulu plays along. It dawns on them that since Dwight is a justice of the peace, they are now legally married. Ninian proposes that he and Lulu depart for Savannah together right after the theater.

Act 2 is set on the Deacons' side porch a month later. Dwight and Ina are manipulated by their daughters, whose behavior has become more obnoxious without Lulu's steadying influence. Suddenly, Lulu arrives. She left Ninian when he confessed that he might have a long-lost wife somewhere. Yet she insists that she loves him still and that he loves her. Dwight sets a condition for taking her back into the household: She must not disgrace the family by revealing the possible bigamy but must let people think that she is to blame for the failure of her marriage to Ninian.

The following evening Dwight lies to his daughters: "The truth is Lulu's husband has tired of her and sent her home." Then Lulu enters and asks Dwight for his brother's address in Oregon. Lulu displays a new assertiveness as she presses Dwight to write a letter asking Ninian to confirm whether he was indeed previously married.

A week later Lulu and Cornish sing together at the piano. She can express herself while Dwight and Ina are away on a trip. An unopened letter from Ninian awaits Dwight's return, but Mrs. Bett opens it to reveal Ninian's proof that he had indeed been married and thus that he really wanted Lulu and had not invented an excuse to get rid of her. Cornish proposes marriage, but Lulu is evasive. Lulu prevents Di's attempt to elope with Bobby. When Dwight and Ina return, Lulu stands up to Dwight to salvage her pride, but he reduces her to silence again by saying that Ninian could be jailed for bigamy if others learn the truth.

The published play offers two versions of act 3. In the revised text, written two weeks into the run and substituted for an ending that audiences had found too dark, Lulu leaves the house determined to make her own way in the world. Ninian arrives in time to catch her. Having tracked down proof that his first wife died, Ninian can offer Lulu an honest future as his wife. The original act 3 is set in Cornish's piano store. Lulu comes to say good-bye on her way out of town. In this version, the letter from Ninian includes a lawyer's letter testifying that his first wife is alive. Cornish proposes marriage, and Lulu will consider it eventually, but first she must go away to see life through her own eyes and to make her own choices.

Themes and Meanings

The subtitle of the published play, *An American Comedy of Manners*, signals the ironic tone of the work. The term "comedy of manners" implies sparkling drawing-room repartee, but the verbal interactions in this middle-class domestic setting, presumably in Zona's Gale's native Wisconsin, achieve their comic effect by means of their utter banality. In the first scene, for example, Dwight puts on patriarchal airs yet harps on the food and the cost of small items and then declares: "The conversation at my table must not deal with domestic matters." Ina's frequent (mis)corrections of Dwight's mispronunciations are an amusing inversion of the sophisticated wordplay in traditional comedies of manners. The first two scenes of act 2 contain sequences of virtually identical dialogue spoken by the same characters, a forceful yet humorous illustration of the smallness of these characters' lives. Thus, the play might well be described as a satire on small-town American, middle-class life, emphasizing the limited horizons, lack of imagination, self-delusion, excessive concern for what others might think and the selfish pursuit of petty comforts.

Compounding the limitations of this middle-class mentality were some generally conflicted attitudes about the place of women in the changing American social landscape of the early twentieth century. Although women had begun entering the American workforce even before World War I, spinsterhood was viewed as an embarrassing circumstance. Many families in the 1920's still harbored "maiden aunts" who had never held outside jobs. As a single woman (until she was fifty-three) who supported herself by writing, Zona Gale understood firsthand the social dynamics of spinsterhood. While Miss Lulu Bett's strength of character and dramatic development ensure that this play will be examined as a portrayal of conditions faced by women in the early twentieth century, one might fold this concern into the larger problem of people whose potential is stifled by various restrictions: the lack of education, having to care for an ailing family member, racial quotas, or economic barriers.

Family relationships are an interesting feature of this play. Well before psychologists had explained certain behaviors, Zona Gale demonstrated them in action. Dwight and Ina make the most basic mistakes of parenting in the inconsistency with which they make and apply rules for their daughters, "performin' like a pair of weathercocks" in Mrs. Bett's view. Dwight and Ina do not serve as role models, as their own behavior contradicts the standards they expect of the children. Sibling rivalries are shown, notably between the daughters Di and Monona, but also between brothers Dwight and Ninian and to a lesser extent between Ina and Lulu. Mrs. Bett gives little indication that she is anything other than a dependent, querulous old woman—until she twice releases a brief torrent of pent-up memory that hints at a generation's hardship that enabled the middle-class comforts available to her remaining children.

Dramatic Devices

As a political and social activist involved in reform movements, Zona Gale had a broad agenda to create a climate in which people could be enlightened and uplifted. Yet, her dramatic method avoided didacticism. She allowed her characters to be themselves in ordinary circumstances, and audiences could draw their own moral lessons from the attitudes and behaviors on display. It could be argued that *Miss Lulu Bett* approaches melodrama in the polarity between unsympathetic and sympathetic characters.

Dwight might be a stock melodramatic villain, except that he is blissfully unaware of how awful he is. His mask of joviality allows him to get away with mendacity, vulgarity, hypocrisy, insults, and patronizing exploitation of others. His lack of self-awareness is laughable even as it is horrifying in the hurt it causes him to inflict. Even when he is most cruel, he sees himself as a paragon of generosity. The docile Lulu appears to be little match for him at first, especially as she sees herself as having nothing to offer anyone, apart from her cooking. Yet her finer impulses as well as the mettle that lies dormant within her are suggested early in the play. Dwight criticizes her for spending money on the potted pink tulip she has placed in the center of the table. Later in the scene, while Dwight is ranting about something else, Lulu reenters and calmly throws the flowerpot out the window. Still later, Lulu wears the tulip, which she has picked and pinned to her dress, a small act of defiance that prepares for her growing self-confidence once Ninian begins paying attention to her. The play abounds with many such artful bits of business that work subtly to enhance characterizations and plot points, but Gale was also not above deploying such time-tested melodramatic devices as keeping a crucial letter unopened and visible to the audience throughout a scene. The mock marriage that turns out to be binding is another hokey device that proves both credible and theatrically amusing in Gale's hands.

Critical Context

In its basic plot structure, *Miss Lulu Bett* is a Cinderella story: The good-hearted young woman has been virtually enslaved by her domineering, self-serving brother-in-law and sister, with the passive assistance of the other family members. Her trap is sprung by a Prince Charming of sorts, but a truly happy ending depends upon her learning to make her own choices, whether or not they will involve a man. The dramatic arc of Lulu's gradual progress toward discovering her own self-worth—not defined in terms of what she contributes to the domestic comfort of others, but as an individual—has led some critics to compare the character to Nora in Henrik Ibsen's *Et dukkehjem* (pr., pb. 1879; *A Doll's House*, 1880; also known as *A Doll House*).

In 1920 *Miss Lulu Bett* was hailed as innovative in several respects and was the first Pulitzer Prize-winning play by a woman. In his foreword to the published play, Robert C. Benchley commented:

> Zona Gale is the first author, to my knowledge, who has dared to write genuinely dull dialogue . . . [b]ut Miss Gale saw the truth and kept it whole. She was depicting uninspired American family life (almost for the first time in our literature) and she held fast to the ideals of American family conversation.

Benchley also signaled the originality of the "old lady who is not sweet, and a child who is not cute." Ludwig Lewisohn declared that "no other American dramatist has succeeded in so fully and richly transferring to the stage the exact moral atmosphere of a class, a section, and a period, as Miss Gale."

Sources for Further Study

Barlow, Judith E. *Plays by American Women, 1900-1930*. New York: Applause Theatre Books, 1985.

Schroeder, Patricia R. "Realism and Feminism in the Progressive Era." In *The Cambridge Companion to American Women Playwrights*, edited by Brenda Murphy. Cambridge, Mass.: Harvard University Press, 1999.

Shafer, Yvonne. *American Women Playwrights, 1900-1950*. New York: Peter Lang, 1995.

Simonson, Harold P. *Zona Gale*. New York: Twayne Publishers, 1962.

Felicia Hardison Londré

MISTER ROBERTS

Authors: Thomas Heggen (1919-1949) and Joshua Logan (1908-1988)
Type of plot: War; tragicomedy
Time of plot: Mid-1945
Locale: A navy cargo ship on the Pacific Ocean
First produced: 1948, at the Alvin Theatre, New York City
First published: 1948

Principal characters:
LIEUTENANT ROBERTS, a cargo officer
DOC, the ship's physician
THE CAPTAIN, a sadistic, ambitious leader
ENSIGN PULVER, the laundry and morale officer

The Play

A two-act play, *Mister Roberts* is set aboard a navy cargo ship on the Pacific Ocean during World War II. As the play begins, the setting reveals a typical cargo ship in the middle of the Pacific Ocean, shortly after dawn. The ship's crew is sleeping; in fact, there is no sign of life, a condition the play explores. As the drama unfolds, each member of the crew struggles with, and overcomes, the figurative absence of life: the tediousness, dissatisfaction, and monotony of life aboard the ship. The central action of the play evolves from the interplay between Lieutenant Roberts and the tyrannical Captain to the interplay between Lieutenant Roberts and the crew, who try to find life in the midst of boredom.

Roberts is frustrated with his role as cargo officer, delivering toilet paper and toothpaste while other men are participating in combat. Disillusioned with his noncombat duty, Roberts writes letters to the Bureau of Naval Personnel requesting a transfer to a destroyer ship. As he says, "I'm sick and tired of being a lousy spectator. I just happen to believe in this thing. I've got to feel I'm good enough to be in it—to participate!" However, his incessant letters put him on a collision course with the eccentric Captain, who wants to use Lieutenant Roberts's skills as a cargo officer to advance his own career. Jealous of Roberts's relationship with the crew, his demeanor, and his educational background, the Captain takes Roberts's letters as an affront to him and his future rather than as an opportunity for Roberts to attain a dream. The Captain wants gold bars on his uniform cap more than he wants a unified crew.

The contentions between the Captain and Roberts are exacerbated when Roberts promises to stop writing letters and to stop challenging the Captain's authority in front of the men, but only if the Captain will grant the crew a liberty, an opportunity they have not had for more than fourteen months. The loss of liberty has dramatically impacted the crew: They fight among themselves, rebel against authority, and stop functioning as a unit. Roberts thus sacrifices his own dream to restore the crew's unity and sense of purpose.

Initially, Roberts's sacrifice reaps positive rewards: The crew finds a humorous outlet for its anger and tedium. Tempers are assuaged and as one member of the crew states, "it was worth it. That liberty was worth anything!" Ironically, Roberts becomes embittered by his sacrifice and as the war draws closer to its conclusion, he distances himself from the crew, referring to them as an "ungrateful mob." Using them as scapegoats for his own frustrations, he puts men on report for minor infractions. As a result, the crew begins to regard him as a "sell-out," which further separates him from the crew.

Eventually, Roberts gets his transfer by defying the Captain, and by an act of selflessness on the crew's part when they learn what he sacrificed for them. Even though Roberts dies at the end of the play, his spirit, humanity, and selflessness live on through Ensign Pulver, who swallows his fear and confronts the Captain. During the interplay between Roberts and the crew, the crew reveals the importance of sacrifice and defines the true qualities of heroism.

Themes and Meanings

Mister Roberts is a tragicomedy that relies more on character development to convey its major conflict and themes than it does on plot. The play delves into the universal conflict of good versus evil as the reluctant crew struggles not only with ennui but also with their contempt for the Captain, a self-absorbed man whose cruelty unifies, rather than separates, them. As they struggle, they discover the importance of self-sacrifice, a sense of humor, and the human face of heroism.

The need for self-sacrifice is given immediate importance in scene 1, when Roberts, an intelligent, sensitive, college-educated man who is idolized by the crew, makes a pact with the Captain. Roberts will sacrifice his dream of being transferred to a combat ship if the Captain will grant shore liberty for the crew. The Captain, a jealous, self-serving individual who is concerned only with getting a promotion and forcing Roberts to adopt a demeanor of respect toward him in front of the crew, agrees.

While the sacrifice seems to be insignificant, its effects are initially disastrous. The crew believes Roberts has broken faith with them. However, when the crew learns of Roberts's sacrifice, they emulate his actions, sacrificing their careers and futures to get him transferred to a combat ship by writing letters to the Naval Command and forging the Captain's signature.

The generosity of subordinating one's own dreams for someone else's good has a ripple effect on Ensign Pulver, the morale officer, who is an ingenious and humorous, but ineffectual, officer whose fear of the Captain curtails his activities. When Roberts is transferred, Pulver unwillingly inherits Roberts's job. Yet, at the end of the play, learning of Roberts's death, Pulver asserts himself in Roberts-like fashion, throws the Captain's beloved palm trees overboard (an action Roberts took earlier in the play), and confronts the Captain. Pulver thus displays the noble impact of self-sacrifice in a simple but heroic manner.

Dramatic Devices

Thomas Heggen and Joshua Logan use several dramatic devices to universalize the experiences of the reluctant crew. In essence, this play is a study of character and the heroic virtues of men like Roberts, Pulver, and Doc, as well as members of the crew, who are ordinary human beings but who rise to heroic stature through a series of simple actions.

In addition to a character study, *Mister Roberts* includes the symbolic use of objects to define the characters and conflict. One prominent symbol is the Captain's "revered" palm tree, the "trophy" the crew earned for "superior achievement for delivering more toilet paper and toothpaste than any other navy cargo ship." While the Captain admires the trophy, caring for it almost as if it were a child, the crew despises it because it epitomizes the futility of their role in the war and their hatred for the Captain. While they cannot openly defy the Captain, they subtly display their attitude through the tree. In the first scene, one member of the crew spits tobacco on it. Later, as the radio encourages the crew to stamp out the enemy as if it were a "malignant tumor," Roberts, in a major act of defiance, grabs the palm tree and throws the "malignant growth" overboard. His action intensifies his conflict with the Captain but resolves his conflict with the crew when they hear of it. When Roberts leaves the ship at the end of the play, the crew rewards his action by giving him a brass medal shaped like a palm tree, "for action against the enemy, above and beyond the call of duty on the night of eight May, 1945." Finally, at the end of the play, when Ensign Pulver learns of Roberts's death, he throws the Captain's new palm trees into the ocean, takes responsibility for his action, and asserts himself for the first time by standing up to the Captain.

Another important element in the play is humor. At times the humor is ribald, as when the crew peers through a spy glass and fights over it to watch nurses shower on a nearby island, or when they return from a shore leave that was wild with revelry and debauchery. At other times, the humor ranges from being self-disparaging to being uproariously funny, as occurs when Pulver creates a firecracker to throw under the Captain's bed and it explodes in the laundry room. The use of humor balances the pathos and tragedy at the end of the play and keeps the plot from becoming maudlin.

Critical Context

Although the play opened to rave reviews, and many critics considered it to be the major comedy hit of the season and the best play produced during World War II, *Mister Roberts* is the only play that Heggen and Logan produced. Heggen, the author of the novel on which the play is based, died in 1949.

Despite the fact that the play is classified as a war play, the war is not the major focus of the action: Only one member of the crew is actually involved in the war, and he only sees brief action at the end of the play. The play is more concerned with the simple but poignant human struggles as the crew battles restlessness and a sadistic Captain with decency, humanity, a sense of humor, and selflessness. At its conclusion, the characters reaffirm the importance of sacrifice in being truly human.

Sources for Further Study

Bonin, Jane F., ed. *Major Themes in Prize-Winning American Drama*. Metuchen, N.J.: Scarecrow Press, 1975.

Cerf, Bennett. *Plays of Our Time*. New York: Random House, 1967.

French, Warren, ed. *The Forties: Fiction, Poetry, and Drama*. Florida: Everett/Edwards, 1969.

Leggett, John. *Ross and Tom: Two American Tragedies*. Rev. ed. New York: Da Capo Press, 2000.

Lewis, Allan, ed. *American Plays and Playwrights of the Contemporary Theater*. New York: Crown Publishers, 1970.

Logan, Joshua. *Josh: My Up and Down, In and Out Life*. New York: Delacorte, 1976.

Sharon K. Wilson

A MOON FOR THE MISBEGOTTEN

Author: Eugene O'Neill (1888-1953)
Type of plot: Psychological
Time of plot: The 1940's
Locale: Connecticut
First produced: 1947, at the Columbus Theater, Columbus, Ohio
First published: 1952

Principal characters:
JOSIE HOGAN, an unwed farmer
PHIL HOGAN, her father
MIKE HOGAN, her youngest brother
JAMES TYRONE, JR., an alcoholic and second-rate actor

The Play

A Moon for the Misbegotten begins on a hot, clear day at roughly noon at the Hogans' run-down farm, the house weathered gray and congruous with the parched and barren land that surrounds it. Attached to the house's left side is a small bedroom, its walls and roof covered with tar paper; three steps lead up to the door of this room, and it is from this door that a very large woman emerges, her feet bare and her body clothed in a sleeveless cotton dress. She is Josie Hogan, and she is obviously anxious about something as she looks around the right corner of the house toward the field and then sighs with relief when she sees Mike Hogan, her younger brother, running toward her. They have planned Mike's escape from the farm, just as—the audience learns—she did for her other two brothers years earlier.

Because much of the dialogue in act 1 serves as exposition, the audience learns from Mike's puritanical chiding of his older sister that she has a bad reputation in town for being promiscuous, has never seemed to care about her virtue, and is like her father, Phil Hogan, insofar as she helps him cheat people in various ways. In fact, Mike says, he would not be surprised if Josie and Hogan try to trick their landlord, James Tyrone, out of some of his recent inheritance: Mike imagines Josie will lure Tyrone into her bedroom some night and then, while he is there, have Hogan burst into the room with a shotgun, accuse Tyrone of compromising his daughter, and blackmail him into giving them some restitution. Although she proudly acknowledges her reputation, Josie denies having thought of such a scheme, says she would never take part in such a plot, and—suddenly seeing their father walking toward the house—commands Mike away to his freedom.

After Hogan's initial rage over Mike's escape has dissipated, he dismisses the boy as annoyingly prudish, especially considering the way Mike chastised Josie for her putative liaisons with local men. Josie tells Hogan about the scheme Mike accused them of plotting. Hogan seems interested in this idea, saying that Tyrone's promise not to sell the farm out from under them cannot be trusted, because when he gets drunk he becomes forgetful. Besides running the risk of losing the farm, Hogan says, there is this to think about: Josie and Tyrone are two of a kind, they like each other, and Josie could reform Tyrone and keep him sober. Nevertheless, Josie will have no part in any scheme, and she believes that Tyrone will keep his word about not selling the farm to anyone but Hogan. When Tyrone arrives unexpectedly at the farm, he tells them that T. Stedman Harder, their wealthy neighbor, is coming to complain about their pigs encroaching upon his ice pond. A short time later, Harder arrives but is verbally abused and quickly frightened away by Hogan and Josie. Act 1 ends with Tyrone promising to come back to the farm in the evening to see Josie.

Act 2 opens in darkness illuminated by light from a full moon. Josie sits on the steps leading to her bedroom, her big body clothed in her Sunday dress. She mutters to herself about being stood up by Tyrone; he was supposed to arrive at nine o'clock, and it is now roughly eleven. Her private humiliation is interrupted when her father arrives from the bar in town, where he has left Tyrone and one of Harder's employees talking about the sale of the farm. Only gradually does he reveal to Josie the cause of his deep anger; as he does so, her humiliation is compounded with a similar anger and sense of betrayal. She does not want to believe that Tyrone would break his promise to them about the farm, but she is already suffering one broken promise. At Hogan's prompting, therefore, she agrees to take part in the scheme to lure Tyrone into her bed. Once again, Tyrone arrives unexpectedly; Hogan pretends to be drunk and staggers back to town, and the act ends with Josie getting whiskey from the house and Tyrone waiting on the steps outside.

Act 3 begins where the preceding act ended; Josie comes back outside with a bottle of whiskey. Initially, she attempts to affect the brazen demeanor of a hussy, but Tyrone tells her that he is tired of whores and wants her to be herself. Despite his urge to prove that she is a virgin, he says, he wants this night to be different from those he has spent with tarts. Telling her that she is the only woman he loves, he adds that she is beautiful because she is kind, wholesome, and strong. Josie struggles against her desire to be close to Tyrone, until he informs her that he fooled Hogan into thinking he was going to sell the farm. Upon learning that Tyrone intends to keep his promise to Hogan, Josie drops her defenses, tells Tyrone she loves him, and admits to being a virgin—one who, nevertheless, wants to go to bed with him. He would ruin their relationship, he says, like he ruined the one with his mother. Indeed, the guilt he feels for having failed his mother, as well as his need for forgiveness, has compelled him to seek maternal solace from Josie. The third act ends as they sit on the bedroom steps, Tyrone asleep in her arms.

Act 4 opens at dawn the following morning; Josie is awake and still holding the unconscious Tyrone, and Hogan is peering around the corner of the house at them. She acknowledges his presence, tells him that she believes he knew Tyrone was kidding about selling the farm, and vows to leave him for his duplicity. Hogan is apologetic, but Josie orders him into the house until after Tyrone has awakened. Tyrone soon wakes, expresses gratitude and affection to her, and says good-bye. As she watches Tyrone disappear, Hogan begs her to believe that he schemed only to gain happiness for her; she says that she believes him and will stay on the farm.

Themes and Meanings

Characteristic of many, if not all, of Eugene O'Neill's plays is his portrayal of neurotic or self-divided individuals, people who cannot approach wholeness until they first learn self-acceptance. In this respect, *A Moon for the Misbegotten* is typical, for both James Tyrone and Josie Hogan discover through each other that they possess within themselves the means for achieving such acceptance.

In an earlier play about the Tyrones, *Long Day's Journey into Night* (pr., pb. 1956), Mary Tyrone, mother and morphine addict, says to her younger son, "The past is the present, isn't it? It's the future, too. We all try to lie out of that but life won't let us." Elsewhere she expresses such fatalism when talking about her elder son, James Tyrone, Jr., when she says, "He can't help being what the past has made him." Mary herself is haunted and consumed by her past, just as her elder son James is in this later play; thus it is not surprising when Tyrone says to Josie, "There is no present or future—only the past happening over and over again—now. You can't get away from it." Whereas his mother used morphine to escape herself and her present life, Tyrone uses alcohol and sex to kill all thoughts about how he failed his mother. He failed her by becoming an alcoholic, by not crying over her death, by attempting to forget the loss through drunkenness and whoring, and by blaming her for dying and leaving him alone. In other words, for Tyrone there is no present or future because he is being consumed by his feelings of guilt about the past. He is impelled into Josie's arms because he needs to forgive and be forgiven, and because Josie is, he says, "like her [his mother] deep in your heart."

Although Josie is strong and maternal, she is also self-consciously large and—she thinks—unattractive as a woman. To compensate for her appearance, she has affected a hard, bawdy, and promiscuous self-image; she pretends to have gone to bed with numerous local men, none of whom contradicts her tales for fear of losing face among other men who supposedly have been to bed with her. She knows that Tyrone is accustomed to being with prostitutes, and she mistakenly thinks that she must seem like one of them to get him to desire her as a woman. Only gradually—after he has revealed his great grief and guilt regarding his mother—does Josie come to understand that Tyrone does not need her as a woman, but in a nonsexual way. Indeed, not only does she confess to him that she is a virgin, but she also realizes that the love he needs from her is, because it demands she subordinate her own personal desire for him, "the greatest of all—because it costs so much." Josie proves herself equal to such a selfless love's demands; she listens to Tyrone's tortured confession and as his mother's surrogate forgives him: "As *she* forgives, do you hear me!" Josie says to Tyrone. "As *she* loves and understands and forgives!"

Dramatic Devices

An autobiographical play about Eugene O'Neill's alcoholic older brother, *A Moon for the Misbegotten* is dramatic realism direct in its simplicity and—like the Hogans' life and farm—stripped of all but what is essential to its integrity.

The play's set itself is stark: What the audience sees in all four acts is a side view of the Hogans' small farmhouse; all of it but Josie's bedroom is a weathered-gray clapboard, and the bedroom itself is covered with tar paper. Before the house and the three steps leading to the door of Josie's room is a dirt yard in the middle of which is a large, flat-topped boulder that Tyrone uses as a sort of table on which to set his whiskey during act 3. O'Neill calls for the removal of the house's living room wall for all of act 2. With the wall removed, the audience is allowed to watch Josie rise from the front steps, as the act opens, and stumble around in the living room until she lights a kerosene lantern, revealing the room's sparse furnishings and, on a bureau, an alarm clock that indicates the time, five minutes past eleven—two hours after Tyrone was supposed to have come to visit her. Clearly O'Neill intends to show that, while the little the Hogans own is old and rudimentary and not worth much, what they themselves bring to it makes it a home. Most important, the playwright intends for the house to be emblematic of Hogan and Josie, insofar as, like them, it is "placed so perfectly in its setting that it appears a harmonious part of the landscape, rooted in the earth."

Aside from the set, noteworthy are the demands this play imposes upon the actors portraying Josie and Tyrone, for O'Neill requires that the latter deliver a monologue during the third act that extends over several pages, and he requires that the former appear natural and attentive as she listens to it. Furthermore, Tyrone's monologue about his mother and his guilt, as well as about the hatred he feels toward his dead father and himself, demands an actor of consummate skill to keep the audience's attention and avoid a maudlin, monotonous tone. As for the actor who portrays Josie, she must be "so oversize for a woman that she is almost a freak. . . ." While she "is more powerful than any but an exceptionally strong man," O'Neill indicates in his directions that "there is no mannish quality about her. She is all woman." In the course of the play, Josie must appear strong but vulnerable, bawdy but sensitive, lusty but maternal, hard as nails but compassionate. Indeed, Josie Hogan is considered by many to be one of the great heroines of twentieth century drama.

Critical Context

The third of three intensely autobiographical plays that Eugene O'Neill wrote between 1939 and 1943, *A Moon for the Misbegotten* has as its two autobiographical predecessors *The Iceman Cometh* (pr., pb. 1946) and *Long Day's Journey into Night*. All three plays represent what O'Neill called faithful realism: the starkly realistic portrayal of individuals and their environments, stripped of all romantic hues except those the given characters themselves impose upon their situations.

While some critics have suggested that most of O'Neill's plays are realistic in form, and while he began his playwriting career in 1913 by writing realistic one-act plays, much of his career was marked by his experimentation with dramatic technique. From the realism of his earliest efforts, he moved into the tragic fatalism of such full-length plays as *Beyond the Horizon* (pr. 1920) and *Anna Christie* (pr. 1921, pb. 1923); he experimented with expressionistic techniques in *The Emperor Jones* (pr. 1920, pb. 1921); he complemented his expressionism with choral speeches, recognizable social types, and symbolic settings in *The Hairy Ape* (pr., pb. 1922); he employed Freudian psychology in *Desire Under the Elms* (pr. 1924); he complemented his expressionistic techniques with masks for the major characters in *The Great God Brown* (pr., pb. 1926); he experimented with stream-of-consciousness asides in *Strange Interlude* (pr., pb. 1928), and in *Days Without End* (pr., pb. 1934) he went so far as to have two actors portray the conflicting sides of one character's mind; and he attempted to retell in modern terms the Aeschylus trilogy about the house of Atreus in *Mourning Becomes Electra* (pr., pb. 1931).

Not without valid reasons do many consider O'Neill the father of modern American drama and one of the greatest playwrights of the twentieth century. That his last plays were his most painfully personal, and yet were rendered with the least amount of artistic contrivance of any but his earliest plays, suggests that he achieved mastery over both his craft and his turbulent past.

Sources for Further Study

Carpenter, Frederic I. *Eugene O'Neill*. Rev. ed. Boston: Twayne, 1979.

Falk, Doris V. *Eugene O'Neill and the Tragic Tension: An Interpretative Study of the Plays*. 2d ed. New York: Gordian Press, 1982.

Frank, Glenda. Review of *A Moon for the Misbegotten*. *Theatre Journal* 44 (December, 1992): 527-528.

Gassner, John, ed. *O'Neill: A Collection of Critical Essays*. Englewood Cliffs, N.J.: Prentice-Hall, 1964.

Gelb, Arthur, and Barbara Gelb. *O'Neill: Life with Monte Cristo*. New York: Applause, 2000.

Houchin, John H., ed. *The Critical Response to Eugene O'Neill*. Westport, Conn.: Greenwood Press, 1993.

Miller, Jordan Y., and Winifred L. Frazer. "Eugene O'Neill: From Nobody to the Nobel." In *American Drama Between the Wars: A Critical History*. Boston: Twayne, 1991.

Raleigh, John Henry. *The Plays of Eugene O'Neill*. Carbondale: Southern Illinois University Press, 1965.

Ranald, Margaret Loftus. *The Eugene O'Neill Companion*. Westport, Conn.: Greenwood Press, 1984.

Tiusanen, Timo. *O'Neill's Scenic Images*. Princeton, N.J.: Princeton University Press, 1968.

David A. Carpenter

MORNING'S AT SEVEN

Author: Paul Osborn (1901-1988)
Type of plot: Comedy; realism
Time of plot: 1939
Locale: Two backyards in an American town
First produced: 1939, at the Longacre Theater, New York City
First published: 1940

Principal characters:

THEODORE "THOR" SWANSON, an older man who lives with his wife, Cora, and her sister Aaronetta
CORA SWANSON, an older woman and the wife of Thor
AARONETTA "ARRY" GIBBS, single sister of Cora who lives with Thor and Cora
IDA BOLTON, sister of Cora, Aaronetta, and Esther who lives next door to the Swansons' house
CARL BOLTON, husband of Ida who is prone to having "spells"
HOMER BOLTON, a forty-year-old bachelor and son of Carl and Ida
MYRTLE BROWN, a woman engaged to Homer for eight years
ESTHER "ESTY" CRAMPTON, sister of Cora, Aaronetta, and Ida who lives up the street
DAVID CRAMPTON, Esther's husband

The Play

This three-act play is set in a Midwest American town during the 1930's. The plot centers on the long relationship of four elderly Gibbs sisters and the secrets that remain unspoken in order not to disturb the tranquillity of their family. The younger sisters Cora, Arry, and Ida have lived next door to one another for fifty years. The oldest sister, Esther, who is nearly seventy, lives only one and a half blocks away. However, the sedentary lives of the sisters and their quirky husbands are disrupted when Homer Bolton, son of Ida and Carl, decides to bring home his fiancé of eight years, Myrtle Brown. Homer, who still lives at home, is terrified by sex and commitment. When his mother suggests that Myrtle and Homer share a double bed, he is deeply embarrassed. Homer's parents and his uncles and aunts are thrilled to finally meet the girl Homer has been dating for twelve years. Myrtle, who is just as naïve as Homer, demonstrates her childlike attitude throughout the play with syrupy comments like, "I've just never had so many people so nice to me all at once!"

The backyard setting, with the Bolton and Swanson porches positioned next to each other, functions well in demonstrating how the proximity of the relatives has taken its toll on the psyches of the sisters and the men with whom they share their lives. It is Homer's return home that initially propels the action of the play. Homer's father, Carl, who cannot stop thinking about what his life might have been like had he become a dentist, reveals his quiet desperation by leaning his head up against a backyard tree and by wandering for hours through the neighborhood looking for the "fork" in the road he missed years earlier. These "spells" that Carl endures recur throughout the play. Homer reacts to his father's "spells" by distancing himself from Myrtle Brown and by comforting his mother. Finally, he tells Myrtle that he can no longer marry her because he needs to take care of his mother while his father is away.

Cora finds out that the house that Carl Bolton owns and had promised to Homer and Myrtle when they marry is no longer needed. The availability of the house propels Cora to act on the long-standing resentment she has felt toward her younger sister Arry, who has been living with Cora and Thor for fifty years. Cora persuades Carl to lease Homer's house to her for twenty years. Cora now feels that she can finally have Thor to herself and that she can put an end to her suspicions that Thor and Arry have been carrying on a long-term relationship in the house that the three of them share.

Esther listens to Cora's plan to persuade Thor to move out of their house and leave Arry behind, but Esther has problems of her own. Her husband, David, does not think much of her relatives and considers her sisters and their husbands to be "morons." Furthermore, he forbids Esther to visit her sisters. Esther refuses to listen to David and continues to visit Cora, Arry, and Ida. Consequently, David devises a plan in which he and Esther can live independently of one another but in the same house: "From now on, I will be living on the lower floor; Esther on the second."

The action of the play picks up when the sisters finally acknowledge the family secret that they have kept for many years. Arry, who discovers Cora wants her out of the house, shares a letter she has written with Esther. The letter reveals that Arry and Thor did indeed have romantic feelings for each other when Arry first came to live with Thor and Cora. Esther gives the letter to Cora to read, but instead of angering Cora the contents of the letter make Cora see the difficulty Arry has had through the years of living in a home that is not her own with a man she cannot have. Meanwhile, Homer learns that Myrtle is going to have a baby, causing him to resume their plans to marry. Cora gives up her wish to lease Carl's house, and the house is once again given to Homer and Myrtle. Arry packs her belongings and prepares to move out of Thor and Cora's house. Dressed as if she is going on a long journey and with luggage in hand, she steps down from Thor and Cora's porch. Arry reminds Ida and Carl that they had earlier promised she could live with them and she walks up the steps of the Boltons' house, determined to begin her new life.

Themes and Meanings

Morning's at Seven provides audiences with a backyard look at how a family secret almost destroys a sisterly bond that has held the Gibbs sisters together for forty years despite their schoolgirl jealousies, the quirkiness of the three brothers-in-law, and a forty-year-old oddball nephew.

The main conflict of the play arises when Cora decides she wants her single sister Arry to move out of her house. After so many years, Cora is tired of providing a home for her younger sister. She wants a place of her own and a house where she can have her husband Thor all to herself. The family structure is shaken, however, when Arry admits to an affair that she had with Thor years earlier while Cora was in the hospital.

Paul Osborn's story is filled with long, drawn-out conversations and pointless philosophical tirades as the Gibbs sisters and their husbands talk extensively about medical checkups and the complications of adding a downstairs bathroom to a house. Initially these discussions come across as trivial; however, beneath the "nice" talk lies the psychological damage that quickly reveals itself in the unfulfilled lives of the play's characters. Homer's father, Carl, who suffers from "spells," laments about what his life might have been if he had only become a dentist: "That's not so much to ask! Just to be a dentist. Charlie Watson went on and became a dentist! But I wasn't up to it!" Homer seems to be headed in the same direction as his father as he struggles with the transition from being a "momma's boy" to a man who is supposed to marry a woman he has been dating for twelve years. The connection between father and son is made quite evident in act 2, when Thor discovers Homer leaning his head against the same tree that his father had leaned against earlier in the play during one of his spells.

Like the tree in the Boltons' backyard, the characters in this story appear on the surface to be happy: Life to them is "nice" and their deep roots and closeness keep them grounded. However, the audience quickly sees the quiet desperation that lies beneath the surface of their kindness to one another. Most of the characters struggle with what life might have been like if they were able to go back to Carl's "fork" in the road. This idea is perhaps best expressed by Arry when she tells Thor she really never had a home: "Nope. That's what I found out. It wasn't ever my home. I haven't got a home. That's what I mean about getting old. I guess it's nice and peaceful if you got a home. If you got a husband. If you got somebody to get old with—. But I haven't."

Dramatic Devices

Morning's at Seven is a realistic comedy. The play calls for a typical midwestern 1930's backyard setting with two houses sitting adjacent to each other and with back porch areas that suggest that privacy may be difficult for the occupants of the homes to find. Through his elderly characters' initial dialogue, Paul Osborn quickly reveals the everyday ups and downs of two neighboring families who not only are blood related but are able to remain civil to one another after being neighbors for more than forty years.

The wit and humor of the play come from the quirky and oddball characters that Osborn created. Each of the four Gibbs sisters seems to play a distinctive role in the dynamics of the family. Late in the play, Cora recites a poem the girls' Papa used to say to them: "Esty's smartest/ Arry's wildest/ Ida's slowest/ Cora's mildest."

In true dramatic fashion, Osborn slowly begins to reveal the secret desires and stilted dreams of the Gibbs sisters and their husbands. The audience knows that all is not well with the family when Carl Bolton begins to lean his head against a backyard tree, signifying his dissatisfaction with his place in life. The tree continues to function symbolically throughout the play as a reminder of the unmoving life force that cannot be uprooted despite the unsettling questions many of the other characters have about their lives.

Critical Context

Paul Osborn's title *Morning's at Seven* was taken from Robert Browning's poem "Pippa Passes" (1841). The title functions ironically to suggest to readers and audience members alike that, unlike the last line in Pippa's song, all is *not* right with this world.

First produced on Broadway in 1939, *Morning's at Seven* did not achieve commercial success until its revival in 1980, when it won a Tony Award and seven Drama Desk Awards. Paul Osborn's other well-known plays include *The Vinegar Tree* (pr. 1930, pb. 1931), *On Borrowed Time* (pr., pb. 1938), *A Bell for Adano* (pr. 1944, pb. 1945), and *The World of Suzie Wong* (pr. 1958). Osborn also enjoyed a career as a screenwriter and wrote the screenplays that included *Madame Curie* (1943), *Cry Havoc* (1943), *The Yearling* (1946), *East of Eden* (1955), *Sayonara* (1957), and *South Pacific* (1958).

When *Morning's at Seven* was finally recognized by audiences as a critical success in 1980, the producers moved the time of the play from 1939 to 1922 in order to create an even greater sentimentality than the original production had when it opened in "the present" in 1939. Filled with oddball characters and representative of other nostalgic plays of the period, such as Moss Hart and George S. Kaufman's *You Can't Take It with You: A Play* (pr. 1936, pb. 1937) and Joseph Kesselring's *Arsenic and Old Lace* (pr. 1941, pb. 1942), Osborn's play refrained from relying too heavily on the oddity of the characters to develop the play's effectiveness. Instead, Osborn strengthened the play by developing a warm-hearted look at family values and contrasted them with the secrets families keep and the potential those secrets have to destroy even the strongest of families.

Sources for Further Study

Birdwell, Christine. "Paul Osborn and His Gals of Kalamazoo." *Midwestern Miscellany* 13, 1985.

Clurman, Harold. Review in *The Nation* 244 (May 3, 1980): 540.

Gill, Brendan. "The Theatre: The Age of Innocence." Review in *The New Yorker*, April 21, 1980, 77.

Kalem, T. E. "Close Relations." Review in *Time*, April 21, 1980, 84.

Kroll, Jack. "The Way We Were." Review in *Newsweek*, April 21, 1980, 112.

Weales, Gerald. "Unhappy Families: Mixing Laughter and Cliché." *Commonweal* 107 (June 6, 1980): 335-336.

Daniel W. Landes

THE MOUND BUILDERS

Author: Lanford Wilson (1937-)
Type of plot: Existential
Time of plot: The 1970's
Locale: Urbana and Blue Shoals, Illinois
First produced: 1975, at the Circle Repertory Theater, New York City
First published: 1976

Principal characters:

PROFESSOR AUGUST HOWE, the senior archaeologist of an expedition to Blue Shoals, Illinois, age forty
CYNTHIA HOWE, his wife, age thirty-five
KIRSTEN, his daughter, age eleven
D. K. "DELIA" ERIKSEN, his sister, a writer, age thirty-eight
DR. DAN LOGGINS, his twenty-nine-year-old assistant
DR. MARY JEAN LOGGINS, Dan's wife, a gynecologist, age twenty-five
CHAD JASKER, the landowner's son, age twenty-five

The Play

The Mound Builders opens in August Howe's study in Urbana, Illinois, on a February morning. August, an archaeology professor, begins to dictate a report on the previous summer's failed expedition to Blue Shoals, in southern Illinois. As he dictates, slides depicting scenes from the expedition are projected onto a screen at the back of the stage. The slides show the lake that threatened to flood his team's excavation, the old farmhouse where the team and their families lived, construction of a dam close to the house and their excavation, a bulldozer, and their excavation site.

As August narrates over the slides, the scene fades into the previous summer, and the lights come up on an interior: the large living, dining, and working area of the old farmhouse. Most of the play's action takes place here, in a series of brief scenes that introduce the central characters, detail their personal lives, and follow the progress of their expedition to discover evidence of early American Indian cultures. Scenes of the summer in Blue Shoals are interrupted by interludes in which August provides commentary in order to introduce background information or heighten suspense.

In the act's second scene, Dan and Jean Loggins arrive at the farmhouse, the archaeological team's summer home for the previous three years. Dan Loggins, also an archaeologist, is August Howe's junior partner; Jean Loggins, a gynecologist, is Dan's wife. Chad Jasker, the landowner's son and a friend of Dan, has driven them to the house and helps to carry in their belongings. Dan tells August privately that he wants to keep the pregnancy of his wife, Jean, a secret from the students helping with the dig. The next evening Chad and August arrive at the house with Delia, August's ill sister, a well-known writer. Dan describes a difficult day at the dig. A bit of a poet, Dan believes the early American Indians built mounds for essentially the same reasons motivating builders today. "A person isn't happy," he says, "unless he's building something."

The quick passage of summer at Blue Shoals is represented in a series of short scenes separated by abrupt blackouts, like slides in a slide show. In one scene, alone with Jean, Chad asks her to go with him to see a model of the county as it will look, he says, after Jasker's development is built. An interstate highway will soon pass close to Blue Shoals, he says, and the new dam will create a large lake. On the lakeshore, resort accommodations will be built on land owned by Chad and his father, making them rich. Jean is happy for Chad but is fascinated with the process by which rural areas can be transformed by "the signing of an energy bill in Washington." As Jean begins to leave the room, Chad suddenly expresses his desire for her. Jean tells him to "get lost." Later, when Chad and Cynthia Howe are alone, he asks Cynthia for money, which she gives him. Events subsequently reveal that Chad and Cynthia are lovers.

The scene shifts back to Urbana in February. Alone in his study, August attempts to organize what he calls "shards" from the expedition. He catalogs a personal tragedy, including a separation from his wife and daughter and an impending resignation from his position at the university.

One night toward the end of June, Dan and Chad return drunk from a fishing trip. Dan tells Chad that the archaeologists have found something unusual under the roundhouse they are excavating. After Chad leaves, Dan tells Jean and Delia that Chad saved him last summer from drowning. Dan goes to bed, and a short scene between Delia and Jean ends the act. Delia believes that men and women burden themselves with too much pain. She envisions how the world ends: "A sad old world of widows . . . lined up on beaches . . . looking out over the water and trying to keep warm."

When act 2 opens, the team has made an exciting discovery beneath the roundhouse: remains of an even earlier culture. Dan believes that they may have discovered a burial mound of the Mississippian culture, which had disappeared from southern Illinois many centuries before. The rest of the act focuses on the team's increasingly more significant discoveries. The archaeologists work under extreme pressure as heavy summer rains threaten their excavation and cause the water level of the lake to rise, further endangering their project. Chad continues his affair with Cynthia and attempts once more to seduce Jean, who again rejects him.

In the longest speech of the play, Dan eulogizes a vanished member of the Mississippian culture, whom he calls Cochise. Cochise, he says, did not vanish "without a trace." He left behind him burial mounds, remains of dwellings and tools, and enough evidence of his culture to attract admirers like Dan, who mourn his passing.

August and Dan's team has unearthed the burial mound of a god-king, the first discovered in North America, only days before the lake would have flooded it. The team begins to collect artifacts from the mound, including the first gold ornaments known to be made by North American Indian cultures. Seeing the gold and copper beads, Chad admires August and Dan's attempt to make something of themselves, not for money but for a reason he understands but is unable to express. The team has discovered a gold burial mask, which Dan puts on almost inadvertently.

While the team cleans and preserves gold and copper ornaments, Chad discovers that Jean is pregnant and becomes extremely agitated, perhaps because he thinks that everyone has been withholding this information from him. Chad tells the team that they will not be able to work on his father's land next summer. Dan and he argue over the use of his father's land, and Dan eventually tells Chad that the interstate highway on which Chad had been counting to bring vacationers and their money to Blue Shoals has been rerouted to the other side of the lake owing to the importance of the Native American monuments in the area. August and Dan have known this information for two years but kept it from everyone else, including Cynthia and Chad. When he learns this, Chad is furious, believing that he had been betrayed by the people he most respected and admired. Dan cannot convince Chad that the land has immense value as a repository of important indigenous dwelling places and artifacts. Instead, Chad howls at the loss of his dream of commercial success and abruptly leaves the stage.

Later that night, Chad returns, and Dan catches him about to leave the house with the god-king's golden mask and other valuables. Chad then lures Dan outside, telling him that he has something to show him. The next morning, the team learns that Chad has run the bulldozer over the site, ruining the project, and has driven the machine into the lake. Moreover, Chad and Dan are missing. Telling August that Chad is "capable of anything," Cynthia then destroys the photographic evidence of their finds. After discovery in the lake of an oar from Chad's boat, a search for Chad and Dan is begun. Dan is missing, and Jean says, "WHY DID HE TRUST PEOPLE, WHY DID HE BELIEVE IN THINGS? . . . Vanished without a trace."

The last scene in the play contrasts tableaux of August Howe in Urbana in February and three women—Cynthia, Delia, and Jean—in Blue Shoals in August. August says that he had imagined the house being carried off by a "great brown flood" when the lake rose; in fact, when he returned in January to see it, the house was on the same spot, half covered by the lake waters. In imagery reminiscent of the ending of act 2, the three women, alone in a house at the edge of rising waters, lament the loss of their men. The women fade into black. Motionless and speechless, microphone in hand, August cannot put his emotions into words as the lights fade on him.

Themes and Meanings

The Mound Builders is a play about the need of human beings to lead meaningful lives and to discover sustaining values: to identify themselves with something of significance and permanence amid the constant change inherent in existence. The characters in the play attach meaning and significance to the vagaries of ordinary existence but eventually have the truly consequential thrust upon them in the inevitable clash of values and desires.

Through not so much a series of events as a series of apparently spontaneous conversations, Lanford Wilson underscores the folly of the myth of self-importance, showing men and women who delude themselves in order to maintain an aura of importance, respectability, and humanity. Humankind builds—things, relationships, works of art, lives—because it is only happy when building something. Wilson shows that within the builder is also the destroyer. The roundhouse was built over a burial mound of an earlier culture. Chad Jasker and his father want to build over the roundhouse.

The archaeologists who dig in the earth for evidence of vanished cultures, the engineers constructing interstate highways and erecting a dam, the planners and builders of Holiday Inn hotels, the farmers plowing new lands for planting—all are destroying what was on the land before they began. Similarly, the desires of the various builders and destroyers inevitably collide. Chad Jasker's father plowed under burial mounds in his desire to work his land, and Chad himself bulldozes the project of Dan Loggins and August Howe in his frustration over the collapse of his dreams. In her passion for Chad Jasker, Cynthia Howe gives away her honor, destroys her marriage, and brings confusion to her daughter. Thus on one level the metaphors of the burial mounds, highway, dam, and Holiday Inn demonstrate humankind's quest for permanence, meaning, and happiness, but they also operate as symbols of destructive elements in humankind. As people search out what meaning and happiness they must, perhaps creating their own myths, they destroy the past and the relationships, and even the people, they most need to cling to. According to the evidence of the burial mounds and the roundhouse, entire cultures can vanish without a trace of the values that sustained them. The present age cannot look to the past for answers. Each culture must discover its own meanings, values, and happiness in the context of the ordinary pains and pleasures of existence.

Wilson resists judging his characters, but for the most part, they are ordinary people, driven by the usual human desires for sex, money, possessions, power, fame. Some of them, such as Dan, Delia, and Jean, repress these desires or attempt to fulfill them as harmlessly as possible. Others, such as Chad and Cynthia, are slaves to their passions and eventually cause misery and destruction. The world is a difficult, unpredictable, dangerous place, Wilson demonstrates, and humankind does not make life easier for itself. Its survival may depend on finding a way to happiness that values preservation more than destruction. Must humanity vanish without a trace, or can it transcend its baser impulses in order to leave behind a record that documents its nobility, courage, and goodness? *The Mound Builders* provides no answers but suggests by its own existence that only the truth about human nature will suffice to indicate its potential for greatness.

Dramatic Devices

Through a variety of dramatic devices that invite the audience to interpret the play metaphorically as well as literally, *The Mound Builders* directs the playgoer's attention to the struggle of the characters to find meaning and purpose in their lives as well as in the course of all human existence. The play suggests that the meaning of human existence is not inherent in events themselves, but rather must be discovered, if not made. Wilson employs three major devices to make this point: a self-conscious stylized structure, numerous parallels between the culture of the mound builders and the present culture, and symbols suggesting that time itself works against humankind's effort to build lasting monuments to itself.

The story of the failed expedition to Blue Shoals is told in flashback, six months after its climactic event, by August Howe, leader of the archaeology team. While attempting to organize a report on the expedition from the archaeologists' notes and his wife's slides, he recalls the events that brought about the end of his marriage, the failure of the expedition, and the death of Dan Loggins. This frame functions as a device to summarize and organize much diverse material, but Wilson uses it primarily to foreshadow the climactic revelation of the play and its consequences, thus suggesting the role played in subsequent events by the otherwise apparently random conversations and confrontations preceding it.

In the first scene of the play, for example, August says that he intends to "go through what is left of the wreckage of last summer's expedition." In the second framing scene, he refers to his wife as "ex-relation by marriage" and to his daughter as "alleged daughter." In the fourth and final framing scene of act 1, August says, "There was no September goodbye this summer." Early in act 2, in the last framing scene before the climax of the play, August says, "By the time the lake overran the site, it didn't at all matter." August's apparent interruptions of the events of the summer thus frequently remind the audience that the events witnessed will eventually culminate by association in meanings and causation. In addition to the framing device, Wilson also foreshadows the outcome of the action by drawing numerous parallels between mound-builder culture and the present. These might represent coincidences, the action of fate, or merely plot machinations. Though their meanings are debatable, the parallels certainly add urgency and significance to ordinary human actions, motivations, needs, and desires.

Wilson's stylized technique serves to remind the audience that what is being watched is not random behavior but a play. The lake water covering a multitude of sins at the end of this play also obliterates the past, making it appear that Dan, Chad, the roundhouse, and the burial mound have all vanished without a trace. Soon the old farmhouse will also disappear. The meaning of this place, then, exists only in human memory and in the spoken and written records made by those struggling to understand the meaning in their own lives.

Critical Context

The Hot l Baltimore (pr., pb. 1973), Lanford Wilson's eleventh play, won two major awards, an Obie and the 1973 New York Drama Critics Circle Award for Best American Play of 1973. Wilson's next play, *The Mound Builders*, though not as popular, has been produced often in the United States and abroad. In addition, it has been made into a film for the Public Broadcasting Service (PBS). Like *The Hot l Baltimore*, *The Mound Builders* received high critical praise for its complexity of thought and language. Critics were divided on its central meaning but generally found evidence in the play of a playwright of great promise.

In *The Mound Builders*, Wilson continued developing ideas, concerns, and techniques along the same daring lines he pursued in *The Hot l Baltimore*. In both plays, as well as in many successful plays in the years since, Wilson provides an authentic American base—the decaying hotel in *The Hot l Baltimore*, rural middle America in *The Mound Builders*, a small town in Missouri in his Talley family trilogy. In his plays, as well, character, not action, dominates. Events often seem ordinary and insignificant, but they accumulate meanings and can prove to be loaded with significance. Some critics have likened Wilson to Tennessee Williams, others, to George S. Kaufman, but for his focus on character rather than action, Wilson's roots might be traced back to Anton Chekhov, whose quirky yet endearing characters also often passively accept a fate they seem powerless to change. Moreover, Wilson, like Chekhov, often employs melodramatic confrontations and climaxes to suggest meanings inherent yet unexpected in the ordinarily uneventful lives of his characters.

Wilson contributed a number of new plays to his oeuvre in the 1990's and early twenty-first century, many of which continued the themes developed in his earlier plays. These works included *The Moonshot Tape* (pr., pb. 1990), *Eukiah* (pr., pb. 1992), *Redwood Curtain* (pr. 1992, pb. 1993), *Day* (pr., pb. 1996), *A Sense of Place: Or, Virgil Is Still the Frogboy* (pr. 1997, pb. 1999), *Book of Days* (pr. 1998, pb. 2000), and *Rain Dance* (pr. 2000).

The Mound Builders is representative of Wilson's best work. In his many full-length plays and one-acts, this major American playwright eloquently states his conviction that each individual is the sum total of what he or she has been. In *The Mound Builders*, as in all of his best plays, characters look to the past for the values to sustain them, and, if they are lucky, discover that personal relationships in the present are their only salvation.

Sources for Further Study

Barnett, Gene A. *Lanford Wilson*. Boston: Twayne, 1987.

Busby, Mark. *Lanford Wilson*. Boise, Idaho: Boise State University Press, 1987.

Clurman, Harold. Review in *The Nation*, March 15, 1975, 315-316.

Cohn, Ruby. "Lanford Wilson." In *New American Dramatists, 1960-1980*. New York: Grove Press, 1982.

Dasgupta, Gautam. "Lanford Wilson." In *American Playwrights: A Critical Survey*, edited by Bonnie Marranca and Gautam Dasgupta. New York: Drama Book Specialists, 1981.

DiGaetani, John L. "Lanford Wilson." In *A Search for Postmodern Theatre: Interviews with Contemporary Playwrights*. New York: Greenwood Press, 1991.

Gussow, Mel. "Lanford Wilson on Broadway." *Horizon* 23 (May, 1980): 30-36.

Savran, David. "Lanford Wilson." In *In Their Own Words: Contemporary American Playwrights*. New York: Theatre Communications Group, 1988.

Williams, Philip Middleton. *A Comfortable House: Lanford Wilson, Marshall W. Mason, and the Circle Repertory Company*. Jefferson, N.C.: McFarland, 1993.

James W. Robinson, Jr.

MRS. WARREN'S PROFESSION

Author: George Bernard Shaw (1856-1950)
Type of plot: Social realism
Time of plot: The 1890's
Locale: England
First produced: 1902, by the Stage Society, London
First published: 1898, in *Plays Pleasant and Unpleasant*

Principal characters:
Mrs. Warren, the owner of a chain of brothels in Europe
Vivie Warren, her daughter
Sir George Crofts, her friend and business partner
The Reverend Samuel Gardner, a clergyman
Frank Gardner, his son
Praed, a friend of Mrs. Warren

The Play

Act 1 begins on a summer afternoon in a cottage garden near Haslemere, Surrey, not far from London. Vivie Warren, a middle-class, well-educated young woman, sits on a hammock reading and writing, with a pile of serious-looking books nearby. Praed, a friend of her mother, arrives and tells Vivie that her mother is coming down from London. Vivie hardly knows her mother, who lived abroad while the girl was sent away to school and college in England. Through the ensuing conversation, the audience learns of Vivie's success in gaining a high mathematics degree at the University of Cambridge, and that she intends to use her expertise by securing employment in London, as either an actuary or an assistant to a barrister. Praed expresses regret that she appears not to have any romance or beauty in her life. She replies that she does not care for either.

Mrs. Warren arrives with her longtime companion, Sir George Crofts, a successful businessman. Immediately attracted to Vivie, Crofts asks Praed who her father is, but Praed does not know. Crofts is concerned that he may himself be her father. Young Frank Gardner, a charming but idle young man who is also keen on Vivie, joins the group and then sidles off to engage in some disrespectful banter with his clergyman father, the Rev. Samuel Gardner, a bustling, seemingly important man who is, however, incapable of winning anyone's respect. It is revealed that Frank's father was something of a rake in his youth and wrote some compromising letters to a woman; he warns Frank not to fall into the same trap. The act ends when the Rev. Gardner meets Mrs. Warren, who, to his great embarrassment, recalls him enthusiastically from days gone by.

Act 2 begins that evening in the cottage. There is a dispute over Frank's wish to marry Vivie, which is opposed by his father (partly because he fears that he may be her father) and by Crofts. Mrs. Warren rebukes Crofts for his interest in Vivie and rules out Frank's suit when she discovers that he has no money. Frank, however, is undaunted by her refusal. The climax of the act is a long discussion between Mrs. Warren and her daughter. Vivie declares her intention of earning her own living, but she wants to know about her mother's occupation and who her father is. Mrs. Warren denies that her father is Crofts, but in a manner that does not reassure Vivie. Vivie's attitude is dispassionate and indifferent, refusing to acknowledge her mother's authority over her. Mrs. Warren talks about her own upbringing. She had been a scullery maid and a waitress, until she and her sister Liz became partners and operated a brothel in Brussels. Mrs. Warren justifies herself; her work was not pleasant, but the women were better treated in the brothel than they would have been in a factory. It is not possible, she argues, to maintain self-respect in starvation and slavery (one of her sisters had worked for many years at "respectable" jobs that barely paid a living wage). Mrs. Warren is proud of the independence she has won and the fact that she had been able to give her daughter a good education. After these revelations, Vivie regards her mother with new respect, although she is disturbed by what she has heard.

Act 3 takes place the following morning. Crofts proposes marriage to Vivie, but she immediately rejects him. He counters by explaining how much Mrs. Warren owes him: He had put forty thousand pounds into her business. Then he reveals that the business is still in existence and yields an excellent profit. Vivie, who thought that the business had been wound up, is horrified, and she surprises Crofts by her knowledge of what the business is. Pointing out that the proceeds have paid for her education, he justifies his investments by saying that everyone makes money in a tainted way—from the Church of England, which allows some of its properties to be used for questionable purposes, to those who make money from employing people at starvation wages in factories. Vivie is shaken; she insults Crofts and he is furious. Frank appears with a rifle and taunts Crofts. Crofts hits back by saying that Vivie is Frank's half sister. Frank aims his rifle at the retreating figure of Crofts; Vivie grabs the muzzle and turns it against herself, and Frank drops the gun immediately. She pushes Frank away and goes off to work in the legal offices of her friend Honaria Fraser in Chancery Lane, London.

In the final act, Frank calls on Vivie in London. He declares once more his romantic feelings for her and also says that he does not believe they are related. Vivie agrees with this, but does not return his love. She tells both Frank and Praed, who is on his way to Italy and has called to say good-bye, what her mother's profession is. Praed is amazed but declares his respect for Vivie; Frank says that he cannot now marry her, because he could not use her money and he is incapable of making any himself.

Mrs. Warren enters, distraught, and tries to win Vivie back. Vivie announces that she intends to support herself in the future. Mrs. Warren attempts to persuade her that she is throwing away her chances for no good reason; she does not realize the hypocritical way the world operates. Vivie says that she would feel bored and worthless if she took her mother's money and asks her mother why she does not leave her business behind her, as her sister Liz had done. Mrs. Warren replies that she needs work and excitement; she is suited to the life. Vivie, unmoved, says they must part, and she gets Mrs. Warren reluctantly to acknowledge that her decision is the correct one. Mrs. Warren leaves angrily, and Vivie is relieved. She tears up a note which Frank had left, turns to her work, and is soon absorbed in it.

Themes and Meanings

In *Mrs. Warren's Profession*, George Bernard Shaw set out to challenge the complacency of his audience and subvert some of their most ingrained notions. In his preface to the play, he said that it was written "to draw attention to the truth that prostitution is caused, not by female depravity and male licentiousness, but simply by underpaying, undervaluing, and overworking women so shamefully that the poorest of them are forced to resort to prostitution to keep body and soul together." He argued that Mrs. Warren's defense of herself was valid, although it was not meant to be a justification of the vice in which she was involved. In the play Shaw draws attention to the hypocrisy of a society in which a man like Crofts is considered respectable because no one of any breeding would be so indelicate as to inquire about the nature of his business activities. Shaw also suggests, through Mrs. Warren, that in a capitalist society that denies opportunities to women, even the relations between "respectable" women and their men are morally not very different from those between a prostitute and her client. All women are dependent on men in one way or another: A respectable upper-class girl must marry a rich man so that she can enjoy his wealth; the only difference between her and the working-class girl or the prostitute is that the latter cannot expect the men of means to marry them.

Another theme in the play is the emergence of the emancipated "New Woman": resourceful, independent, career-oriented. Shaw was responding to a suggestion made by his friend Beatrice Webb that he "should put on the stage a real modern lady of the governing class—not the sort of thing that theatrical and critical authorities imagine such a lady to be." The result was the cigar-smoking Vivie Warren, who is a complete contrast to the submissive, sentimental heroine to which popular Victorian taste had become accustomed. Vivie is self-assured and knows exactly what she wants: "People are always blaming their circumstances for what they are. I dont believe in circumstances. The people who get on in this world are the people who get up and look for the circumstances they want, and, if they cant find them, make them." Vivie has reached a point at which she can exercise freedom of choice, and she chooses the pleasures of productive work over those of love or family ties.

An underlying theme is incest. It is conveyed in the suggestion that Vivie and Frank may be half brother and sister, although it is not clearly established that they are, and neither of them believes that they are. Some critics have argued that the theme is brought in unnecessarily, and Shaw has also been criticized for bringing it in but not developing it. Shaw insisted, however, that it was a necessary part of the play. In an early draft the theme was much more explicit—there was no doubt that Vivie and Frank were half brother and sister, and they became mildly sexually involved before Vivie broke off the relationship.

Dramatic Devices

Following the model of the Norwegian playwright Henrik Ibsen, whom George Bernard Shaw admired, Shaw attempted to create plays in which the central interest lay in dialogue rather than action. He thought that the dialogue should revolve around ideas, in such a way that the audience would have their habitual opinions and attitudes challenged. Shaw achieves the effect he wanted primarily in the two confrontations between Mrs. Warren and Vivie, which conclude acts 2 and 4. He does this even while making concessions to the stage conventions of the day: Progressive revelations about guilty pasts and shady associations, as well as hints of incest and some odd coincidences, keep the action moving and satisfy the audience's need for surprises, although the facts that unfold are anything but conventional.

The emotional center of the play is reached at the end of act 2. In the early stages of the discussion between Vivie and her mother, it appears that Vivie's view will easily prevail. Her rational assurance seems to carry moral authority with it. In two significant stage directions, however, Shaw suddenly shifts the balance of the argument. After chiding Vivie for her heartlessness, Mrs. Warren "suddenly breaks out vehemently in her natural tongue—the dialect of a woman of the people—with all her affectations of maternal authority and conventional manners gone, and an overwhelming inspiration of true conviction and scorn in her."

This sudden eruption of deeply felt emotion has considerable force. It shifts the sympathies of the audience in the direction of Mrs. Warren, and when her spirited defense of herself follows immediately after, the audience is less sure of its own moral positions. The effect is compounded by the next stage direction, in which Vivie, moved by her mother's explosion of true feeling, is to sit "down with a shrug, no longer confident; for her replies, which have sounded sensible and strong to her so far, now begin to ring rather woodenly and even priggishly against the new tone of her mother." Having established some measure of equilibrium in the tension between opposing views, and broken down some of the prejudices of the audience, Shaw can then drive the wedge in further in the remainder of the play, as he continues to expose the many layers of hypocrisy on which he believed capitalist society rested.

Critical Context

Mrs. Warren's Profession was first published in *Plays Pleasant and Unpleasant* (1898). It was George Bernard Shaw's third "unpleasant" play, following *Widowers' Houses* (pr. 1892, pb. 1893), which dealt with the problem of slum landlords, and *The Philanderer* (pb. 1898, pr. 1905), about marriage and the restrictions it imposed on women. The plays were described as "unpleasant" because they attack existing social conditions in a way that forces the audience to question their own basic assumptions. "I must . . . warn my readers that my attacks are directed against themselves, not against my stage figures," Shaw wrote in his preface.

There are similarities between *Widowers' Houses* and *Mrs. Warren's Profession*. In the earlier play, Harry Trench hears that his independent income is in fact derived directly from the profits made by Sartorius, the slum landlord, his prospective father-in-law. This puts him in a situation similar to that of Vivie Warren. Later in *Widowers' Houses*, it transpires that Sartorius's mother had been an exploited washerwoman—an explanation in part for his later attitudes, just as Mrs. Warren's profession resulted (in her opinion) from her early experiences as a victim of an unjust system. *Mrs. Warren's Profession*, however, is a more powerful drama than the earlier play, particularly in the skill with which Shaw handles the two confrontations between Vivie and Mrs. Warren in acts 2 and 4.

Because *Mrs. Warren's Profession* deals with prostitution and hints at incest, it was for many years banned from public theaters. It was first performed in 1902 by the Stage Society, a private club that gave a performance for its own members and so escaped the censorship imposed by the Lord Chamberlain. The play was performed in New York in 1905 but was closed down immediately by the police; the producer and the entire company were arrested, although they were later acquitted and the play was allowed to continue. It was not until 1925 that the play received its first legal public performance in England, at the Regent Theatre in London. As late as 1955, the play was banned in Paris because it was considered "amoral."

Sources for Further Study

Bertolini, John. *The Playwriting Self of George Bernard Shaw*. Carbondale: Southern Illinois University Press, 1991.

Bloom, Harold. *George Bernard Shaw*. Broomall, Pa.: Chelsea House, 1987.

Davis, Tracy. *George Bernard Shaw and the Socialist Theatre*. Westport, Conn.: Greenwood Press, 1994.

Ervine, St. John. *Bernard Shaw: His Life, Work, and Friends*. New York: Morrow, 1956.

Greene, Nicholas. *Bernard Shaw: A Critical View*. London: Macmillan, 1984.

Holroyd, Michael. *Bernard Shaw*. New York: Random House, 1988.

Hugo, Leon. *Bernard Shaw: Playwright and Preacher*. London: Methuen, 1971.

Page, Malcolm, and Margery Morgan. *File on Shaw*. London: Methuen, 1989.

Bryan Aubrey

MY DINNER WITH ANDRÉ
A Screenplay

Authors: Wallace Shawn (1943-   ) and André Gregory (1934-   )
Type of plot: Problem play
Time of plot: The late 1970's
Locale: New York City
First produced: 1981, as a film directed by Louis Malle
First published: 1981

Principal characters:
WALLY and
ANDRÉ, the authors, as themselves

The Play

My Dinner with André takes the form of a conversation between the work's authors, playwright/actor Wallace Shawn and theater director André Gregory. Shawn's interior monologue at the work's beginning provides some biographical information about Gregory; during the subsequent conversation only their first names, "Wally" and "André," identify the speakers. Even so, they clearly play themselves, for their conversation has to do exclusively with matters related to the theater, to aesthetics, and, frequently, to actual persons. Events to which they refer, though focused, highlighted, or slightly altered for purposes of their presentation, are basically factual. The play's action proceeds without intervals and, except for brief interior monologues which attend Wally's arrival and departure, is set entirely at the table of an exclusive New York City restaurant. The two men enjoy a fine meal as they talk.

Wally trudges along on his way to the restaurant as the work begins. He is thirty-six years old, though he looks older; he is a playwright, turned actor in order to eke out some form of living. It bothers him that his girlfriend Debby has to work three nights a week as a waitress to help support them. Routine errands, such as making telephone calls, buying envelopes, mailing copies of unproduced plays, and checking with his answering service in hope of some acting work have made his day more discouraging than usual. Worst of all, Wally is uneasy about his dinner engagement with André and wishes that instead he were on his way home to see Debby and eat a good dinner there.

André had been a close friend and colleague, had discovered Wally, and had directed Wally's first play, but immediately after this had dropped out of sight. Wally has heard all sorts of strange tales about André's doings: that André had become a devotee of Buddhism, that he had talked to trees, that he had appeared in odd parts of the world at unpredictable times, always traveling alone and for no ostensible purpose. In short, Wally worries for his old friend's sanity and feels unprepared to cope with André's problems in addition to his own. He is also quietly resentful that André appears to have the money to indulge these eccentricities.

These feelings exacerbate the awkwardness with which the evening begins. André appears almost immediately after Wally has arrived. Though the warmth of his greeting dispels some of Wally's attempt at disengagement, Wally is still nervous. He wonders whether he will survive the meal and thinks that André looks "crazy." The audience does not know what to think. André is painfully thin, looks vaguely haunted, and, though dressed neatly and with considerably more style than Wally (who wears a tie and poorly cut sports jacket), has nevertheless chosen to wear a shawl-collar sweater and open-neck shirt to an elegant restaurant.

André looks younger and more alive than Wally, though he is actually ten years older; however, to Wally's pleasantry, "You look terrific," he replies, "I *feel* terrible."

André begins to talk even as Wally is having these negative thoughts. The audience hears only a phrase or two beneath Wally's negativism, about an actual Polish director named Jerzy Grotowski who had dropped out of the theater, had returned to Poland, and had begun to run avant-garde workshops for actors there. Grotowski had invited André to participate in one of these, held in a forest from sunset to ten or eleven o'clock the next morning. A group of forty, none of whom spoke English, would sing, dance, and eat in a kind of living improvisation, then sleep from noon until the next sunset. André enjoyed these sessions immensely, though he also found them frightening because all plan and structure was absent. There was no security of routine, let alone script, and anything could happen. André himself directed one of these events, which Grotowski called "beehives," unified only by a song of Saint Francis, in which the singer thanks God for eyes, heart, friends, and life. The group sang this song for hours, in countless repetitions, until something happened.

Partly because he had feared nothing would happen, André grabbed a huge teddy bear one of the women had brought and threw it into the air. Immediately, the group began to dance in two circles, one clockwise, the other counterclockwise, still singing the song, but with a thumping, persistent rhythm. Before even André had realized it, he was holding the teddy bear to his breast as though nursing it, then tossing it to Grotowski who did the same, all this time to the infectious rhythm and the playing of a flute and drum two of the participants had brought. At the height of this ritual, during one of what André describes as one of its "improvisations," Grotowski and André were able to place their hands in a flame without pain or harm. The ritual ended as suddenly as it had begun; all were convinced that something important had happened, but nobody could say for certain what it was. On André's final day with the group, its members christened him in a ceremony with thousands of flowers and hundreds of candles and torches.

Other strange events happened to André after his return from Poland, and these seemed to impel important decisions that he made. In a country field, while walking alone, he heard a voice call out, "Little Prince," and immediately thought of *Le Petit Prince* (1943; *The Little Prince*, 1943), the fantasy by Antoine de Saint-Exupéry. André had disliked the book intensely but determined to reread it because of this experience. That same day, he received from one of the women in his workshop in Poland a letter in which she had written that André had "dominated" her; she had crossed out this word, however, for English was still new to her, and substituted "tamed." André's answer, guided by his rereading of *The Little Prince*, was simply an outline of his own hand with the words "Your heart is in my hand" written in the center. No sooner had he done this than he came across a complete run of the classic Surrealist magazine *Minotaur*, which reproduced the *A* from Sir John Tenniel's illustrations for Lewis Carroll's *Alice's Adventures in Wonderland* (1865). André recalled his own realization of that work as a stage play. Then he saw the handprints, traced on subsequent pages, of surrealist André Derain, André Breton, and Antoine de Saint-Exupéry; moreover, he discovered that the magazine's first issue had appeared on May 12, 1934, one day after his own birth. André soon afterward decided to work on a stage version of *The Little Prince*, in the Sahara Desert in the company of two actors and a Japanese Buddhist priest he had met in New York.

André continues to relate the series of bizarre events that had happened after he last had seen Wally—from eating sand in the Sahara to returning to New York and discovering that the Buddhist, who was still with him, dominated André's wife and children, ate huge amounts of food, and wore Gucci shoes under his monk's robes. After André imagines that he sees a six-foot, eight-inch blue minotaur at Mass in a Long Island Roman Catholic Church, he feels oddly consoled and believes this creature is there merely to assure him that all this strangeness is part of life's journey.

As a result, André decided to pursue the odyssey with enthusiasm. He had a flag made for himself, purple and bearing the Tibetan swastika (the reverse of the Nazi symbol). Ultimately, however, he allowed the flag to be destroyed, since so many friends found it disturbing. He went to India and to Findhorn, Scotland, where people set aside fields of vegetables for the insects to eat in order to ensure a good harvest, refer to "the god within," and give names to their machines and household appliances. André even allowed himself to participate in a Halloween ritual at Montauk, Long Island, in which he was buried alive; details of this ceremony recall the executions of the Nazi death camps.

Since these adventures, André feels becalmed but maudlin. He thinks of death often, and people often appear, to varying degrees, as insensitive, insincere, or hypocritical. Because people are always, in effect, acting, theatrical performance is vapid, and daily life has become its substitute. He muses that if a director of a modern performance of Euripides' play *Bakchai* (405 B.C.E.; *The Bacchae*) were to order that a severed human head actually be passed around the audience to represent the head of Pentheus, the audience and many of the actors would be scandalized and revolted; yet the arts have resorted to such sensationalism, primarily out of desperation. People have become bored and spoiled, taking an elevator to the top of a skyscraper rather than climbing Mount Everest, or even imagining climbing Everest.

By this time, as suddenly as it had begun, the conversation has ended. All the other diners have left the restaurant, and since André has paid the bill, Wally finds himself with enough money to take a taxi. As he rides home, Wally sees familiar buildings and sights in terms of his childhood memories: the place where he bought a suit with his father, where he had an ice cream soda after school. He looks forward to telling Debby everything about his dinner with André.

Themes and Meanings

Extreme and harrowing as André's experiences are, they come about as a result of what he perceives as contemporary art's inability to portray life. He recognizes that reality has become surreal, and theater has become a tranquilizer that protects its audience from discomforting ideas. Ancient Greek theater, in its purest sense, was a celebration of Dionysus, the god associated with the fertility of the wine grape. André's experience in Poland, though he likens it to an American Indian tribal festival, also parallels the orgiastic rites of Dionysus insofar as it relied on music and ecstatic chant to induce a new state of consciousness above conventional sense perception. The baptism that concluded the workshop signals rebirth; that André is only partly prepared for his rebirth is clear from his inability to place his right as well as his left hand in fire. Saint Francis of Assisi, before his religious awakening, participated in a medieval version of this fertility rite, in the form of uninhibited group dances known as *farandoles*. Even so, Francis quickly recognized that such rituals confer only a short-term benefit. André, like Francis, desires closer communion with the world in which he lives, to become a better artist as well as a more complete human being. It is, therefore, appropriate that the principal activity of his group session is a sustained chant in Saint Francis's honor.

André's sudden fascination with synchronicity, which occurs when he examines his brother's copies of *Minotaur* magazine, indicates his need to continue his search for pattern, structure, and meaning in his art as well as his life. He wishes to believe that all things have connections with past, present, and future, so he fastens on coming upon the Tenniel *A* with bibliomantic fervor, as a mystic reference to his own name, as a connection with his own past staging of *Alice's Adventures in Wonderland*, as an indication that Surrealism in the manner of Breton and Derain should be the artistic path he ought to follow, and that he should pursue as well the cult of the self, as represented by Saint-Exupéry's *The Little Prince*. This clearly will take him in precisely the opposite direction from the communion his Poland experience implied; with a certain bathos, André shifts allegiance from the secular Saint Francis to the solipsistic Saint-Exupéry.

A variety of literary cult has formed about Saint-Exupéry, all of whose works champion the strong individualist willing to pass into nothingness so long as it is possible do so while pursuing a personal destiny of greatness. That Saint-Exupéry, an aviator as well as a writer, disappeared without a trace while flying a solo mission during World War II has added romantic appeal to his ideas. André eventually condemns Saint-Exupéry's philosophy as implicitly fascist, but not before attempting to prepare his own version of Saint-Exupéry's *The Little Prince* with a Japanese Buddhist in the surreal Sahara and adopting a personal flag with the Tibetan swastika emblazoned upon it.

The experience at Findhorn provides André with answers that are closer to, even if not perfectly, satisfactory. Vegetables raised for insects to consume imply respect for life. Naming household possessions denies the value of conspicuous consumption. Recognizing "the god within" ties the individual to environment. Stereotypic Scottish independence is attractive in itself; yet Findhorn is a community as well, with surreal elements that appeal to an artist such as André.

Clearly, André has not found precise answers to the questions that impelled his five-year odyssey; nevertheless, his very conversation forces Wally, who is more sedentary, less intellectual, yet just as troubled in his life and art, to ask less traumatizing but no less meaningful questions about his own circumstances. That Wally comes from the meal with a reawakened awareness of how well he fits into the city in which he lives is a measure of the service André has done for his old friend.

Dramatic Devices

Though André's experiences extend more than five years, his vivid recounting of them takes less than two hours. Conversation, or more precisely André's narrative with Wally's sometimes significant interjections, is the medium that gives *My Dinner with André* an Aristotelian triple unity of time, place, and action. Change occurs, for André is certainly different from the man Wally had known five years earlier, but Wally undergoes a more sudden and possibly more lasting change from hearing André's experiences in a single evening. Wally arrives at the restaurant rumpled from the subway ride and worried about his career, his finances, and his life in general, but he returns home in a taxi, recalling the scenes of his youth and eager to tell his girlfriend all that he has heard.

Clearly, Wally serves as a conversational foil for André's brilliance. Except for Wally's interior monologue, delivered on his way to the restaurant, nearly all of his words are monosyllables that indicate agreement with what André says. This is not to imply that Wally is unimportant in the action. Wally is alternately pathetically and bathetically humorous: worried about affording the necessities of life, yet dining in a restaurant far beyond his means; a professional writer, yet filling his conversation with monosyllables and trite analogies; from New York City, yet a mere provincial when compared to André.

My Dinner with André lacks act divisions, time lapses, and other conventional intervals, but the meal, served as the narrative proceeds, has several courses. André is forced to stop whenever the waiter takes the order, pours the wine, or changes the table settings. The waiter has the only other speaking role, aside from André and Wally, and his place is very important. Directions specify that he have the face of a man who has seen life. He observes every detail as the men converse, though he limits his comments to the meal. Initially, at least, the waiter views the two men with a disdain amounting almost to suspicion. Their appearance clearly does not inspire his confidence in a paid check, let alone a satisfactory tip. Even so, he remains passive and unobtrusive, like a one-man chorus in whose features one can read the results of a lifetime of acceptance. He is not a broken man, but he is older than André and in his own way has seen as much. When he asks the men whether everything is satisfactory, it might be tempting for them to give an answer that encompasses more than the excellent meal and the way he has served it. It is affecting and ironic that both Wally and André immediately offer him the conventional assurance that everything is fine, though their conversation reveals clearly that little in life is completely acceptable.

Structuring the conversation around Wally's interior monologues at arrival and departure is a final and important dramatic device. Though Wally speaks more, and even ventures to express mild disagreement when André asserts that modern city life is devoid of reality, both Wally and the audience can clearly see the differences between the two men. However, Wally is hopeful, even excited, as a result of his reunion with André, and one cannot help but think that this augurs well for Wally's own creative work.

Critical Context

My Dinner with André represents a collaboration by two authors with very different personalities and experiences in the arts. André Gregory, true to his persona in this play, has never hesitated to engage in avant-garde and even outrageous projects. In 1979, for example, he and a group of nondancers performed, with complete seriousness, a ballet choreographed by Twyla Tharp at Town Hall in New York City. He was the former director of the Manhattan Project, an experimental theater group, and it was there that he first met Shawn. Gregory's stage adaptation of *Alice in Wonderland* (pr. 1970) received great critical acclaim in its five-year New York run and won an Obie Award (given to outstanding Off-Broadway plays). Like Alice, Gregory has never hesitated to follow his own White Rabbit, wherever it might take him.

Wallace Shawn's career in the theater has been equally distinguished, though certainly more traditional and circumspect. His play *Our Late Night* (pr. 1974, pb. 1984), which also won an Obie Award, was directed by Gregory and represented their first collaboration. Shawn's characters, like his own persona in *My Dinner with André*, are often sedentary. Though they live wild and intense lives within their imaginations, some element of their circumstances (perhaps only psychological, yet overwhelming) anchors them to an apparently more controllable environment.

This theme remains a feature of his subsequent works. *Aunt Dan and Lemon* (pr., pb. 1985), for example, focuses on a young recluse who, though born "Leonora," retains the implicitly pejorative name "Lemon," given her as a child by "Aunt Dan," a family friend whose real name is Danielle. Aunt Dan, an eccentric professor, controls Lemon's life completely, even after Dan herself has died, through a series of conversations that effectively sour and poison the younger woman's adult life. In the 1990's Shawn added two plays to his oeuvre: *The Fever* (pr. 1990, pb. 1991) and *The Designated Mourner* (pr., pb. 1996).

Sources for Further Study

Brewer, Gay. "He's Still Falling: Wallace Shawn's Problems of Mortality." *American Drama*, Fall, 1992, 26-58.

Buford, Bill. "My Lunch with Wally." *Vogue* 176 (January, 1986): 56.
Gingold, Alfred. "Shawn with the Wind." *New Republic*, February 9, 1987, 10.
King, W. D. *Writing Wrongs: The Work of Wallace Shawn*. Philadelphia: Temple University Press, 1997.
Lahr, John. "Wallace Shawn." In *Show and Tell: New Yorker Profiles*. Woodstock, New York: Overlook, 2000.
Rose, Lloyd. "The Art of Conversation: Wallace Shawn." *Atlantic*, November, 1985, 125.
Savran, David. "Wallace Shawn." In *In Their Own Words: Contemporary American Playwrights*. New York: Theatre Communications Group, 1988.

Robert J. Forman

NIGHT AND DAY

Author: Tom Stoppard (Tomas Straussler, 1937-   )
Type of plot: Psychological
Time of plot: The 1970's
Locale: Kambawe, a fictitious former British colony in Africa
First produced: 1978, at the Phoenix Theatre, London
First published: 1978

Principal characters:
GEORGE GUTHRIE, a British photographer for the *Sunday Globe*
DICK WAGNER, his partner, an Australian roving reporter
JACOB MILNE, a young, idealistic British correspondent
GEOFFREY CARSON, a British colonial survivor
RUTH CARSON, his wife
MAGEEBA, the president of Kambawe

The Play

Night and Day begins with a dream sequence in which the photographer Guthrie is gunned down by machine-gun fire. The scene quickly changes to the reality of a comfortable colonial veranda where the audience meets the hostess, Ruth Carson, the attractive wife of mine-owner Geoffrey Carson. Guthrie has arrived, uninvited, to await his colleague, Dick Wagner. Both are journalists in the midst of a revolution in the fictitious Kambawe. President Mageeba is beset by the insurgent Colonel Shimbu, and the wealthy Carson will act as middleman in their peace talks. The journalists have heard rumors of this meeting and thus intrude themselves on the Carsons in order to be on the scene of the action. They also need access to the telex machine Carson possesses. An anonymous special correspondent has, meanwhile, scooped the two professionals by obtaining an exclusive interview with Shimbu and sending it to their own London paper, the *Sunday Globe*. This same reporter, the young and idealistic Jacob Milne, arrives on the scene with Carson and has information for another potential scoop: Shimbu's forces have secretly attacked and captured Carson's mines.

Dick Wagner is furious with the idea of the younger reporter's success, but even more so when he learns that Milne had worked previously for the Grimsby *Evening Messenger* and was the "Grimsby Scab," the reporter who broke ranks by refusing to join the journalists' union in the strike against management. Wagner is a staunch union man, a good old boy of the old school. The three journalists debate the rules of the profession, while each plays his own game in trying to be the first to get the story of the African war to the waiting world. Wagner remains at the Carsons' home knowing of the secret meeting to take place there between Mageeba and Shimbu, and Wagner sends Milne with Guthrie to the scene of the fighting to pass on to Shimbu the president's reply to his request for peace negotiations.

Act 1 also introduces the subtext of the play, the special relationships of Wagner and Ruth and of Ruth and Milne. It is revealed that the week before the above action begins, Ruth was in London to fetch her eight-year-old son from school and met Dick Wagner, with whom she had a one-night stand. She had previously been faithful to the older, dour Carson, and she feels considerable remorse about her interlude with Wagner. He avoids a direct confrontation when they meet again in her home but alludes to their liaison and seems quite agreeable to a continuation of the affair. This possibility is abhorrent to her. Her special rules allow her one extramarital event or, if consumed by passion, a thousand. She asserts that "twice, Wagner, *twice*—a lady might think she'd been taken for a tart." In the meantime, she is attracted to Milne, his youth and idealism, his purity of profession, his total difference from Wagner.

As the second act begins, the lines are drawn. Wagner is determined to scoop Milne on the peace talks in the African war and to preserve his "old pro" way of life and of journalism. Ruth has a fantasy encounter with Milne, but in reality she and Carson await the secret visit of the president when Wagner intrudes, determined to be present during the negotiations. Mageeba arrives and proves to be a match for Wagner. London-educated, articulate, and perfectly in control, Mageeba conducts the interview on his own terms and intrudes his own view of the fifth estate; his has to be a "relatively free press . . . I mean a free press which is edited by one of my relatives." He concludes by shouting a diatribe against Wagner and the *Sunday Globe* and strikes Wagner's head with his weighted cane. Guthrie bursts into the room shouting that Milne has been killed—shot in the cross fire as his Jeep approached Colonel Shimbu's headquarters.

The play ends in a final irony: The war in Africa and the Fleet Street journalistic wars converge. Milne's final story has been "blacked" by the union, because of his anti-union stance in Grimsby. There is a strike and all the weekend papers are shut down. Wagner's great scoop, his interview with President Mageeba, will not be printed. The alliance of Ruth and Milne will never be. The gentle, idealistic side of her nature that she revealed to Milne during the brief meeting at the end of the first act and the more elaborate scene of seduction at the beginning of the second act are now subverted. She gives in to Wagner: "I want to be hammered out, disjointed, folded up and put away like linen in a drawer." She will have a second night with Wagner after all. Wagner uses the telex to reach the *Sunday Globe*—not to transmit his scoop of a lifetime but to dictate Jacob Milne's obituary.

Themes and Meanings

Night and Day encompasses the duality of theme that its title implies. The more obvious examination is of journalistic responsibility. Guthrie and Wagner, the grizzled veterans of the wars and natural disasters of the age, have traveled the globe covering events from earthquakes to assassinations. They are workmanlike, cynical, both consummate professionals. They arrive at the scene, take the pictures, write the story, and move on. They abandoned their idealism long ago. Their only enduring loyalty is to "the business," the newspaper world itself. Jacob Milne, on the other hand, is young, fresh, dedicated, and enthusiastic. He has just scooped the veteran Wagner on a story to the *Sunday Globe*, Wagner's own paper, and, more seriously, was a scab when the union closed the shop. He believes that a free press is the last line of defense, and that with it, all things are correctable. Milne and Wagner implicitly debate the issues of "junk journalism" and the young reporter's ideal of them as "part of a privileged group inside society and yet outside it, with a license to scourge it and a duty to defend it night and day."

The play is also as much about Ruth Carson as it is about journalism. To balance the debate of journalistic ethics, Tom Stoppard adds another about private morality. Ruth acts as her own confessor and examines the issues of her (probably first) infidelity to her husband, what path she will take in the future, and whether, as she sings, "The Lady Is a Tramp." She has coupled with Dick Wagner in the neutral world of a London hotel room. Now, in her own domain, she debates with herself the possibility of a night with the attractive, somewhat innocent young Milne and what such an encounter will cost her. A part of her realizes that in the end the practical Carson and the pragmatic Wagner are likely to triumph over the fantasy match with Milne. As she takes Wagner to her bed for a second encounter, she accepts that in the real world of sex, as in the real world of journalism, compromise and expediency triumph. She has her freedoms and choices dictated to her as clearly as the press has its freedoms to act purely and idealistically—or not. Milne is dead, Ruth has fallen, and Wagner is, in his weary way, triumphant.

Dramatic Devices

Night and Day introduces both acts with an attention-grabbing flight from reality. The first act opens to the beauty of an African sunset shattered by a helicopter, the headlights of a Jeep driving onstage, machine-gun fire, and a spotlight following the photographer Guthrie as he darts about. A burst of gunfire catches him and he falls. This image immediately changes over to Guthrie in a garden chair, the machine-gun fire the noise of a telex, the Jeep an approaching car. It has been a dream but a projection of the play's action: the attacks on the press and the war in Kambawe, which will provide the backdrop for the dramatized debate to follow.

The second act begins with Ruth Carson in the night section of the play, verbally seducing Jacob Milne. It concludes with her walking naked after him into the darkness outside, but this entire action is illusion. In the play's reality, Milne is dead, and Carson, Ruth, and Wagner await a visit from the embattled President Mageeba. With his arrival and their subsequent conversation, the topic of the ethics and responsibilities of journalism again takes precedence.

Probably the most outstanding device Stoppard uses to clarify the play's issues and draw the audience into the action is the interior dialogue between Ruth the character and "Ruth." She is inside the action as Carson's wife and as Wagner's former and Milne's potential lover. She comments wryly on their elevated views of the press and its freedoms and responsibilities and brings a humor and perspective to the debate, and to the play, which make both more interesting. As "Ruth," she reveals herself as a bruised, lonely, self-questioning woman, seeking in fantasy a life of romance that neither the cynical Wagner nor the practical Carson can provide. "Ruth" has a morality that prods her to confess her one-night fling with Wagner to her husband, an idealism that desires the youthful Milne, and a self-destructiveness that moves her to a second coupling with Wagner. Her debates with her inner self reveal a contrasting personality attracted to both sides of the larger journalism issue: Wagner, the unromantic opportunist to whom career and tomorrow's edition are all-important, and Milne, the gentle neophyte who believes that a free press and human decency must endure at all costs. In the real world of both sex and journalism, Stoppard implies, principle will give way to compromise and expediency.

Ruth is given to snatches of song that offer interesting comment on the play's tensions. When she finds herself confronted with Wagner and attracted to Milne, she sings lines from "Night and Day" and the Beatles song "Help!" In questioning her own morality and wondering at her moral future, she sings "The Lady Is a Tramp." Her sardonic eloquence lends a color and an appeal to the play's entire action, elevating it from a wordy debate on press ethics to a human conundrum of personal morality.

Critical Context

In *Night and Day*, Stoppard's fourth full-length play, the author moves into a stage naturalism without sacrificing his verbal dexterity. The playwright's usual formula—a marriage of serious ideas with high comedy—was set aside for this play. With *Rosencrantz and Guildenstern Are Dead* (pr. 1966, pb. 1967), *Travesties* (pr. 1974, pb. 1975), and *Jumpers* (pr., pb. 1972), the astounding verbal and intellectual gymnastics are so effective that the plays are always highly entertaining but not totally accessible. Puns are piled upon puns; characters engage in fast and furious convoluted exchanges. Language itself is one of Stoppard's prime concerns, a concern that links his work with that of the German linguistic philosopher Ludwig Wittgenstein. In Stoppard's relativistic world, no absolute meaning seems possible; language's very usefulness and reliability are therefore under constant examination. There are strong absurdist elements in his plays—Rosencrantz and Guildenstern, for example, in *Rosencrantz and Guildenstern Are Dead*, remind one of the hapless Vladimir and Estragon of Samuel Beckett's *En attendant Godot* (pb. 1952; *Waiting for Godot*, 1954)—but to Stoppard, language is ultimately an extremely valuable quantity; to the absurdists, it is most often meaningless and incomprehensible.

Stoppard combines the theater of ideas with an acute perception of twentieth century chaos and confusion, infusing the mixture with the brisk entertainment and humor of an Oscar Wilde play. Stoppard's *Travesties*, in fact, parodies Wilde's *The Importance of Being Earnest* (pr. 1895) while incorporating Vladimir Lenin and novelist James Joyce as characters who are filtered through a narrator's only partially reliable memory. The linguistic and philosophical gymnastics of *Jumpers* become literal gymnastics as well: The members of a university philosophy department are also members of an amateur gymnastics group. Their human pyramids tumble, however, and the philosophical issues remain unresolved, just as in his whodunit *The Real Inspector Hound* (pr., pb. 1968) the murder mystery remains unsolved—and insoluble.

Night and Day contains the Stoppardian coda; clever quips and repartee abound. Words are taken at their face value, then stretched, wrung out, and put back into context, to the delight of the audience. In *Night and Day,* however, the message, not the mode, dominates, and the audience is, if less dazzled, certainly more aware of Stoppard's intention. It is not so much a play for the intelligentsia as it is one for the thoughtful.

Sources for Further Study

Anchetta, Richard A. *Tom Stoppard: An Analytical Study of His Plays*. Chicago: Advent, 1991.

Bigsby, C. W. E. *Tom Stoppard*. Harlow, England: Longman, 1976.

Cahn, Victor L. *Beyond Absurdity: The Plays of Tom Stoppard*. Rutherford, N.J.: Fairleigh Dickinson University Press, 1979.

Dean, Joan Fitzpatrick. *Tom Stoppard: Comedy as a Moral Matrix*. Columbia: University of Missouri Press, 1981.

Gabbard, Paquet Lucina. *The Stoppard Plays*. Troy, N.Y.: Whitston, 1982.

Gitzen, Julian. "Tom Stoppard: Chaos in Perspective." *Southern Humanities Review* 10 (1976): 143-152.

Gussow, Mel. *Conversations with Stoppard*. New York: Grove-Atlantic, 1996.

Harty, John. *Tom Stoppard: A Casebook*. New York: Garland, 1987.

Hayman, Ronald. *Tom Stoppard*. London: Heinemann, 1977.

Londre, Felicia Hardison. *Tom Stoppard*. New York: F. Ungar, 1981.

Whitaker, Thomas. *Tom Stoppard*. New York: Grove Press, 1984.

Maureen DesRoches

NIGHT MUST FALL

Author: Emlyn Williams (1905-1987)
Type of plot: Psychological
Time of plot: The 1930's
Locale: England
First produced: 1935, at the King's Theatre, Edinburgh, Scotland
First published: 1935

Principal characters:
THE LORD CHIEF JUSTICE
MRS. BRAMSON, a fifty-five-year-old invalid
OLIVIA GRAYNE, her niece, twenty-eight
HUBERT LAURIE, Olivia's pompous admirer, thirty-five
NURSE LIBBY, a young north-country woman
MRS. TERENCE, Mrs. Bramson's middle-aged Cockney cook
DORA PARKOE, Mrs. Bramson's maid
INSPECTOR BELSIZE
DAN, a page boy

The Play

The prologue to *Night Must Fall* begins in darkness, and there is solemn music. As the lights gradually come up, the Lord Chief Justice is revealed in the imposing robes of his office. He has reached the peroration of his summing up and declares that there are no grounds for interfering with the sentence of the appellant, a young man convicted of two brutal murders. The solemn music is heard again and the stage darkens.

Act 1, set in the sitting room of Mrs. Bramson's bungalow in a forest in Essex on a fine October morning, begins with Olivia reading from the melodramatic novel *East Lynne* (1861) to her aunt, Mrs. Bramson. The latter is a selfish, parsimonious hypochondriac who controls the lives of those around her, although she gains little sympathy from the cheerful Nurse Libby and is frequently insulted by her cook, Mrs. Terence. Olivia is tied to Mrs. Bramson financially, but continues to reject Hubert Laurie's continual offers of marriage. Dora, the maid, reveals that there are several men poking about in the neighboring woods. Hubert renews his courtship of Laura, who declares that he is a bore but promises him an answer soon.

Dora incurs Mrs. Bramson's wrath when she breaks some Derby china and then reveals she is pregnant. The father is Dan, a page boy at the Tallboys, a nearby hotel. Mrs. Bramson agrees to speak with Dan so that he will marry Dora. Shortly afterward Inspector Belsize calls, inquiring whether anyone in the household has noticed anything unusual. He tells them that Mrs. Chalfont, a guest at the Tallboys, is missing and might have been murdered. Olivia muses on how murder can suddenly intrude into ordinary life and how the murderer can be "a man walking about somewhere, and talking, like us."

Dan enters wearing his hotel uniform. He smokes frequently, speaks with a rough accent (which could be Welsh), and possesses a variable personality which only the discerning can perceive. Mrs. Bramson interrogates him about his relationship with Dora, which was based only on momentary lust. Dan is also questioned about his knowledge of Mrs. Chalfont and reveals his observational powers in his description of her. Alone with Dan, Olivia is both fascinated and repelled by him. His attempts to seduce Olivia fail, but he does ingratiate himself with Mrs. Bramson by playing on her hypochondria. When Dan says she reminds him of his mother, he wins her over completely. Shortly afterward, a newspaper story reveals that a man with the missing Mrs. Chalfont was heard singing a song, "Mighty Lak a Rose." The act closes with Dan singing the same song and Olivia's strong suspicion that he may be the murderer.

Scene 1 of the second act begins twelve days later; it is afternoon, and the weather is duller. Mrs. Bramson's appearance is remarkably improved and Dan, now working for her, is obviously her favorite. There is a sensational moment when Dora discovers a belt which could have belonged to the murdered woman; instead, it belongs to Olivia (although this device does serve to draw the audience's attention to parallels between Mrs. Chalfont and Olivia). While Dan is out "walking" Mrs. Bramson in her wheelchair, Olivia and Hubert have a chance to discuss how well Dan has ingratiated himself with Mrs. Bramson. Olivia realizes that Dan acts all the time, disguising his thoughts very well.

Olivia interrogates other members of the household (Mrs. Terence and Dora) to gauge their reactions to Dan. They know that Dan is far from honest but are not troubled greatly. Dora, however, declares that Dan is vain, prompting Olivia to remark that murderers characteristically possess "incredible vanity." She is now sure that Dan has murdered Mrs. Chalfont and, with Hubert, Dora, and Mrs. Terence, searches Dan's luggage looking for evidence. Apart from a photograph of Mrs. Chalfont, they find nothing incriminating. They are about to examine an extraordinary hatbox when Dan returns unexpectedly. He toys with them until he notices the hatbox, and they begin to grill him about Mrs. Chalfont; he manages to deflect their questions. Left alone with Dan, Olivia tells him she thinks that he is acting all the time, that he is living in "a world of [his] own imagination." The scene finishes dramatically with news that a hand is sticking out of the garbage pile and with Olivia staring at Dan in horror.

By act 2, scene 2, the area is attracting sightseers, especially since Mrs. Chalfont was decapitated. Hubert presses Olivia to marry him; Dan is even more Mrs. Bramson's favorite, calling her mother. Another duologue between Olivia and Dan reveals they both resent their dull lives, though Dan becomes wildly excited when he talks about his life and fears. Inspector Belsize returns and extracts a confession from Dan that he was having an affair with Mrs. Chalfont. He also wants to examine the hatbox, but Olivia claims it is hers. The curtain falls as Dan faints.

Dan has recovered at the beginning of act 3, scene 1, while Olivia is now too frightened to stay in the bungalow overnight. She fails to alert Mrs. Bramson to her suspicions, and the latter is left alone as the other employees also leave for the night. Mrs. Bramson reveals momentarily that she is not confined to her wheelchair. Dan returns, reads the Bible to her, and then prepares to smother her with a cushion.

Act 3, scene 2 opens with Dan taking Mrs. Bramson's cash box and preparing to burn the evidence of his latest crime after dousing everything in paraffin. Olivia returns and is surprised to discover how "ordinary" murder is. Dan enjoys another outburst of vain self-confidence and threatens to make Olivia another victim. Inspector Belsize arrives and, despite an effort by Olivia to protect Dan, arrests him, alluring him with all the attention and notoriety a murder trial will bring.

Themes and Meanings

Night Must Fall examines the inner workings of a murderer's mind and explores the fascination murder holds for the remainder of ordinary humanity. Dan clearly has an enormous power to attract and fascinate other people, whom he derides and scorns. The women he draws to him cover a broad spectrum of English society—Mrs. Chalfont, the hotel guest; Dora, the maid; Olivia, the poetic but poor niece; and Mrs. Bramson, the wealthy invalid. Even Mrs. Terence and Nurse Libby appear to be favorably disposed toward Dan. Of this group, Olivia is most attracted to him, as their several exploratory duologues indicate. Olivia believes that crime, and murder in particular, is something extraordinary, something quite outside humdrum, mundane experience. When she actually encounters murder, however, she sees it as surprisingly ordinary.

Dan, throughout his life, has tried to lift himself out of his lowly rut, to make himself more than ordinary. He has apparently attempted a seafaring life, and when that failed, acted his way through different situations employing various guises. It is significant that his first appearance in *Night Must Fall* is in a page boy's uniform, since there is very little difference between a uniform and a costume. Olivia comments repeatedly on Dan's acting and so points to the murderer's inability to deal with reality. Dan's arrogance also plays a major role in his constantly shifting personality.

Ironically, the murderer attracts others to him. All the women appear to realize that Dan is far from innocent, but they still allow him to take advantage of them. Dora is pregnant by Dan, Mrs. Bramson gives him her complete confidence (preferring him to a close relative), and Olivia tries to cover up for him even after he has murdered her aunt. The very unreality of the ultimate crime seems to draw murderer and victim together. At the same time, Emlyn Williams creates a convincing picture of genteel life in the English countryside. The bungalow is described in realistic detail, and there is a fair sprinkling of humor, usually derived from the lower orders: Mrs. Terence comments that, though she has found no dead bodies in the woods, she has stumbled across the live bodies of loving couples.

Dramatic Devices

It is clear from the prologue to *Night Must Fall* that Dan is the culprit and that he has already been arrested, tried, and convicted for murder. Thus there is no true element of suspense; the emphasis falls rather on character development and motivation. As in all good dramas, however, the audience suspends its disbelief and remains interested in the way events unfold.

Dan's entry into the action is delayed until act 1 is well under way and until the audience has already learned much about him. This device has the effect of making the audience just as curious about him as are the characters in the play. Williams employs other theatrical tricks from the school of the "well-made" play. Various pieces of information are carefully placed here and there to be used later at a crucial moment. Hence the bungalow is made of wood and paraffin is delivered—both essential elements for Dan's planned conflagration. The suspected murderer of Mrs. Chalfont sang a particular song, which Dan also sings later, and each act ends with a "sensational" curtain which reminds the audience of the judge's words in the prologue: "I cannot help thinking that the deplorable atmosphere of sentimental melodrama which has pervaded this trial has made the *theatre* a more fitting background for it than a court of law." Nor should the famous hatbox in which Mrs. Chalfont's head is hidden be forgotten.

A subtler theatrical device is the way in which each act is set later in the day: The play begins on a fine morning and ends at night. Subliminally, this device conveys a sense of inevitability and eventuality, that night must indeed fall. Rather like fine acting, this progression is not noticed until the play is over and the theatrical people have succeeded with their tricks. The bad actor's devices are eventually penetrated, and he is caught out.

Critical Context

Night Must Fall was very popular when it first appeared and remains one of the plays most associated with Emlyn Williams's name. Well-known, too, are *A Murder Has Been Arranged* (pr., pb. 1930), *The Late Christopher Bean* (pr., pb. 1933), and *The Corn Is Green* (pr., pb. 1938).

Williams's fascination with murder is also evident in *A Murder Has Been Arranged* and his account of the famous English Moors murders of 1965, titled *Beyond Belief: A Chronicle of Murder and Its Detection* (1967). *Night Must Fall* is itself based on at least three murders which took place in the 1920's and 1930's. First there was Henry Jacoby, a hotel employee, who was executed in 1922 for killing a hotel guest; then in 1924 there was Patrick Mahon, who murdered his mistress in a Sussex bungalow; and in 1934 Toni Mancini attempted, very clumsily, to conceal his victim's body in his Brighton lodging house. Moreover, Dan is based on Fess Griffith, a working-class ne'er-do-well who forged a check which Williams had given him to buy a motorbicycle and with whom Williams was infatuated for a time.

Perhaps, ironically, that infatuation eventually helped Williams understand the character he had created, for he scored a great success acting the role of Dan. Indeed, Williams's reputation now rests as much on his acting as on his playwriting. He gave a celebrated one-man show as Charles Dickens in 1951, following that up with *Dylan Thomas Growing Up* (pr. 1955). Both shows were theatrical coups—which points to the basis of Williams's success: a sure sense of what will work in the theater and what will hold an audience.

Sources for Further Study

Borowitz, Albert. "'The Sinister Behind the Ordinary': Emlyn Williams's *Night Must Fall*." In *A Gallery of Sinister Perspectives: Ten Crimes and a Scandal*. Kent, Ohio: Kent State University Press, 1982.

Dale-Jones, Don. *Emlyn Williams*. Cardiff: University of Wales Press, 1979.

Findlater, Richard. *Emlyn Williams*. London: Rockliff, 1956.

Harding, James. *Emlyn Williams: A Life*. London: Weidenfeld & Nicolson, 1993.

O'Casey, Sean. "Murder in the Theatre." In *The Flying Wasp*. London: Macmillan, 1937.

Stephens, John Russell. *Emlyn Williams: The Making of a Dramatist*. Chester Springs, Pa.: DuFour, 2000.

J. P. Wearing

THE NORMAN CONQUESTS

Author: Alan Ayckbourn (1939-)
Type of plot: Comedy
Time of plot: The 1970's
Locale: England
First produced: 1973, at the Library Theatre, Scarborough, England
First published: 1975

Principal characters:
NORMAN DEWERS, a librarian
RUTH DEWERS, his wife, a businesswoman
REG, Ruth's brother, a real estate agent
SARAH, Reg's wife
ANNIE, Ruth and Reg's younger sister
TOM, Annie's friend, a veterinarian

The Play

The Norman Conquests is a trilogy of full-length plays, *Table Manners*, *Living Together*, and *Round and Round the Garden*, each taking place during the same July weekend in different parts of a house and garden in suburban England. *Table Manners*, set in the dining room, opens on a Saturday evening as Reg and Sarah arrive to look after Reg's invalid mother while Annie, his youngest sister, goes away for the weekend. Annie is going alone, leaving behind her friend Tom, a veterinarian who prefers animals to people and is, according to Sarah, "a trifle ponderous." Tom has never touched Annie, who believes that he visits only when he has nothing to do.

Annie reveals that she is leaving with her sister Ruth's husband, Norman, with whom she had sexual relations the previous Christmas, but prudish Sarah vows to stop them. Reg, on the other hand, is happy that his sister is finally going to have some romance in her life. The naïve Tom appears and says that he would have gone with Annie if she had asked. Even though Norman is in the garden waiting for her, Annie decides not to go.

Scene 2 of act 1 occurs the following morning, as Norman tries to convince Annie that he only wants to make her happy. Then Ruth appears, having been summoned by Sarah. Ruth and Norman argue about their marriage, with Ruth claiming that he has held her career back ten years. Norman discloses his adulterous plans with Annie, and Ruth laughs when he claims that they are in love.

Act 2, scene 1, takes place that evening, with Tom threatening to punch Norman for upsetting Annie. Norman attempts to enlist Sarah's support by explaining how they are both sensitive. Ruth tells Annie that Tom loves her but needs to be coerced into action. Annie apologizes to her sister for her would-be romance with Norman. Over dinner, Norman and Ruth squabble, and dim Tom, thinking that Norman is insulting Annie, strikes him. Norman and Sarah unite in feeling misunderstood. In act 2, scene 2, the following morning, Norman suggests that Sarah needs a holiday and volunteers to go with her, promising to make her happy. She invites him to call her later. Annie tells Tom that she agreed to leave with Norman only because she was lonely, but he, as usual, fails to get the point. The play ends with Annie asking Norman to take her away.

Living Together is set in the sitting room and opens on the same Saturday evening as the previous play. Norman tries to explain to Sarah how innocent his weekend with Annie would have been, how no one would have been hurt if Annie had not told her about it. Annie tells Norman that she is fond of Tom but that communicating with the veterinarian "is terribly heavy going. Like running up hill in roller skates." Norman continues attempting to seduce Annie, and Reg catches them kissing. Tom realizes that "something seems to be going on which I'm not being let into." Norman takes out some of his frustrations by advising Tom to win Annie's affection through treating her roughly. Norman begins drinking wine made by Annie's mother before she became confined to her bed, gradually becomes very drunk, and passes out on the rug on which he and Annie made love. Reg persuades the others, in act 1, scene 2, to play a complicated board game he has invented, trying to instruct them while the drunken Norman talks to Ruth on the telephone and shouts at his mother-in-law on the extension. Becoming assertive, Tom tells Annie, "You're damned lucky to have me around," and threatens to slug her. The act ends in total confusion.

Act 2, scene 1, opens the following morning, with Ruth complaining of Norman's wasting her time: "I almost wish to heavens he'd gone away with Annie, had his weekend and got it over with." She also complains of never getting along with the "evil woman upstairs," referring to her mother's many adulteries while her children were growing up. Sarah finds Annie and Norman kissing and tells her, "You're just a tart like your Mother." Norman enjoys watching Annie and Sarah almost come to blows. Finally exasperated, Ruth slaps Norman. He accuses her of being less upset by his infidelity than by his effect on her work. He claims to have arranged the weekend with Annie simply to gain Ruth's attention and seduces his wife on the rug. The next morning, in act 2, scene 2, Ruth is embarrassed when Reg finds them asleep there. Tom is also ashamed of his behavior toward Annie. The play ends with Sarah saying she wants to go to Bournemouth alone and Reg shocked at the implications.

Round and Round the Garden begins slightly earlier and closes a bit later than the other two plays. Tom, who uses the old lady's cat as an excuse to visit Annie, is in the garden trying to coax it out of a tree so he can examine its paw. Though they were to meet in the nearby village, Norman arrives because he is afraid that Annie has changed her mind about their holiday together. They are going to unfashionable East Grinstead, he explains, since he was unable to book Hastings. He tries to hide before Tom can see him. Reg shows up thinking Annie is going off with Tom and jokes with Norman about the "bit of stuff" he is to meet in East Grinstead, but Sarah comes outside to announce that Annie is not going anywhere. Act 1, scene 2, takes place that night as the drunken Norman flirts with Sarah. He induces her to lose control, and they kiss. Having decided that she is a coward for not following through on her plan, Annie invites Norman to her room. Insisting that women manipulate and dominate men,

Norman wants Reg and Tom to take a holiday with him. Annie and Sarah find him professing his affection for Reg and crying that no one loves him.

Act 2, scene 1, occurs late the next morning. Ruth tells Sarah that she cannot take Norman seriously; he is annoying, but she does not want to be rid of him. Sarah denies that Norman has made advances to her. When Ruth tries to encourage Tom to express his emotions, he misunderstands and thinks that she is in love with him. In front of them all, Norman and Annie embrace passionately, so Tom grabs Ruth and kisses her. In the play's final scene, the visitors begin leaving, but Ruth's car will not start. Reg and Ruth wonder whether their mates are becoming involved with each other, but Norman swears he would never consider such an affair. Haltingly, Tom finally proposes, but Annie wants to go away and think about it. While Reg tows his sister's car, Norman rams into his, disabling both. The play ends with Norman telling all three women that he can make them happy, as each walks away from him.

Themes and Meanings

The Norman Conquests is about people's dissatisfaction with their lives, misunderstandings that hamper relationships, and the need for romance. Sarah cannot understand how her unambitious husband can run a business, and Reg, though reconciled to Sarah's bossiness, wishes that he could be a boy again, insulated from the world in his room, lost in his hobbies. Sarah feels unfulfilled by the monotonous life of a housewife (even though she wants to get home in time to clean the house before the cleaning lady comes), and Annie is bored with being her mother's nurse and housekeeper. Ruth tries to use business as an escape from the rest of life, trying so hard to be unlike her lascivious mother that she is in danger of becoming hardened. Norman complains of his wife, "Don't you think I'd take Ruth away. . . ? If she'd come. But she won't. She has no need of me at all . . . except as an emotional punch bag."

Alan Ayckbourn makes his characters and situations more completely human with an ironic layer of inconsistency. Sarah tells Annie that everyone needs a "nice dirty weekend somewhere," becomes morally outraged when she discovers that Annie is going with Norman, and finally tentatively agrees to go with him herself. Reg tells Norman that although he has always been faithful, he thinks that adultery might keep any marriage from going stale and would not mind if Sarah "went off for a few days with someone"; yet when he realizes that she may be planning such a move, he is alarmed. A major irony of *The Norman Conquests* is that while the mother, who makes Annie read lurid romances to her, has led a very active sex life, Reg, Ruth, and Annie, in the midst of the sexual revolution, are relatively inhibited.

Mother's spiritual child is Norman, though he is less obsessed with sex itself than with romance. Throughout *The Norman Conquests*, the title character presents himself as a romantic idealist while acting like a romantic fool. When Ruth mentions divorce, Norman is outraged by her attitude that marriage is a legal contract and defines it as "sharing and giving." When Sarah deprecates Annie's plain appearance, he responds, "Anybody I love is automatically beautiful." Norman finds romance being destroyed "by the cynics and liberationists," and Ayckbourn seems to wonder whether it can survive in such an age. While Norman proclaims, "I want to make everyone happy. It's my mission in life," most of the time he creates only anger and confusion.

Dramatic Devices

The three plays that compose *The Norman Conquests* are meant to stand on their own and be seen in any order. With this approach, Alan Ayckbourn achieves considerable irony and humor, especially when his audience is seeing its third play and knows what is going on offstage. Tom's effort, in *Living Together*, to describe the argument going on in the dining room between Reg and Sarah is more amusing for those who have already experienced this scene. After Reg catches Annie and Norman kissing in the first play and Sarah does the same in the second, it is hilarious in the third to find all the others staring, amazed, at the passionate couple. Ayckbourn also seems to be using this device to comment on the nature of truth. The audience for one part of the trilogy thinks that it fully understands the characters and their predicaments, but each play fills in details needed for full comprehension. (The playwright may be satirizing the theatrical convention of relying on offstage events to move the action forward.)

The plays are best seen or read in the order Ayckbourn presents them in the published version. When Norman's entrance is delayed until the second scene of *Table Manners*, the protagonist begins to take on almost mythic proportions and is clearly the catalyst for all the action of the trilogy. Since *Table Manners* ends with Annie clinging to Norman and *Living Together* with Sarah considering going to Bournemouth with him, *Round and Round the Garden* should be seen last: As all three women walk out on Norman, Ayckbourn suggests that the modern age has turned its back on the romantic.

Ayckbourn uses only occasional visual humor lest the play become farce. Ruth's refusal to wear her glasses, resulting in her pouring hot water instead of milk on her cereal, reveals her vanity and stubbornness. Because she cannot see well enough, she is unable to open a collapsible garden chair all the way and, placing it on its side, sits on it anyway. Tom arrives and arranges his chair similarly, showing his courtesy, conformity, timidity, and general eccentricity.

More typical of Ayckbourn's humor is the use of two unseen characters, the invalid mother upstairs and her treed cat, as silent commentators hovering, like ironic gods, above the fray. Mother's needs and whims must be attended to regardless of the turmoil downstairs. Though Ayckbourn's style of comedy depends primarily on character and situation, it is frequently verbal as well. Ruth tells Norman that when Sarah telephoned her "she sounded as if she was summoning relatives to your bedside," and he replies, "I suppose she was, in a manner of speaking." Of his wife, Reg says, "She's like those toy animals you see in the back windows of cars. Any violent movement from me and she's nodding her head reproachfully for days."

Critical Context

Alan Ayckbourn writes what seem to be conventional comedies but creates unusual staging techniques for many of them. In *How the Other Half Loves* (pr. 1969, pb. 1972), two sets are superimposed to create the illusion that actions occurring at different times and places are happening simultaneously. The characters in *Bedroom Farce* (pr. 1975, pb. 1977) crisscross among three bedrooms in three houses. *Taking Steps* (pr. 1979, pb. 1981) is set on multiple levels of a house, and *Way Upstream* (pr. 1981, pb. 1983) takes place on a boat floating in a fiberglass tank of water. For *Sisterly Feelings* (pr. 1979, pb. 1981), Ayckbourn wrote two versions of the second and third scenes of a four-scene play and allows the actors to choose which to perform. Most unconventional is *Intimate Exchanges* (pr. 1982, pb. 1985), in which two performers portray ten characters and whose thirty-one scenes may be presented in sixteen combinations. *The Norman Conquests* has been called the most effective of these experiments for the mathematical precision with which its various parts dovetail. *"House"* and *"Garden"* (pr., pb. 2000) were two productions played in adjacent theaters, performed at the same time, and employing the same characters, who move back and forth between the two theaters during the course of the same evening's performance. Doubtless *The Norman Conquests*, using a similar concept, sparked the idea of simultaneous performances.

The relatively sober ending to *Round and Round the Garden* is appropriate. Ayckbourn's subsequent comedies have grown increasingly dark as the playwright strives to find the comic side of the alienation, frustration, and even tragedy of modern life. Although Ayckbourn has been criticized for being repetitive and too absorbed in middle-class mores, he has, for a highly successful commercial playwright, shown remarkable growth, as with his increasingly complex and sympathetic female characters, and an enthusiastic willingness to experiment.

Sources for Further Study

Billington, Michael. *Alan Ayckbourn*. London: Macmillan, 1984.

Blisten, Elmer M. "Alan Ayckbourn: A Few Jokes, Much Comedy." *Modern Drama* 26 (March, 1983): 26-35.

Dukore, Bernard F. *Alan Ayckbourn: A Casebook*. New York: Garland, 1991.

Hayman, Ronald. "Innovation and Conservatism." In *British Theatre Since 1955: A Reassessment*. New York: Oxford University Press, 1979.

Howarth, W. D. "English Humor and French *Comique?* The Class of Anouilh and Ayckbourn." *New Comparison* 3 (Summer, 1987): 72-82.

Kerensky, Oleg. "Alan Ayckbourn." In *The New British Drama: Fourteen Playwrights Since Osborne and Pinter*. London: Hamilton, 1977.

Taylor, John Russell. "Art and Commerce: The New Drama in the West End Marketplace." In *Contemporary English Drama*, edited by C. W. E. Bigsby. London: E. Arnold, 1981.

Watson, Ian. *Conversations with Ayckbourn*. 1981. Rev. ed. Boston: Faber and Faber, 1988.

Michael Adams

THE OCTOROON
Or, Life in Louisiana

Author: Dion Boucicault (1820?-1890)
Type of plot: Social realism
Time of plot: Prior to the American Civil War
Locale: A plantation in Louisiana
First produced: 1859, at the Winter Garden Theatre, New York City
First published: 1953

Principal characters:
ZOE, the daughter of a slave and Judge Peyton
GEORGE PEYTON, the judge's nephew
MRS. PEYTON, the judge's widow
DORA SUNNYSIDE, a southern belle
JACOB M'CLOSKY, a Yankee and former overseer of the Peyton estate, who still owns one half of it
SALEM SCUDDER, a Yankee and current overseer of the Peyton estate
PAUL, a slave boy
WAHNOTEE, a Native American man

The Play

The Octoroon is a drama of plantation life and miscegenation in antebellum America, written by an Irishman who visited the South. As act 1 begins, the selling of Terrebonne Plantation, the Peyton estate, is imminent. Various liens have been placed on the property, and the most substantial is the one held by Jacob M'Closky, Terrebonne's former overseer. He tricked the late Judge Peyton into mortgaging one thousand acres, the plantation's richest half, to him. After the judge's death, Salem Scudder, who replaced M'Closky as overseer, plummeted Terrebonne into further debt as a result of bad "inventions and improvements" on the estate. Two years have elapsed since the judge's death, and George Peyton, the judge's nephew and heir of Terrebonne, has recently arrived from Paris. Although Dora Sunnyside falls in love with George, he loves Zoe, the beautiful daughter of Judge Peyton and one of his slaves. The judge's widow also loves Zoe; the widow treats her as if she were her daughter and worries what will happen to Zoe, who has not been raised as a slave, after her death. M'Closky intends to own the plantation and make Zoe his concubine. When he reveals his intentions to Zoe, she wants nothing to do with him. M'Closky stops her from leaving his presence until Scudder, who is also in love with Zoe and regrets his role in Terrebonne's demise, intervenes, draws his knife, and warns M'Closky to let her walk away. M'Closky acquiesces.

As act 1 ends, M'Closky steals the paper signed by the judge proclaiming Zoe's freedom. M'Closky knows that the paper is now invalid, since liens have been placed on the Peyton estate. Paul and Wahnotee go to the landing to get the mail from the steamboat: Mrs. Peyton anxiously awaits a letter from England that would stop the plantation's sale. She expects a sizable settlement for a twenty-year-old debt owed to her late husband. M'Closky plans to steal the letter.

In act 2, the wealthy Dora urges Zoe to encourage George to marry her, and consequently she will purchase Terrebonne. When Zoe approaches George on Dora's behalf, he expresses his love for Zoe. He proposes to her only to have her reject him because interracial marriage is illegal. George argues that they could live abroad, but Zoe still refuses his offer because she knows his aunt would not accept their marriage. M'Closky overhears the young couple's conversation just before he spies on Paul and Wahnotee as they are returning to Terrebonne with the mail. They discover Scudder's camera, and Paul poses as Wahnotee is about to take his picture. M'Closky sneaks up on Paul and strikes him on the head with Wahnotee's tomahawk, killing Paul. M'Closky then steals the mailbags and finds the letter from Liverpool. Wahnotee smashes the camera, believing that he has killed Paul, and carries his body away.

Act 3 begins with people assuming that Wahnotee killed Paul and talking of lynching the Native American on the very day that the auction of Terrebonne is to take place. When Mrs. Peyton learns that Dora wants to marry George and that George loves Zoe, she encourages him to marry Dora. George tries to propose to Dora, but he and Zoe confess their love for each other. Then the auctioneer informs Zoe that her status has been changed: She is now a slave and must be sold at the auction along with the house and other slaves. Dora's father buys Terrebonne at the auction on her behalf. M'Closky is the highest bidder for Zoe.

In act 4 the photographic plate is found and reveals that M'Closky is Paul's murderer. In act 5 Wahnotee murders M'Closky. Mrs. Peyton receives the letter that saves Terrebonne from the auction block. George gains control of Terrebonne but loses his love. Unbeknownst to the major characters, Zoe swallows poison and dies with George at her side. So ends Boucicault's original *The Octoroon*. The British demanded a different outcome; thus he drafted "The English Happy Ending" which he acknowledged the British public "composed" and he "edited." In the revised version, George rescues Zoe, and the audience may infer that they will marry.

Themes and Meanings

Dion Boucicault's drama was inspired by his visit to the American South and *The Quadroon* (1856), a novel by Thomas Mayne Reid. Ironically, *The Octoroon* premiered in New York four days after famed abolitionist John Brown was executed for his October 16, 1859, raid at Harpers Ferry, Virginia. Boucicault's play, which focuses on the denial of liberty, identity, and dignity, opened during a period in American history when antislavery and pro-slavery sentiments were at near-zenith level.

The play is subtitled *Life in Louisiana*. Boucicault's portrayal of antebellum life is an indictment of slavery. Thus he crafted a drama of social criticism. As an Irishman from a subjugated country, Boucicault was more sympathetic to the plight of the enslaved than many of his American contemporaries. Like Boucicault, George is an outsider who cannot fathom slavery's complexities. His love interest, Zoe, is a young, compassionate, educated, beautiful woman who merits love and respect. George is sensitive to the way others interact with her; he cannot understand why some people act in a condescending manner to her. Although he has lived a shallow lifestyle in Paris, he redeems himself in Louisiana. His love for Zoe causes him to ignore material concerns and empowers him to eagerly defy barriers imposed by race, class, and tradition. Zoe, who has been raised and educated as a proper southern lady, rejects his marriage proposal because she is black. She understands southern life far better than George. He naïvely believes their "love can conquer all" obstacles. Zoe, on the other hand, is cognizant that their love cannot overcome prejudice. In addition to criticizing the southern lifestyle, Boucicault blames northerners: His two transplanted characters from the North, M'Closky and Scudder, adapt to the southern status quo as overseers, and although they are romantically interested in Zoe, they cannot imagine how it would be possible for Zoe and George to marry.

Two themes prevalent in Boucicault's other plays are also present in *The Octoroon*. There is an obsession with materialism. The very reason Terrebonne is to be auctioned off is that the judge mismanaged his money, and M'Closky deliberately helps the judge out of his financial dilemma in order to gain control of the plantation's best acreage. Yet the didactic message here is that an overemphasis on wealth leads to less than desired ends. The mistreatment of the weak is another theme found in Boucicault's plays. In *The Octoroon*, this is most vividly seen in act 2, when Paul, a boy who is defenseless and unaware of the threat that M'Closky poses, is murdered. Violence against the weak is followed by abuse of the weak in act 3, when the slaves are subjected to the auction block.

Dramatic Devices

Boucicault's dramatic adaptation of Mayne Reid's novel, *The Quadroon*, was not the first to bring the issue of slavery to the stage; various adaptations of Harriet Beecher Stowe's famous novel *Uncle Tom's Cabin: Or, Life Among the Lowly* (1852) preceded it, and like the dramatic versions of Stowe's novel, *The Octoroon* relies heavily on melodramatic devices. There is the required conflict between good and evil; in this case, freedom and slavery clash. Thus the conflict exists between Zoe, the virtuous victim, and the villain M'Closky, who purchases her. Zoe is an ideal heroine according to the standards of melodrama; she is morally upright, and she is terrorized by the despicable M'Closky and slavery. Melodrama manipulates the emotions of the audience, who pity and have sympathy for the oppressed Zoe as she is not free to marry the man she loves and is sold to the man she detests. Zoe tells George that although she loves him and has hopes as well as ambitions, she can only know despair and suffering.

Melodrama also depends upon plot twists by the villain, and M'Closky does this on at least two occasions: He gains ownership in Terrebonne and intercepts the letter that would halt the auction. Once he possesses the letter, he knows that the auction will be held and that he can purchase Zoe. Melodrama may also employ sensational physical acts, and in *The Octoroon*, Boucicault creates a spectacle with a fire on board the steamer in the American version, and the steamboat's explosion in the British version.

Another dramatic device of interest is Boucicault's inclusion of the camera. At first, it appears to be merely another of Scudder's "improvements." Ironically it convicts M'Closky of Paul's murder. Boucicault, who apparently read of the inadvertent photographing of a murder in Albany Fonblanque's novel *The Filibuster: A Story of American Life* (1862), is credited as the first dramatist to use the camera to reveal the villain on the stage.

Critical Context

Writing plays was not Dion Boucicault's only contribution to theater. He was an actor, director, and manager. Yet he is best known as a dramatist. Boucicault created at least 141 extant plays that span a period of fifty-four years. His comedy of manners *London Assurance* (pr., pb. 1841) was Boucicault's first highly successful play and revealed his potential to create quality drama. Boucicault's first successful American play was the melodramatic *The Poor of New York* (pr., pb. 1857). This play was followed two years later by a better-written melodrama, his controversial *The Octoroon*; the play was extremely popular during its time and remains a noteworthy example of earlier American drama. Boucicault, a nineteenth century dramatist, is primarily remembered in the twenty-first century for three Irish plays: *The Colleen Bawn* (pr., pb. 1860), *Arrah-na-Pogue: Or, The Wicklow Wedding* (pr. 1864, pb. 1865), and *The Shaughraun* (pr. 1874, pb. 1880), which was his greatest artistic and commercial success. *Arrah-na-Pogue* was the only one of this trio of Irish plays that did not premiere in New York.

Like the various dramatic adaptations of *Uncle Tom's Cabin*, *The Octoroon* is classified as a slavery play. Unlike its predecessors, Boucicault's play is a more unified and polished work. During the nineteenth century, autobiographies by former slaves such as Frederick Douglass, William Wells Brown, and Harriet Jacobs were potent tools in the antislavery crusade. Many readers of these narratives were awakened to the evils of slavery. In a similar manner, *The Octoroon*, with its ability to evoke various antislavery sentiments, served as an important tool for abolitionists. More than a century later, *The Octoroon* remains a valuable resource that reveals the insight and courage of a nineteenth century playwright who dared to bring the inflammatory issue of slavery to the stage.

Sources for Further Study

Fawkes, Richard. *Dion Boucicault: A Biography*. New York: Quartet Books, 1979.
Hogan, Robert. *Dion Boucicault*. New York: Twayne, 1969.
Parkin, Andrew. Introduction to *Selected Plays of Dion Boucicault*. Washington, D.C.: Catholic University of America Press, 1987.

Richardson, Gary A. "Boucicault's *The Octoroon* and American Law." *Theatre Journal* 34 (1982): 155-164.

Roach, Joseph R. "Slave Spectacles and Tragic Octoroons: A Cultural Genealogy of Antebellum Performance." *Theatre Survey* 33 (1992): 167-187.

Thomson, Peter, ed. Introduction to *Plays by Dion Boucicault*. New York: Cambridge University Press, 1984.

Watt, Stephen, and Gary A. Richardson, eds. *American Drama: Colonial to Contemporary*. New York: Harcourt Brace, 1995.

Linda M. Carter

OFFENDING THE AUDIENCE

Author: Peter Handke (1942-)
Type of plot: Social realism
Time of plot: Concurrent with the evening's production
Locale: Unspecified
First produced: 1966, at the Theater am Turm, Frankfurt, West Germany
First published: Publikumsbeschimpfung, 1966 (English translation, 1969, in *Kaspar and Other Plays*)

Principal characters:
FOUR SPEAKERS, who are neither named nor differentiated

The Play

Before the speeches of *Offending the Audience* begin, Peter Handke's script contains a section titled "Rules for the actors." The four speakers are urged to seek out forms of popular art and other experiences which, presumably, would help to free them from the methods of delivery or acting inculcated by their previous training. The actors are told to strive for a sameness of sound, without individual inflection, as if in a crowd or ritual situation; they are also told to make up the partially inarticulate lines and deliver those lines very fast in overlapping and even simultaneous fashion.

Before the curtain opens and the lights onstage and in the auditorium are turned up, the audience is to have the typical pre-performance experiences: formally attired ushers, proper programs, and noises from behind the closed curtain that sound like a crew setting up. When the curtain parts, the equal lighting of both stage and auditorium, a stage without props or scenery, actors who rehearse invectives which cannot be completely heard, all signal to the audience that the play will not be traditional, and perhaps not entertaining. The audience is welcomed, the piece is announced as a "prologue," and the actors proceed with a series of lines, the grammatical subject of which is "you."

The first task of the speakers is to disillusion the audience as to what it will see and hear. Attention is caught by a paradox: On one hand the audience will not see what it usually sees; on the other hand it will see nothing that is really unusual. The play or prologue will not create another world, with props, fictional characters, and compelling plot. The stage does not represent a room, with an invisible wall between the actors and the audience, as in realistic theater where members of the audience are in the position of onlookers and eavesdroppers. Gestures and speeches are not meant to suggest anything other than what they would in normal, direct communication. In this sense, the audience will not experience anything unusual.

In the course of disillusioning the audience, the speakers make it aware of the illusions or assumptions it brings into the (any) theater. It expects a different time, a suspension of real time; it expects a transformed space; it expects a story told in actions (words, deeds) of people who are spotlighted in that space. In this prologue, the time is now, the world is this theater tonight, the action is what happens to the audience. Meaning will come from what the audience realizes about itself and most theater audiences. The speakers "review" the audience, the way a spectator or critic might review a play: The audience is characterized variously as "charming," "breathtaking," and "not a brilliant idea," unconvincing in its debut performance. Later, in the "name-calling section" of the play, the audience is likewise characterized as completely convincing and realistic even while it is criticized for being nothing but cheap imitations.

Being onstage, what does the audience do? The speakers have described the audience's expectations; now they turn to a singular "you" in their address and begin to describe the typical viewer's self-consciousness—of the body, the muscles, the heartbeat, breathing, blinking, salivating. The speakers ask the members of the audience to try not to blink, breath, hear, salivate—in short, not to live. Then the speakers ask the audience why it continues to do these things. They order the audience to cease. Then they order the audience to do these things. Now, the speakers assert, members of the audience are fully aware of themselves as being at the center of this world. The speakers begin to taunt the audience, gently, by telling it that they could well have represented another reality or significance, but they did not. In speaking, they do not imitate fictional characters and they do not even represent themselves; they merely communicate with the audience. They repeat the opening statement, "This piece is a prologue," explaining that it is prologue to attending theater and to living. The speakers sketch the immediate future of the audience, the shifting in seats, the rising, the passage out of the theater, the fragmenting and dispersing of the audience into individual lives.

Up to this point, the piece is also prologue to the speakers' "offending the audience," which some critics have thought to be the main action. Beginning with favorable comments on the audience as players in the drama of the prologue, the speakers move into several paragraphs of such names as "ass-kissers," "scum of the melting pot," "sitting ducks," "dirty Jews," "napalm specialists," "killer pigs," and "farts." The outpouring does not really define a single despised object, but there are two themes to the invective: The audience, like all audiences, sits passively and takes whatever the playwright/actors dish out; the audience, like all humanity, contains the full range of types and vices. The last name applied to the audience, in fact, is "you fellow humans you." The speakers close politely: "You were welcome here. We thank you. Good night." The curtain closes, then opens again to reveal the actors standing, looking into space. Recorded applause and noise plays over the loudspeaker system until the audience disperses.

Themes and Meanings

Peter Handke's prefatory note to *Offending the Audience* provides a helpful entrance to its themes and meanings. He calls the piece a *Sprechstucke*, translated as "speak-in." As such, the piece is to be regarded as a self-contained presentation of words which refer to nothing outside of themselves. The play is a dismissal of and, in some sense, a rebuke to the conventions of theater, particularly as they shape or limit the expectations of the audience. The audience is deliberately "offended" in the name-calling section, but it is clear that the particular audience of any given night need not take offense.

In a sense, Handke's piece seems to indicate that the audience is not to blame, and that all the speakers want to do is shake the audience out of its complacency. In turning attention to the audience, the speakers stress the extent to which the audience "creates" the full experience of any drama by allowing its expectations to operate. *Offending the Audience* simultaneously makes the audience aware of its usually unconscious role in structuring the details into a whole and denies that this play will allow them to do that. Instead, the drama wants spectators to understand themselves and possibly restructure their roles in drama. They will hopefully understand that plays are made of language, of words that do not necessarily transcend themselves. The piece does this by stressing the informational or communicative functions of language over its imaginative functions.

Offending the Audience does not, however, reject theater. It is, in fact, quite theatrical in its performance of complaints, analysis, and attacks. It takes place in a theater before an audience which paid to be admitted. So the viewer is confronted with the irony of a protest against institutionalized theater that supports the institution. The name-calling even suggests that the conventions of theater are so strong that the audience can "create" theater where there is none.

Dramatic Devices

As a "speak-in," *Offending the Audience* deliberately undercuts or omits the traditional devices of drama. Scenery, props, lights, story, fictional characters, and action are not factors. The normal devices of poetic-dramatic language are undercut or omitted too. Peter Handke wants no metaphors, analogies, or images to suggest another level of reality.

Offending the Audience is not another existential or absurdist play about meaninglessness or the absence of all value. Language communicates meaning in this play. The speeches set up and develop ideas with some logic, although the frequent contradictions and repetitions tend to mask the logic. First, the piece seeks to expose and deny the traditional expectations of theater. Second, the speakers seek to turn the audience's attention on itself, in particular to the way the audience really "creates" the full dramatic experience by seeking or adding significance to the dialogue, scenic elements, and actions onstage. The speakers emphasize the audience's role both in this piece and in traditional drama by engaging in a mocking "review" of the audience's performance on this night. This review inevitably leads to the most dramatic part of the prologue, the offensive name-calling. Third, in the outpouring of names, an epic catalog of positive and negative categories of humanity, the audience is made aware that the world of theater and the world of reality are similar in that they are constituted by language.

In a real sense, Handke believes, language and the categories it creates structure all of humanity's consciousness. Once the audience realizes this, the speakers remind them, in a fourth stage, that they as actors could easily have created imaginative drama and that the audience, as a group of separate individuals, can now better appreciate what happens in normal drama through language and gestures. Hence, this piece is a "prologue" to normal drama, which is evoked by the recorded audience reaction to other dramatic events that is played over the sound system at the end of the piece.

Other devices that structure or order *Offending the Audience* are linguistic. The speakers speak very simple, direct sentences, with a limited vocabulary and much repetition. The use of "you" as plural subject puts the emphasis on the audience as a group; the use of the present tense put the emphasis on the present moment, a moment of expectation, denial, and (Handke hopes) enlightenment. Once the piece has focused attention on the collective audience, the speakers can shift to a singular "you" and imperative sentences, to raise individual consciousness of how one is alive during the drama and how one thus participates in creating the meaning of the drama. The offensive invective or name-calling marks a peak of drama, but also a peak of words as words, since the names are not part of larger, meaningful sentences. Further, by piling up names that do not add up to one type of person or even one moral perspective, by setting up phrases of names that are approximately equal in length and similar in order, the speakers empty them of their usual application, and the audience should become aware of language as a rhythm of sounds, as acoustical pattern. Perhaps the audience even realizes that the meaning of language, too, is something people add to ordered sounds, not something the sounds have in and of themselves.

Critical Context

The term "speak-in" situates this piece in the cultural upheaval and literary experimentation of the 1960's. "Be-ins," "guerrilla theater," "street theater," and "happenings" were terms applied to dramatic events designed to break outside forms and physical restrictions of conventional theater. They were often loosely scripted so as to create maximum involvement of the audience. The aim of these events was to create an "experience" that would be unique for each occasion, perhaps never repeated in exactly the same way.

Although Peter Handke's piece is more conservative in its staging, deliberately setting itself on a stage in a theater even while it denies the conventions of the theater, it does have a measure of the spontaneity of these earlier forms in that the actors are instructed to make up speeches when they approach the front of the stage in the beginning and, once they are positioned, to choose their parts in whatever order they decide. On different nights, each speaker might deliver different lines. There are, however, limits to the openness of this piece: Apart from the fact that the order makes logical sense, it is a self-contained work with no scripted "openings" for the audience. The audience is expected to "sit and take it," just as if it were watching traditional drama.

This factor opens up the other aspect of the category, "speak-in," that Handke sets up. If the title suggests certain spontaneous and loosely constructed dramatic experiences popular in the 1960s and 1970's, it also suggests the political protests of that period. *Offending the Audience* features a strong measure of argumentation, didacticism, and harangue. The audience is lectured, chastised, and even called names for the purpose of education or, to use a phrase popular in the 1960's, consciousness-raising.

Offending the Audience, Handke's first published play, is often read less as a manifesto than as a thematic guide to his early works. It connects to a protest Handke made the same year (1966), when he accused a distinguished gathering of German authors of clinging to old forms of moral realism. In *Selbstbezichtigung* (pr., pb. 1966; *Self-Accusation*, 1969), one speaker confesses to the audience, but, as in *Offending the Audience*, he or she ends up emphasizing how character was and is created by language. Both "speak-ins" are at least "prologues" to *Kaspar* (pr., pb. 1968; English translation, 1969). Based on the famous case of an adult who had been reared alone, without hearing or learning speech, and then left in the care of town authorities, *Kaspar* analyzes and criticizes the ways in which society (re-) constitutes human character through its education of this "blank mind."

Peter Handke's concerns with the operations of language in cultural and individual character formation are often linked to the work of modern linguistic philosophers Ferdinand de Saussure and Ludwig Wittgenstein and to the theories of structuralists and deconstructionists. Both of the latter groups are concerned with the tradition-bound relationships between words and meaning and how the interrelationships of words in sequence (syntax) alter their meaning. Deconstructionists, such as Jacques Derrida, have stressed the need to demystify language, to strip it of its hidden transcendental meanings. Handke's attempt to deny, for at least one night, the power of dramatic language to evoke another world seems similarly deconstructive.

Sources for Further Study

Barry, Thomas. "Postmodern Longings for the Static Moment: On Recent Peter Handke Criticism." *German Quarterly*, Winter, 1987, 88-98.

Berman, Jaye. "*Offending the Audience:* A Dramatic Example of Postmodern Parabasis." *Antithesis* 1, no. 1 (1987): 93-100.

DeMeritt, Linda C. *New Subjectivity and Prose Forms of Alienation: Peter Handke and Botho Strauss*. New York: P. Lang, 1987.

Firda, Richard A. *Peter Handke*. Boston: Twayne, 1993.

Klinkowitz, Jerome, and James Knowlton. *Peter Handke and the Postmodern Transformation: The Goalie's Journey Home*. Columbia: University of Missouri Press, 1983.

Ran-Mosely, Faye. *The Tragicomic Passion: Clowns, Fools, and Madmen in Drama, Film, and Literature*. New York: Lang, 1994.

Schlueter, June. *The Plays and Novels of Peter Handke*. Pittsburgh: University of Pittsburgh Press, 1981.

W. M. Hagen

THE OLD MAID

Author: Zoë Akins (1886-1958)
Type of plot: Social realism
Time of plot: 1833-1854
Locale: New York City
First produced: 1935, at the Empire Theatre, New York City
First published: 1935

Principal characters:

DELIA RALSTON (née LOVELL), a socially respectable woman
CHARLOTTE LOVELL, Delia's cousin and mother to Clementina
DR. LANSKELL, Delia's confidante
MRS. MINGOTT, a sophisticated relative of the Ralstons
JAMES RALSTON, Delia's affluent husband
JOSEPH RALSTON, the wealthy brother of James Ralston and Charlotte's fiancé
CLEMENTINA "TINA," Charlotte's illegitimate daughter
LANNING HALLEY, Tina's socially unfit suitor
DELIA "DEE" HALLEY, Delia's daughter
JOHN HALLEY, Dee's husband
NORA, Delia Ralston's maid

The Play

The Old Maid consists of five acts, or episodes, which span the twenty-one-year period from 1833 to 1854. The first episode is set on the day of Delia Lovell's marriage to Mr. James Ralston. Nora, Delia's maid, is superstitious about Delia's wedded future and wants to be sure that the bride has something borrowed and something blue. Delia agrees to borrow Nora's garter but carefully averts her head when Nora lifts her skirt. This incident calls attention to the conservative social conventions of the era. Parts of the body are treated with great delicacy and modesty; polite society disapproved of any discussion or suggestive hint of sex. Charlotte, Delia's cousin, gives her something blue, a turquoise from Clem Spender, Delia's rejected suitor. Delia is still in love with Clem, but she has chosen to marry the more affluent and so more socially acceptable James Ralston. Delia asks Charlotte to console Clem after her marriage to James. Charlotte, who is also in love with Clem, proudly announces that, had he returned Charlotte's affections, she would have waited for him forever. In a statement that has ironic resonance and becomes prophetic, Charlotte passionately claims that she would even be willing to be an old maid for his sake.

The second episode occurs five years later in the home of Charlotte and Delia's grandmother on Mercer Street. In a room above the stable, Charlotte has opened a nursery for the children of poor working women and has become engaged to Joseph

Ralston, the wealthy and equally conventional brother of Delia's husband. One of the poor children, whose name is Clementina, is a foundling who was left on the porch of a black family with a one-hundred-dollar note pinned to her dress. Several of the children torment five-year-old Tina and cruelly taunt her that she must live with "niggers" because her father and mother do not want her. When Charlotte reveals that she plans to continue to visit the day-nursery after her marriage, Joseph, her fiancé, disapproves. Charlotte is torn between the prospect of a safe future as a married woman secure in her respectability and the pain of parting with Tina and the other children.

The third episode takes place later that evening in the drawing room of James and Delia Ralston. Mrs. Mingott, a worldly-wise relative, explains the respectability of the Ralstons to Delia, who is still wearing Clem's turquoise around her neck, by saying that their family was not founded by gentlemen but by people who wanted to move up the social ladder, implying that this is also Delia's motive. Charlotte enters and begs Delia to persuade Joseph to let her continue with her nursery school, but she also reveals the secret that she had a love affair with Clem and that Tina is their daughter. On his own, Joseph decides to let Charlotte keep her nursery after they marry.

Meanwhile, Delia, intervening in Charlotte's future, tells Joseph that Charlotte coughed blood in front of her and is too ill to marry. Shortly afterward Delia confesses her knowledge of Charlotte's indiscretion to Dr. Lanskell, and he warns her that it is unethical to intervene in another person's destiny. Delia excuses herself by saying that she cannot allow Charlotte to marry Joseph in good conscience. She also reports that she plans to rear Charlotte's child. Later, Delia tells Charlotte that she cannot marry Joe, but that Charlotte can keep her daughter. As this act concludes, Charlotte, crying softly, grabs a skein of bright silk embroidery, threads it through her engagement ring, and then throws it on the table before she rushes from the room.

The fourth episode is set fourteen years later in 1853. Charlotte, now a colorless, "typical old maid," is known to her daughter Tina as Cousin Charlotte. Charlotte has concealed from Tina that she is her mother and practices what she will say so that she will sound like an "old-maid aunt" to her daughter. Tina and Dee, Delia's daughter, regard the very composed and still beautiful Delia as their mother. Dee is married to the respectable and dull John Halley. Charlotte interrupts a passionate and potentially compromising scene between Tina and Lanning Halley, a suitor as undesirable as Clem had been. Later, Charlotte says that she will tell Tina the truth about her own past and take her away. Delia intervenes in Charlotte's life again. She counters with a different solution to the problem of Tina's future by offering to adopt Charlotte's daughter and give her the Ralston name and her personal fortune.

The fifth episode occurs six months later, in June, 1854, on the eve of Tina's wedding to Lanning Halley. Delia confides to Dr. Lanskell that although she and Charlotte are giving Tina up, the girl will now be safe from the truth of Charlotte's past and her own illegitimacy. Everyone is aware that Lanning's parents have decided to let him marry Tina because she now has money and a name. Tina credits Delia with her good fortune, exclaiming that she owes her everything. In a scene overheard by Charlotte, Tina tells Delia that she would rather have her as her mother than anyone else in the world and reveals Charlotte's jealousy by noting that there is less affection between Delia and her daughter Dee than exists between Delia and Tina. Tina also shows Dr. Lanskill the turquoise that Delia has given her and recalls her early memory of sitting on the lap of a beautiful lady who let her play with the turquoise.

Charlotte's jealousy erupts in a confrontation with Delia over control of Tina. Charlotte accuses Delia of hating her because she is the mother of Clem Spender's child; Delia retorts that Charlotte has always hated her. Announcing that she will tell Tina the truth about her birth, Charlotte leaves the room. Dr. Lanskell, who sympathizes with Delia for having had to live with Charlotte and put up with her jealousy, comforts Delia. Dee then tells Delia that she is glad that Delia decided to adopt Tina and informs Delia that she is going to have a child. Charlotte returns to report that she has not told Tina the truth about her illegitimacy. She acknowledges to her cousin that Delia has always been the mother whom Tina wanted and urges Delia to go to Tina. This concession seems to soften Delia's feelings about Charlotte because, in her final scene with Tina, she tells her that Charlotte is an old maid because Charlotte would not give Tina up.

Delia does not confront the issue of Tina's illegitimacy; she merely tells the young woman that Charlotte gave up a man who loved her very much and would have given her everything she wanted. Tina asks why no one has ever told her about Charlotte's sacrifice, and somewhat uncertainly Delia replies that sometimes people are selfish and fail to think. In a concession to her cousin, Delia tells Tina to kiss Charlotte as her last gesture of farewell to her family and home. The play concludes with Delia listening as she hears from a distance Tina calling out, "Cousin Charlotte."

Themes and Meanings

The Ralstons are identified as descendants of middle-class English colonists who came to the colonies not for religious reasons but to gain financially in the New World. Their affluence enables them to impose a set of rigid codes on society. Akins satirizes their middle-class morality, but her deepest sarcasm is reserved for their callous indifference to the poor and less fortunate. For example, although Charlotte places Tina with her own childhood nurse, the other characters dismiss the black family as unworthy of caring for a white child.

In *The Old Maid*, Akins focuses more on social character than on ideas. She deftly establishes the stifling social orthodoxy of New York in the 1850's but avoids overtly moralizing about the crushing conventionalism represented by the Ralstons. Instead, she focuses attention on the lifelong psychological duel between Delia and Charlotte over who is to be Tina's mother. To Delia, the child Tina symbolizes a youthful, romantic love with Clem that she rejected in favor of social acceptance and affluence. Delia controls the play's action, twice intervening decisively in Charlotte's life. She prevents Charlotte from marrying into the Ralston family, and she adopts her illegitimate daughter to keep Charlotte from taking her away. In the character Delia, Akins creates a protagonist as fascinating as she is frightening.

Dramatic Devices

The shift in time from 1839 to 1853 is suggested by changing the style of the set's furnishings from Empire to Victorian. The continuity, however, is important; the room is still the same. Like society, the setting has not really changed. Tina, a young woman without an identifiable social status or fortune, is as unacceptable as her father was. This parallelism is emphasized by beginning the play with a scene occurring just before Delia's wedding and concluding the play with a scene just before Tina's wedding to Lanning Halley.

At the end of the third episode, Delia, after revealing to Charlotte that she has broken her cousin's engagement to Joseph Ralston, promises Charlotte that she will live by herself with Tina. Charlotte picks up a skein of bright silk from Delia's embroidery and draws it through her engagement ring. She stands hesitating and then slips the silk through the ring and lets the ring swing away from her. Symbolically, she accepts her future as an old maid. Without looking at Delia, she rushes from the house.

Critical Context

Zoë Akins merits more attention than she has received in the history of modern American drama. Even defenses of Akins often begin with the assumption that she wrote melodramas. Predictably, *The Old Maid* was dismissed as sentimental and out of date when it received the Pulitzer Prize for drama in 1935. Many critics thought that the Pulitzer Prize should have been awarded to the Lillian Hellman's more controversial *The Children's Hour* (pr., pb. 1934), but *The Old Maid* was a popular success in New York City and on tour.

Akins adapted *The Old Maid* from Edith Wharton's novella, which appeared as one of four studies in a collection published under the title *Old New York* (1924). Wharton was so confident of Akins's adaptation that she did not insist on approving the script before it was produced. Akins, like Wharton, was willing to oppose the prevailing approval of naturalism. Akins's interest in character results in a compelling study of the conflict between society and the individual.

Sources for Further Study

Bradley, Jennifer. "Zoë Akins and the Age of Excess: Broadway Melodrama in the 1920's." In *Modern American Drama: The Female Canon*, edited by June Schlueter. Rutherford, N.J.: Fairleigh Dickinson University Press, 1990.

McDowell, Margaret B. "Edith Wharton's *The Old Maid:* Novella/Play/Film." *College Literature* 14, no. 3 (Fall, 1987): 246-262.

Shafer, Yvonne. "Zoë Akins (1886-1958)." In *American Women Playwrights, 1900-1950*. New York: Peter Lang, 1995.

Sutherland, Cynthia. "American Women Playwrights as Mediators of the 'Woman Problem.'" *Modern Drama* 21 (1978): 319-336.

Wharton, Edith. *The Old Maid*. New York: D. Appleton, 1924.

Jean R. Brink

THE OLDEST LIVING GRADUATE

Author: Preston Jones (1936-1979)
Type of plot: Psychological
Time of plot: Summer, 1962
Locale: West Texas
First produced: 1974, at the Dallas Theater Center, Dallas, Texas
First published: 1976, in *A Texas Trilogy*

Principal characters:
COLONEL J. C. KINKAID, a World War I veteran
FLOYD KINKAID, his son
MAUREEN KINKAID, Floyd's wife
CLARENCE SICKENGER, Floyd's new business partner
MARTHA ANN SICKENGER, Clarence's wife
MIKE TREMAINE, a handyman

The Play

The Oldest Living Graduate concerns an important week near the end of Colonel J. C. Kinkaid's life. The audience is immediately introduced to him in the first scene through his exchange ("conversation" is hardly the word) with his daughter-in-law, Maureen Kinkaid, and their neighbor Martha Ann Sickenger. The setting, as it remains throughout the play, is the den of his son's ranch-style house on the outskirts of Bradleyville, Texas. This dialogue is important not so much for the information it conveys as for the personalities it reveals. The colonel is seventy-five, wheelchair bound, cantankerous, and more than a bit dotty, his mind often moving through a series of associations to the most comical conclusions. However, he still has drive and spunk, along with an indomitable will that he tries to impose on others. Even in his dotage, his insights are often keen. Both likable and irritating, he is by turns admired and merely tolerated by Maureen, whose own personality at times resembles his.

Martha Ann is an empty-headed chatterbox who perpetually annoys Maureen. A few nuggets of information important to the development of the plot do appear among the humorous arguments and misunderstandings that ensue. The audience learns that the colonel was shell-shocked during the trench warfare of World War I; there is also mention of the Genet farm, which is dear to his heart. After he has left to have a look at this property, Martha Ann lets slip that her husband and Floyd Kinkaid, the colonel's son, hope to capitalize on the farm as part of a lakeside development.

The husbands return, there is more banter revealing the essential barrenness of small-town life, and finally Maureen and Floyd are alone. Wealthy, childless, they have few aims. Maureen realizes that Floyd needs a challenge, but she is taken aback by his callous plans not only to develop his father's cherished property but also to manipulate to his advantage the fact (it is now revealed) that his father is "the oldest livin' graduate" of the Mirabeau B. Lamar Military Academy in Galveston. The school is moving to a new location, and its officials have decided to use the occasion to honor Colonel Kinkaid. Since the latter cannot make the trip to Galveston, the ceremony will be held in Bradleyville. Floyd envisions the sudden influx of government officials, businessmen, and military dignitaries as the perfect springboard to launch his lakeside development.

Act 1, scene 2, is decidedly different in tone. The first part is a conversation between Colonel Kinkaid and Mike Tremaine, a hired hand who occasionally looks after the colonel and takes him for drives. The colonel reveals the accumulating sense of loss that time has brought him: his present immobility, the death of his older (and favorite) son, what in his eyes amounts to the destruction of the land under the barrage of development, and the end of his first romance. Now the audience discovers the reason for the colonel's attachment to the Genet farm: It was there that a group of French settlers had come, and the colonel had fallen in love with Suzanne Genet. Forced by drought to move on, the Genet family, including Suzanne, disappeared. The colonel keeps the property untouched "for rememberin'." Thus, the audience is prepared for the second part of the scene: a confrontation between Floyd and the colonel, during which Floyd asks for permission to develop the farm, and the colonel refuses.

The arrival in act 2, scene 1, of two representatives of the military academy sharply focuses the conflicts that have been building within the colonel's mind and between him and his son. Colonel Kinkaid graphically disabuses the young cadet who has accompanied the school commandant of any notions about the romantic nature of his military career. Filled with sorrow when he learns how each of his classmates has died, the colonel abruptly declines any part in the school's ceremonies: "It ain't no honor to be the oldest livin' *anything*. Oldest living *graduate*, oldest living *Indian*, oldest living *armadillo*, oldest living *nuthin'*, 'cause that means that you're all alone!" Floyd wheels angrily on his father. In the dispute that follows, Floyd reveals, among other matters, the bitterness and the pain that he has felt from having his dead brother constantly idealized as a paragon of filial behavior. Even Maureen, much as she admires the colonel's feisty independence, begs him this once to show his love for Floyd by giving his son what he wants. The scene ends inconclusively, however, with Floyd driving his father to a lodge meeting.

The Sickengers return in scene 2. Clarence reveals that actually Floyd does not need permission from his father to develop the farm, for a week earlier Floyd has had his father declared incompetent and has received power of attorney over his affairs. Maureen can comprehend neither Floyd's motives nor the elaborate game that he has played with his father trying to secure permission. Floyd attempts to explain that just once he wanted his father to show tangibly that he recognizes his son's worth. Maureen, however, insists that Floyd be honest with his father. Just as Floyd agrees, a telephone call comes announcing that Colonel Kinkaid has suffered a stroke during his lodge meeting.

A short scene concludes the play. The colonel has refused to stay in the hospital. He reminisces with Mike about his vanished past and the changed West. Facing the imminence of his death and the uselessness of clinging to the past, he gives Floyd the land.

Themes and Meanings

The Oldest Living Graduate is a play about the effects of time: the change it brings and the way the past intrudes into the present. Even the plot's father-son conflict is related to this theme. Floyd wants to turn his back on the past, to transform the land where he lives. This desire stems largely from his need to avenge a past that he cannot escape. Always he has been measured against his elder brother, who is forever secure from failure because he is dead and consequently never to be equaled. Floyd is begging for his father to recognize his younger son in Floyd's own right, not in comparison to the dead brother. At the same time, Floyd is trying to assert his real role as the family's benefactor, preferably by having Colonel Kinkaid acknowledge that he has been the one to hold their properties together for seventeen years, but if necessary by certifying that the old man is senile and incompetent. It is thus important to the colonel's own character development that he presents the Genet farm to Floyd without knowing that it is no longer his to give away.

Few of the colonel's memories are romantic ones. He does reminisce with gusto about his career with General John Pershing in the Philippines and especially in Mexico. None of these military exploits performed in the grand old style, however, had prepared him for the realities of trench warfare in France. That experience broke the colonel's spirit, leaving him a shell of a man. Thus, he is fighting to preserve the few romantic memories that he does have. For this reason he refuses to let the Genet farm be disturbed. As he says, "That's important to an old feller like me, havin' places that stay the same for rememberin' on." His first love retains its romantic glow as long as he can keep the place inviolate, for then he can keep the memory inviolate. It is significant that Colonel Kinkaid explains the farm's importance to Mike, who more than anyone else in the play stands for the enduring values of the past. At the end of the play the colonel is forced to acknowledge that a person cannot stem change: "The things ah seen and remember in this country is all gone now. Even the sounds of things is gone." The very title of the play suggests the inevitability of time's progress. The colonel is the oldest living graduate, but many died to leave him in that position, and soon he will join them: He will be "graduated," to another plane and will leave another to inherit the title.

Dramatic Devices

The story line of *The Oldest Living Graduate* constantly skirts sentimentality, which Preston Jones avoids through generous doses of comedy. The colonel is the primary source of much of the humor. One of Jones's favorite devices is to let the colonel start an incongruous chain of associations that leads him further and further into fantasy, only to pull up short and shoot off again in a totally unexpected direction. For example, early in the play Maureen receives a telephone call from a preacher involved in the planned ceremony. Colonel Kinkaid intercepts the call on the den's extension and decides, for some obscure reason, that it is an obscene call, whereupon he informs the caller that he has wasted a dime if he thinks that Maureen is sexually attractive. When Maureen finally makes the colonel realize that it is the preacher on the telephone, the colonel proceeds to denounce him for losing his religious calling. By the time Maureen finally grabs the receiver from the colonel's hand, the minister has hung up. The colonel takes full credit for having shamed him, then declares, "Don't like preachers anyway." When Maureen demands to know why, however, Colonel Kinkaid denies having made such a statement and accuses Maureen of trying to get him into trouble with God in order to keep him out of Heaven.

Another comic device that Jones uses with both the colonel and Maureen is allowing them to tell the truth about a social situation when politeness would call for keeping quiet. For example, the colonel cannot understand why Martha Ann has married such an unattractive man as Clarence. He demands to know if she had become pregnant before the wedding and then, when she reacts in shock, blurts out the probable truth: "Must have been the money then." Though never obscene, some of the humor is sexual.

Many lines in the play are almost throwaway zingers that crisply reveal the area's cultural barrenness, its racial and ethnic prejudices, and its closed-mindedness. In particular, the Sickengers are vehicles for Jones's satire against small-town mentalities. Martha Ann is close to being a caricature of a young, empty-headed woman whose only interests are clothes, her new sports car, and gossip. Clarence is the stolid, unimaginative businessman who prefers women who do not talk back. Dramatically, they both function to make Maureen more understandable and even likable for her cattiness, for the Sickengers represent personality types and attitudes that both the Kinkaids have managed to avoid. In total contrast to the Sickengers' Babbittry stands the handyman Mike. Dramatically, he represents the values of the Old West, based on a closeness to the land, a closeness that the Sickengers and the younger Kinkaids have lost. It is between these two poles that the Kinkaids battle toward some sense of community within the family.

Critical Context

In centering his plot on a conflict between father and son, Preston Jones placed *The Oldest Living Graduate* squarely in one of the great American dramatic traditions. Plays such as Arthur Miller's *Death of a Salesman* (pr., pb. 1949), Tennessee Williams's *Cat on a Hot Tin Roof* (pr., pb. 1955), and Eugene O'Neill's *Long Day's Journey into Night* (pr., pb. 1956) come instantly to mind as examples of this tradition. Jones's satiric exploration of small-town values is also part of a long American literary tradition dating from Edgar Lee Masters's *Spoon River Anthology* (1915) and Sherwood Anderson's *Winesburg, Ohio* (1919). Examination of an old person's confrontation with his own mortality is a universal theme, but it is particularly instructive to compare Jones's play with Flannery O'Connor's short story about the death of a Civil War veteran while attending his granddaughter's graduation, "A Late Encounter with the Enemy" (1953).

In Jones's own development, *The Oldest Living Graduate* is the third play of *A Texas Trilogy*, his first works to be presented to the public. Each play stands alone dramatically, but each becomes richer when seen in relationship to the other two. All are set in the same locale (an imaginary town modeled on Colorado City, Texas), and names dropped casually in one play become full-fledged characters in another. Thus, the practical nurse who accompanies Colonel Kinkaid home from the hospital in *The Oldest Living Graduate* is the offstage mother of a character in the first play, *The Last Meeting of the Knights of the White Magnolia* (pr. 1973, pb. 1976) and a prominent character in the second play, *Lu Ann Hampton Laverty Oberlander* (pr. 1974, pb. 1976). The former takes place during the time of act 2, scene 2 of *The Oldest Living Graduate*; in it the colonel suffers his stroke. In *Lu Ann Hampton Laverty Oberlander* it is revealed that the town erects a statue to the colonel after his death (a statue so ugly that even the pigeons will not defile it) and that Floyd and Clarence are successful with their lakeside development (though they have trouble getting the grass to grow on the golf course).

Jones's reputation rests entirely on this trilogy. It has received public acclaim in regional theaters and at the Kennedy Center in Washington, D.C. Critical reviews were decidedly mixed when the trilogy opened on Broadway in September, 1976, and it closed there after a brief run. Still, Otis L. Guernsey, Jr., chose both *The Oldest Living Graduate* and *The Last Meeting of the Knights of the White Magnolia* for inclusion in *The Best Plays of 1976-1977*. *The Oldest Living Graduate* was televised in 1980 with Henry Fonda as Colonel Kinkaid. Jones returned to a West Texas setting for a one-act play examining racial attitudes, *Juneteenth* (pr. 1979), but the other three full-length plays that he completed before his death were all set in his natal state of New Mexico: *A Place on the Magdalena Flats* (pr. 1976, pb. 1984), *Santa Fe Sunshine* (pr., pb. 1977), and *Remember* (pr. 1979). None of the four received much attention, though they reflect Jones's continued interest in the themes he had developed in *The Oldest Living Graduate* and the other plays of *A Texas Trilogy*.

Sources for Further Study

Anthony, Ole. "The Long Nights of Preston Jones." *Texas Monthly* 7 (December, 1979): 180-189.

Bennett, Patrick. *Talking with Texas Writers: Twelve Interviews*. College Station: Texas A&M Press, 1980.

Busby, Mark. *Preston Jones*. Boise, Idaho: Boise State University Press, 1983.

Cook, Bruce. "Preston Jones: Playwright on the Range." *Saturday Review* 3 (May 15, 1976): 40-42.

Kerr, Walter. "The Buildup (and Letdown) of *Texas Trilogy*." *New York Times*, October 3, 1976, p. D3, D6.

Prideux, Tom. "The Classic Family Drama Is Revived in *A Texas Trilogy*." *Smithsonian* 7 (October, 1976).

Reynolds, R. C. "Humor, Dreams, and the Human Condition in Preston Jones's *A Texas Trilogy*." *Southern Quarterly* 24, no. 3 (1986): 14-24.

Drewey Wayne Gunn

ONCE IN A LIFETIME

Authors: George S. Kaufman (1889-1961) and Moss Hart (1904-1961)
Type of plot: Comedy
Time of plot: The late 1920's
Locale: New York City and Hollywood
First produced: 1930, at the Music Box Theatre, New York City
First published: 1930

Principal characters:
JERRY HYLAND,
MAY DANIELS, and
GEORGE LEWIS, vaudevillians who have fallen upon hard times
SUSAN WALKER, an aspiring actor
HELEN HOBART, a Hollywood gossip columnist
HERMAN GLOGAUER, a studio executive

The Play

Once in a Lifetime opens in a rundown apartment in New York City in 1929, where George Lewis, whose passion is eating Indian nuts, is conversing with the witty May Daniels. Jerry Hyland, the third to enter, completes the team for their vaudeville act. The three have only $180 between them, and their prospects seem dim.

Jerry, an ambitious man in his early thirties, proclaims that the new "talkies" have made the theater extinct and that he has just sold their act for five hundred dollars. He has decided to take his chances in Hollywood, inspired by Al Jolson in *The Jazz Singer* (1927). May, hiding her affection for Jerry, agrees to the move. She reasons that they could make their fortune by opening a school of elocution to teach silent stars the proper way of speaking. George, who appears to be more interested in his Indian nuts than in any of the action going on around him, is reluctant to commit himself to the move. Soon, however, he is persuaded of the possibilities in the land of "talkies." The first scene ends with all three singing "California Here I Come!"

In act 1, scene 2, the setting is a Pullman car headed west. George eats his Indian nuts as May nervously looks through a book on elocution in order to be ready to teach it in Hollywood. She reads aloud to George, "We strongly urge the use of abdominal breathing as a fundamental principle in elocutionary training." Irritated by his continual crunching, she asks whether "those things come without shells"; impatiently, she leaves the coach. In his first sign of affection for May, Jerry tells George that they must keep her spirits up.

Having seen Helen Hobart, a well-known gossip columnist from Hollywood, on another car, May returns to the coach. It seems that May and Hobart are old acquaintances. The travelers hatch a scheme to enlist Hobart's support for their new school of elocution, taking advantage of the contacts and funds to which she has access. The threesome decide to impress her, going so far as to give George the fictitious title "Doctor."

Hobart is easily convinced that such an enterprise would be worthwhile and offers financial support as a 50 percent owner of the school. She decides that it should be housed in the studios of Herman Glogauer. Since he passed up an opportunity to own the technique used in the making of "talkies," the vitaphone, he would be a most likely help in this cause, if for no other reason than embarrassment. Hobart's promise is made as the scene moves toward conclusion. Susan Walker then enters the car. It quickly becomes obvious that she and George are a perfect match—both naïve and blindly hopeful of success.

The main action of act 1, scene 3 is the closing of the deal to open the school of elocution at the Glogauer Studios. Hobart sets up a meeting with Glogauer at the Stilton Hotel. Susan and her mother are the first to arrive and are barraged by movie star look-alikes and those hopeful of being discovered. George, May, Jerry, and Hobart appear. The last to arrive is Glogauer with a police escort. He agrees after some discussion to take on the threesome to educate his actors to speak properly. Two of the stars from his studios, Phyllis Fontaine and Florabel Leigh, have terrible regional accents. As the scene comes to an end, viewers are introduced to Glogauer's closest competition, the twelve Schlepkin brothers. George introduces Susan and asks her to recite "Boots," by Rudyard Kipling, in order to impress Glogauer. She begins the recitation; simultaneously, the Schlepkin brothers make an offer for merging the two studios.

The second act takes place in the reception area of Glogauer's Hollywood studios. It is a lavishly decorated room. Telephones ring, important-looking people rush in and out, and those of minor importance are doomed to wait at the leisure of the studio's boss, Glogauer. Miss Leighton, the receptionist, is deftly handling the studio's pages, who enter with signs announcing where Glogauer is. In the reception area, an underworked New York playwright, Lawrence Vail (a role initially played by Kaufman himself), is waiting in the hope of seeing Glogauer. Miss Leighton and the lot stars Phyllis and Florabel are boasting of the new elocution skills taught to them by May.

May enters and confidentially talks to Jerry, who she thinks is beginning to be swept up by the Hollywood scene too quickly and thoroughly. Jerry exits, pained by the suggestion, which has hit home. Helen Hobart enters looking for a story on lot star Dorothy Dodd but also informs May that Glogauer is very unhappy with the results of the school and is going to close it. She exits with a "Bon voyage!" To make matters worse for George, Susan is planning to return home to Columbus, upon the request of her father.

The plot twists quickly when Glogauer finds that his German-imported director, Kammerling, does not want to work with the actor he has been given, Dorothy Dodd, a known star. He refuses to do the picture unless a cast change is made. Glogauer agrees with him, but has no immediate suggestion as to whom to engage to replace Dodd. George quickly suggests that Susan would be perfect for the role of an innocent country girl.

When Glogauer scoffs at the suggestion, George, in a fit of insight, suggests that no one in the studio is competent, not even Glogauer himself, for he turned down the chance to be the first to use the vitaphone. Ashamed, and impressed with George's forthright manner, Glogauer quickly agrees to use Susan. He then schemes to present Susan in New York City as a new discovery of his from England. He puts George in charge of the entire operation and accedes to George's demand to rehire May and Jerry.

The last act is broken down into three fast-moving scenes that bring the action of the play to its climax while further emphasizing the power of the quick decision that is clearly the modus operandi of Hollywood. The first scene takes place on the set of *Gingham and Orchids*, George's project, which stars Susan. It is the last day of shooting, and May is coaching Susan with her only line in a wedding scene: She must say "I do." Glogauer is to visit the set, for he is amazed that the film has actually come in under the shooting schedule, something that has never occurred in the history of the studio.

At the ending, Glogauer becomes confused and realizes that George has filmed the wrong scenario. He is so furious at this waste of time and money that he again fires George, May, and Jerry; he tells Susan that the film will be the end of her career. Jerry tries to save his job by talking Glogauer out of his rash decision, but May seizes the opportunity to attack the studio executive with her sharp wit. As the scene ends and Glogauer exits, the three are served their notices.

Act 3, scene 2 takes place on the same Pullman car that brought the threesome to California. May is the only one of the three on the train. At the first stop, Vail climbs aboard, having left a sanatorium for underworked Hollywood playwrights. In this institution, as part of their cure scenario writers are allowed to stand in front of life-size reproductions of the executives of the studios to say whatever they like to them. The porter comes into the car with notices of *Gingham and Orchids*, and to May's surprise the reviews are overwhelmingly positive. Some of the remarks described the use of bonglike sound reminiscent of Eugene O'Neill's tom-toms in *The Emperor Jones* (pr. 1920). That sound was actually George cracking his Indian nuts on the set during the filming. It seems that all George's mistakes turn out to be innovations. A telegram is delivered to May from George, begging her to help him. She quickly changes her plans and decides to return to Hollywood.

The final scene of the play revolves around the reuniting of May with George and later with Jerry. There is a sense of closure; May and Jerry are together again, as are Susan and George. Just as all seems to be in harmony, Glogauer comes into the scene to fire them all for the third time. He has just been informed that George has bought two thousand airplanes so that he can get one free. In the nick of time, Glogauer receives a message that all the rival studios are clamoring to buy the airplanes from him: There is a new interest in making airplane pictures, but George has bought all the airplanes that were available. Again, Glogauer recants, perceiving George as a film genius. Miss Leighton then informs Glogauer that the studio is being torn down, on orders from George. When George explains that it is being torn down to build an even bigger studio, Glogauer exclaims, "Tell them to go ahead."

Themes and Meanings

Once in a Lifetime is a play of unbridled optimism. May and Jerry succeed, and the most naïve character, George, becomes the farcical counterpart of the self-made man. Just as the Depression was getting well under way in the United States, George S. Kaufman and Moss Hart offered hope to every person through this play, and especially the character of George. George flies in the face of conventional wisdom by challenging the power structure of Hollywood embodied in Glogauer.

As a counterpoint to George, Kaufman and Hart present the character of the New York playwright who was lured to Hollywood with a lucrative contract. Not only is Vail unable to see Glogauer in his office, but also he eventually has a nervous breakdown and must seek help in a sanatorium. In spite of the seemingly serious nature of Vail's breakdown, it serves a comic function in the play.

The play was written at a time when the use of sound in films was in its nascent stages. It pokes fun at the film industry, showing overworked executives being forced to make major decisions much too quickly. Some of those decisions—for example, Glogauer's decision not to use the invention that made talking pictures possible—are made without much foresight. Those quick decisions at times come back to haunt the executives. Certainly in the play Glogauer is swayed by financial considerations, but he is also motivated by the embarrassment he suffered by not being farsighted enough to see the possibilities inherent in the use of sound in film.

Romantic themes are also prevalent in the play. May, a strong-headed woman with a sharp wit, is portrayed as very much in love with her vaudeville partner Jerry. In this male-oriented play, she eventually comes back to him. The relationship between George and Susan represents a union of the naïve. It seems fitting that the play should end with these characters together again. Here the values of the playwrights, as well as those of American society in the late 1920's, are displayed. Though Kaufman and Hart were willing to disparage the film industry of Hollywood, they remained content with representing conventional ideals of romantic love.

George's rise to the top suggests the value of spontaneity. His character displays the optimistic attitude many Americans had toward Hollywood in the 1920's, and he embodies the hope for fame and fortune that many cherished in the early days of the industry. In this play, the motion-picture world can be seen as a metaphorical microcosm of the United States itself, a country where individual success is dependent on luck as well as courage and creativity.

Dramatic Devices

Once in a Lifetime relies on the audience's empathy with the main characters, George, May, and Jerry. The play begins in a seedy New York City hotel, a setting that immediately suggests the characters' hard luck and the unsettledness of their situation. The play's two Pullman car scenes further help to express the idea of the great American frontier. Mobility and flexibility are essential if one is to pursue a better life.

The play's structure is dependent on the comic technique of quick reversals. For example, when George berates Glogauer for incompetence, instead of being physically removed from the premises, he is given complete artistic control over a film. Later, when it is learned that he has bought two thousand airplanes in order to receive one free of charge, he is applauded rather than condemned, for Glogauer discovers that all the competing studios are interested in purchasing airplanes.

The character of Lawrence Vail, with his despair at being a playwright in Hollywood, as well as his trip to the sanatorium for writers, embodies the fear of many playwrights of the time that film would entirely displace live theater. The nature of theater as a critic of the forces of its demise helps to push the drama forward and creates many comic moments. Notably act 3, scene 1 takes place on a film set and so serves as a sort of play-within-the-play. In it, the actor Susan is being asked to memorize a line of dialogue, the lifeblood of drama, but she finds the chore difficult. However, the press eventually hails her as a fresh new talent.

Critical Context

Once in a Lifetime was the first commercial play written by Moss Hart. He is generally considered the creator of the play; it is thought that he later collaborated with George Kaufman so as to make it a commercial success. This venture was the first between Kaufman, by this time an established playwright, and Hart. Before their collaboration came to an end they had created such successes as *Merrily We Roll Along* (pr., pb. 1934), *You Can't Take It with You* (pr. 1936), and *The Man Who Came to Dinner* (pr., pb. 1939). The fascination Kaufman felt with actors and backstage life is reflected in *Once in a Lifetime*. He used similar characters, people both mistrusted and adored by their public, in plays such as *Merton of the Movies* (pr. 1922, pb. 1925), *Dinner at Eight* (pr., pb. 1932), and *Stage Door* (pr., pb. 1936). Merton Gill, the prototype for George Lewis, is a naïve character who has boundless belief in his ability to succeed in the silent film industry. He reads all the glamour magazines, takes a correspondence course in acting, and refuses to believe in anything other than his possible success. In *Stage Door* the protagonists are actors who are seeking success in New York's theater world. The main characters of *Dinner at Eight* are stars who have seen better days.

Kaufman and Hart's characters are basically true-to-life people in outrageous situations. The best known of the two playwrights' collaborations is *You Can't Take It with You*, in which the American Dream is viewed through the Vanderhof family, an odd collection of individualists who pursue their respective hobbies passionately. The Vanderhofs symbolize the American value of individualism, which had already been reflected in the main characters of *Once in a Lifetime*.

The work of Kaufman is generally accepted as classic American comedy, and his work with Hart is viewed as some of his best. Their strength lay in their ability to draw character and to create situations that are simultaneously believable and outrageous. Kaufman's success on Broadway was tremendous, and his collaborations with some of the best Broadway writers of the 1920's, 1930's, and 1940's were a testament to his desire to create and explore new avenues of theatrical expression.

Sources for Further Study

Bach, Steven. *Dazzle*. Cambridge, England: DaCapo, 2000.

Goldstein, Malcolm. *George S. Kaufman: His Life, His Theater.* New York: Oxford University Press, 1979.

Hart, Moss. *Act One: An Autobiography*. 3d ed. New York: St. Martin's Press, 1989.

Mason, Jeffrey D. *Wisecracks: The Farces of George S. Kaufman*. Ann Arbor: University of Michigan Research Press, 1988.

Meredith, Scott. *George S. Kaufman and His Friends*. Garden City, N.Y.: Doubleday, 1974.

Pollack, Rhoda-Gale. *George S. Kaufman*. Boston: Twayne, 1988.

Teichmann, Howard. *George S. Kaufman: An Intimate Portrait*. New York: Atheneum, 1972.

John R. Wilk

OPERETTA

Author: Witold Gombrowicz (1904-1969)
Type of plot: Problem play
Time of plot: 1910 and after World War II
Locale: Himalaj Castle
First produced: 1969, at the Teatro Stabile, Aquila, Italy
First published: *Operetka*, 1966 (English translation, 1971)

Principal characters:
MASTER FIOR, a famous fashion designer
PRINCE HIMALAJ
PRINCESS HIMALAJ, his wife
COUNT SZARM, their son
ALBERTYNKA, a beautiful girl
BARON FIRULET, Count Szarm's rival
COUNT HUFNAGIEL, a former valet, now a revolutionary
TWO THIEVES, hired by Szarm and Firulet

The Play

The first act of *Operetta* takes place before World War I, around the year 1910, in a church square near the Castle Himalaj. The protagonist, Count Szarm, son of the prince and princess Himalaj, desires to seduce a young girl named Albertynka. The problem is that he has never been introduced to her. Thus, he searches for a way to start up a "casual" acquaintance with her. He hires a petty thief to steal a medallion from her neck while she is sleeping on a bench. The count then "catches" the thief, retrieves the stolen medallion, and thus has a pretext for an introduction. During her sleep, however, Albertynka feels the hand of the thief, and from this time onward will constantly fall into sleep in order to relive the experience of that touch. The touch was not that of a thief but, rather, that of a lover. Count Szarm's plans are thus foiled, for Albertynka has come under the spell of someone else. From this time on, she dreams of "nudity," which is especially unfortunate for the count, as he is ashamed of nudity and loves to dress up. He would like to dress the girl in clothes from the best stores, while she only desires that he undress her.

At this time, Master Fior, a world-renowned fashion designer, arrives. A ball is subsequently arranged at the Castle Himalaj, in connection with a fashion show. Fior, who is to rule the fashion world for the next few years, is unsure what his next famous style will be. Acceding to the advice of Count Koniarz Hufnagiel, Fior decides that all guests at the ball will create and present their own "styles of the future." All are to cover themselves (and their creations) with large bags, which they are to take off at an appointed moment, uncovering their new clothes. In this way, Fior hopes to get some ideas for his new line. A committee will give out awards to those judged best.

In act 2, the guests arrive in their bags at the Castle Himalaj, where they are greeted by the prince and princess. Court Szarm arrives with the overdressed Albertynka. He is also leading on a leash the thief he had hired in the first act, as he fears the results should that person again touch Albertynka, who had been so moved by the first contact with him. (Albertynka, meanwhile, does not know that he is the man who had touched her.) Baron Firulet, the count's copycat rival, also arrives at the ball with his own thief on a leash. The sleepy Albertynka becomes the cause of a duel between the rivals, though neither of them is hurt.

The confusion grows in the ballroom. The count and the baron unleash their thieves, who steal everything they can lay their hands on and touch everyone. During the ball, it becomes known that Hufnagiel is neither a count nor a stableboy, as his first name indicates: He is in reality the prince's former valet, who is now a revolutionary activist. He came to the ball under an assumed name to smuggle in a new, bloody "fashion"—revolution. The lights go out in a general confusion of bodies, masks, and clothes; a revolution bursts forth under Hufnagiel's leadership. Fior turns on a flashlight and sees that the general has taken his bag off to reveal the uniform of a Nazi officer. The marquise is dressed as a Nazi turnkey in a concentration camp.

In the third act, which takes place after World War II (and the revolution), the transformed characters make their appearance against the background of the ruined castle. Hufnagiel gallops on the back of a professor, chasing after the Fascists. After they have been captured, Fior wishes to place them before a tribunal. Hufnagiel is judge, his "horse" is the procurator, and Fior is the attorney for the defense.

A seemingly magical thunderstorm takes place, after which all are in accord: Szarm and Firulet are chasing butterflies together. After them come two thief-gravediggers, carrying a black coffin. The rivals sadly look for Albertynka, who disappeared after the ball; only her clothes remained. Convinced that she was raped and murdered, they wander the earth searching for her naked body. Meanwhile, each character places in the coffin his own personal sufferings and failures. At the end, when Fior, master of fashion, curses the very existence of clothing and places in the coffin his own holy, common human nudity, Albertynka rises up from the coffin.

Themes and Meanings

The principal theme of *Operetta* is one that preoccupied Witold Gombrowicz throughout his career. He defined it clearly in the first volume of his *Dziennik* (1957; *Diary: Volume I*, 1988). Writing in 1954, and at the height of the Cold War, Gombrowicz said that the "real battle in culture" is not the conflict between opposing worldviews—communist versus Roman Catholic, for example. Rather,

> the most important, most extreme, and most incurable dispute is that waged in us by two of our most basic strivings; the one that desires form, shape, definition and the other, which protests against shape and does not want form. Humanity is constructed in such a way that it must define itself and then escape from its own definition. Reality is not something that allows itself to be completely contained in form.

In his various works Gombrowicz approached this conflict from different angles. In *Operetta*, the conflict between form and reality is expressed in the opposition between clothing and nakedness.

In one important respect the treatment of this theme in *Operetta* differs from Gombrowicz's treatment of it in his other works. In most of his writings, while insisting that the individual must continue to struggle against the confinements of form, Gombrowicz nevertheless stresses the futility of the quest for authenticity. He shows how rebellions against form quickly harden into mere forms themselves. In *Operetta*, however, the triumphant resurrection of Albertynka concludes the action with a striking image of youth, of eros, and of unconstrained authenticity.

Dramatic Devices

As *Operetta* is a drama that sets in metaphorical opposition images of clothing and nakedness, the most obvious and important dramatic device in the play is that of pretentious "dressing up" versus Albertynka's desire to be denuded. In the first act, Albertynka's unconscious desire to be undressed, which dramatizes her authenticity and unpretentious nature, is excited by the touch of Count Szarm's hireling thief. In stealing her medallion, the thief is indeed "undressing" her for the first time, giving her the subconscious impetus she needs to express her true self. From this time forward, she longs for nudity—that is, unpretentious authenticity.

The other characters of the play, and especially Szarm himself, are stifled by their own particular masks. Ashamed of nakedness, afraid of realizing their own authentic selves, they hide behind the various uniforms they show to the outside world. Perverted as they are as to appearances, they have not lost their reason. Knowing full well that their masks are unauthentic, yet ashamed to strip down to the nakedness of their own true nature, they strive to mask the nakedness of other, authentic personages so as not to be aware of their own falsity. This can be seen in Szarm's overwhelming desire to dress (indeed, overdress) Albertynka, as well as in his leashing of the thief.

As a matter of course, however, falsity cannot cover up truth for very long. When Szarm and Firulet, in a moment of passion, let loose the thieves from their collars, they "undress" them and allow them to act according to the laws of their own true natures. Chaos breaks loose, and one would think that, with the revolution, the house of cards would come tumbling down, and Albertynka (and truth) would come out triumphant. However, she disappears, and the court is left in the hands of the valet-count-revolutionary Hufnagiel (himself a twice-over devotee of appearances), under whose rule the star of fashion reaches its zenith.

The storm, which arrives at the height of idiotic falsity in the third act, magically transforms the scene into a veritable idyll. This dramatic device symbolizes the eventual triumph of human nature over falsity. Humans cannot sustain their mask for long—it will eventually fall from them, if they do not throw it away first. The great ceremonial denuding with which the play ends symbolizes the resignation of the characters from their masks, which they are physically unable to uphold any longer. When Fior, the master of masks, so to speak, curses fashion and places his own "holy" nakedness in the black coffin, Albertynka arises to assume her rightful place at the top of a rejuvenated, authentic society, as in a mythical resurrection. It is no coincidence that the main proponent of nudity and truth should be a young woman.

Critical Context

It has been remarked (and by Gombrowicz, at that) that *Operetta* can be seen as a farcical look at humanity's political nature and the desire to dress up in uniforms and masks which represent something that is quantitatively (though not qualitatively) bigger than the individual self. This idea is certainly present in the play. *Operetta*, however, is not a political drama. Like all Gombrowicz's works, it centers on the individual, on the inner soul, provoking the members of the audience to take a hard look at themselves and their own particular masks.

The entirety of Gombrowicz's literary output centers on the individual. An important writer little understood by his contemporary public, a Polish author living at a great distance from his nation and readership, Gombrowicz had much time and occasion for musing on the solitariness of individual human existence. This philosophical search for the individual's authentic essence can be found in works which span the entirety of the author's corpus. In the early short story "Pamiętnik Stefana Czarneckiego" (the diary of Stefan Czarnecki), Gombrowicz explores the problem of individual identity in relation to the masks that national tradition and adolescent experiences force upon one. Both these themes were taken up and developed at greater length; the former in the semi-autobiographical novel *Trans-Atlantyk* (1953) and the latter in the author's most famous work, *Ferdydurke* (1938; English translation, 1961).

Iwona, księżniczka Burgunda (pr. 1938, pr. 1957, revised pb. 1958; *Ivona, Princess of Burgundia*, 1969) may be considered a forerunner and sister-play of *Operetta*. The prince in *Ivona*, however, is unable to liberate himself from his mask; as noted above, *Operetta* is uncharacteristically optimistic in its conclusion.

Sources for Further Study

Goldmann, Lucien. "The Theatre of Gombrowicz." *Drama Review* 14, no. 3 (1970): 102-112.

Gombrowicz, Witold. *Diary, 1961-1966*. Edited by Jan Kott. Evanston: Northwestern University Press, 1994.

Junker, Howard. "Sweet Violence." *Newsweek*, May 29, 1967, 94.

Przybylska, Krystyna. "The Modern Polish Theater." *Queens Slavic Papers* 1 (1973): 68-79.

Taborski, B. "Witold Gombrowicz." In *Crowell's Handbook of Contemporary Drama*. New York: Crowell, 1971.

Ziarek, Eva. *Gombrowicz's Grimaces: Modernism, Gender, Nationality*. Albany: New York State University Press, 1998.

Charles S. Kraszewski

OTHERWISE ENGAGED

Author: Simon Gray (1936-   )
Type of plot: Comedy
Time of plot: The 1970's
Locale: London
First produced: 1975, at the Queen's Theatre, London
First published: 1975

Principal characters:
SIMON HENCH, a well-to-do publisher
STEPHEN HENCH, his brother, a public-school teacher
BETH HENCH, Simon's wife
DAVE, a student, tenant of the Henches' upstairs apartment
JEFF GOLDING, a boorish friend of Simon's
DAVINA SAUNDERS, Jeff's manipulative mistress
BERNARD WOOD, a former schoolfellow of Simon's

The Play

Otherwise Engaged begins in silence. In his luxurious London living room, whose expensive high-fidelity equipment and shelves of records attest his love of music, Simon Hench unwraps a new record, settles on a comfortable sofa, and begins to listen to Richard Wagner's opera *Parsifal* (1882). Then the interruptions begin which will make up the substance of the play.

The first intruder is the upstairs tenant. Dave, who enters uninvited, makes it clear that he has no intention of paying his rent and complains because Beth Hench was not present on the previous evening to supply food for his girlfriend. Desperate to get rid of him, Simon offers him a loan. Just as Dave is leaving, however, Simon's brother Stephen Hench arrives, seeking sympathy because he is certain that he has failed in his application for the position of assistant headmaster at his school; perhaps, he speculates, because he has too many children, perhaps because he went to the wrong university, perhaps simply because he is a loser. When Simon mentions the possibility of his friend Jeff Golding coming by, Stephen rather proudly recounts an incident at a dinner party when he responded to one of Jeff's insults with a physical attack on him. Unfortunately for Stephen's sense of importance, Jeff then appears, obviously drunk, and it is clear that he does not remember Stephen at all, much less the episode at the party.

Unlike Stephen, Jeff needs no ego-building. His conversation consists of glib generalizations, boasts, and insults, delivered amid a steady stream of profanity. After Stephen leaves, indicating his anger with a slam of the door, Jeff reveals his reason for coming to Simon. He wants someone to listen to his problem: He thinks that he is in love with his former wife, Gwendoline, who is now married to a University of Cambridge don and even has a child, and whom he is meeting regularly twice a week in the rooms of a friend of the don. In mid-monologue, Jeff mentions another mistress, Davina Saunders, with whom he is angry for some reason; just then the doorbell rings and Davina appears.

Davina has followed Jeff to Simon's place in order to express her own anger, to return her lover's key, and in the nastiest terms to give him some news: Gwendoline's husband has telephoned to report her attempted suicide and to threaten to assault Jeff. Throwing his drink at Davina, Jeff slams out. After Jeff's exit, Davina admits that she has made up the whole story and offers herself to Simon. When Simon offers to give serious consideration to the book which Davina is writing, however, she leaves, contented with his promise, and Simon, hopeful that he may yet be able to concentrate on *Parsifal*, places an "otherwise engaged" message on his telephone answering machine.

Unfortunately, Dave wanders in again, and this time Simon has to give him a bottle of sherry in order to get rid of him. As he leaves, Dave admits a man whom Simon does not recall, even though the stranger, Bernard Wood, says that he was at school with Simon. Wood has come to search for his daughter, who had applied for a job at Simon's publishing house and has since disappeared. Wood accuses Simon of having sexual intercourse with her, and, after a shocked denial, Simon suddenly admits that he did, and the act ends.

The second act continues in the same setting: The actors have not changed posture, and evidently only a few seconds have elapsed. Since he has obviously made no headway in shaming Simon, Wood reveals the fact that the missing girl is not his daughter but the girl for whom he has left his family and who consistently uses and humiliates him. He envies Simon, hates him enough to kill him, Wood says. Just then, Stephen returns. He says that Wood reminds him of a "plop" or loser he knew at school, and Wood exits.

Stephen's news justifies Simon's attempts to cheer him. He has indeed been given the assistant headmastership and is on his way to have a drink with the headmaster, the price he must pay for advancement. At this point, Dave returns, drunk on Simon's sherry. When Simon refuses to lend him his coffee maker, Dave abuses him, threatens to move out, and leaves, slamming the door. Immediately, Stephen returns, accuses Simon of sneering at him, and informs Simon that his wife, Beth Hench, is miserably unhappy with him and is having an affair with a fellow teacher. For the first time in the play, Simon is surprised.

Soon afterward, when Beth returns home, Stephen seems to realize what he has done; he tries to attribute his words to foolish spite and then leaves hastily. Even though their conversation begins in an ordinary fashion, the old ease requires a new effort. With some relief, Beth realizes that Simon knows about her affair. In fact, Simon says that he has known from the beginning. He has preferred to ignore it, he says, assuming that eventually she would tire of the relationship; to Beth, Simon's detachment is infuriating, implying that he does not really care about her. Beth has news, however, which shatters Simon's composure: She is pregnant, and she does not know by whom. With this, she leaves.

In the final minutes of the play, Dave enters, announcing that two more of his ilk are moving in upstairs; Simon hears a message on the answering machine from Wood, who is committing suicide; and Jeff rushes in to accuse Simon of reporting his drunkenness to the police, an accusation which turns out to be another of Davina's lies. This is too much for Simon. He throws his drink on Jeff and announces firmly that he is going to listen to *Parsifal*. Jeff apologizes and sits down with Simon. As the play ends, the words stop, Simon puts on the record, the music fills the theater, and the lights go down.

Themes and Meanings

The question of theme in *Otherwise Engaged* depends on the interpretation of Simon's character. If Simon is meant to be a victim, a man so pressed by the demands of others that he has no time for himself, then he could be considered the prototype of modern human, or at least of civilized human in a society which has lost its manners. On the other hand, if Simon is at fault, if through his coldness and self-centeredness he regularly gives pain to others, then he is the villain of the piece.

The first interpretation is the most obvious. Although traditionally the Englishman's home is said to be his castle, Simon has no retainers to guard his gate, and callers seem to wander in and out at will, disregarding his desire to be alone. At first, only the disreputable lodger Dave demands more than his attention. Dave seizes the opportunity for a kind of blackmail; to get rid of him, Simon offers an extension on the rent, money, and a bottle of sherry. Later, when Simon refuses the loan of his elaborate coffee-making equipment, Dave repays him with abuse.

If this kind of treatment might be expected from someone of Dave's level, it is more surprising from Simon's friends and his relatives. Unlike Dave, they begin politely, merely asking Simon to listen to their problems. As the play proceeds, however, they become as insulting as Dave. Whatever their problems, it is Simon who is blamed. For example, when Jeff returns, drunk, he falsely accuses Simon of betraying him to the police. Simon's brother and his wife are no different. Even though Simon has attempted to build up Stephen's confidence and then has rejoiced with him about his promotion, Stephen cannot forgive his brother for his greater worldly success, and he deliberately strikes out at him by reporting Beth's affair.

Nowhere does Simon Hench appear to be the long-suffering victim more than in the final moments of the play. Instead of asking forgiveness for her deception, Beth casts all the blame for her actions on Simon. At this point, a sympathetic audience is ready for Simon to strike back; when he throws the drink on Jeff, the action seems long past due. If the play is viewed in this way, Simon can be seen as the victim of a society in which everyone demands that his own needs be met while ignoring the needs of others.

On the other hand, some critics see Simon himself as the prototype of a modern sickness: the selfish detachment from feeling. A careful reading of the play supports this interpretation as much as it does the sympathetic view. For example, Dave points out that Simon would not rent an apartment to unmarried mothers, who would have troublesome children, or to old people, who might become senile and even die. If this kind of avoidance of involvement in life is really Simon's motive, then he deserves Dave.

Furthermore, there is evidence that despite his seeming benevolence toward others, Simon has no real compassion for them. To Wood, Simon admits that when he was in school, he profited—unintentionally, he insists—from the desire of other boys for him. In maturity, he still takes what he likes, as he took Wood's young mistress, callously handing her some pills in case he has given her a sexually transmitted disease. When Simon switches on his answering machine and hears what seem to be Wood's final words, he does not call the police. He simply hangs up.

It might be argued that such actions are the result of a real compassion, that Simon is retreating because he fears involvement in life, fears that he will feel too deeply. Beth does not agree. She attributes Simon's detachment to a deliberate refusal to feel anything. Whatever his motivation, he consistently uses words either to mask his emotions or to substitute for emotions. Thus when Beth tells him of her affair, Simon avoids a real response by making his longest and most pointless speech of the play. Shortly after she tells him of her pregnancy, he makes another retreat, this time into music. At the end of the play, the audience is left wondering whether Simon is indeed simply a music lover with a new recording, kept from his music by the selfishness of others, or a selfish man who uses music, as well as words, to keep the needs and the concerns of others at a safe distance from his own life.

Dramatic Devices

Otherwise Engaged is structured as a series of scenes, in each of which someone demands Simon's attention and prevents him from listening to his new recording. His intentions are made clear in the first moments of the play. The set itself, the Hench living room, is filled with records. This is clearly a room for relaxing. As the curtain rises, Simon is unwrapping a new record. Obviously his next step is to sit down and listen to it. With Dave's entrance, however, Simon Gray begins the series of interruptions upon which the development of the play is based. By the second interruption, the audience perceives the comic pattern. The suspense no longer depends on whether an interruption will occur, but instead on the form that it will take. Like a magician, Gray varies his tricks. Characters enter from the kitchen (stage right) or from the hallway (stage left); sometimes they simply barge in, sometimes they ring, then enter, sometimes they are actually admitted, as Wood is announced by Dave. As the play progresses, another variation is introduced: The callers begin to vilify Simon, and whether one considers their insults just or unjust, the result is hilarious. As they become angry with each other and then with Simon, the exits become stormier. Furious with Jeff, Stephen slams out; furious with Davina, Jeff slams out. The insults and the exits are the more amusing because Simon spends most of his time sitting down, as if he is waiting for the storm to spend itself.

Simon's own stage business expresses his internal conflict. On one hand, as a well-bred person, he must offer his guests a chair, a drink, even a handkerchief, and he must turn off his record player so that he can listen to them. On the other hand, he has his own life, symbolized by his record player and by the answering machine, which is the modern equivalent of a butler, trained to repel intruders. Simon's actions suggest the conflict between his private desires and his public role.

At the beginning of the play, for example, Simon is playing his record and assuming that Dave will leave; only when Dave sits down does he switch off the record. Halfway through the play, Simon actually starts back toward his record player; it is at this point, attempting to ensure his privacy, that he stops to put his "otherwise engaged" message on the answering machine. Then, just as he begins to put on his record, Dave enters again. Although it can answer Simon's calls, the machine cannot bar the door.

Periodically, Simon again takes up his record, but he is interrupted every time. Furthermore, his servant, the answering machine, adds to his burdens; when he turns it on again, it is waiting to play Wood's suicide threat.

Throughout the play, Simon, the unwilling host, has been dutifully offering drinks, even allowing Jeff to get drunk at his expense. When at last he throws a drink at Jeff, it seems likely that with his gesture Simon is expressing his attitude toward the whole concept of hospitality. In a moment, however, he has reverted; he offers Jeff a handkerchief, then a drink. Nevertheless, he does what he has not previously done: He announces his intention to play his record, he puts it on, and at last is uninterrupted. He may have lost his wife, but he has gained an interlude for his music.

Critical Context

Simon Gray's protagonists are usually men, who are often sexually ambivalent and who are trapped in difficult situations by the persistence of their companions and by their own personality defects. In Gray's early plays, the situations were treated farcically. In *Wise Child* (pr. 1967, pb. 1968), for example, a criminal who is masquerading as a woman cannot escape from his male lover, and in *Dutch Uncle* (pr., pb. 1969), a husband, who has fallen in love with a male police officer, fails again and again in efforts to murder the wife who stands in his way. It is *Dutch Uncle*, with its continual interruptions, which most clearly foreshadows *Otherwise Engaged*; similarly, inept protagonists reappear in *Butley* (pr., pb. 1971) and in *Quartermaine's Terms* (pr., pb. 1981).

With *Butley*, his first major hit, Gray established the pattern of his later plays, which concentrate on intellectuals whose confusion and frustration is reflected in their indulgence in word games. Ben Butley is a university professor who detaches himself from others, especially from his young homosexual office mate, by the use of language; at the end of the play, unlike Simon Hench, he realizes that his troubles are of his own making. Gray's next professor, St. John Quartermaine, is one of his most sympathetic protagonists. As anxious to become a part of others' lives as Hench and Butley are to distance themselves, Quartermaine drives people away because of his dullness and his banal conversation. Despite his real kindness, he is used, snubbed, and finally fired. Probably he is as close to a tragic character as any of Gray's protagonists.

A later play, *The Common Pursuit* (pr., pb. 1984), brings together a group of college friends, five men and one woman; fifteen years after graduation they have attained some measure of success but have lost their reasons for living. Like *Butley*, *Otherwise Engaged*, and *Quartermaine's Terms*, it focuses on the pervasive sense of alienation and purposelessness in society, which is the stuff of tragedy. Critics generally praise Gray's skill in turning such materials to comic uses, pointing out that in masterful plotting, in verbal subtlety, and in psychological insight, he excels among contemporary playwrights.

Sources for Further Study

Barnes, Clive. "London Likely to Be *Otherwise Engaged*." *New York Times*, August 18, 1975, p. 33.

Burkman, Katherine H. *Simon Gray: A Casebook*. New York: Garland, 1992.

Ellmann, Richard. "Simon Gray's New Play Anatomizes a Likable Creep." *New York Times*, August 17, 1975, sec. II, p. 5.

Jones, John Bush. "The Wit and the Wardrobe: Simon Gray's Tragic (?) Comedies." *West Virginia University Philological Papers* 25 (1979): 78-85.

Kerensky, Oleg. "Simon Gray." In *The New British Drama: Fourteen Playwrights Since Osborne and Pinter*. London: Hamilton, 1977.

Nelson, Byron. "The Unhappy Man in *Otherwise Engaged*." In *Contemporary British Drama, 1970-1990*, edited by Hersh Ziefman and Cynthia Zimmerman. Toronto, Ont.: University of Toronto Press, 1993.

Nothof, Anne. "Simon Gray's Comedy of Bad Manners." *Essays in Theater* (May, 1988): 109-112.

Novick, Julius. "Looking Down on the Plops." *Village Voice*, February 14, 1977, p. 81.

Stafford, Tony. "Simon Gray." In *British Playwrights, 1956-1995: A Research and Production Sourcebook*. Westport, Conn.: Greenwood Press, 1996.

Rosemary M. Canfield Reisman

OUR COUNTRY'S GOOD

Author: Timberlake Wertenbaker (1946-)
Type of plot: History
Time of plot: 1787-1789
Locale: Sydney, New South Wales, Australia
First produced: 1988, at the Royal Court Theatre, London
First published: 1988

Principal characters:

CAPTAIN ARTHUR PHILLIP, governor of New South Wales
MAJOR ROBBIE ROSS, a Scotsman and senior officer in charge of the Royal Marine contingent
CAPTAIN JEMMY CAMPBELL, Ross's assistant and a fellow Scotsman
CAPTAIN DAVID COLLINS, advocate general of New South Wales
REVEREND JOHNSON, a minister of the Church of England
SECOND LIEUTENANT RALPH CLARK, the director of the play
MIDSHIPMAN HARRY BREWER, provost marshall of New South Wales and the hangman
DUCKLING SMITH, Brewer's mistress
THE ABORIGINE, a native Australian
JOHN ARSCOTT,
BLACK CAESAR,
ROBERT SIDEWAY,
JOHN WISEHAMMER,
MARY BRENHAM,
DABBY BRYANT,
LIZ MORDEN, and
KETCH FREEMAN, convicts who take part in the play

The Play

Our Country's Good takes place in two acts, each with short scenes that are titled. In a production the titles are usually announced or flashed onto a screen. The first scene, "The voyage out," takes place in the hold of a convict ship bound for Australia in 1787. The stage is in semi-darkness with a group of convicts huddled together. Robert Sideway is being flogged offstage on the deck as Lieutenant Ralph Clark counts the lashes. When Sideway is thrown into the hold and collapses, the other convicts begin to speak longingly of the England from which they have been exiled. The action of scene 2 is described by its title: "A lone Aboriginal Australian describes the arrival of the first convict fleet in Botany Bay on January 20, 1788." The next scene, "Punishment," finds Captain Phillip and other officers shooting birds and discussing the punishment the convicts should receive for stealing and other offenses. Captain Phillip objects not only to the regular floggings but also to the hangings that are scheduled for the next day, while the other officers defend such punishment.

Scene 4, "The loneliness of men," opens with Clark reading aloud what he is writing in his diary concerning events in the prison colony. Harry Brewer enters and reveals that the man he hanged is haunting him. Clark tries to comfort him and mentions the possibility of doing a play with a convict cast. In scene 5, titled "An audition," George Farquhar's comedy *The Recruiting Officer* (pr., pb. 1706), gets under way, and the dialogue takes a comic turn as the convicts react to the unfamiliar situation of actually being in a play. Theatrical performance has never been a part of their wretched experience in England.

The play's theme emerges in scene 6 as the scene title notes: "The authorities discuss the merits of the theatre." Several of the officers, especially the stern Major Ross, object to the production as inappropriate and frivolous for a prison colony. Captain Phillip, however, defends the idea and points out that "The theatre is an expression of civilization." The seventh scene, "Harry and Duckling go rowing," shows one of the personal relationships that have formed in the insular world of the remote prison. In the eighth scene, "The women learn their lines," several of the female convicts discuss the play and in the process reveal much about their own pathetic lives. Scene 9 opens as "Ralph Clark tries to kiss his dear wife's picture." Clark paces about talking aloud to the picture of his wife, which he finally kisses. The convict Ketch Freeman interrupts him, and after telling Clark the sad history of his life, Freeman begs to be in the play. In scene 10, "John Wisehammer and Mary Brenham exchange words," Brenham, one of the few convicts who can read and write, makes a copy of *The Recruiting Officer*. Another literate convict, Wisehammer, displays his knowledge and love of words.

The first act's final scene follows the difficulties at "The first rehearsal." As usual the convict players argue among themselves about the play, which they take literally and confuse with their own lives. Major Ross and his assistant Captain Campbell interrupt the rehearsal to announce that some of the cast members have stolen food and attempted escape. At this point it appears that the play will never be produced.

The opening scene of act 2, "Visiting hours," finds four of the convict players—Morden, Wisehammer, Arscott, and Caesar—in chains awaiting their punishment for theft and attempted escape. Morden recalls her ill-fated life in England that led her to being imprisoned and transported. The others talk about escape, but are interrupted by fellow cast members who have come to rehearse the play. In scene 2, "His excellency exhorts Ralph," Captain Phillip argues against canceling the play, even though half of the cast has been arrested. Here the captain develops further his idea that the theater will be a redeeming force in the prison colony and expresses his belief in the essential dignity of all humans, no matter how mangled their lives may have become. Scene 3, "Harry Brewer sees the dead," revisits the haunted hangman, who is overwhelmed by the spirits of those he has killed. The Aborigine appears again in scene 4 and "muses on the nature of dreams." Scene 5 covers "The second rehearsal," with the arrested players in chains. The presence of the cruel Major Ross disrupts the proceedings as he harasses and humiliates the convicts. "The science of hanging" is the title of scene 6, which first focuses on the attempt to measure Morden in order to determine the length of the rope that will be used to hang her. The action then moves to the haunted Brewer, who hears the voices of the dead and finally collapses.

Scene 7, "The meaning of plays," opens with the Aborigine asking how his people can rid their land of these white interlopers, whom the Aborigines consider a swarm of ancestors' spirits. Following his speech, another rehearsal takes place, again with constant interruptions as the cast argues over the play's meaning. Scene 8, "Duckling makes vows," finds Duckling Smith sitting beside her lover, Harry Brewer, and promising to treat him better if he will not die. She then discovers that the doomed Brewer is already dead, having succumbed to the voices of the hanged ones who have haunted him day and night. Titled "A love scene," the next episode takes place on the beach as the play's director Ralph Clark and the leading lady Mary Brenham carry on a private rehearsal, but passion overtakes them. Soon they are undressing in the warm night and become lovers. Scene 10 addresses "The question of Liz," who has been sentenced to hang for her part in the food theft and escape attempt. Morden has refused to defend herself because she does not want to be branded as an informer on her fellow convicts. She finally explains what took place and is reprieved. Captain Phillip encourages her to play her role well in the forthcoming production.

The play's final scene is simply called "Backstage." The Aborigine appears alone at the outset and describes the symptoms of his illness. He does not know that he has contracted smallpox from the unwanted visitors. Then the actors bustle in excitedly. Wisehammer has written a prologue for *The Recruiting Officer*, which contains the words "our country's good," suggesting that the transportation of the convicts had actually benefitted their beloved England, to which they are still loyal. The director and cast members decide that the prologue, although well written, should not be used because it is too political. The play ends with the cast waiting nervously for their entrances and listening intently as one of the actors delivers offstage the opening speech.

Themes and Meanings

The play is an adaptation of Australian writer Thomas Keneally's novel *The Playmaker* (1987), which is based on historical fact. The convicts' performance of *The Recruiting Officer* actually took place in the Sydney prison colony in 1789; the performance was just a year after the arrival of the First Fleet, which carried several hundred male and female convicts, along with their keepers, from England to Australia. Many of the characters in the play, such as Captain Phillip and Major Ross, are historical figures. Nothing is known about the circumstances surrounding the rehearsal and performance of the play, except that it is mentioned in historical documents. Keneally in his novel imagines what might have happened and creates a convincing picture of the colony and its reluctant inhabitants engaged in such an improbable project. Unlike Wertenbaker, though, he does not draw any themes from the action but is more interested in telling a story.

Wertenbaker uses the voice of Captain Phillip to express the central theme of the play. Through his speeches, the playwright stresses the important contribution that theater makes to a civilized society. At one point, the captain even cites the ancient Greeks' strong belief in theater's redemptive power. Another theme that emerges in the captain's speeches is respect for all people, no matter how degenerate they may appear. The real Captain Phillip, unlike some of his fellow officers, believed that the convicts could reform and gain dignity if they were given the chance.

Wertenbaker has long been involved in prison theater in England and is convinced that the theater has the capacity to change lives. When asked to adapt Keneally's novel to the stage, she immediately accepted, seeing in the story a vehicle for her ideas. The play first appeared when the Margaret Thatcher administration in England was cutting back on arts funding, a connection that was made in the reviews and discussions of the play's initial production.

Dramatic Devices

The succession of short scenes in varied locales has become a familiar way for contemporary dramatists to construct a complex plot. In production, *My Country's Good* would be performed on a basic set, most likely on several levels, so that one scene could flow into another without interruption. Lighting and simple properties along with period costumes would establish the necessary atmosphere.

Announcing or projecting on a screen the names of the scenes—a device borrowed from playwright Bertolt Brecht—helps the audience to follow the complicated plot and to keep track of the numerous characters who appear so briefly that they cannot be developed fully. While the present condition of the convicts and their past histories are grim, the script moves easily from the dramatic to the comic, a pace which shows Wertenbaker's sound grasp of theatrical devices. She manages to make the convicts and some of the officers, especially Captain Phillip and Ralph Clark, humane even though they are in an inhumane world. Nevertheless, the violence and cruelty hover over the play in a subtle manner. Many of the convicts' speeches contain eighteenth century slang typical of the low class, a device that adds to the play's authenticity.

Critical Context

Wertenbaker has written for the stage, screen, and television. She has also translated plays into English, including dramas by Jean Anouilh, Maurice Maeterlinck, and Luigi Pirandello. Widely recognized at home in England and in the United States, her work is noted for its strong dramatic qualities and its commitment to the theater of ideas. Some of her best-known plays include *New Anatomies* (pr. 1981, pb. 1984), *Three Birds Alighting on a Field* (pr. 1991, pb. 1992), and *After Darwin* (pr., pb. 1998). In 1990 she wrote the screenplay for Edith Wharton's *The Children.*

Our Country's Good was first produced in London, then saw several major productions in the United States. Its success early in Wertenbaker's career helped to establish her reputation internationally. The drama received the 1988 Laurence Olivier Play of the Year Award in London, and in 1991 received the New York Drama Critics Circle Award for Best New Foreign Play. It continues to be one of Wertenbaker's most widely performed and read plays.

Sources for Further Study

Hornby, R. "Broadway Economics." *Hudson Review* 44 (Fall, 1991): 453-461.

LaRue, M. "*Our Country's Good*." Review in *Theatre Crafts* 25 (March, 1991): 40-52.

Rabey, D. I. "Defining Difference: Timberlake Wertenbaker's Drama of Language, Dispossession, and Discovery." *Modern Drama* 33 (December, 1990): 518-529.

Ramsden, Timothy. "Prison Therapy." *Times Educational Supplement* (September 25, 1998): 30.

Speirs, L. "Current Literature." *English Studies* 71 (December, 1990): 535-562.

Weeks, Stephen. "The Question of Liz: Staging the Prisoner in *Our Country's Good*." *Modern Drama* 43 (Summer, 2000): 147-157.

Wilson-Smith, A. "*Our Country's Good:* Theatre, Colony, and Nation in Wertenbaker's Adaptation of *The Playmaker*." *Modern Drama* 34 (March, 1991): 23-35.

Robert L. Ross

PAINTING CHURCHES

Author: Tina Howe (1937-   )
Type of plot: Psychological
Time of plot: The early 1980's
Locale: A townhouse in Beacon Hill, Boston
First produced: 1983, at The Second Stage, South Street Theatre, New York City
First published: 1984

Principal characters:
FANNY SEDGWICK CHURCH, a woman in her sixties from a fine old Boston family
GARDNER CHURCH, Fanny's husband, an eminent poet in his seventies from an even finer New England family
MARGARET "MAGS" CHURCH, Gardner and Fanny's daughter, a painter in her early thirties

The Play

As the play begins, Fanny and Gardner Church have sold their Boston town house and will move in a week to their much smaller cottage on Cape Cod. Their daughter Mags, whose arrival from New York they eagerly await, plans to paint their portrait and help them pack. When she arrives she tells them about her success as an artist. Although they express their delight, they do so with their mouths full of crackers, and they continue to be absorbed in eating crackers as Mags goes on about her success. Later Mags is dismissive when Fanny tells her how impossible Gardner is becoming in his mental wanderings. Scene 1 ends with Fanny and Gardner playfully practicing poses for their portrait by making silly faces.

In scene 2 Mags nails up a crimson tablecloth as a portrait backdrop, oblivious to her mother's protests about the damage she is doing. Her parents clown by miming Grant Wood's painting *American Gothic*, and Mags complains they do not take her seriously. She talks about her first group show, at which her mother called attention to herself and disparaged her daughter's paintings in front of an important art critic. While Mags relates this humorous story of her embarrassment and exasperation, her parents continue to amuse themselves by posing as Michelangelo's sculpture *Pietà*, and his fresco *The Creation of Adam*.

Scene 3 ends on a grimmer note. Mags reminds her parents that at age nine she was banished from the dinner table for playing with her food. Oblivious to her mother's requests to stop her account, she explains that, sent to her room with a tray, she would flush the food down the toilet and melt crayons on the radiator. Every week she would use her allowance to buy and melt more crayons, imagining a taste for each color and becoming more and more hungry. By the time her parents discovered her creation, it had in Mags's mind come to resemble a "gigantic Viennese pastry." However, Fanny thought it disgusting and got rid of it. Act 1 ends with Fanny and Gardner left speechless as Mags rushes from the room after insisting they knew nothing of her artistic abilities—that she had and has them.

In act 2, scene 1, Gardner tells Mags he has been having disturbing dreams in which he is a child, strangers move into his house and take over his things, and his bed is empty as if he were dead or never existed. As his wife packs his books and papers, he becomes agitated. Mags reads a few pages her father has been typing and is surprised to see evidence of what Fanny told her earlier, that his mental wanderings make no sense. Later Fanny laughs about Gardner's incontinence and need for diapers. Mags is appalled and, after Fanny engages her husband in a game of dive bombing his papers into a packing carton, Mags berates her for treating him like a child. Fanny replies that Mags should open her eyes and see the reality of her aging parents. What is wrong with trying to have some fun in a grim situation? Fanny asks, and adds that she and Mags's father are moving to their small cottage so she more easily can care for him. She tells Mags to paint them as they are and points to Gardner playing on the floor with a paper glider.

In the play's final scene, a parrot Gardner has been training to recite Thomas Gray's "Elegy Written in a Church Courtyard" (1751) does so. Mags recalls a magical night when phosphorus was in the ocean and she and her father swam together, iridescent and laughing. In fifteen minutes a car will come to take her parents away, and she begins to panic about their reaction to her portrait of them, which she finished by staying up all night. They insist on seeing it, and Mags's panic turns to joy as she realizes they like it. It is inspired by a Pierre-Auguste Renoir café scene with dancers, Fanny says, and Gardner begins to dance her around the room. Offstage a car horn honks. The curtain falls as Mags watches her dancing parents with tears in her eyes.

Themes and Meanings

After the premiere of *Painting Churches*, Tina Howe remarked that every child must make the journey "to find his legs in his own household" and asked how one could obtain parental acceptance "not as a child, but as an artist." Gaining such acceptance is the desire of Mags Church, the daughter of a famous poet father and a flamboyant and critical mother. Thus a major theme of *Painting Churches* is a child's need to establish independence from his or her parents and the concomitant desire for parental approval. Mags's desire to paint the Churches reflects her craving for their admiration and her need to empower herself. As she says, "The great thing about being a portrait painter . . . is it's the *other* guy that's exposed." Although Mags has established herself in the world, when home she is back in the role of a child, subject to motherly criticism of her hair, her "arty friends in New York," the "wretched art school" where she teaches, and her clothes. In a reversion to the time she was banished from the dinner table at age nine, Mags finds herself constantly hungry. When her mother remarks on how much she eats, Mags replies: "I only do this when I come home." What she eats onstage is never a proper adult meal: It is Saltines, Sara Lee banana cake, tapioca—in short, nursery food. Her physical hunger is symbolic of her even greater hunger to have her parents' recognition.

Still, Mags's parents are formidable people, and in the Church household one must vie for attention. When Mags reports her success as an artist, Fanny insists on showing off her own creation, a decorated lamp shade. One motif of the play is the tendency of the characters to be so involved in their own concerns that they slight or are oblivious to the concerns of others. So, for example, Fanny says about posing for her daughter: "I don't know what we're doing fooling around with Mags like this when there's still so much to do." Mags is so self-absorbed she fails at first to take in the serious difficulties besetting her parents.

Her parents' difficulties evoke another of the play's themes, ephemerality. At one point the Churches discuss friends who have Parkinson's, Hodgkin's, and Addison's disease, and those who have died. Fanny does not look forward to the change from her life in Boston, where she can see the few friends she has left, to a life of rustication as Gardner's nursemaid. Gardner's situation is even more desperate, his fears of oblivion movingly suggested by the dreams he describes to Mags. When Mags reminisces about the night she swam with her father, she recalls "wishing the moment would hold forever" and becoming "panicky because I knew it would pass; it was passing already."

Related to the ephemeral is a third major theme of *Painting Churches*, the artist's ability to stop time. Howe says her heroes are writers who have tried "to hold on to what's changing in front of their eyes." Mags attempts this in her portrait of her parents, as does Howe in the image of the Churches dancing. Mags gazes at them, giving in "to their stolen moment."

Howe acknowledges that in *Painting Churches* she was examining her own coming of age. Like Mags, for example, whom people ask, "Gardner Church is YOUR father?!," Howe had to deal with the insecurity common to children from well-known families who face living up to high expectations. "The reason to pick up the pen or the paint brush," she says, "is to fight back." Like the Churches, Howe's parents were from Boston families, but her father was a well-known radio and television newsman rather than a poet, and Howe herself is a playwright, not a painter. When people ask her how much the Churches resemble her family, she replies that "all of it is true, but none of it happened."

Dramatic Devices

Howe's single set has "three soaring arched windows," suggestive of a church, with its air of authority and awe. By going home, Mags reenters that which was in her childhood a space of parental authority and awe (surely Howe chose her characters' family name for its significance). The changing light pouring through the windows functions to transform what it touches: At play's end, for instance, it should be "dreamy and dappled" as the Churches dance in a gentle moment out of time. The Chopin waltz heard when they dance also communicates that they are removed from everyday reality, just as the honking car horn symbolizes the flow of time to which they are being summoned back. Their furnishings, a mix of the tasteful and the odd, reflect their personalities. Fanny's very clothing when the audience first see her echoes this mix as she sits wearing a worn bathrobe and a stylish hat. Mags, who has gone off to New York and become her own person, "wears wonderfully distinctive clothes and has very much her own look."

The packing cartons on stage are another dramatic device. They are empty, then overflowing, then filled with clothing as well as household items, then fewer in number, and finally gone. They symbolize the passing of time as the Churches move toward their end. The gradual stripping of the house also accompanies "the psychological stripping bare of the characters," as critic Christopher Bigsby has noted.

Gardner's recitations function powerfully in the play, the gorgeous language emphasizing his love of poetry and the nobility of his calling. Yet, he now can only parrot words, not write them, symbolized by his teaching a parrot to recite the elegy by Gray. That poem itself suggests Gardner's declining faculties and imminent end.

Finally one should note the play's tableaux. Such instantly recognized images suggest art's power to inhabit consciousness and, as frozen moments, its ability to arrest time. The Churches' delight in enacting these tableaux communicates the fun they share. Insofar as they do so while Mags wants them to take her seriously, their play suggests that aspect of a couple's relationship which is separate from their children. However, the fact that the final tableau is inspired by Mags's painting, as well as by Renoir's, makes her a part of her parents' dancing even while she is apart from it.

Critical Context

Sigmund Freud noted the painful necessity for individuals, if they are to develop, to become free of their parents' authority. Freud's observations seem relevant to Mags's traumatic childhood experience of banishment from the table and the destruction of her composition of melted crayons. The distancing from her parents, who did not recognize what she considers to be her first masterpiece, went in tandem with the beginning of her development as an artist. By writing a drama treating the psychological dynamics at play among the Churches—their tensions, rivalries, shifting alliances, and rejoicings—Howe engages that recurrent subject in American theater going back to Eugene O'Neill, the nuclear family.

The subject is common to Howe's other plays, as is her obsession with artists and art, and with the losses attendant upon time, especially death. In all her work she explores these subjects with humor while moving toward an epiphany, a moment of reconciliation or redemption. Because of the epiphanies, Howe speculates, her true mentors are not other playwrights, but the novelists Virginia Woolf and James Joyce. Howe attributes audiences' warm reception of *Painting Churches* to the "sheer fantasy" of the reconciliation at the play's end: "In real life, we all know perfectly well there's rarely that moment when our parents finally say, 'You are a wonderful artist, and I admire your work.'"

Sources for Further Study

Barlow, Judith E. "The Art of Tina Howe." In *Feminine Focus: The New Women Playwrights*, edited by Enoch Brater. New York: Oxford University Press, 1989.

Bigsby, Christopher. "Tina Howe." In *Contemporary American Playwrights*. Cambridge, England: Cambridge University Press, 1999.
Howe, Tina. *Coastal Disturbances: Four Plays by Tina Howe*. New York: Theatre Communications Group, 1989.
_______. "Tina Howe." In *Interviews with Contemporary Women Playwrights*, edited by Kathleen Betsko and Rachel Koenig. New York: Beech Tree Books, 1987.
_______. "Tina Howe." In *A Search for a Postmodern Theater: Interviews with Contemporary Playwrights*, edited by John L. DiGaetani. New York: Greenwood Press, 1991.
_______. "Tina Howe." Interview by Judith E. Barlow. In *Speaking on Stage: Interviews with Contemporary American Playwrights*, edited by Philip C. Kolin and Colby H. Kullman. Tuscaloosa: University of Alabama Press, 1996.

Jack Barbera

PANDORA'S BOX

Author: Frank Wedekind (1864-1918)
Type of plot: Tragedy
Time of plot: The 1890's
Locale: Germany, Paris, and London
First produced: 1904, at the Intimes Theater, Neürnberg, Germany
First published: Die Büchse der Pandora, 1904 (English translation, 1918)

Principal characters:

LULU, a beautiful, amoral woman
ALWA SCHÖN, a writer
RODRIGO QUAST, an athlete
SCHIGOLCH, a vagrant
COUNTESS GESCHWITZ, an artist
MARQUIS CASTI-PIANI, a police spy and slave trader
HERR HUNIDEI, a mute giant
KUNGU POTI, the crown prince of Uahubee, Africa
DR. HILTI, a university lecturer
JACK THE RIPPER, the infamous murderer

The Play

Frank Wedekind originally planned to make his revolutionary Lulu character—the ultimate embodiment of female eros—the focus of a single *Monstretragödie* (gigantic tragedy). The unwieldiness of this project, however, coupled with severe restrictions imposed on his works by German censors, forced him eventually to break the gigantic tragedy down into two separate plays: *Erdgeist* (pb. 1895, pr. 1898; *Earth Spirit*, 1914) and *Pandora's Box*.

Earth Spirit introduces many of the characters who will later play an important role in *Pandora's Box:* Lulu, her lesbian admirer Countess Geschwitz, the vagrant Schigolch, and Alwa Schön, a writer who eventually becomes one of Lulu's many lovers. This play also provides background information on Lulu herself: that she is known by many other names (her lovers call her Nelli, Eva, and Mignon), that she has no parents, that she was reared by the mysterious Schigolch and later educated—in Pygmalion-like fashion—by Alwa's father, the newspaper editor Dr. Schön, and that she possesses no conscience, no soul, no feelings, and no morals and consequently represents the complete antithesis of bourgeois society as it existed during the Victorian age.

In *Earth Spirit*, the ravishingly beautiful Lulu, using a lethal combination of naïveté and charm, lures a number of respectable German burghers into her web of sexual excess, moral debasement, and, in certain cases, even death. Her husband, Dr. Goll, becomes her first victim. This elderly gentleman, who constantly attempts to keep Lulu's eros in check, finds her in the arms of the painter Schwarz; he dies of a heart attack as he rushes to separate the pair. Lulu then marries Schwarz, who hopes to transform her into a perfect middle-class wife. After learning of Lulu's immoral past, however, he commits suicide, thus becoming her second victim. Lulu's final victim in *Earth Spirit* is Dr. Schön, her educator and mentor, who had previously kept her as a mistress. The play ends as Dr. Schön, who succumbs to Lulu's eroticism and marries her despite his earlier resistance, is shot to death by his new wife as he attempts to force her to commit suicide for having transformed the Schön household into a veritable bordello swarming with lovers.

In *Pandora's Box*, Lulu in turn becomes the victim, the haunted creature. She is sent to prison for the murder of Dr. Schön but soon breaks out with the help of Countess Geschwitz, whose ingenious and extremely complex plan of escape elevates her (by Wedekind's own admission) to the actual heroine of the play. Now a fugitive from the law, Lulu is forced to flee Germany. Together with Alwa Schön she relocates to Paris, where she goes by the assumed name Countess Adelaide d'Oubra.

In a remarkably short time Lulu is again surrounded by a circle of men, each of whom is now intent not on making love to her as would have been the case in *Earth Spirit* but instead on capitalizing on her precarious position. To all outward appearances she is, after all, a rich widow trying to elude justice. The first to prey upon her is the somewhat dim-witted athlete Rodrigo Quast, who threatens to turn her in to the authorities if she does not provide him with a large sum of money. Using sex as bait, she successfully overcomes this threat. She is not nearly so fortunate in the case of Marquis Casti-Piani, a police spy and slave trader who will have her arrested unless she consents to being sold to a bordello in Cairo. For a time Lulu succeeds in dissuading Casti-Piani from carrying out his plan by offering him her "fortune" in blue-chip stocks. These stocks turn out to be worthless, and an incensed Casti-Piani immediately calls in the police. Lulu only very narrowly avoids being captured.

This time she flees to London, where she is followed by Alwa, now her fourth husband, as well as by her "father" Schigolch and the slavishly devoted Geschwitz. Devoid of money and of her earlier vitality and sexual energy, Lulu is no longer a desired object of the burgher class and must—as a symbol of her utter degradation—eke out a meager existence as a common prostitute, working out of the dingy Soho tenement she shares with Alwa and Schigolch.

Lulu's customers represent a bizarre mix of characters. Herr Hunidei, a man of gigantic stature, is mute and communicates solely through gestures. Kungu Poti, an African crown prince, refuses to pay Lulu in advance and, when Alwa intercedes, brutally strikes him down, killing him instantly. Dr. Hilti, a Swiss academician, is engaged to be married and goes to Lulu to gain sexual experience; when he stumbles over Alwa's corpse, however, he hastily departs. Lulu's last client, Jack the Ripper, is a sex maniac intent on murdering her. As he is about to make his kill, he is surprised by the returning Countess Geschwitz, whom he fatally stabs in the stomach. He kills Lulu in the same way only moments later.

Themes and Meanings

On the surface, *Pandora's Box* and its predecessor, *Earth Spirit*, appear to be little more than graphic representations of the havoc wreaked on modern, civilized society when the most basic human drives are allowed to exist unchecked. In this case, it is Lulu's sexuality, a dark, primeval force of almost mythic proportions, that—to use the positivistic terminology of Frank Wedekind's day—"causes" the destruction of all people with whom she comes into contact. Indeed, most characters in the Lulu tragedies are incapable of reconciling their middle-class morality (and especially their concept of respectability) with the sexually uninhibited, bohemian lifestyle portrayed by Lulu. As soon as they succumb to Lulu's charms, they seemingly are fated to die. Dr. Goll suffers a heart attack, Schwarz commits suicide, Dr. Schön is shot, Alwa is struck down, and Geschwitz is stabbed. Even Lulu herself, who cannot help being a beautiful temptress, must die at the end as a victim of her own sexuality.

Beyond the mere observation that unbridled drives, sexual and otherwise, may have dire consequences for the individual, it is possible to identify a much deeper meaning within Wedekind's plays, a meaning that may have important implications for modern society. This deeper meaning has been unlocked in part through Freudian theory, the proponents of which have asserted that *Pandora's Box* and *Earth Spirit* represent the collision of two antithetical principles constantly vying for power in the world: that of reality and that of pleasure.

In order for society to be successful and productive, it must be governed by the reality principle, which entails hard work, personal sacrifice, deferred gratification, and, above all, the restraint of personal feelings and drives. This is the principle embraced by such people as Dr. Goll and Dr. Schön, whose goal is the perfect burgher existence and who must, at least in public, repress anything not congruent with the middle-class ethic.

Lulu, in turn, represents the pleasure principle, which involves immediate gratification, joy, the absence of repression, and the suspension of all sexual taboos. Her every action stands in direct contradiction to the established values of society. She is perceived as a menace: As the *Urweib* (archwoman), she can lead respected men to break with bourgeois norms, to flirt with decadence, as it were, and thus to rock the very foundation of civilized society.

If *Earth Spirit* represents Lulu's triumph over bourgeois society, *Pandora's Box* shows society's defense against Lulu's naïvely decadent nature. At first, men repeatedly attempt to force her into the accepted role of the devoted and loving wife. When these attempts at "domestication" fail, society has no alternative, and must destroy Lulu and with her any hope of freeing civilization from the shackles of repression, false morals, and exaggerated puritanism. When Jack the Ripper murders Lulu, he is actually reasserting society's old values, thus depriving it of all vitality and freedom.

Seen in this light, it would appear that Wedekind viewed Lulu's sexuality as a means of enlightening, of lifting sexual taboos, and of giving humanity a new lease on life. Constantly attacked by puritanical censors, Wedekind realized, however, that the repression-free world he envisioned was still very distant. Indeed, it was not until the

1960's, with the advent of the sexual revolution, that Western society took its first real steps in Wedekind's direction.

Dramatic Devices

Pandora's Box and *Earth Spirit* utilize a number of dramatic devices, which characterize not only these plays themselves but also Wedekind's entire dramatic oeuvre. Most prominent among these devices is the use of grotesque characters to symbolize the unnaturalness and repressiveness of modern society vis-à-vis Lulu's natural, innocent, and almost childlike attitude toward sexuality and life in general. In *Pandora's Box*, examples of such characters are Herr Hunidei, the mute, who represents a repressed society's inability to discuss sexual matters; Dr. Hilti, a hypocrite, who feigns respectability yet seeks out the services of a prostitute; and Jack the Ripper, a maniacal killer, who reflects society's wish to repress and ultimately to destroy all elements that do not accord with its highly artificial and inhumane moral standards.

Another important device is the use of an impressionistically arranged series of situations in lieu of a traditional plot in both *Earth Spirit* and *Pandora's Box*. Each situation affords a slightly different picture of the confrontation between middle-class morals and Lulu's lack of sexual inhibition. The order of these situations is largely insignificant. They do not contribute to one another, but only to the symbolic value of the plays themselves. The only real order to be found in the Lulu tragedies exists in the fact that *Earth Spirit* represents Lulu's rise in society, whereas *Pandora's Box* depicts her utter downfall.

Related to the observation that each scene (or situation) graphically portrays the clash between Lulu and society is the fact that Wedekind's dramas rely much more heavily on actions than on words to express emotions and ideas. Feelings of anger, disappointment, and hate are never vented in dialogue, but in brutal acts of violence. When people do speak, they talk past one another, each totally consumed by his or her own thoughts. Wedekind's dialogue shows the egotistical and antisocial nature of modern society.

A final important device is Wedekind's detailed description of stage decorations and costumes, particularly in *Pandora's Box*. Not unlike his contemporaries the German naturalists, he did everything possible to establish a visual bridge between his audience and the characters portrayed onstage. Only if his audience—mostly middle-class Germans—could identify themselves with the likes of Goll, Schön, or Hilti could he hope to make them aware of their own narrow-mindedness, their hypocrisy, and their blind adherence to false and stifling morality.

Critical Context

The Lulu tragedies *Pandora's Box* and *Earth Spirit*, with their sharp attack on all forms of sexual repression, represent the climax of a long line of plays in which Frank Wedekind waged war on traditional morality, established social norms, and middle-class values, and in which he proclaimed a "new morality" based on a totally liberated view of human instincts and drives. The first in this line of plays was *Frühlings*

Erwachen (pb. 1891, pr. 1896; *Spring's Awakening*, 1960), which directs its criticism against inhibited middle-class parents who do not enlighten their teenage children about sexual matters, yet chastise their daughters when they become pregnant and even endanger their lives by forcing them to undergo illegal abortions.

A different type of attack against society is contained in *Der Marquis von Keith* (pr., pb. 1901; *The Marquis of Keith*, 1955). Here, the false values of German bourgeois society are mirrored in Keith's use of fraud and deception to fulfill his dream of achieving material wealth and a luxurious lifestyle. By contrast, the play *Tod und Teufel* (pb. 1905, pr. 1912; *Death and Devil*, 1952) seeks to expose the discriminatory treatment of women, who are, Wedekind alleges, bred by the system to be subservient to men and to respect the patriarchal order underlying German society.

In one of his last plays, *Die Zensur* (pb. 1908, pr. 1909; censorship), Wedekind suggests a reconciliation between the earthly world of sexuality and instinct and the loftier world of moral values and rationality. This work is largely confessional in nature, as it was Wedekind's lifelong ambition to unify within himself the sexual and the spiritual and thereby to emerge as a liberated individual characterized by inner peace and harmony. Significantly, no such harmonious individuals ever emerge from Wedekind's dramas, and least of all from the Lulu tragedies, making it appear as if tension between the sexual and the spiritual (or rational) will always be a hallmark of human existence. This message, that inner discord will eternally plague individuals and society, was further developed by German expressionism, a literary movement whose major proponents, Carl Sternheim, Oskar Kokoschka, Georg Kaiser, and Bertolt Brecht, were all greatly inspired by Wedekind's plays and by the revolutionary worldview contained therein.

Sources for Further Study

Best, Alan. *Frank Wedekind*. London: Wolff, 1975.
Brustein, Robert. *The Theatre of Revolt*. Boston: Little, Brown, 1962.
Garten, Hugh. *Modern German Drama*. 2d ed. London: Methuen, 1964.
Gittleman, Sol. *Frank Wedekind*. New York: Twayne, 1969.
Hill, Claude. "Wedekind in Retrospect." *Modern Drama* 3 (1960): 82-92.
Lewis, Ward B. *The Ironic Dissent: Franc Wedekind in the View of His Critics*. Willowdale, Ont.: Camden House, 1997.
Sokel, Walter H. "The Changing Role of Eros in Wedekind's Drama." *German Quarterly* 39 (1966): 201-207.

Dwight A. Klett

PANTOMIME

Author: Derek Walcott (1930-   )
Type of plot: Comedy
Time of plot: The 1970's
Locale: Tobago, the West Indies
First produced: 1978, at the Little Carib Theatre, Port of Spain, Trinidad
First published: 1980, in *"Remembrance" and "Pantomime": Two Plays*

Principal characters:
HARRY TREWE, an Englishman in his mid-forties, the owner of the Castaways Guest House and a retired actor
JACKSON PHILLIP, a forty-year-old Trinidadian who is Trewe's handyman and a retired calypsonian

The Play

As the curtain rises on the sparse set of *Pantomime*, the audience watches Harry Trewe, dressed in white, start a tape recorder and begin a light song and dance routine based loosely on the story of Robinson Crusoe. Unhappy with his initial effort, Harry stops the machine, then starts it and tries a few more lines of the song before stopping the recorder once more. Finally, he exits with it, leaving an empty stage for a few moments before Jackson Phillip, dressed in an open, white waiter's jacket and black pants but barefoot, enters to serve Harry his breakfast. Finding Harry gone, Jackson calls to him and, hearing no response, speculates halfheartedly that Harry has jumped into the sea below the gazebo at the Castaways Guest House, where the play is set. As Jackson exits, Harry enters with a goatskin hat and parasol, notices Jackson's shoeless footprint in the dirt around the breakfast table and continues his song with the essential but subtle question of the play: "Is this the footprint of a naked man,/ or is it the naked footprint of a man . . .?"

When Jackson returns, the quick-paced dialogue commences with mutual greetings wherein Harry admits a desperate boredom and, without explanation, casts Jackson as Friday in his version of the Crusoe story. Responding to Jackson's refusal to play along, which apparently has happened before, Harry jumps up on the ledge overlooking the sea and feigns a suicide attempt. Jackson, protesting that he will be accused of murder, threatens to quit his job, but Harry jumps back down, complaining about the lack of entertainment for guests due to arrive in less than a week. Jackson, however, argues that the guests will be "casualties" if he does not complete repairs to the guesthouse instead of humoring Harry with work on his pantomime.

While Harry attempts to persuade Jackson to play Friday to his own Crusoe, Jackson protests the insistent refrain of Harry's pet parrot, "Heinegger, Heinegger." Threatening the parrot in playful banter, Jackson tells Harry that "language is ideas . . ." and "this precolonial parrot have the wrong idea." Although Jackson wishes only to serve breakfast and continue the repairs, Harry persists in his plans for the pantomime of Crusoe, reminding Jackson of his talent for singing calypsos. Suddenly, Harry stumbles on the idea of reversing the roles: The white Harry will play the part of the black Friday while the black Jackson will play the white Crusoe. Still reluctant, Jackson argues that he must finish his work; however, Harry, professing his liberal views, all but coerces Jackson to take Crusoe's role.

Jackson, disconcerted by Harry's penchant for wandering around in his underwear and realizing that Harry will not drop the project, consents and quickly adapts the improvisations in progress to his own perspective: that of a colonial subject who becomes the colonizing authority. As Jackson begins to dominate the pantomime's development, Harry becomes visibly more hesitant to continue the reversal of roles. Jackson substitutes an invented religion and language that inverts the colonial dominance of the British Empire. Including references to Harry's divorced wife and his dead son, Jackson, in essence, gives the worldview of Man Friday to the part of Crusoe—reversing the perspectives of master and slave as well as the skin colors of the two actors in their respective roles.

Harry, unnerved by the very improvisation that he had asked of Jackson, decides that the pantomime has become too serious. Jackson, now fully engaged in the role of a black Crusoe who is educating a white Man Friday on the dynamics of colonialism, sees the pantomime as "nothing less than" a reenactment of "the history of imperialism." When Harry realizes that he has been recast as a Christian cannibal, that "he'd have to be taught by this—African . . . that everything was wrong, that what he was doing . . . for nearly two thousand years . . . his civilization, his culture . . . was . . . *horrible*," he stops the work on the pantomime, offering as an excuse his fear of creating "a play."

As the first act closes in an increasingly tense exchange, Harry threatens to fire Jackson if he persists in his improvised role; however, Jackson, while agreeing to stop, reminds Harry that they have just enacted "the history of the British Empire" and explains:

> You come to a place, you find that place as God make it . . . you civilize the natives; they try to do something, you turn around and you say to them: "you are not good enough, let's call the whole thing off, return things to normal, you go back to your position as slave or servant, I will keep mine as master, and we'll forget the whole thing ever happened."

Jackson, however, will not accept the loss of his dignity and independence, even though he cannot afford to lose his job. As the lights fade, the two men face each other rigidly while Jackson insists that Harry get out of his way so that he can straighten up the breakfast table.

When act 2 begins, it is noon, and Harry is trying to escape the tension with a paperback thriller. Jackson's hammering in the process of making repairs distracts Harry, but he tries to ignore it by attempting to nap. After a long pause in the noise, Harry jumps up from his deck chair, startled by Jackson standing very close, shirtless, with hammer in hand. Recovering from his mock fear of Jackson's mock threat, Harry invites Jackson to sit and drink with him. Harry's treatment of Jackson has grown somewhat; through considerable exposition of racial and cultural understanding, the two men begin work again on the pantomime, but, despite the reconciliatory tones, the improvisation digresses frequently with intermittent discussions of equality and acting styles.

Harry sees Crusoe as a lonely, suffering romantic, entrapped by the self-conscious loss of his wife and son. Jackson sees Crusoe as a practical realist who must create a new life for himself from the material immediately at hand; he wants to include the slaughter of a goat in the pantomime. The men dub the two styles as classical and Creole acting, respectively. Harry reveals a despairing emptiness in the wake of a wife who had been far more successful in theater than he had been but who, because of her alcoholism, had been driving when their son was killed in a car wreck. In his grief and inability to accept the loss, Harry had divorced his wife and fled to the West Indies. Jackson quickly sees that Harry's Crusoe is little more than his projection of sentimental agony onto the Crusoe character, and he argues that Crusoe—unlike Harry—had a wife and child to whom he could return.

Pushing Harry to accept the reality of his situation, Jackson theorizes that Crusoe was the first true Creole because he had to adapt to his environment so that he could not only survive but also achieve dignity in the "art" of living. As Jackson presses Harry further to accept his failures as an actor and as a husband, Harry mimics an earlier story of Jackson's that involved a threat with an ice pick. When Jackson responds to the mock attack by strangling the parrot, Harry's racism erupts viciously: "You people create nothing. You imitate everything." Jackson, switching to Friday's role, pretends, on his knees, to beg forgiveness while Harry puts on the goatskin attire of Crusoe.

As the tension wanes, Jackson exits and returns with a photograph of Harry's former wife Ellen. Assuming Ellen's voice, Jackson provokes an emotional catharsis in Harry, who forgives Ellen as Jackson—still playing her—feigns suicide while standing on the ledge above the sea. In his catharsis, Harry seems to be crying and laughing at the same time, uncertain whether he is playing Crusoe, Friday, or himself. Eventually, both men emerge from the uneasiness of Harry's genuine vulnerability and, exchanging puns on the words *goat* and *ego*, agree to get the pantomime finished before the guests' arrival.

As the play closes, they seem to have reached a more intimate but tentative understanding of personal equality. Harry now appears free from his self-indulgent romantic liberalism, and Jackson affirms his faith in his own Creole acting by dressing again as Crusoe. Jackson's closing song asserts the unity of their acting styles for the project at hand, but, as Harry and the audience join in applause, Jackson requests a raise, suggesting that social equality must be followed by economic equality. If he is to act, he expects to be paid as an actor—not as a handyman.

Themes and Meanings

Pantomime embraces several issues of racial and cultural equality, of colonial history, and of artistic methods, but these issues are all subordinate to the play's faith in the integrity of the artist's vision of diversity yet unity within humanity. While both characters change in the course of the drama, Jackson's recovery of respect for the cultural origins of calypso and "Creole acting," the ability to improvise according to immediate circumstances without the loss of self-dignity, serves as the catalyst by which Harry can come to terms with his largely unconscious racism and with his sexism—the jealousy over his wife's success—which had provoked the tragic events of his past. Jackson's forgiveness of Harry—without accepting a position of inferiority—becomes Harry's forgiveness of Ellen, and, just as important, Harry's forgiveness of himself for his failures. What Jackson offers Harry is a sense of common humanity that is free from suppressing racial, historical, and cultural differences. Rather than blurring differences in a universalist concept of art, Derek Walcott, paradoxically, affirms those differences as a prerequisite to understanding the essential unity of humanity.

Those differences are governed by language and history. Harry's flight to the West Indies enacts symbolically the expansion of the British Empire and the colonial conquests of any empire. He arrives with enough capital to assume the role of master, but, in his cultural assumptions embedded in the language of empire, he remains oblivious to the potential for independent critical thought and creation, despite the fact of West Indian political independence. Consequently, he is also oblivious to Jackson's personal dignity and pride in that independence. Jackson, having freed himself from psychological dependence on colonial acculturation, seizes the opportunity to play master (Crusoe) and, in so doing, educates the unwilling Harry in the feelings of being cast as an inferior human being. As Harry realizes Jackson's effectiveness, primarily through his poetic play with the English language, as a "Creole actor," he is intimidated by Jackson's successful synthesis. Not only has Jackson assimilated what of Western culture is useful to him by spiking his improvisations with allusions to canonical English literary texts such as Samuel Taylor Coleridge's *The Rime of the Ancient Mariner* (1798), but he also demonstrates his ability to turn Western language and culture to his own quest for artistic integrity. Jackson's faith in the equality of art—Western and Creole—founded on the uniqueness of language permits Harry to grasp their equality as people.

Walcott's larger theme of forgiveness as a crucial motive for artistic vision offers a resolution to the dialectical struggles between race and class. While Harry and Jackson represent the dialectic between master and slave, management and labor, and colonizer and colonized, the reversals implicit in the play and explicit in the satire of the pantomime are merely methods by which the two men can establish mutual respect for each other's differences and yet use those differences to create a new version of the Crusoe story—the story of emergent racial equality in the inextricable destiny of all humankind. As Jackon puts it: "*I tell you: man must live*! Then, after many years, he see this naked footprint that is the mark of his salvation . . ." Consequently, the crucial ability to move beyond perpetual dialectical reversals rests on the artist's capacity to create as a witness to the essential goodness of humanity, but such an effort does not erase the legacies of shame or obliterate the differences of historical power.

Dramatic Devices

From the title itself, much of the fast-paced comedy of *Pantomime* depends on linguistic play and the two actors' effective employment of proper British and West Indian Creole English accents. Near-melodramatic gesture reinforces the language play of puns and allusions, but Derek Walcott's inclination to offer his actors limited freedom for improvisation permits some adaptation of gesture, depending on the shifting tones of confrontation and intimacy and the audience's reaction to various scenes. By using a sparse set, Walcott forces the audience to be more attentive to language and gesture. The relative simplicity of lighting, sound, and props also helps keep the audience's attention on nuance and innuendo in the rapidly moving dialogue.

The subgenre of the pantomime has a relevant etymology suggesting that, beyond the literal action on which Harry and Jackson are seeking to create a pantomime, Walcott has chosen his title quite consciously. Originating in Augustan Rome, where one actor played all parts in a dumb show, the pantomime implies both empire and its consequential parallel effects on both actors. The unity of the two characters has for its precedent the dominance of both; in short, both Harry and Jackson suffer the legacies of imperialism. As the pantomime's evolution progressed through the farce of the *commedia dell'arte* in medieval Italy and France into eighteenth century British plays for children, the subgenre suggests a colonial paradigm in which the colonized are treated as children, incapable of participating in a rational world—just as Harry often responds to Jackson.

Anchored in the Roman emphasis on the portrayal of character and in the gestures of grand opera, pantomime indicates a necessity to act on one's principles, just as Harry must finally act on his liberal views and Jackson must act on his belief in the validity of Creole art. Finally, with origins in the dumb show of the mime, whose actors were suppressed by Christian Roman rulers in the fifth century, *Pantomime* evokes speech as the complement to exaggerated expressive behavior such as that in the mime; the Latin *pantomimus* means "complete mime." Hence, for Walcott, Jackson's refusal to conform to Harry's version of the Crusoe story is the refusal of the colonized to conform to the dumb show of colonial rule in which behavior—submissive or revolutionary—not language, is the principal means of compliance or resistance.

Artistic independence as well as sociopolitical independence requires confidence in one's worldview articulated in language and performed in the face of colonial attitudes such as Harry's. Jackson's invented language in the first act underscores the importance of linguistic identity: the source of ideas, of worldview, is language. Thus, Jackson's Creole grammatical structures, accents and puns, such as "Trewe" and "true," are the dramatic establishment of an identity capable of creating an independent artistic vision. Similarly, Jackson's gestures, while at times feigning subservience to meet Harry's expectations, are often ironically confrontational; he can play the role of servant, but he demands an identity of equality—the stance of the artist freeing himself through his own language in order to affirm his faith in humanity.

Critical Context

Derek Walcott, winner of the 1992 Nobel Prize in Literature, is widely regarded as the best West Indian playwright and, according to Robert Graves, is one of the best poets anywhere writing in English. Along with such playwrights as Wole Soyinka, Athol Fugard, and Ngugi wa Thiong'o, he is a non-Western, postcolonial playwright who has used the drama to illuminate issues of colonialism and racism. Choosing the obscurity of the West Indies over exile and prominence in London (such as that achieved by Trinidadian novelist V. S. Naipaul), Walcott founded the Trinidad Theatre Workshop in 1959, writing, directing and producing more than forty plays before his resignation from the workshop in 1977. His dedication to West Indian drama is unsurpassed; he might well be described as the founder of modern West Indian theater.

Walcott's growth as a dramatist parallels his development as a poet. Just as Walcott's poetry becomes increasingly more confident in its use of Creole culture and language, so, too, does his dramatic development move toward confidence in the use of Creole styles. In his one-act drama *The Sea at Dauphin* (pr., pb. 1954), Walcott emphasizes the folk idiom of St. Lucian French-English patois and the character of ordinary fishermen who survive the whimsical forces of nature and empire. *Ione* (pr., pb. 1957) and *Drums and Colors: An Epic Production* (pr. 1958, pb. 1961) further evoke the folk tradition of St. Lucia, and the latter shares some of the didactic qualities of *Pantomime*. These early plays, alluding frequently to Stephen Dedalus (James Joyce's artist-hero) and to the mythic Icarus, suggest Walcott's resolve both to experiment with the materials of his predecessors and to forge his own wings with which to fly into the sun of the British Empire, which had not yet set on the West Indies.

Walcott's poetry in his collection *The Castaway and Other Poems* (1965) centers on the very Creole Crusoe figure that Jackson fully develops in *Pantomime*. Jackson brings much humor to the Creole Crusoe's quest for identity, and Walcott's *Jourmard* (pr. 1967) had provided an early foray into comedy. With *Dream on Monkey Mountain* (pr. 1967, pb. 1970), Walcott received considerable acclaim. The Crusoe figure must create from whatever materials are at hand, for there are no indigenous cultures that survive in the West Indies upon which the artist might base his identity. The protagonist Makak in *Dream on Monkey Mountain* can use language only to achieve racial identity; he has not yet found the humor that Jackson possesses to sustain a quest for personal identity. Makak is still caught in the perennial reversals of dialectical power between master and slave.

After the farce in *Jourmard* and the steadfastness of Makak's resolve not to be duped into accepting the illusion of colonial supremacy in *Dream on Monkey Mountain*, Walcott's plays of the early 1970's explore the ambivalence of racial identity. *In a Fine Castle* (pr. 1970) presents the protagonist Brown (of black and white ancestry) caught in a struggle to resolve the conflicts inherent in the newly emerging black consciousness with the legacies of colonial culture, and *Franklin* (pr. 1973) explores the complex hierarchies of complexion in the emergent black pride movement. In his book-length poem *Another Life* (1973), Walcott, through an autobiographical examination of his childhood and early development as a poet, offers an account of the artist's evolution, akin to the project in William Wordsworth's *The Prelude: Or, The Growth of a Poet's Mind* (1850).

Of necessity, Walcott must resolve his own multicultural ancestry in pursuit of a language both faithful to the monuments of beauty from the West, which his colonial education had offered, and capable of defining a West Indian artistic identity in its own terms. While *O Babylon!* (pr. 1976, pb. 1978), set in a Jamaican squatter community of Rastafarians, uses the vehicle of a reggae musical to argue that the source of identity is within each person, it is not until *Pantomime* that the individual artist's accommodation to place, to history, and to race becomes explicitly located within the integrity of the artist's inner life. Both Harry and Jackson find that only by finding themselves at home within can their mutual language of English articulate an authentic identity that heals the damage of colonial rule and creates the freedom of Creole art.

Sources for Further Study

Asein, Samuel O. "Drama, the Church and the Nation in the Caribbean." *Literary Half-Yearly* 26 (January, 1985): 149-162.

Baer, William, ed. *Conversations with Derek Walcott.* Jackson: University of Mississippi Press, 1996.

Brown, Stewart. *The Art of Derek Walcott.* Chester Springs, Pa.: Dufour, 1991.

Cooper, Carolyn. "A Language Beyond Mimicry: Language as Metaphor and Meaning in Derek Walcott's Œuvre." *Literary Half-Yearly* 26 (January, 1985): 23-40.

Fox, Robert Elliot. "Derek Walcott: History as Dis-Ease." *Callaloo* 9 (Spring, 1986): 331-340.

Hamner, Robert D. "Caliban Agonistes: Stages of Cultural Development in Walcott's Plays." *Literary Half-Yearly* 26 (January, 1985): 120-131.

_______. *Derek Walcott.* Rev. ed. Boston: Twayne, 1993.

_______, ed. *Critical Perspectives on Derek Walcott.* Boulder, Colo.: Reinner, 1997.

Taylor, Patrick. "Myth and Reality in Caribbean Narrative: Derek Walcott's *Pantomime.*" *World Literature Written in English* 26 (1986): 169-176.

Michael Loudon

PASSION PLAY

Author: Peter Nichols (1927-)
Type of plot: Psychological
Time of plot: The early 1980's
Locale: London
First produced: 1981, at the Aldwych Theatre, London
First published: 1981

Principal characters:
JAMES CROXLEY, age fifty, a restorer of damaged paintings
ELEANOR CROXLEY, his wife, a forty-five-year-old music teacher
JIM, his alter ego
NELL, Eleanor's alter ego
KATE, James's mistress, a twenty-five-year-old photographer
AGNES, a fifty-year-old widow

The Play

In their twenty-fifth year of married life, James and Eleanor Croxley undergo what in contemporary jargon is glibly referred to as a mid-life crisis. Both of their children, now grown, have left home, and both James and Eleanor are, to all appearances, successful in their respective professions—restorer of modern religious art and musician—and comfortable in the solidity of their marriage. The catalyst for the action of the play is the death of a friend, Albert, who, having left his wife, Agnes, had been living with Kate. Younger even than one of the Croxley daughters, Kate loses no time in forming a liaison with James. The action of the play consists of the slow change from what at first appears to be an innocent diversion to a complex, all-consuming passion which, feeding on itself, eventually leaves the marriage intact but hollow. In the last scene, a daughter and her husband join James and Eleanor for the beginning of Christmas festivities; the audience is left with the devastating contrast between appearance and reality, even as guests arrive and all wish one another "Happy Christmas." James and Eleanor perfunctorily perform their duties as host and hostess, although their alter egos, Jim and Nell, are at total variance with the appearance of things.

The play opens with James and Eleanor entertaining Kate, sometime after the funeral of Albert, a "crusading editor," as Agnes describes him. Comfortable with themselves, neither James nor Eleanor suspects Kate's admiration for James, even though she has expressed it to Eleanor, with the object of having Eleanor relay that bit of information to James. James yawns repeatedly, and Kate apologizes for keeping her hosts up. As Kate leaves, the parting dialogue is drowned by a loud burst of choral music from Wolfgang Amadeus Mozart's "Dies Irae" to "Stricte discussurus" (1791); Peter Nichols frequently uses such musical techniques during moments of passion between Jim and Kate or during other climactic moments in the play. After Kate's departure, James and Eleanor retire, sexually comfortable with each other. Kate's plan, however, has succeeded, for Eleanor has casually informed James of Kate's attraction to him. For the time being, James throws off Eleanor's comment.

In the next two simultaneously staged scenes, James meets Kate for a professional lunch, and Agnes visits Eleanor for a coffee chat. Kate begins her seduction of James, and Agnes, even though she herself is currently enjoying a male friendship, vents her hostility toward Kate. As Agnes leaves, James arrives, Eleanor commenting on his sexy smell as they kiss. Then, for the first time Jim, dressed as James, enters, as in answer to Eleanor's question he lies, blaming the traffic for his lateness. So begin the small deceptions, lies, more assignations, telephone calls, and eventually letters, intercepted by Agnes and shown to Eleanor. Intelligent and broad-minded, Eleanor does not enter as Nell until she reads the letter Jim has written to Kate. Now Nell joins Jim to engage Eleanor and James in a tug of war, reaching a dramatic climax in a scene at the end of act 1 in which all four, along with Kate, indulge in accusations and counter-accusations. Nichols describes this scene as a "fugue of voices with the written speeches predominating and improvised dialogue continuing behind." Kate then leaves for the Far East, and Eleanor's confusion about what to do becomes acute.

In act 2 Kate returns from her travels, and Eleanor visits a psychiatrist, speaking to him as both Eleanor and Nell, as she tries to explain the trap in which she finds herself. James tells Eleanor that she must learn to play the new game of marital freedom, and Eleanor responds with her accusation that he wants "to have his cake and eat it." Both watch as Nell swallows a whole bottle of pills, one at a time. As Eleanor, Nell justifies her attempted suicide as the only card left for her to play. Finally, for the monogamous Eleanor, there is the sad departure of Nell during the Christmas festivities, but for James, who has returned to art restoration in his home workshop, there is Jim, who furtively reads one letter and addresses another.

Themes and Meanings

Banal though his mid-life crisis plot of marital infidelity may seem, Peter Nichols places still another version of what he has called the "genetic family trap" under the unblinking, microscopic eye of a steady observer of human passions to produce the kind of detailed texture found in the works of Gustave Flaubert, August Strindberg, Émile Zola, and Leo Tolstoy, all of whom examined marital infidelities and their destructive consequences.

Nichols gives outward forms to those passions in the alter egos or doubles. Stunning though his technique is, it is the ironic truths that technique conveys that place *Passion Play* in the forefront of modern British dramas about marital infidelity. Those truths reach into psychological, social, and religious arenas of conflict. The deepest personal urges are represented by the instincts of Nell, who comes from a provincial, working-class family, in which the major outlet for her passion (like that of Emma Bovary of Flaubert's novel) was the church, particularly the music of the church. It was the only place in her rundown village that seemed alive, a place where she heard stories and poetry, joined in the hymns, and enjoyed the streets thronged with people twenty minutes before the service. When her confidence in her marriage crumbles, she realizes that the freedom she and James had eagerly anticipated once their children were gone was in itself an illusion. "Out to lunch, as they say in America," she repeats at intervals in the play. Her music and James's art restoration provided each with an out, until the arrival of the seductress Kate. Reanimated, James, who had always found religion silly and Christianity "a terrible disaster forced on the rest of us by madmen in the Middle Ages," discovers a vitality in middle age that he had never experienced in his work. He describes himself as "an unemotional man who's inspired a passion in my partner. And I needn't tell you what passion means? Suffering. Self-inflicted torture. Masochism. All that's holy. Like that exquisite depiction of a bleeding corpse that's waiting for me in Zurich. . . ."

Kate, from a prosperous middle-class background, has assimilated all the freedoms of the new age, unhampered by the disillusionment of the monogamous Eleanor and by the conscience of James. Of a new generation, she is agile in claiming the sexual attention of one married man after another.

Socially, the two main characters (of the lower middle class) have moved up, but they still remain on the borders of the world the sexually liberated Kate inhabits. James works at his restoration of modern religious paintings (a seeming contradiction in terms) with a craftsmanship that is technical rather than artistic. His cultural mediocrity is suggested by the lack of passion in his work. Before his seduction by Kate, he yawned constantly and had to have eight hours of sleep every night. Eleanor, on the other hand, has come a long way from her provincial origins, having known something like passion in her early church associations. She continues teaching pupils and singing in a choir. She feels emptiness and pain, the former because of the loss of her illusionary marital comfort and the latter because of her loss of a friendship with Kate. Despite their age difference, she has found a vitality in her friendship with Kate that she could not enjoy with her own daughters, both of whom are about Kate's age. Thus she suffers the double loss of husband and friend. Agnes, on the other hand, acts in traditional modes, continuing to harbor desires for revenge on Kate and going so far as to take advantage of her access to Kate's apartment to steal the letter responsible for the emergence of Nell.

In *Passion Play*, Nichols continues his stripping away of illusions from reality, a theme that is at the core of all of his plays. Here, however, his comic wit takes a more somber tone, and the ironies as they multiply become darker than in the earlier dramas.

Dramatic Devices

Peter Nichols's main device is his doubling of the two main characters into ego and alter ego and having four different actors play those roles. Another device used to stunning effect is the simultaneous doubling of scenes, such as the one in which Eleanor reads Jim's letter to Kate, even as the audience sees Jim writing that letter. Both reader and writer slip the letter into its envelope at the same time, in one of the finely tuned details that proliferate in the play. The scene is an important one, as it is at this point, when Eleanor and Agnes are discussing the letter in a tea shop, that Nell enters for the first time, dressed like Eleanor and taking her place between the two women. She becomes an antagonist to Eleanor until her unnoticed departure from the Christmas party at the end.

Perhaps the most moving of Nichols's dramatic devices is his use of music. As mentioned earlier, Mozart's last work, *Requiem* (1791), crashes in a "sudden, fortissimo burst of choral music" as Kate leaves the Croxley home in the first scene. When James and Eleanor turn off the lights in their bedroom, the "Dies Irae" bursts out again. At the end of act 1, after Jim and Kate discuss Kate's trip, Kate assures Nell that they will go shopping and talk like girlfriends again when she (Kate) returns. Once more, the *Requiem*, which has been swelling during the scene, drowns out the voices. Following her departure, James and Eleanor go upstairs for their ritual "liedown," and the "Dies Irae" resumes. In a final burst of irony, at the end of act 2, the music to which Nell leaves the house is no longer Mozart's but that of hollow Christmas carols.

With music and art as the paradoxical metaphor for his play about modern marriage and about two middle-class, middle-aged professionals and parents, Nichols evokes the passionless nature of a whole age.

Critical Context

In the context of modern British drama, *Passion Play* joins a tradition of dramatic treatments of marital infidelity, including earlier plays such as Arthur Wing Pinero's *Mid-Channel* (pr. 1909) and Terence Rattigan's *The Deep Blue Sea* (pr., pb. 1952), both of which feature suicides or attempted suicides. Peter Nichols updates this tradition, keeping intact the universality of the experience.

Having earned a reputation for his skill in manipulating complex plots (*The National Health: Or, Nurse Norton's Affair*, pr. 1969, pr. 1970, and *Forget-Me-Not Lane*, pr., pb. 1971, for example), Nichols here surpasses the inventiveness of those plays. His creation of the alter egos knits the inner and outer events more seamlessly than, for example, do the interior monologues of *A Day in the Death of Joe Egg* (pr., pb. 1967), in which the two main characters step out of their roles to address the audience directly.

Having earned acclaim for total honesty in exploring relationships in a family with a retarded child (*A Day in the Death of Joe Egg*), he surpasses even that honesty by the convincing subtlety with which he details the painful breakdown of a passionless marriage. Ironically witty, both dialogue and events move rapidly, with the doubling techniques creating an orderly confusion that evoked strong critical approval, especially of the first act. Unlike dramatists such as Harold Pinter, who express subtextual realities of characters in pauses and silences, Nichols uses alter egos, a device Irving Wardle of *The Times* (London) describes as "so comically fertile that it is amazing that nobody to my knowledge has used it before."

Described by Philip Barnes as Nichols's most acclaimed work since *A Day in the Death of Joe Egg*, *Passion Play* seems a culmination of the artistry Nichols has progressively demonstrated since his early, prolific writing for the television medium. The winner of a number of *Evening Standard* awards, Nichols is highly respected and has been called an uncompromising moral allegorist of his times. He is an outspoken critic of directors' whims and philistine management, on occasion expressing his intention to leave the theater for other kinds of writing.

Sources for Further Study

Barnes, Philip. "Peter Nichols." In *A Companion to Post-War British Theater.* Totowa, N.J.: Barnes & Noble, 1986.

Glendenning, Victoria. "Only Four Can Play." *Times Literary Supplement*, January 23, 1981, p. 83.

Jones, Kim L. "Peter Nichols." In *British Playwrights, 1956-1995: A Research and Production Sourcebook*, edited by William Demastes. Westport, Conn.: Greenwood Press, 1996.

Parkin, Andrew. "Casting the Audience: Theatricality in the Stage Plays of Peter Nichols." In *British and Irish Drama Since 1960*, edited by James Acheson. Houndsmill, England: Macmillan, 1993.

Storm, William. "Adulteration as Clarification: Dramaturgical Strategy in Peter Nichols's *Passion Play.*" *Modern Drama*, Fall, 1994, 437-450.

Taylor, John Russell. *The Second Wave: British Drama for the Seventies.* New York: Hill and Wang, 1971.

Wardle, Irving. "Doing Justice to the Theme of Adultery." *Times* (London), January 14, 1981, p. 11.

Susan Rusinko

THE PELICAN

Author: August Strindberg (1849-1912)
Type of plot: Psychological
Time of plot: The early twentieth century
Locale: Unspecified, probably Sweden
First produced: 1907, at the Intimate Theatre, Stockholm, Sweden
First published: Pelikanen, 1907 (English translation, 1962)

Principal characters:
ELISE, the mother, a widow
FREDERICK, the son, a law student
GERDA, the daughter
AXEL, the son-in-law, married to Gerda
MARGARET, the cook

The Play

The Pelican opens in a living room with a chiffonier, a writing table, a chaise lounge with a purple-red lap rug, and a rocking chair. Mother, dressed in mourning clothes, listens to the music of Frédéric Chopin. She is bothered by the smell of funeral flowers and the sight of the chaise lounge, Father's deathbed, but she cannot get rid of the furniture until the estate has been settled. Harboring a guilty conscience, she is bothered by a mysterious presence lingering outside the house and always wants the door shut. Although she believes that she has sacrificed for her children, she has needlessly scrimped on food and has refused to light fires, despite the fact that her husband earned a considerable sum of money. As a result, her children are weak and sickly, and Margaret, her cook, tired of ill treatment, threatens to leave. Mother, however, will not be needing Margaret, because Mother is going to live with her newly married daughter, Gerda, and her son-in-law, Axel, whom she likes. Margaret intimates that Mother's devotion to Axel is more than platonic.

When Margaret has left, the son, Frederick, cold and drunk, comes in coughing. Mother accuses Frederick of being callous because he is concerned about his inheritance, yet she herself cannot understand why there is no will. She even tries to pry information out of Frederick. Frederick is an impoverished law student, but Mother will give him no money for warm clothes. Frederick, who has no love for his mother, accuses her of spending money on trips abroad and eating at fancy restaurants while depriving her family of necessities and feeding them food that either lacks nutritional value or is overseasoned. Throughout her argument with Frederick, Mother is still bothered by a presence outside the house, and she tells Frederick to take down his father's portrait because it has evil eyes.

After Frederick leaves, Axel enters and is greeted warmly by Mother. Axel has been bored on his honeymoon with Gerda and remembers that at his wedding he danced with Mother and wrote her a poem, calling her a pelican. Most of all, however, Axel wants to know what has happened to the estate. They search the chiffonier and pull out a hidden document just when Gerda is knocking on the door. Gerda voices suspicions about the locked door, but Mother changes the subject. Axel and Gerda decide to live in the house with Mother. As they exit, the wind blows, papers fly, and a picture falls off the wall.

Mother returns. Startled by the swaying rocker, she recovers, but she will continue to be bothered by the rocker throughout the play. The hidden document turns out to be a letter from Father, accusing Mother of ruining and murdering him. Appalled, Mother wants to leave, but Axel, who has married Gerda for the inheritance, sees no other option but to stay and live on Mother's money. Mother and Axel had murdered Father legally by driving him to despair; when Mother left Father to spend the night with Axel, Father howled outside their window like a madman. Axel and Mother, compatriots in crime, are doomed. As Axel abandons both Gerda and Mother to go to a meeting, Mother realizes his hypocrisy.

In scene 2, Gerda and Frederick become closer and start to wake up to Mother's deceitfulness. Unwilling in the past to face the truth, Gerda has always defended Mother. The two siblings realize that their parents' marriage was deeply unhappy, despite hypocritical displays of affection such as they performed at their silver anniversary celebration. When Gerda continues to defend Mother, Frederick accuses all the women of being conspirators, a secret Mafia. As he goes to light the fire, Frederick discovers his father's letter, pieces it together, and becomes distraught when he reads it. The letter reveals how Mother stole money from the household budget while she deprived her family and how Axel borrowed money from Mother, then married Gerda for mercenary reasons. Gerda suspected this ruse, but did not want to believe it. Frederick reminds her that Axel slapped her on their wedding night. Knowing they are doomed, the two siblings vow to avenge their father. They taunt Axel with innuendos, and when Mother comes in with pudding, Gerda deliberately takes the group out to eat steak and sandwiches; now Axel and Mother know something has happened.

In scene 3, the group turns against Mother. Gerda accuses Mother of cooking tasteless meals and hoarding the best food for herself. Axel orders Mother to light the fire and to eat weak porridge, ignoring Mother's threats to throw herself out the window. Next, Frederick reminds Mother that she gave him over to nursemaids, who took him to prostitutes who abused him. Even when confronted with such charges, Frederick realizes, she will remain blind to her complicity in murdering her husband and destroying her children's lives. Panic-stricken, Mother finds that Frederick's rocking sounds like knives being whetted. Finding her so evil that he pities her, Frederick leaves as Mother opens the window and sees Father's ghost. Frightened by the blast of wind, Mother turns on all the electric lights, but Gerda turns them off and tries to feed Mother oatmeal. She accuses her deluded mother of teaching her how to torment Father and steal from him.

Defending herself, Mother claims that she also had an unhappy childhood and learned her wiles from her family; all families are guilty of treachery. If life is so dismal, Gerda does not want to live. Suddenly, they smell smoke: Frederick has set the house on fire. Mother jumps out the window as Frederick and Gerda hug each other. The ugly memories of the house go up in flames as Gerda remembers a happy Christmas and Frederick recalls a boating trip when Mother joined them on the boat. They huddle close to the floor consumed in flames as the stage is bathed in red light.

Themes and Meanings

In *The Pelican*, August Strindberg intertwined a number of themes that had obsessed him for most of his career as a dramatist. Though naturalist in tone, the play is symbolic in its form. The characters are called Mother, Father, Son, Daughter. In this manner, Strindberg suggests the symbolic reconstruction of the human family in a world that is fallen and lost. In myth, the pelican is supposed to feed its young from its flesh. It not only symbolizes ideal mother love but also represents Jesus Christ as redeemer of the world. Strindberg's use of this symbol is deeply ironic, for the human family is living in a post-lapsarian world. The mother does not nurture her young; instead, she skims the cream off their food, forces them to live in a freezing environment, abandons them when they are sick, gives her son over to a prostitute, and steals her daughter's husband. In this world of perverted values, marriage is a hell. Axel is bored on his honeymoon and strikes his wife on her wedding day. Frederick sees the role of husband as that of a pimp for a tramp who will carve him up. Father and Mother's silver wedding anniversary is a sideshow, for Father has been persecuted and has often abandoned his house to flee to barrooms.

The children of the marriage are stifled. Both Frederick and Gerda are bottle babies who have been undernourished on rye bread and vinegar. Gerda's breasts have never developed and she is sterile: For the next generation, motherhood is an impossibility. Frederick is weak, sick, and weary of life. He will never marry and has given up pursuing a career.

In this fallen world, people commit psychic murder—a form of psychological warfare used to destroy a person's will to live. By abandoning Father and tormenting him, Mother has driven Father to his death even though she has not legally killed him. She is also starving and poisoning the minds of her children and slowly "murdering" them. Furthermore, this nightmare family is built around lies and deceit. Gerda is taught to lie to Father and is able to make her debut only when she has become a consummate liar. Conversation in this house is a form of idle chatter, a way of hiding thoughts. All his life, Frederick has heard nothing but lies; he notes that even the legal system is based on deception. The family members are sleepwalkers; for Strindberg, sleepwalkers go through life in a self-induced trance, unable to see their demeaning condition. Gerda is sleepwalking and does not want to face the fact that her mother is having an affair with her husband. Mother is the biggest sleepwalker. She is a congenital liar and thief who cannot give up her illusions that she is a good mother and that Axel loves her.

Caught in a world of lies, deceit, and illusions, the human family is trapped and doomed. Mother cannot leave, nor can she even move the furniture until the landlord comes. Margaret, the cook, has always wanted to leave but has always stayed. Caught in their own web of intrigue, Axel and Mother are doomed to live in poverty in the house of their crime. Gerda, too, wants to run away, but there is nowhere to go. When Frederick sets the house on fire, she tells him to run, but he is doomed to stay in the house. Thus, the house itself represents the human condition, from which there is no escape.

Mired in sin and guilt, weak and helpless, Frederick decides to burn down the house of shame, guilt, and death with the fire of purification. As the two children hug each other and dream of the ideal of a happy family, they are consumed by flames. For Strindberg, the world is a form of purgatory where one must simply endure suffering. Mother says she was taught lies in her own family; the chain goes back to Adam and Eve. She supports Strindberg's position that underneath family life lies human corruption.

Dramatic Devices

August Strindberg makes use of many dramatic devices in *The Pelican*. Food becomes a symbol for emotional nourishment. The absence of this emotional nourishment is seen in the food that provides no sustenance. Food in Mother's house is light as air, overseasoned, and overcooked. The milk is skimmed; the tea, weak; and the fish, rancid. People are fed porridge, oatmeal, rye bread, and vinegar. Thus, the children are weak and undernourished, both physically and emotionally. The physical coldness in the house represents the emotional coldness brought on by a lack of love. Frederick is always coughing because he is freezing, and Mother will not give him the money to buy warm clothes. Even the maids are freezing, but Mother refuses to light the fire and hides the firewood. Also, the house is dark, without the light of human joy, for Mother will not let anyone turn on more than a few electric lights.

The most effective dramatic device is the symbolic presence of the dead father, who is a focal character. The odor of his death is still in the house, forcing Mother to open windows. His presence is felt stalking the garden and haunting Mother. His portrait stares at Mother with "evil" eyes. Frederick's howls of agony echo Father's fiendish cries the night he found Mother unfaithful. Moreover, Father's rocker keeps rocking, sounding like knives being sharpened. The chaise lounge where he died looks like a "bloody butcher's block." Even the letter his son finds is a sign of Father's voice speaking from the grave and condemning Mother. Like a vengeful god, he is embodied in the storm raging outside the house.

In the end, the tide turns: Mother must eat mush, feel the freezing cold, and have the electric lights turned off against her wishes. She falls down in panic on the death-couch of her husband. And when she jumps out the window, she falls toward Father's ghost, which haunts the garden.

In this play, Strindberg employs two literary motifs: the Orestes theme and the Hamlet theme. In the myth of Orestes, Orestes and Electra plot the death of their mother Clytemnestra, who has killed their father Agamemnon. The purple-red covering on the chaise lounge could allude to the red carpet used to trap Agamemnon, and the image of the bloody butcher's block might serve for the bloody bath where he was stabbed. In William Shakespeare's *Hamlet* (1603), the ghost of Hamlet's father appears and tells Hamlet to avenge his murder, which was plotted by his wife's lover. Like Hamlet, Frederick has a disdain for life and its falsehoods, avoids marriage, broods over his father, hears the voice of his dead father proclaiming a foul murder, and dies in the process of avenging his father's murder. Through the use of these scenic effects and dramatic devices, including the musical pieces that open each scene and the red lighting at the end, Strindberg creates compelling theater.

Critical Context

Strindberg explored the themes of sleepwalking and psychic murder in such early works as *Fröken Julie* (pb. 1888, pr. 1905; *Miss Julie*, 1912) and *Fadren* (pr., pb. 1887; *The Father*, 1899). Later, he moved toward a more expressionist form of drama. *The Pelican* was written late in Strindberg's career, after the psychological turmoil of his inferno period. In 1907, Strindberg opened the Intimate Theatre in Stockholm with *The Pelican*, one of a series of experimental dramas. These "chamber plays" were based on the interweaving of thematic movements rather than on linear plots. They displayed a series of theatrical images juxtaposed and intertwined as themes are in a piece of chamber music. The plays were short, with small casts and simple staging. They focused on a world of discord, sin, shame, guilt, retribution, and reconciliation. Their mood was somber and elegiac, their structure compressed. Combining realistic scenes with grotesque symbolic images, they enveloped the audience in a muted spectacle of sight and sound that was almost surrealistic.

Strindberg called these plays his "last sonatas." *The Pelican* is, indeed, a last sonata, for it incorporates a number of themes Strindberg had already explored: the vampirish woman who drives a man to his death, the presence of a dominant father hovering over a cast of characters, the torments and hypocrisy of married life, the victimization of children in troubled marriages, the sacrificial death scene, and the hopelessness of living in a sinful world.

The Pelican was not only a culmination but also a new beginning, for the play bears characteristics that would become hallmarks of modern drama: a cast of mysterious characters haunted by vague anxieties; grotesque images interspersed with realistic dialogue; a confined setting from which there is no escape; language that conceals rather than reveals meaning; and a stark, apocalyptic ending. According to Eugene O'Neill, "Strindberg was the precursor of all modernity in our present theater."

Sources for Further Study

Carlson, Harry G. *Out of the Inferno: Strindberg's Reawakening as an Artist*. Seattle: University of Washington Press, 1996.

Dahlström, Carl E. W. L. "*The Pelican*." In *Strindberg's Dramatic Expressionism*. 1930. 2d ed. New York: B. Blom, 1965.

Johnson, Walter. Introduction to *The Pelican*. In *A Dream Play and Four Chamber Plays*. Seattle: University of Washington Press, 1973.

Lamm, Martin. "*The Pelican*." In *August Strindberg*. Translated and edited by Harry G. Carlson. New York: B. Blom, 1971.
Marker, F. J., and Christopher Innes, eds. *Modernism in European Drama*. Toronto, Ont.: University of Toronto Press, 1998.
Robinson, Michael, ed. and trans. *Strindberg and Genre*. Chester Spring, Pa.: Dufour-Novik, 1991.
Sprinchorn, Evert. "The Chamber Plays." In *Strindberg as Dramatist*. New Haven, Conn.: Yale University Press, 1982.
Törnqvist, Egil. "*The Pelican*." In *Strindbergian Drama*. Atlantic Highlands, N.J.: Humanities Press, 1982.
Ward, John. "*The Pelican*." In *The Social and Religious Plays of Strindberg*. Atlantic Highlands, N.J.: Humanities Press, 1980.

Paul Rosefeldt

A PENNY FOR A SONG

Author: John Whiting (1917-1963)
Type of plot: Comedy
Time of plot: 1804
Locale: England
First produced: 1951, at the Haymarket Theatre, London
First published: 1957, in *The Plays of John Whiting*

Principal characters:
TIMOTHY BELLBOYS, a country gentleman
LAMPRETT BELLBOYS, his brother
HESTER BELLBOYS, Lamprett's wife
DORCAS BELLBOYS, the daughter of Lamprett and Hester
HALLAM MATTHEWS, a dandy from London
EDWARD STERNE, a blind soldier
GEORGE SELINCOURT, a leader of local volunteer forces
WILLIAM HUMPAGE, a lookout

The Play

A Penny for a Song, set in 1804, illustrates "the finer lunacies of the English at war" in a typically English mixture of farce and romantic comedy. The setting is a sheltered garden on the Dorset coast, bounded by orchard, sea, and sky, with an elegant eighteenth century house in the background. In the foreground stands a tree with a man crouched on top, who is oddly attired in scraps of old uniforms and holds a telescope as well as green and red wooden signals. This is Humpage, the lookout, ordered by the two eccentric brothers Timothy and Lamprett Bellboys to maintain his precarious position day and night. Timothy wants Humpage to report on any sign of Napoleon Bonaparte on British shores, for he is determined to defeat the Beast of the Apocalypse single-handedly. Lamprett, obsessed with using an old fire engine—so much that he himself starts fires so that he can extinguish them—insists that Humpage pay attention only to fires. Meek in anything that does not concern fire fighting, Lamprett is married to an imposing and bossy woman, Hester. Although Hester enjoins her daughter Dorcas, who is seventeen, to put off her childish ways, none of the older people has done so yet; they all behave like unruly children. The Bellboys family is joined by Hallam Matthews, a dandy from London who is determined to take a holiday from life in this idyllic setting. In fact, however, Hallam, who becomes everyone's confidant, not only is implicated in the farcical confusions but compounds them.

While Dorcas, not quite ready to follow her mother's advice, turns somersaults, she is suddenly confronted by a young man and a boy who ask for refreshments on their journey. Edward, blinded in the French war, is traveling to London to show his blindness to the mad king George III, to persuade him to stop the war. The boy, who met

Edward on a battlefield, is an orphan who cherishes his own romantic mission. Hearing the Christmas story, he recognized Jesus as his lost brother and now is determined to go to Bethlehem in search of him, for the storyteller had forgotten to mention that it all happened centuries ago. These young people for a moment inject the reality of war into the sunny Dorset garden, although their quests are no less fantastic than those of the older farcical eccentrics.

Timothy next explains to Hallam why he had asked him to bring a wardrobe from a London theater. Though his countrymen are doing nothing to defend their nation against the French threat, and even have denied him leadership of his own volunteer corps, the Bellboys Fencibles, Timothy has conceived a charmingly simple rescue. Taking advantage of what he considers his remarkable resemblance to Napoleon, he will don a French National Guard uniform and appear from a tunnel at the rear of the French army. Then, with words borrowed from a French phrasebook, he will order the men to retreat, saying that all is lost.

Timothy departs, but Hallam's rest is again interrupted by George Selincourt, who has been put in charge of the local volunteers instead of Timothy. Selincourt explains that the forces under his command are going to stage a mock battle and leaves him with posters bearing the single word "INVASION," suggesting that Hallam purchase at least one hundred of them at a bargain price. When Timothy discovers a poster, he is galvanized into action. He dons his disguise (in which his brother mistakes him for Lord Nelson) and, clutching the French phrasebook, prepares to descend the well which leads to the tunnel. Before he can finish his farewell speech, which is incomprehensible to all but Hallam, the rope gives, and he disappears with a bump.

Act 2 opens with a picnic during the mock battle, which Hester and Lamprett assume to be real. "There is great comfort, I find, in resorting to good food during a crisis," says Hester and commands her husband to shut the gate after a second cannonball has come bouncing into the garden. Lamprett feels frustrated by the lack of fires, although he has moved his fire engine into the garden, ready for action. Hallam remains aloof, enjoying the commotion, even when Selincourt returns to inform him that what was intended as a maneuver has become a war in earnest: One of the volunteers has spotted Napoleon.

Selincourt proves himself no less idiosyncratic than Timothy in his attempt to defeat the enemy. Believing that Napoleon's men are hiding in a tunnel under the sea while their emperor is on shore spying, Selincourt resolves to capture Napoleon. As soon as Selincourt leaves, Timothy appears overhead in a balloon which he captured from the volunteers, having mistaken them for the French. He is gleefully munching biscuits when the balloon descends; protesting, Timothy once again goes down into the well. The moment he is out of sight, Selincourt reappears in a fury, complaining that some fool is putting out all of his warning fires. Nevertheless, he is confident that Napoleon cannot elude his forces, for the volunteers are sealing the entrance to the tunnel with a ton of explosives. Hearing this, Hallam loses all ironic detachment, fearing that he has allowed the joke to be carried too far. He even wonders whether the real Napoleon has not landed after all.

Selincourt's men, however, use an excessive amount of explosives, so that the false Napoleon is propelled through the air and lands safely beyond the cordon of volunteers. A dirty, tattered, but invincible Timothy establishes his identity by his knowledge of cricket, and the warring parties are reunited in characteristic English manner by the planning of a game, volunteers included, for the next day. The men then retire into the house for a candlelight dinner. Only Hallam and Dorcas remain outside. Edward has left to continue the quest that he knows to be hopeless; Dorcas, who has found and lost her love in one day, has indeed grown up, so that together with the disillusioned dandy she can appreciate a song about life's brevity and illusions. Humpage's bell sounds softly as he stirs in his sleep, and from the house can be heard the sound of the men's voices singing "gay and gentle." Hallam takes up the melody on his flute "with an infinite tenderness. . . . A single star stands in the sky."

Themes and Meanings

Inspired in 1940, when England was under another threat of invasion, but written at a time of "great personal happiness" for playwright John Whiting, *A Penny for a Song* combines a dark vision of the violence and futility of life with gentle and forgiving comedy. Like all Whiting's other works, it is set in a time of war and pours scorn on elaborate schemes for outfoxing the enemy. The play stands apart from Whiting's others, however, in that it depicts the human quest for grandeur not only as destructive, deluded, and vain but also as somehow endearing. As a result, the mood is one of wistful humor tinged with melancholy, rather than of anger and despair. Even the most obsessive eccentrics in the play, Timothy and Lamprett, can stand back at times to reflect on the futility of their efforts. Hallam, the Byronic outsider without commitments of his own, comments throughout on human folly but never loses his compassion, being well aware of the vulnerability that underlies each person's posturing: "We never give up our rattles: our thumbs will go to our mouths on our death-beds." He knows that everyone plays the clown because he seeks to escape an unbearable reality and an intolerable self.

The main spokesman, however, is not the disillusioned and rhetorical Hallam but Edward, blind and alone, dedicated to the hopeless mission of stopping men from waging war. Edward falls in love with Dorcas, but despite his present happiness, despite their laughter and tenderness, he feels compelled to continue his journey. Trying to explain the urgency of his quest to Dorcas, he says, "You see, my life-loving darling, the dark journey to the dark home is sometimes sweeter than the summer's day." Many Whiting characters share this longing for "the dark home," which really is the other side of their juvenile idealism. The inevitable failure of their monumental yet childish schemes leaves them nothing but death. It is the only home they can hope to reach.

Despite such somber musings, however, *A Penny for a Song* succeeds as a boisterous farce of mix-ups and misunderstandings, all of which are happily resolved in friendship and love. The audience is assured that on this sunny day in a far distant time the heavens are not about to fall. "All [the play] states, in very simple terms, is the idea of Christian charity," according to Whiting. Still, a full thematic analysis must take account of the characters' violent delusions and their loneliness, frustration, and desire for death. The dual genesis of the play is reflected in the interplay between the older and younger groups of characters, so that comedy, despair, and love are intertwined.

Dramatic Devices

A Penny for a Song is a play in two acts, each of which alternates scenes of frantic action, involving the eccentric older characters, with contemplative exchanges between the young lovers, while Hallam serves as a link between the two groups. The play takes place on one day, beginning with Timothy tearing apart his bedroom curtains, throwing open the window, and shouting at Humpage. Act 1 ends with his abrupt disappearance down the well, which unleashes the madcap action of the second act. The play ends in a quiet, thoughtful mood, with Hallam and Dorcas's ruminations on the transitoriness of life and with a series of solicitous good-nights. This ending corresponds to the title, derived from a William Butler Yeats poem, which reflects on the passing of youth. Whiting is said, however, to have preferred the title of the German translation of his play, *Wo wir fröhlich gewesen sind* (where we were happy), which makes a similar statement without literary reference.

A Penny for a Song uses many of the traditional devices of farce: precisely timed entrances and exits, mistaken identities, misunderstandings, and acceleration (act 2 moves at a faster pace than act 1). Costumes and props add to the comic effect. Humpage wears an odd military get-up, including satin knee-breeches and worsted stockings. In act 2 he is ordered to put a saucepan on his head as protection in his exposed position on the tree. Timothy appears dressed as Napoleon, and Hester takes leave of her family in what appears to be a suit of golden armor as she sets forth to join Lady Jerningham's corps of British amazons, accompanied by her diminutive maid Pippin. Props, such as the colorful balloon and the fantastic fire engine, contribute visual comic effects.

The chief source of the humor, however, is the language. The eccentrics reveal their idiosyncrasies through their speech. Lamprett, for example, is exasperated at the subordination of the fire brigade to "ephemeral activities such as agriculture." Timothy sums up his position by telling Hallam, "The situation is roughly this: myself, versus one hundred and seventy-five thousand Frenchmen." While Timothy and Lamprett are mainly unconscious of the effect of their words, Hallam uses language self-consciously. He is elegant with words, believing in "the music of civilised conversation," especially "the fugue of argument" and "the bravura passage." Such fugues and bravura passages occur in *A Penny for a Song* and indeed in all Whiting's plays. Hallam, for example, discoursing on youth and age, applies metaphors such as "the morning, sweet as a nut" and "the early evening, sad as a mustard pot." Edward's language is poetic rather than rhetorical, in keeping with his romantic vision of homelessness and death.

Although in the mid-1950's, a few years after *A Penny for a Song*, Whiting claimed that his early work suffered from his "hangover from the English lyric tradition," he never abandoned his heightened use of language. The rhythm of his plays is controlled by the alternation of fast-moving dialogues and extended monologues, which often serve as dramatic climaxes.

Critical Context

Although *A Penny for a Song* is John Whiting's only comedy, the play conforms to the pattern of his other works. Like *Saint's Day* (pr. 1951, pb. 1952), *Marching Song* (pr., pb. 1954), and *The Gates of Summer* (pr. 1956, pb. 1969), it features an isolated house beset by the threat or imagined threat of invasion and inhabited by a group of eccentric recluses who plan an attack to defend themselves. They see themselves as heroic figures but are actually childish and often cranky people, careless of anyone and anything but their mission. Their mostly preemptive attack, however, tends to collapse as soon as they put it into action, and they continue to hide in their isolated fortress-nursery. Ensconced in domesticity, they still harbor dreams of aggression, fears of invasion, and, ultimately, a desire for death. Whiting's other plays present this condition in all of its violence, moodiness, and incoherence; early critics were baffled and sometimes infuriated. *A Penny for a Song* takes up the same themes, but subdues and controls them by the comic action, to which they serve to lend depth.

In 1962 a revised version of *A Penny for a Song* appeared; in this version Whiting altered the character of Edward, making him into a revolutionary who constantly spouts radical philosophy and quotes from *The Rights of Man* (1791-1792). He is no longer blind, nor is he in love with Dorcas, whom he leaves without pain. This revision is inferior to the original, for it replaces scenes of poignant comedy and lyrical charm with heavy didacticism. The 1951 *A Penny for a Song*, however, succeeds completely as a whimsical comedy, frantic yet lyrical, one of the "finer lunacies" of the English comic spirit.

Sources for Further Study

Hayman, Ronald. *John Whiting*. London: Heinemann, 1969.

Robinson, Gabrielle. *A Private Mythology: The Manuscripts and Plays of John Whiting*. Lewisburg, Pa.: Bucknell University Press, 1988.

Salmon, Eric. *The Dark Journey: John Whiting as Dramatist*. London: Barrie & Jenkins, 1979.

Trussler, Simon. *The Plays of John Whiting: An Assessment*. London: Gollancz, 1972.

Gabrielle Robinson

PENTECOST

Author: David Edgar (1948-)
Type of plot: Political
Time of plot: 1989 to the early 1990's
Locale: An unnamed southeast European country, presumably Bosnia Herzegovina
First produced: 1994, at The Other Place, Stratford-upon-Avon, England
First published: 1995

Principal characters:
GABRIELLA PECS, an art curator in her thirties
DR. OLIVER DAVENPORT, an English art historian in his forties
MIKHAIL CZABA, a minister for monuments in his twenties
LEO KATZ, an American art historian in his thirties
ANNA JEDLIKOVA, a former dissident and present magistrate in her fifties
YASMIN, a stateless Palestinian and leader of asylum-seekers in her thirties

The Play

In an abandoned Romanesque church in an unnamed Balkan country (presumably Bosnia Herzegovina) Gabriella Pecs shows Dr. Oliver Davenport a lamentation fresco said to date from the early thirteenth century. She tells him how she has tracked it down by following the story of its provenance as it is set out in the (fictional) "Old Nagolitic" national epic (c. 1215). A foreign traveler headed for Persia is captured by villagers and threatened with death but saves his skin by offering to paint on their church wall the famous scene of the Virgin and Christ's followers mourning the dead Jesus. The fresco uncannily recalls Florentine painter and architect Giotto di Bondone's *Lamentation* (1304-1306) in Padua, Italy, both in its verisimilitude and in its skillful deployment of perspective, although it was created a century before the Italian masterpiece. If authentic, it would rank as the art discovery of the century, since only 1 percent of Byzantine era paintings are known to have survived. Even more, it would mark the beginning of the Renaissance and the great shift in the West from a theocratic to a humanistic perspective.

Contemporary representatives of church and state—an Orthodox priest, a Roman Catholic priest, a hardline right-wing nationalist leader with skinhead support, and a swinging American-slang-talking minister for the preservation of national monuments—contend among themselves and with Davenport and Pecs regarding the disposition of the fresco, which was hidden by bricks for centuries and which was, until the play's opening, covered by a "grand heroic revolutionary picture," a piece of agitprop kitsch. To this sextet joins a brash, fast-talking, erudite American art historian, Leo Katz, who not only doubts the account of the provenance of the fresco but also, and more important, opposes removing it from the wall by an elaborate procedure of chemical transfers. Katz has been brought in by the Orthodox priest as an expert witness to forestall the removal. Anna Jedlikova, a fifty-year-old former student dissident and political prisoner under the former communist government that recently ended after a forty-year tenure, then enters. She has become a magistrate and has been brought in to adjudicate the dispute.

The stage is nearly set. However, at the end of act 1 a motley group of eleven armed refugees plus an infant—a Palestinian Kuwaiti, an Azeri (Azerbaijani), a Mozambican, a Bosnian, a Russian, a Ukrainian, an Afghan, a Sri Lankan, two Bosnian Roma, and a Kurd—together with two British hostages, burst in seeking sanctuary. Each speaks his or her language for the duration of the play (translated in the text), whereas before the audience heard the language of the country (presumably Serbo-Croatian, actually Bulgarian) now and then along with various kinds of English. The intruders take the others hostage (a few manage to escape), force them to exchange clothes with the refugees, and lock the church. The act ends with a police loudspeaker outside telling the refugees they are surrounded and must surrender.

Act 1 covers about one month. In the accelerated act 2, covering about eighteen hours, the asylum-seekers demand safe passage and work permits to Western Europe, threatening the hostages' lives if their demands are not met. Phone messages pass back and forth, skinheads plan an assault, and the police surround the church. The Roman Catholic priest, who left earlier, enters naked to show he is not wired and says that some can go but not all. Anger and confusion and a babel of tongues follow.

Yasmin, the Palestinian leader, threatens to kill Katz to demonstrate her seriousness, but Davenport intervenes. He overheard the word for "rock" (uttered by the skinheads), connects it with the Italian for "hunchback" (the words are near homonyms), and, since there is a hump-shouldered person in Giotto's fresco, imagines someone describing the Padua *Lamentation* to the fresco painter. This leads him to oppose the priest's contention that the provenance of the fresco has not been proven and, subsequently, it has little value. He now conjectures, amid rising tension, that the painter was not an Italian traveling east but an Arab colorist coming west, who had seen the mosaics of Constantinople and frescos in Serbia or Macedonia. The artist hears the strange story of the woman whose son dies on a tree but comes back after three days. Fascinated, he paints the scene using a deep ultramarine blue (powdered lapis lazuli) unknown in the West. Unmoved, Yasmin orders the fresco doused with gasoline and, in a desperate last act, threatens to burn it if they are not freed. Then a stunning *coup de théâtre* occurs: An explosion and sirens are heard, smoke rises, and masked German-speaking commandos burst through a hole in the fresco wall and start shooting. After this chaos, four refugees, including Yasmin and Davenport (he is dressed as a refugee), lie dead.

In the last scene the audience learns that the authorities outside the church have heard all along what has been going on inside from a bug they slipped in with Davenport's insulin medication and never had any intention of granting safe passage. The play ends with cryptic one-word exchanges between Pecs and Katz.

Themes and Meanings

The play premiered five years after the Berlin Wall came down and takes place in the shadow of that great event. It scrutinizes the consequences of the "new freedom" for Eastern Europe; the unnamed country evokes Bosnia with echoes of the events that took place in Sarajevo. Initially it seems an intellectual detective story, but, when the refugees enter, the discussion of the fresco changes from an academic contemplation of the rise of humanism and uneasy relation of East and West to an actual and tensely dramatic issue: What should be done with the stateless persons in the aftermath of the collapse of communism? Will the West accommodate them? Echoing Emma Lazarus's poem on the Statue of Liberty, "The New Colossus" (1883), the last words of the play—"Huddled." "Yearning." "Free."—provide no closure to these questions.

Given the scope of the play and its historical sweep and tragic violence, it is surprising that it is often also very comical. Verbal play abounds (an Edgar trademark), not always advertent on the characters' parts. The non-English speakers have some wonderful lines. Early in the action, Gabriella Pecs responds to Oliver Davenport's query as to whether the church was Orthodox: "When we are Hungary, it Catholic, when we are holy Slavic people, Orthodox, when we have our friendly Turkish visitor who drop by for few hundred years, for while it mosque. When Napoleon pass through, it house for horses." The play is a Babel of languages, from English being spoken as a second language to American English to what is ostensibly Serbo-Croatian to all the tongues of the refugees.

The mixture and clash of languages symbolize the clash of cultures and ideologies and evoke the biblical Tower of Babel (Gen. 11.1-9), a parable of hubris. Humankind speaks but one language, and, presumably working cooperatively, raises a tower to heaven. God will have none of this and causes the original linguistic monad to fall into multiplicity, so that there is no common understanding. The audience is supposed to see communism as an attempt to remake that monad composed of an infinitude of cooperating entities. It fails, and its proponents are cast into confusion and doubt. This parable dominates act 1.

Another biblical parable prevails in act 2, lending itself to the title of the play. The parable of Acts 2.1-6, however, is optimistic, since on the day of Pentecost (the seventh Sunday after Easter), amid rushing winds and cloven tongues of fire, the Paraclete descends to humankind and miraculously brings about mutual understanding, though each person speaks his or her language. In the play, this miracle is alluded to as the refugees tell one another stories in their own tongues. If the play ended at this point, it would have been altogether affirmative. However, the actual ending is equivocal, though redemptive possibilities are undoubtedly implied, however faintly.

Dramatic Devices

Pentecost is a play and could only be a play. It displays at every turn a hugely experienced and dyed-in-the-wool dramatist (it is Edgar's thirty-second full-length play). The dramatic devices provide an intense theater experience: the virtuoso use of languages, the set dominated by the bricked-up fresco, which is increasingly revealed as the play proceeds, the noises offstage (for example, the roar of diesel engines, the amplified police voices, the explosions, the solo cello at the end of the sixth scene in act 2), the candles and cooking fires in the darkened church in act 2, and the stunning and violent climax with the German-speaking commandos bursting through the wall and shooting five dead. Indeed, *Pentecost* exploits the possibilities of the medium in such a way as to put to an extreme test the talents of the director, the production designer, the sound and light technicians, and the actors, who are required to learn lines in Bulgarian, Russian, Arabic, Sinhalese, and Turkic, among other languages.

Critical Context

David Edgar has said he would like to be remembered, like Honoré de Balzac, as the secretary of his times. In the case of both Balzac and David Edgar, "recording angel" might be more accurate, since each takes on the burden of attempting to present a grand synoptic view of his era. In Edgar's case, however, the view is largely circumscribed by politics, since he clearly subscribes to Thomas Mann's dictum about the destiny of humankind asserting itself in political terms. Still, his attempt to take the grand synoptic view means that his works must be read collectively; they complement and reinforce one another, much like those of Balzac. Like his great predecessor he finds it impossible to get said what he feels must be said in one work, or perhaps even in one life.

Edgar has written scores of one-act and full-length plays, including the major political dramas *Destiny* (pr. 1972), *Maydays* (pr., pb. 1983), and *The Shape of the Table* (pr., pb. 1990), as well as the hugely successful *The Life and Adventures of Nicholas Nickleby* (pr. 1980, pb. 1982). He has written extensively for radio and television and has done film work. He is the author of a number of essays and reviews exploring the relationship of politics and theater and is a major force at Manchester University in fostering young playwrights. A man on the move and an inveterate sponsor and attendee at international conferences, he is a sophisticated and widely read student of political theory and a political activist with Marxist leanings.

Several works have followed *Pentecost*, but critics agree that *Pentecost* is his crowning achievement. It develops the themes of his other plays—the adversarial relationship between self and state, the place of the arts in an increasingly politicized age, the changing definitions of revolution and the conflict of the hard and soft Left, the power and impotence of the individual vis-à-vis history, the void left by the collapse of the Soviet empire—and refocuses them in an unprecedented and brilliantly original fashion. *Pentecost* is indeed a parable for the modern era and presents its themes with rare dramatic boldness, sweep, and power. It ranks among the most ambitious, the most complex, the most profound, and the most successful political plays of twentieth century drama. It also proves an invaluable study for understanding some of the consequences of the fall of Soviet communism.

Sources for Further Study

Edgar, David. *The Second Time as Farce: Reflections on the Drama of Mean Times.* London: Lawrence and Wishart, 1998.

_______. "Ten Years of Political Theatre, 1968-1978." *Theatre Quarterly*, Winter, 1979.

Grant, Steve. "Writer's Bloc." *Time Out*, May 31-June 7, 1995.

Hanks, Robert. "Speaking in Tongues." *Independent*, October 26, 1994.

Lavender, Andy. "New Pastures Green." *New Statesman*, October 21, 1994.

Page, Malcolm. *File on Edgar.* London: Methuen, 1991.

Painter, Susan. *Edgar the Dramatist*. London: Methuen, 1996.

Swain, Elizabeth. *David Edgar: Playwright and Politician*. New York: P. Lang, 1986.

Stanley Poss

THE PETRIFIED FOREST

Author: Robert E. Sherwood (1896-1955)
Type of plot: Melodrama
Time of plot: The 1930's
Locale: Eastern Arizona desert
First produced: 1935, at the Broadhurst Theatre, New York City
First published: 1935

Principal characters:
ALAN SQUIER, a drifter
JASON MAPLE, the proprietor of the Black Mesa Bar-B-Q
GABBY MAPLE, Jason's daughter
DUKE MANTEE, a gang leader on the run
BOZE HERTZLINGER, Jason's employee and an admirer of Gabby
GRAMP MAPLE, Gabby's pioneer grandfather
MR. and MRS. CHISOLM, travelers

The Play

As if suggesting a play of social protest, the action begins with a conversation between two telegraph linemen about freedom and socialism. The two are sitting in the Black Mesa Bar-B-Q, a filling station and café on the edge of the Arizona desert. Listening is Gramp Maple, the father of the proprietor; he tells the men of his pioneering days, especially of the time he was shot at by Billy the Kid. The talk thus leads to the subject of law and order, or the lack thereof, as evinced by Duke Mantee and his gang, who have massacred six people in an Oklahoma shoot-out and are now reported to be somewhere in the area. Jason Maple, the proprietor, is contemptuous of the gang and vows that he and his American Legion fellows will deal with them. Jason's daughter, Gabby, has come in from the kitchen. Restless, impatient with her shallow father, she seems the controlling force of the place; she is a sensitive young woman who reads romantic poetry that Boze Hertzlinger, a gas-jockey and former college athlete, belittles with the self-assured cockiness of the failure. He is attracted to Gabby, but she curtly parries his advances.

Meanwhile, Alan Squier enters the eatery. Dressed in shabby elegance, shouldering a rucksack, and carrying a walking stick, Squier is a drifter, a sort of noble vagrant, a status that may be better understood in the context of the Depression. Gentle, soft-spoken, almost knightly, he takes a liking to the bluff innocence of Gabby, while she is vaguely attracted to his quiet urbanity. Finding a sympathetic ear, she tells Squier about her French mother, who married her father during World War I but who could not acclimatize to the desert and so returned to France, where Gabby hopes to go someday to visit her. Every year for her birthday her mother sends Gabby books of poems, and it is one of these books that she was just reading. At Squier's request, Gabby recites a love poem by François Villon and expresses again her dream of going to France. Squier is touched by her innocence and sensitivity. He tells her of his own life: He wrote a self-consciously stark novel at age twenty-two; married his publisher's wife, who ran off with him to the Mediterranean; lived as a frustrated, "inarticulate" writer for eight years, then left his wife and came to America to find "something to believe in."

Convinced that she has found a kindred spirit and attracted by his knowledge of the world beyond the petrified forest of Arizona, Gabby shows Squier one of her paintings. He is impressed but bewildered, sensing Gabby's restless, creative energy. He gently reproves her when she urges him to run off with her and take her to France. Instead, he asks her for a kiss as he prepares once more to set out on the road. Boze enters and in a jealous pique tries to throw Squier out, but Gabby checks him. Just then, Mr. and Mrs. Chisolm enter. Well-to-do, they are driving to California and have stopped to refuel. Gabby asks them to take Squier along. She and Squier shake hands in farewell.

After Squier and the Chisolms have gone, Boze romances Gabby, who agrees to walk with him in the desert moonlight. Before they leave, she begins to tell Boze about Squier's remarks concerning man's failure to conquer Nature, but just then the Mantee gang bursts in. Armed, the gang orders Gabby, Boze, and Gramp to stay calm while Duke Mantee orders food and drink. After a moment, Squier reenters to warn them about Mantee, who had intercepted the Chisolms and him on the road and exchanged cars. When Squier sees the gang, he resignedly asks for a drink. As the curtain closes, he raises his glass in a salute.

Act 2 opens half an hour later. Gramp has been recounting his pioneer days of law and disorder. Mantee has been listening to the radio news reports about his escape and the dragnet set for him. He is firm but civil in his demands for food and drink. Boze is openly defiant, but Mantee scornfully ignores him. When Boze grabs for a gun, Duke Mantee shoots him in the hand and warns Boze that next time he will kill him. Gabby comforts Boze, and they are taken out by one of the gang.

Meanwhile, Squier has been watching Mantee. The two have a subtle respect for each other; Squier in particular expresses his admiration for Mantee as a paragon of individualism. Even Mrs. Chisolm, who admits to having led a circumscribed life, declares her respect for Mantee.

This insight into Mantee as a kindred spirit prompts Squier to offer the gangster a startling proposition. Squier's only asset is a life insurance policy to which he has not assigned a beneficiary. Perceiving Mantee as a "man of imagination," Squier quietly asks him, along with Gramp and Mrs. Chisolm, to witness his designation of Gabby as his beneficiary. Then he pleads with Mantee to shoot him dead before leaving the cafe. Mrs. Chisolm at first believes Squier to be mad, but she then realizes that Squier is in love with Gabby and wants to give her a chance at a future. Mantee himself has already perceived Squier's love and gently agrees to his request.

When Gabby returns from tending to Boze, Squier admits his love for her and encourages her to follow her dream. Just then Jason Maple and his fellow Legionnaires come into the café. The gang takes them prisoner, but Jason informs Mantee that the gang is trapped, as the sheriff and his posse are on their way. Shooting is heard outside as the sheriff arrives. There is much gunfire and everyone in the café keeps low. Mantee decides to make a run for freedom, but as he prepares to escape Squier reminds Mantee of his promise. Acknowledging that they will meet each other again soon, Mantee shoots Squier and runs from the café amid a fusillade.

In the final scene, Gabby cradles the dying Squier in her arms. She fights back tears as the men decide to give him a hero's funeral in the petrified forest. As the curtain falls, Jason telephones the police, warning them that Mantee is heading south.

Themes and Meanings

From one point of view, *The Petrified Forest* is a melodrama in the tradition of the Western. In this light, Mantee is a latter-day Billy the Kid or even an American equivalent of Robin Hood. Gramp Maple's constant references to Billy the Kid, together with some of the characters' fearless admiration of Duke Mantee, make an obvious connection between the gangster and that legendary hero-villain. Like the Western hero, Mantee lives beyond the imperatives of social conduct while maintaining an unwavering personal code in which the individual is treated with dignity. Mantee is not a brute. He treats no one meanly. His motives are uncomplicated and there is about him an element of personal honesty, something without hypocrisy. Squier guesses, for example, that there is a bit of the romantic in Mantee, urging him to wait as long as he can for his girl to arrive before fleeing for the border. It is this spirited individualism that Alan Squier sees in Duke which brings the two of them together as spiritual kin.

Squier, too, is independent, free from the shams and delusions of the intellectual world, unconvinced of the conventions of morality, distrustful of belief. As Mantee is the physical outlaw, Squier is the spiritual outcast, and so the drama is in a sense a modern morality play in which the characters are allegorical representatives of body and soul in search of truth or unity.

In this play, however, there is no real resolution. Even as the action ends with Duke on the run and Squier dead, the audience is left with only the insipid denizens of the café—the mediocre, the frustrated, the incompetent, or, as in Gabby's case, the inarticulate. As part of an allegory, Squier is not a full-bodied personality. His cynicism, his worldly ennui, which suggest the played-out characters in many of the novels of the 1920's, make him only an effete victim in a world on the verge of the petrified forest, where meaning has hardened and ideals calcified. Squier's love for Gabby is a love for the innocent, the straightforward, the unsophisticated, and hence the unworldly. Though Gabby is the only figure of hope, the play ends inconclusively, her future uncertain.

The Petrified Forest thus borders on the absurd, in the existential sense of life as a kind of dead end. Squier's final heroism is a piece of romantic melodrama enacted in a context of lawlessness and frustration. That Mantee is not captured but escapes, presumably to wreak further havoc, indicates the chaos which harries society.

Dramatic Devices

Like a well-made classical drama, Robert Sherwood's *The Petrified Forest* observes the unities of time, place, and action. No more than two hours elapse, and the entire action of the drama takes place in the lunchroom of the Black Mesa Bar-B-Q. No attempt is made to use innovative staging or to evoke moods with lighting. Though evening approaches near the end of the play, the darkness beyond the interior of the café is not so much symbolic as simply naturalistic. Everything in the play is intended to enforce the deadening reality of the characters' situation. The lunchroom is minutely depicted—the walls are covered with advertisements. The dialogue is unobtrusively correct, natural. Such colloquialism is suggested rather than conscientiously transcribed, as in many of the realistic plays of the 1930's.

The characters themselves are more stereotypical than profound: Gabby is the young ingénue; Gramp, the garrulous old pioneer; Jason, the shallow, would-be bourgeois; Boze, the failed college athlete. It is in this very clarity of presentation, the direct simplicity of exposition, however, that the play holds the interest of the audience. Sherwood establishes a sense of inevitability early, with the reference to the Mantee gang foreshadowing the subsequent action. When Squier leaves the café and Mantee subsequently enters, the audience is presented with a neat anticlimax, or rather, a double-climax, as Squier reenters and finds himself a captive as the curtain falls on act 1.

The ending of the play echoes the beginning. Just as the telegraph linemen open the action with a discussion of liberty and socialism, so the conclusion is a kind of physical reenactment and interpretation of the argument: Mantee has "freed" Squier from his world-weariness while the gangster himself remains free, though hounded by the State. In addition, Sherwood's flat, almost prosaic dramaturgy, stressing a kind of blunt reality, provides a powerful contrast to the frustrated idealism of Squier, the inchoate dreams of Gabby, and the thwarted individualism of Duke Mantee.

Critical Context

Of the fifteen plays that comprise Robert Sherwood's dramatic compositions, *The Petrified Forest* is the eighth and thus stands almost in the center of his creative work, chronologically as well as artistically. It was the first of his three masterworks composed within a three-year period (*The Petrified Forest*, pr., pb. 1935; *Idiot's Delight*, pr., pb. 1936; *Abe Lincoln in Illinois*, pr. 1938, pb. 1939) and the first to treat seriously the theme of idealism and the decline of Western values.

His first play, *The Road to Rome* (pr., pb. 1927), poked fun at the bourgeois values of ancient Rome—in an analogy to the materialistic American society of the 1920's—and defended the ideal of pacificism through the love affair between Hannibal and Amytis, who persuades her lover to renounce war. After several less successful works, Sherwood produced *Reunion in Vienna* (pr. 1931, pb. 1932), another comedy, this one satirizing Freudian psychology. It was followed by *Acropolis* (pr. 1933), which drew a pointed analogy between the death of the democratic ideal in ancient Athens and the growing totalitarianism of Europe in the 1930's.

These plays clearly show Sherwood as a versatile dramatist, trying his hand at the popular comedy of manners, a form exemplified by the work of his contemporary Philip Barry, at sentimental comedy, and at thinly veiled fables, such as *Acropolis*. As one of the country's foremost film critics during the 1920's, Sherwood understood the popular taste, and some cinematic characteristics are evident in his work, as, for example, in the shoot-out in *The Petrified Forest*. Interestingly, the role of Duke Mantee, both on Broadway and in the screen version, was played by Humphrey Bogart.

Like many of his generation who had served in World War I, Sherwood, who had been wounded, returned with scars deeper than the simply physical. He perceived the world as on the brink—civilization bankrupt, society bereft of values. His plays suggest a need for tolerance and understanding. The compassion of Abe Lincoln in *Abe Lincoln in Illinois*, a play which garnered for Sherwood one of his three Pulitzer Prizes, differs only in degree and circumstance from the kindred understanding of Duke Mantee and the gentle sadness of Alan Squier.

The Petrified Forest thus treats idealism not as a comedy of manners but as melodrama, what the erstwhile film critic himself called a "good show." As such, its themes are clearly related to the earlier works while also looking ahead to the defeatism of *Idiot's Delight* and to the serene integrity of the young Lincoln in Illinois. *The Petrified Forest* makes no claim for the liberal or the conservative, for the Americanism of the workingman or the leftist beliefs of the intellectual. It merely dramatizes the dilemma between them, the polarity between freedom and death, reality and idealism.

Sources for Further Study

Broussard, Louis. "Everyman at Mid-Century: Robert E. Sherwood." In *American Drama: Contemporary Allegory from Eugene O'Neill to Tennessee Williams*. Norman: University of Oklahoma Press, 1962.

Brown, John Mason. *The Ordeal of a Playwright: Robert E. Sherwood and the Challenge of War.* New York: Harper and Row, 1970.

Gould, Jean. "Robert E. Sherwood." In *Modern American Playwrights*. New York: Dodd, Mead, 1966.

Kulshres, Chirantan. "Robert Sherwood." In *Reference Guide to American Literature*. 2d ed. Chicago: St. James, 1987.

Meserve, Walter. *Robert E. Sherwood: Reluctant Moralist*. New York: Pegasus, 1970.

Shuman, R. Baird. *Robert E. Sherwood*. New York: Twayne, 1964.

Edward Fiorelli

PHILADELPHIA, HERE I COME!

Author: Brian Friel (1929-   )
Type of plot: Comedy
Time of plot: The 1960's
Locale: Ballybeg, County Donegal, Ireland
First produced: 1964, at the Gaiety Theatre, Dublin, Ireland
First published: 1965

Principal characters:

MADGE, the housekeeper
GARETH "GAR" O'DONNELL (in public), a twenty-five-year-old Irishman
GARETH O'DONNELL (in private), his thoughts, invisible to everyone onstage
S. B. O'DONNELL, his father, a shopkeeper
KATE DOOGAN, his girlfriend
LIZZY and CON SWEENEY, his Irish-American aunt and uncle
NED,
TOM, and
JOE, his friends

The Play

Philadelphia, Here I Come! begins the evening before Gar O'Donnell is to leave home for Philadelphia. He has finished his last day of work in his father's dry-goods store. He jokes with Madge, the housekeeper, as she prepares his tea, and then he begins to fantasize about life in the United States.

This fantasy, like all of his private thoughts, appears to the audience in the character of Private Gar, unheard by the other characters and unseen by anyone. Gar's first fantasy is wild and exuberant, with images of flying in a plane and playing football. Madge enters, and they briefly discuss his father, who has apparently expressed no thoughts or feelings about his son's departure. While Gar expresses disdain for old S. B. (Private Gar calls him Screwballs), he is clearly pained by the estrangement.

At this moment S. B. enters with a question about a delivery to the shop, and his immediate departure sets off a long fantasy scene between Public and Private Gar. Gar imagines his first day at work in a Philadelphia hotel, then, accompanied by a recording of Felix Mendelssohn's Violin Concerto, thinks of his long-dead mother. He breaks the melancholy mood with some Irish music, but it, too, holds associations, recalling his proposal of marriage to Katie Doogan.

That memory scene appears in its entirety. Kate resists Gar's insistent proposal because he does not make enough money for them to live on. Finally he confesses his secret income from selling eggs. Though the profits are smaller than Kate first imagines, she yields and takes Gar immediately to talk to her father, Senator Doogan.

At the Doogan house Gar can only stutter in front of the self-important senator, who promptly reveals his intentions for Kate to marry someone else. Gar leaves in disgrace, and the next memory is of the newspaper announcement of Kate's wedding. In another attempt to break the mood, Gar imagines a farcical scene with his father, followed by a fantasy of picking up a woman in the United States.

Once again Madge breaks in on the fantasy, calling him in to his meal. She reveals, in passing, that her niece has had a baby girl and has promised to name it for her. As S. B. joins Gar for tea, Private mocks him mercilessly, providing accurate predictions of everything he will say. The pain beneath the mockery emerges as Private reveals, "Screwballs, we've eaten together like this for the past twenty-odd years, and never once in all that time have you made as much as one unpredictable remark." He pleads (in his thoughts) for that unpredictable remark, that one thing that might tempt him to stay. His thoughts are interrupted by the entrance of Master Boyle, the drunken schoolteacher, who has come to say good-bye to Gar and, incidentally, to borrow ten shillings.

The first scene of act 2 begins with more fantasy role-playing. Public and Private act out a scene with Gar as a United States senator. As Gar checks his immigration papers he is thrown back in memory again, this time to the day his uncle and aunt, Con and Lizzy Sweeney, came to visit and offer him the job in Philadelphia. Lizzy dominates the scene, energetic, garrulous, and a bit drunk. Gar wants to hear stories about the mother he never knew, but Lizzy is too easily distracted. She returns repeatedly to the advantages of the United States, with an emphasis on her possessions. At the end of the visit, she admits her plot to bribe her only nephew into her childless home. Undeterred by her selfish motive, Gar agrees to move to Philadelphia.

Scene 2 returns to the present and to a brief criticism of Lizzy's vulgarity and possessiveness. To end the musing, Gar decides to go out to find his friends. He returns almost immediately with Ned, Tom, and Joe. Ned, the leader, can talk of nothing but football and women, with support from Tom. Gar attempts to speak of his departure, but Ned changes the subject. He recounts in graphic detail one of his sexual escapades, while Private counterpoints with what really happened. Finally Ned prepares to lead the group in quest of new women, pausing to give Gar his belt as a good-bye gift.

Joe, the quietest of the group, stays behind, but Gar sends him off with the others. Private realizes that "they're louts, ignorant bloody louts," though he wants to remember that there were good times too. This musing is interrupted by Kate, who has also come to say good-bye. The moment is awkward, and Gar manages to insult her before she leaves. The scene ends with a rush of memory, with disconnected sentences and phrases from the past.

Act 3 begins a short time later. Gar, S. B., and Madge have gathered to say their evening rosary. Gar's imagination, revealed by Private, is again active. He recalls a spring afternoon with his father, fishing from a blue boat on a lake. Prayers over, he tries to ask his father about that day, but he is interrupted by the arrival of Canon Mick O'Byrne.

The canon is a regular visitor, here for his nightly game of checkers. Gar sees the scene as another indication of indifference to his departure. As before, Private mocks mercilessly, then lapses into melancholy. Gar goes to his room to play Mendelssohn, hearing in the music the story of fishing from the blue boat. He regrets that the two participants in that event are unable to talk to each other.

Act 3, scene 2, takes place in the middle of the night. Neither Gar nor S. B. can sleep, and they meet in the kitchen. Wanting to talk, Gar is only able to remind his father of household and business details that need attention. Finally, S. B. awkwardly advises Gar to sit at the back of the airplane, where it is safest. With this opening, Gar asks about the blue boat, only to find that his father cannot remember it. Disappointed, he leaves the room.

Madge returns from a visit to her niece and the new baby, who will be called Brigid, not Madge. To her S. B. is able to say things he could not say to Gar, and in his one long speech of the play he recounts his memory of walking hand in hand with Gar on his first day of school. When he leaves, Madge recalls a memory of her own: When S. B. was Gar's age "he was the very same as him: leppin, and eejitin' about and actin' the clown; as like as two peas." Gar comes in to say good-night to Madge and to utter one more time his doubts about leaving home.

Themes and Meanings

Philadelphia, Here I Come! is, on one hand, a traditional play about a young man's coming of age; on the other it is an experimental presentation of the complex contradictions that form personality. These two themes work together in the study of a family that is pathologically unable to communicate.

The theme of coming of age, tracing a young man's difficult separation from his family and his first halting steps toward autonomy, is familiar in modern drama. Parallels may be seen in Tennessee Williams's *The Glass Menagerie* (pr. 1944), Frank Gilroy's *The Subject Was Roses* (pb. 1962), and Neil Simon's *Broadway Bound* (pr. 1986). In the case of Gar, the process of leaving home is complicated by his role as only son of a father who, though unable to express his love, or any feeling at all, nevertheless depends on him. Gar recognizes this dependence in their final conversation about business details that S. B. must now look after himself. However, like Tom in *The Glass Menagerie*, he must leave, driven away by the dependent parent.

He is driven away by more than his father. He sees few opportunities for himself in Ireland, in contrast to his fantasized world of opportunity in America. Furthermore, at home he has failed in love, having proposed to a woman who soon after married someone else. He has even failed to form significant friendships. America, even with Aunt Lizzie, must offer more than Ireland and his father.

Though Gar seems resolute in his decision to leave home, he is in fact wracked with doubts. He must regularly and deliberately cajole himself back into a mood of optimism. The conflicts and complexities underlying his decision are revealed in the conversations and debates between his public and private selves.

The debates expand to other issues as well, revealing the complexities and contradictions involved in all human behavior. For example, Private Gar reveals his desire to talk to S. B. about something, anything, of significance. Given the opportunity, however, Public Gar remains tongue-tied. On the other hand, he has plenty to say to Kate when she visits, all of it unfortunate, and all in contradiction to what Private wants to say. In fact, Gar's relationships with all the other characters in the play reveal his repeated conflict between inner desires and outer actions.

Significantly, S. B.'s final speech (about his memory of walking Gar to school) reveals that he, too, has the same conflicts. The man who has seemed to the audience to be gruff and unfeeling suddenly tells a warm and sentimental story: "And at the heel of the hunt I had to go with him myself, the two of us, hand in hand, as happy as larks—we were that happy, Madge." Like Gar, S. B. has a private self quite unlike the self everyone sees, and he is equally unable to break through that facade.

Because Gar and his father (and, presumably, the other characters as well) cannot break through their public selves, they cannot ever communicate. Each remains forever unaware of the other's well-hidden inner life. They are unaware, too, of the similarities between them that Madge observes. Gar's departure remains his only hope, though the fact that he maintained his facade when he met his aunt and uncle suggests that he will be no different, thus no happier, in his new home.

Dramatic Devices

The most significant dramatic device in *Philadelphia, Here I Come!* is the use of two actors to play the role of Gar. The convention of a character revealing private thoughts through soliloquies or asides is traditional. On the other hand, Brian Friel's splitting of a character into a public and a private self is highly innovative. Friel explains in his note on staging that "Private Gar, the spirit, is invisible to everybody, always. Nobody except Public Gar hears him talk. But even Public Gar, although he talks to Private Gar occasionally, never sees him and never looks at him. One cannot look at one's alter ego."

The device not only allows Gar to make private observations about the actions of the other characters but also provides opportunity for extensive revelation of Gar's fantasy life. Gar talks to himself, acts out imaginary scenes, and reenacts scenes from his memory. Without the alter ego, these scenes would be available only through asides and soliloquies or through speeches of exposition (which would be uncharacteristic of characters who barely speak in one another's presence).

The closest parallel is Arthur Miller's use of acted memory scenes in *Death of a Salesman* (pr., pb. 1949). As in *Philadelphia, Here I Come!* these memories help to reveal the motives for Willy Loman's present actions. Even more significantly, in Miller's play the character of Ben, Willy's brother, functions as a kind of self-manufactured conscience, goading Willy to action. Ben remains, however, a shadowy figure, an undeveloped alter ego. Friel, in contrast, moved the private self to the center of the play, exploiting all of its possibilities.

One additional technique in the play which deserves brief attention is the masterfully appropriate use of music. On two occasions Gar plays a recording of Mendelssohn's Violin Concerto, a particularly emotional and melancholy composition. In each case the music moves Gar into nearly maudlin reminiscences; with great effectiveness the music works on the audience as well. Playgoers hear it with him and, feeling the effect, understand his reaction.

Critical Context

The critical context of *Philadelphia, Here I Come!* is suggested by the two thematic interpretations of the play. It is at once part of a long tradition of coming-of-age plays and of the experimental movement of the 1960's.

As a play about growing up, Brian Friel's treatment of the theme risks criticism for sentimentality. The subject of leaving home is emotional enough, and the melancholy music of Mendelssohn's Violin Concerto only underscores this sentimental thrust. In the closing moments, when Gar and S. B. privately reveal the significant memories they cannot share with each other, the mood is especially moving. However, Friel rises above sentimentality by his masterful exploitation of comedy. Private's satiric commentary on the action, as well as some moments of pure slapstick, helps to keep the play from becoming maudlin.

So, too, does the experimental technique. The clearly nonrealistic method of presenting one character with two actors helps to dispel the sentimentality invited by the surface of the story. In fact, it is the familiarity of the story that allows the experimental technique to work. Though the 1960's saw significant experimentation in dramatic presentations, the mainstream, popular plays remained fairly traditional. Friel's experiment was an exception. In fact, it enjoyed a long run on Broadway in 1966. It has been characterized by Christopher Fitz-Simon as one of the most important plays of the 1960's. The tension between the familiar, sentimental plot and the highly experimental technique emerged as the decisive factor in creating the play's commercial and critical success.

Sources for Further Study

Coaklay, James. "Chekhov in Ireland: Brief Notes on Friel's *Philadelphia*." *Comparative Drama* 7 (1973): 191-197.

Friel, Brian. *Brian Friel: Essays, Diaries, Interviews. 1964-1998*. London: Faber & Faber, 2000.

Hogan, Robert. *After the Irish Renaissance: A Critical History of Irish Drama Since "The Plough and the Stars."* Minneapolis: University of Minnesota Press, 1967.

Kerwin, William, ed. *Brian Friel: A Casebook*. New York: Garland, 1997.

Leary, Daniel. "The Romanticism of Brian Friel." In *Contemporary Irish Writing*, edited by James D. Brophy and Raymond J. Porter. Boston: Twayne, 1983.

Maxwell, D. E. S. *Brian Friel*. Lewisburg, Pa.: Bucknell University Press, 1973.

Peacock, Alan J. *The Achievement of Brian Friel*. Lanham, Md.: Oxford University Press, 1997.

Bruce H. Leland

THE PHILADELPHIA STORY

Author: Philip Barry (1896-1949)
Type of plot: Comedy of manners
Time of plot: The 1930's
Locale: Near Philadelphia, Pennsylvania
First produced: 1939, at the Shubert Theatre, New York City
First published: 1939

Principal characters:
TRACY LORD, a beautiful twenty-four-year-old high society woman
MARGARET LORD, her mother
SETH LORD, her father
ALEXANDER "SANDY" LORD, her brother
DINAH LORD, her younger sister
GEORGE KITTREDGE, Tracy's fiancé
C. K. DEXTER HAVEN, Tracy's former husband
MACAULAY "MIKE" CONNOR, a newspaper reporter
ELIZABETH "LIZ" IMBRIE, a newspaper photographer

The Play

As the curtain rises on *The Philadelphia Story*, Tracy Lord is in the sitting room of her family's country house near Philadelphia hurriedly writing last-minute thank-you notes as her mother, Margaret Lord, brings in more gifts. Tracy is to be married the following day. During the ensuing conversation, it becomes clear that it is Tracy's second marriage, following an elopement ten months previously, which terminated in divorce. As the scene progresses, the possibility of scandal escalates. Tracy's former husband, C. K. Dexter Haven, is in the vicinity. Furthermore, Dinah Lord has found the proof sheets of an article which a magazine called *Destiny* is about to publish concerning the involvement of her father, Seth Lord, with a dancer, an affair which so angered Tracy that she has refused to invite her own father to the wedding. When Sandy Lord enters, it transpires that, as a journalist himself, he has made a deal with *Destiny:* In return for killing the article about Seth, they will be permitted to print the inside story on Tracy's wedding. Sandy has even arranged for a fake telegram from Seth, regretting that illness will prevent his coming to the ceremony.

Soon the delegation from *Destiny* arrives: Mike Connor, who immediately displays his democratic disapproval of Main Line society, and Liz Imbrie, who is clearly in love with Mike. Although Sandy and Margaret hope to win over their guests, Dinah and Tracy assume the roles of spoiled and brainless socialites. When her fiancé, George Kittredge, enters, Tracy gushes over him; later, in a fit of invention, she introduces her uncle as her father, and pretends to forget the name of C. K. Dexter Haven, her former husband. Just as lunch is announced, Seth arrives, and Tracy's real fury about the journalistic invasion becomes clear. The family troubles are his fault, she indicates, and then suggests the complexity of the situation by addressing him by her uncle's name.

As the second act begins, it is obvious to the audience that in the conflict between the socialites and the reporters, the socialites are ahead; the very fact that Liz and Mike can talk about the simplemindedness of their hosts indicates that they have been deceived by them. As they talk, however, Mike and Tracy begin to draw closer; they have to admit that they both assume a toughness which is only superficial. In a later conversation with Dexter, Tracy again must approach the truth. Dexter's gift to her, a photograph of their boat, brings back memories of their own happiness. Although Tracy has blamed Dexter for their divorce, he tells her that the cause was her own intolerance and that she will not be happy with a man such as George. When George pompously describes his plan to place Tracy on a pedestal, she begins to worry, and at the end of the scene, when her father, like Dexter, accuses her of spinsterish intolerance, Tracy is confused, for perhaps the first time in her life.

The second scene in act 2 takes place some hours later, after an all-night party. Once again, the Lords are scheming to outwit the press. With an inebriated and somewhat infatuated Mike cooperating, Sandy and Tracy plan to blackmail the publisher of *Destiny* in order to get all the publicity about their family stopped. Meanwhile, Tracy continues to spar with Mike; however, when she hears herself accusing him of intolerance, she stops and begins to see herself. Champagne and impulse reign; they kiss, they put in an emergency telephone call to summon the publisher, and they run offstage for a swim without suits. George arrives to check on Tracy's conduct with Mike; Dexter unsuccessfully tries to send him home but at least manages to pocket Tracy's telltale jewelry. When Mike enters carrying the naked Tracy, along with their clothes, however, even Dexter cannot cover up for her. He knocks Mike down, supposedly to prevent George from doing so, and George leaves in a huff.

The third act takes place just before the wedding. Tracy is hung over and confused. She has found a man's watch beside her bed, and she has lost her bracelet and her engagement ring. When Dexter returns the jewelry and Dinah tells her about seeing Mike carrying Tracy into her bedroom, Tracy can only assume the worst. So does George, who sends a nasty note and then arrives in person to demand an explanation. Even though Mike assures George that nothing happened, Tracy sees her fiancé for the stuffed shirt that he is and breaks the engagement. Realizing that all the essentials for a wedding are in place except the bridegroom, Mike proposes, but Tracy refuses, leaving him free for Liz. Because the publisher has arrived and hired Mike back, he is too happy to be hurt by Tracy's refusal. When Tracy admits that she has loved Dexter all along and that she wishes to remarry him immediately, Mike happily agrees to act as Dexter's best man. There is only one more relationship unmended. After the other characters leave the stage to take their places at the ceremony, Tracy tells her father that she has now learned how to be human and therefore to be tolerant of others and, taking his arm, she exits.

Themes and Meanings

It may seem surprising that a comedy of manners set in Philadelphia Main Line society is essentially a plea for tolerance. The two most interesting characters in the play, Mike and Tracy, as well as Tracy's pompous fiancé, George, are all so committed to their own ideas that they cannot accept others as they are, much less enjoy the differences between people. Early in the play, the prejudices of these characters become clear. Both George and Mike are of humble backgrounds; neither understands what the Lords are like. George has developed his own image of the extremely proper aristocrat who is to be his wife and expects the unconventional, mercurial Tracy to fit the pattern. Mike considers people such as the Lords to be brainless, heartless parasites, and he dislikes them even more because he has been pulled from news stories of social significance to cover their extravagant wedding festivities. On her part, Tracy shares with her class the dislike and distrust of reporters, whom she sees as voyeurs without sensitivity or manners, and in addition, she is furious about the fact that her father's indiscretion has forced her to admit the press to her wedding.

Although the play focuses on Tracy's need to change, if she is ever to have a happy marriage, she can only develop through seeing the intolerance shown by George and Mike, who though her social inferiors, behave no worse than Tracy herself. The stage directions make it clear that Philip Barry expects the actor who plays Tracy to reflect her growing understanding more through facial expression than through words. When George describes her future place on the pedestal he is constructing for her, Tracy reacts with distaste and concern. In the middle of a diatribe about Mike's intolerance, Tracy stops, obviously hearing in her accusation of Mike the echo of other characters' criticisms of her. Although Tracy had seemed blithely to ignore the identical assessments of her own flaw which were made by the two men she most loved, her father and her former husband (both of whom she had rejected because of their imperfections), evidently she had heard more than she admitted. Despite all the scheming and the verbal sparring, the audience is allowed to see Tracy thinking deeply.

Dexter had mentioned an earlier episode when Tracy got drunk and discarded her clothes; therefore it is no surprise to the audience when, after the champagne party, she suggests the swim with Mike. The next morning, Tracy remembers nothing, and even when she finds out that nothing happened, she realizes that she must credit Mike's gallantry, rather than her own restraint. The result is a happy one. Because she now sees him as a tyrant, Tracy rejects George; because she has also seen her own tyrannical possessiveness, she must admit her error and be reconciled with the two men she has wronged, her father and Dexter. Unlike George, she has indeed learned to be a human being.

Dramatic Devices

Because *The Philadelphia Story* is a traditional comedy of manners, the dramatic devices used are those typical of the genre. The expensive set decoration establishes the upper-class setting of the story. In this case, a sitting room and a porch are substituted for the usual drawing room, but there is no essential difference, because these are the public rooms which are meant to present the social group, here the Lord family, at its best.

Much of the humor arises from the attempt to keep private scandal hidden from the public, represented in this play by the reporters. Thus when Tracy hears that the reporters are coming, she goes to her room and changes costume, emerging in a demure, high-necked dress that she hopes will establish her propriety. The deception, however, cannot be maintained for long. Later, when Mike carries the naked, drunken Tracy through the other public area, the porch, on the way to her bedroom, Barry is emphasizing the fact that private behavior always becomes public knowledge. This type of revelation scene in comedy of manners is traditional, going back to the screen that falls to reveal the hidden Lady Teazle in Richard Brinsley Sheridan's *The School for Scandal* (pr. 1777). In these plays, that which is hidden is always discovered; the sitting room or the drawing room eventually becomes not a place of successful deception but instead a place where the truth is revealed, so that private lives and public lives become the same.

All traditional comedies also have a quality of magic. As complication follows complication, the audience is in suspense as to how the playwright will ever resolve the knotted strands of his plot. Barry skillfully introduces more confusion than would be necessary for the plot. For example, Sandy plans to explain Seth's absence at the wedding by a telegram stating that he is ill. The telegram is garbled and obviously phony; further, before it arrives, Tracy has decided to pretend that her uncle is her father, and then when her father turns up, she introduces him as her uncle. Another example of the multiplication of complications is the fact that Tracy ultimately has three possible bridegrooms. At the end of the play, while the wedding guests wait, Tracy must quickly deal with a proposal from Mike before she can marry Dexter.

The third traditional element which Barry handles beautifully in his play is the visual expression of comic plot complications. In the public rooms where comedies of manners are set, characters come and go rapidly and unexpectedly, frequently encountering the very characters with whom contact is most awkward. Part of the interest of the play is watching the way in which highly polished ladies and gentlemen deal with this awkwardness. Whether they pretend unconcern, as when the Lords invite Tracy's former husband to lunch, or whether they lapse into plebeian behavior, as when Dexter knocks Mike across the room, their behavior is always unpredictable. As the audience watches the playwright to see how he magically resolves plot complications, so it also watches the characters to see how they will use their own social finesse to deal with the encounters which he arranges for them. In his handling of the traditions of comedy, and particularly of those established for comedy of manners, Barry deserves to be ranked with his predecessors, from William Congreve to Noël Coward.

Critical Context

During his relatively brief career, Philip Barry alternated sophisticated comedies, such as *The Philadelphia Story*, which were highly successful, with serious plays, which rarely pleased the public. His first success, *The Jilts* (pr. 1922), which was later titled *You and I* (pr., pb. 1923), established his reputation as a delightful writer of comedy. He followed it with a similar play, *The Youngest* (pr. 1924, pb. 1925), which Barry himself disliked, but which ran for 104 performances on Broadway. *In a Garden* (pr. 1925, pb. 1926) was admittedly meaningful, but only the outstanding performance of Laurette Taylor kept the play on the boards for seventy-four performances, and the fantasy which followed, *White Wings* (pr. 1926, pb. 1927), lasted for only twenty-seven performances.

During the rest of his career as a playwright, the pattern continued. For example, two of Barry's plays were written simultaneously and produced within two months of each other. The tragedy *John* (pr. 1927, pb. 1929) died after eleven performances; the comedy *Paris Bound* (pr. 1927, pb. 1928) lasted for 234. The serious play which critics admire most is *Hotel Universe* (pr., pb. 1930). The play incorporates the element of fantasy: Through a physicist's manipulation of time, a group of sophisticated people are enabled to relive certain past experiences which have crippled them in the present. In what is a peculiar combination of psychoanalytic therapy and Roman Catholic confession and absolution, the characters are then healed and are able to proceed with their lives.

Although critics recognize Barry's serious intent in such plays as *Hotel Universe* and although the public of his time tended to assume that because they were puzzled, he must be profound, later critical opinion sees him as a fairly pedestrian Catholic moralist rather than as a truly original thinker. The judgment of the public may have been better than his own. In brilliant comedies such as *The Philadelphia Story*, he best expressed his major themes: the folly and the destructiveness of prejudice, the need for tolerance and understanding in human relationships, the importance of forgiveness, and the sanctity of marriage.

Sources for Further Study

Brown, John Mason. "The American Barry." *Saturday Review of Literature* 32 (December 24, 1949): 24-27.

Gassner, John. "Philip Barry: A Civilized Playwright." In *The Theatre in Our Times*. New York: Crown, 1954.

Krutch, Joseph Wood. "Miss Hepburn Pays Up." *Nation*, April 8, 1939, 410-411.

Roppolo, Joseph Patrick. *Philip Barry*. New York: Twayne, 1965.

Weales, Gerald. "Philip Barry." In *Reference Guide to American Literature*. 2d ed. Chicago: St. James, 1987.

Rosemary M. Canfield Reisman

A PHOTOGRAPH
Lovers in Motion

Author: Ntozake Shange (Paulette Williams, 1948-)
Type of plot: Psychological; verse drama
Time of plot: The late twentieth century
Locale: San Francisco, California
First produced: 1977, at the New York Shakespeare Festival, New York City (as *A Photograph: A Still Life with Shadows; A Photograph: A Study in Cruelty*); revised, retitled version, 1979, at the Equinox Theatre, Houston, Texas
First published: 1981, in *Three Pieces*

Principal characters:
SEAN DAVID, a photographer
MICHAEL, a dancer
NEVADA, an attorney
CLAIRE, a model
EARL, an attorney

The Play

A Photograph: Lovers in Motion is set in an old San Francisco flat. The central character is a novice photographer, Sean David, who is sexually involved with a complex triad of women: Nevada is an attorney who wishes to take Sean out of the ghetto and provide him with material comfort; Claire is a model, a cocaine addict, and a nymphomaniac who wants to possess Sean; and Michael is a dancer who wants to help Sean fulfill his dreams. Earl, Sean's boyhood friend, wants Sean for a lover as well.

Act 1 opens with Sean telling Michael of his dream of becoming a famous photographer. As they examine some of his photographs, Earl enters to remind Sean that he is expected to attend a party at Nevada's home. Sean antagonizes Michael when he tells her that she is not invited to the party. Michael retaliates by insinuating that some of the nude women in Sean's photographs are more than mere subjects. Sean nonchalantly reminds her that there are a number of women in his life, but that he will not let them interfere with his relationship with her.

Following Sean's protestations of devotion to Michael, he allows Claire to dance across his bedroom in a scarlet camisole and lace panties. When he does not respond to Claire's need to make love, she makes him jealous by mentioning several of her lovers and their charm. Sean angrily tells Claire that if he ever catches her with a lover, he will take her to a nightclub and personally see to it that she is gang raped. Not willing to be threatened, she flaunts her independence, telling him that she will gladly give herself to the gang and invite him to watch. Becoming animated, Sean picks up Claire and tumbles onto the bed to give the nymphomaniac what she wants.

Though Claire beds Sean, it is to Michael that he gravitates. When he reaches out to her, she tells him that she can no longer sleep with him in the bed where the smells of his other lovers linger. She surprises Sean by telling him that she has resolved not to fight over his lovers because her life is full of her art, dancing; she will not allow herself to be destroyed by jealousy.

When Claire returns to Sean's flat, she encounters Michael, who tries to befriend her by offering whiskey to accompany the cocaine Claire plans to snort. Claire lets down her guard; when she hears Sean approaching, Michael wrestles Claire to the bed and makes it appear that Claire is trying to seduce her. Calling Claire a pervert, Sean orders her to leave his apartment.

Michael then sets out to eliminate Nevada from the love triangle. After Nevada tears up some of Sean's photographs in a fit of jealousy, Michael convinces him that he degrades himself by allowing Nevada to pay his rent in exchange for sex. She tells him that their black ancestors had pride and that many died to pave a way for him. She tries to instill in Sean a love for his work. Sean counters by telling her that he has only known welfare, racism, drugs, whores, and a father who loved a pet monkey more than his son.

When Michael threatens to leave Sean, he hits her, then tries to appease her with sex. She rejects his violent offering and instead reaches inside herself to present him with the gift of tenderness, particularly because Sean has known acute abuse from his father.

Act 2 opens with Earl's attempt to persuade Nevada to give up Sean. Earl's hidden agenda is revealed when he propositions Sean, his boyhood friend. He offers to secure a house for the two of them. Sean, however, refuses Earl's offer and tells him that he and Michael will be getting a place together.

In a climactic gathering of Sean's three loves, Michael, Claire, and Nevada, and his would-be lover Earl, Sean chooses Michael. For the first time in his life, he is able to tell a woman that he loves her. He chooses her because Michael's love has helped him to believe in himself. In a celebration dance, Michael surrounds Sean as he tells her repeatedly that he loves her.

Themes and Meanings

A Photograph: Lovers in Motion, as the title suggests, is about capturing and preserving the essence of life, which is, according to Ntozake Shange, a belief in oneself. Shange places a high value on the wholeness that results when a person learns to accept and love himself. With the exception of Michael, the characters in this play suffer from a lack of self-esteem. Sean is an emotional cripple who sleeps with and abuses three women in an attempt to ease the pain caused by his father. He recalls that his father had a habit of bringing women home, getting them drunk, sleeping with them, and then beating them mercilessly. However, when Sean speaks of arranging for a gang rape of Claire, wrestles with Michael when she threatens to leave him, or verbally abuses Nevada, he does not seem to be aware that he is perpetuating his father's treatment of women. Sean's past incapacitates him, making him unable to love himself or anyone else.

It is not until Michael instills in him a sense of pride in his race and in himself that Sean becomes a whole person. The motion or progression of his relationship with Michael then begins to take on a focus. She serves as a catalyst for his growth by conjuring up ancestral ghosts whose very lives serve to empower Sean to seek a better life, a life that does not involve manipulating women for the sake of survival. He comes to realize that he no longer needs Nevada's money and prestige or Claire's nymphomania to make him feel like a man. Michael also teaches Sean to love his work, his photography, even if prestigious galleries reject it. She teaches him that it is in loving what he creates that he can come to love himself.

A Photograph: Lovers in Motion is also about women's inviolability. Shange deliberately sets up Claire and Nevada as foils to the heroine, Michael, who represents all that is nurturing and regenerative about black womanhood. Michael, though she loves Sean, does not allow him to compromise her values or to debase her as he does the vulnerable, fragmented Claire and Nevada. When Michael senses that she is losing herself to Sean's weakness, she arms herself with memories of her grandmother, who with a shotgun protected her family from a lynch mob. When Michael tells Sean that she is leaving in order to be able to keep loving herself, he heaps obscenities upon her. He insults her by telling her that she should be satisfied that he knows how to appease her with sex. Michael is immune to his chauvinistic barbs, however, because she loves herself, her dancing, and her people. For Shange, this love of oneself is the key ingredient of wholeness.

Dramatic Devices

The central ideas in *A Photograph: Lovers in Motion* are magnified by several dramatic devices. Ntozake Shange constructs this theater piece around a series of alternating long and short scenes, which, like snapshots, convey the richness of the characters' lives. Shange blends experimental poetry with traditional dialogue to demonstrate the fragmentedness and uncertainness of her characters' lives. This poem-play unravels as spontaneously as do the relationships of the characters. As lights rise and fade on a series of scenes, small glimpses are given of the journey that Michael and Sean must take before they can find happiness.

Not only does Shange blend poetic with traditional dialogue, but she also orchestrates the plot by moving the characters back and forth between a nontraditional and a traditional setting. The main action takes place in Sean's San Francisco flat, which is neat and elegant but a potpourri of scavenged objects and furniture. The secondary action of the play takes place in a plain black space, one that is used by all characters except Sean and Michael. For example, the black space becomes the elegant home of Nevada, where she and Earl, in formal attire, discuss what is best for Sean's future. In another instance, the black space becomes Earl's office, where Claire taunts him about his homosexuality and Sean's sexual capabilities. Also in Earl's office, he tries to convince Nevada that she is too refined for someone as coarse and cruel as Sean. The black space also becomes Claire's bedroom, where she, drunk with whiskey and cocaine, yearns for someone to touch her and make love to her.

The setting helps to demarcate the difference between the real and sustaining world of the hero and heroine and the idealistic and transient world in which Earl, Claire, and Nevada operate. Whereas there is hope for Sean and Michael, as evidenced by their spiritual and physical union in Sean's flat, there is an absence of hope and growth for the characters who people the black space. In this black space, the characters strive to give something physical or material to Sean; however, in Sean and Michael's space, Michael gives him not only herself, her spirit, but also Sean himself. He learns to love himself and then is able to reciprocate.

The plot of *A Photograph: Lovers in Motion* is anything but linear; the alternating scenes emphasize that life is made up of a series of steps forward with occasional steps backward. Because this poem-play does not move forward in a tidy sequence, the lives of the characters are crystallized and made poignant. This flexible, highly experimental structure allows Shange to dramatize and explore the lives of characters in a way that traditional flashbacks cannot achieve; the structure frees the playwright not only to go back in time but also—and simultaneously—to explore the present and future.

Critical Context

A Photograph: Lovers in Motion, like other plays by Shange, including *for colored girls who have considered suicide/ when the rainbow is enuf* (pr., pb. 1976), *Boogie Woogie Landscapes* (pr. 1979, pb. 1981), and *Spell #7: Geechee Jibara Quik Magic Trance Manual for Technologically Stressed Third World People* (pr. 1979, pb. 1981), encompasses so imperceptibly the particulars of African American life that the substance of the play becomes recognizable as universal. Shange's aim in the theater has been to evoke an emotional response as the lives of mutilated characters are laid bare.

Women of every race were affected by Shange's *for colored girls who have considered suicide/ when the rainbow is enuf.* Shange's 1976 Broadway smash hit, only the second play by a black woman to reach Broadway, marked the beginning of a new temper in American theater. This play established its author as a serious, innovative dramatist, who gives voice to the pain of all women who have been raped emotionally and physically and perceive themselves as exploited and unappreciated. Furthermore, with this play Shange succeeded in establishing the choreopoem as an acceptable, legitimate form.

Shange's originality in *A Photograph: Lovers in Motion* created additional space for her art form in the American theater. This play demonstrates her interdisciplinary approach to theater, in her portrayal of the lives of visual and performing artists. Her use of poetry, dance, music, and choreographed lighting is her way of bringing to the theater the heart and soul of African American traditions. When Michael dances, her movements symbolize the working out of the tangles of her life. The rhythm in Michael's dance is heightened by the blending of poetry and nontraditional dialogue. This theater piece, with its innovative structure and language, extended the possibilities and alternatives of dramatic art.

Sources for Further Study

Brown-Guillory, Elizabeth. *Their Place on the Stage: Black Women Playwrights in America*. New York: Greenwood Press, 1988.

Griffin, Gabriele. "Writing the Body: Reading Joan Riley, Grace Nichols, and Ntozake Shange." In *Black Women's Writing*, edited by Gina Wisker. New York: St. Martin's Press, 1993.

Lester, Neal. *Ntozake Shange: A Critical Study of the Plays*. New York: Garland, 1995.

Richards, Sandra L. "Conflicting Impulses in the Plays of Ntozake Shange." *Black American Literature Forum* 17 (Summer, 1983): 73-78.

_______. "Ntozake Shange." In *Contemporary Dramatists*. 6th ed. Detroit: St. James, 1999.

Tate, Claudia, ed. *Black Women Writers at Work*. New York: Continuum, 1983.

Waxman, Barbara Frey. "Dancing Out of Form, Dancing into Self: Genre and Metaphor in Marshall, Shange, and Walker." *The Journal of the Society for the Study of the Multi-Ethnic Literature of the United States*, Fall, 1994.

Elizabeth Brown-Guillory

THE PHYSICISTS

Author: Friedrich Dürrenmatt (1921-1990)
Type of plot: Problem play
Time of plot: The twentieth century
Locale: Switzerland
First produced: 1962, at the Schauspielhaus, Zürich, Switzerland
First published: Die Physiker, 1962 (English translation, 1963)

Principal characters:

DR. MATHILDE VON ZAHND, the chief psychiatrist of a private sanatorium
HERBERT GEORG BEUTLER, alias Isaac Newton
ERNST HEINRICH ERNESTI, alias Albert Einstein
JOHANN WILHELM MÖBIUS, a physicist
NURSE MONICA, in love with Möbius
RICHARD VOSS, a police inspector

The Play

The Physicists takes place in the grand villa "Les Cerisiers," formerly the residence of the von Zahnd family, now transformed into a private sanatorium for the mentally ill. Dr. Mathilde von Zahnd, the last descendant of that once vital aristocratic family, makes her living here by treating—at exorbitant fees—the neuroses and psychoses of the "spiritually confused elite" of the Western industrialized nations.

Police Inspector Richard Voss has been summoned to investigate the strangulation of a young nurse. The murder suspect is patient Ernesti, who calls himself Albert Einstein and affects the mannerisms and appearance of the great physicist—even to the point of playing the violin, which he is doing when Voss arrives (the audience hears the agitated strains of Ludwig van Beethoven's "Kreutzer Sonata" in the background). In the first of many ironic sequences, the head nurse refuses to allow the inspector to interrogate the murderer, since the patient is after all "a sick man" who must be allowed to "recover" from the trauma he has just experienced. Furious, Voss demands to see the director of the Institute, Dr. von Zahnd, only to be informed that she is at the moment occupied—accompanying Einstein on the piano.

As the body of the slain nurse is taken away, Voss is joined by a jovial Isaac Newton (patient Beutler in eighteen century costume), who cheerfully recounts his own recent use of a curtain cord—Einstein used the cord to an electric lamp—to murder a nurse who had fallen in love with him. Newton realized, he said, that his purpose in life "consisted in contemplating Gravitation, not in loving a woman."

Inspector Voss is overwhelmed by the flood of Newton's admissions and explanations, including the revelation that "Einstein" is in fact mentally ill, believing himself to be Einstein in reality, whereas "Newton" is on the other hand only *pretending* to be Newton. In truth, however, as Newton explains, it is he who is actually Einstein. In this vein "Newton" assures the inspector that he himself, that is, the *real* Albert Einstein, wishes to take full responsibility for making construction of the atom bomb possible. He then launches into a diatribe against the insensitive misuse of theory by practical-minded technicians, after which he returns to his room.

The hunchbacked Dr. Mathilde von Zahnd enters and reports that Einstein is resting peacefully and seems to have recovered from his trauma. Voss quickly gets to the point: The authorities are convinced that the occurrence of two murders at the Institute within the past three months indicates a certain laxness of security and may well provoke public outrage. Dr. von Zahnd responds glibly that her profession is quite capable of determining which mental cases are dangerous and which are not—the fact that mistakes have been made is not a matter of concern for the legal authorities but for medical scientists alone. She briefly recounts the case histories of Einstein and Newton, who both arrived at "Les Cerisiers" in the past two years, and reveals that yet another physicist shares the ward with them: Johann Wilhelm Möbius, a harmless patient who has been confined for a total of fifteen years.

As Voss departs, Möbius's wife arrives. In a farcical scene typical of Friedrich Dürrenmatt, Frau Möbius enters with her three sons and her new husband, a missionary by the name of Oskar Rose, whom she introduces apologetically. Since the missionary and his burgeoning family—it includes Rose's own six boys by his first wife, who has died—are to be sent to the Mariana Islands, the former Mrs. Möbius informs Dr. von Zahnd that she can no longer afford to pay for her former husband's care. After reassuring the distraught woman that Möbius will be allowed to stay, Dr. von Zahnd brings the timid, middle-aged patient out to say good-bye to his former wife and their three boys. Möbius evidently has one of his frequent hallucinations in which a naked and cowering King Solomon appears to him. In a dark parody of a psalm, Möbius recites a graphically detailed song of humankind's transience and hopelessness. He decries the advancements of space-age technology as futile and hollow. At the end he tells his horrified audience to leave him, and he announces his sincere wish that his family rot at the bottom of the Mariana Trench.

Later Möbius reveals to Monica, the nurse who loves him, that he only pretended to be crazy in order to make it easier for his family to leave him for good—the terrible things he said to them were meant to sever their emotional attachments in a humane way. Besides, he has put the finishing touches on his life's work, an all-encompassing theoretical edifice he calls the "System of All Possible Inventions," which has been dictated to him by King Solomon. Nurse Monica, however, who does not believe that Möbius is really ill, has bad news for him: She is being transferred to another part of the hospital, and he will be left vulnerable to the dangerous attentions of Newton and Einstein.

In the final portion of the act Möbius seeks to convince Monica that his life has become an act of penance for having revealed the existence of King Solomon. On the contrary, Monica argues, he has betrayed Solomon by his cowardly refusal to stand up for him, to proclaim his revelation. Monica then explains that, in order to help, she has arranged for an eminent physicist to review Möbius's manuscript in the expectation that it will be made public. As the stage darkens, Möbius and Monica tenderly embrace before the window. Suddenly Möbius pulls down the curtain, wraps her in it, and suffocates her.

Act 2 begins, as does act 1, with Inspector Voss's arrival at the Institute to investigate the murder of a nurse. This time Möbius is the suspect, and he openly confesses that he killed "Sister Monica" because King Solomon ordered him to do so. Voss admits his powerlessness and leaves the three physicists to their own devices. Alone with Möbius, Newton and Einstein reveal their true identities as scientist-spies who represent competing world powers and whose mission it is to win Möbius over to their respective political systems. The seriousness of their purpose is indicated by their willingness to commit murder to maintain their "cover" of insanity. They argue, threaten, and cajole, but Möbius accepts neither Einstein's pragmatic vision of science in the service of power-politics for the good of humankind, nor Newton's assurance of pure intellectual freedom to pursue research, which for him means freedom without responsibility for the consequences. Work for either side would be imprisonment, not freedom or power, and Möbius prefers the asylum. Finally, all three realize that the point is moot: Their acts of murder have effectively consigned them to perpetual confinement.

The final act takes a sinister turn when Dr. von Zahnd emerges to announce that Möbius indeed destroyed his "System of All Possible Inventions" in order to prevent the consequences of that knowledge from injuring humankind, but too late—she surreptitiously made photocopies of the work dictated by King Solomon. While the startled Möbius insists that there is no King Solomon, Dr. von Zahnd revels in her plans for world conquest in the service, not of political ideology or truth, but of her own bitter egoism. As she exits triumphantly, the physicists appear numb with defeat. "Newton" and "Einstein" take on the roles of the real Newton and Einstein in brief soliloquies, and Möbius takes on the persona of Solomon in a lament for the earth and its inevitable demise.

Themes and Meanings

The Physicists is a play about the ethical dilemmas of modern science in an age of remarkable technological achievement. Can the pursuit of truth ever become immoral? In the case of Albert Einstein and the development of the atom bomb, for example, can the scientist be held responsible for the deleterious results of the technological application of his discoveries? Dürrenmatt explores these questions through his characters, who personify the prevailing contemporary attitudes on the use of power gained through knowledge.

The play revolves around the inevitability of scientific advancement; as Dr. von Zahnd says in act 2, "What can be conceived, will be conceived." Möbius's refusal to allow his work to be used by either side in the Cold War and his withdrawal to the asylum appear as noble, if quixotic, attempts to take a moral stand, yet his tragic mistake lies in thinking he can exert power over knowledge by withholding his talents and the results of his scientific speculations from the world. He must finally conclude at the end of the play that the scientist's work, even if conducted in the presumed safety of a mental hospital, is never ethically neutral, for the scientist is always either the conscious or unwitting accomplice in morally corruptible acts that result from his discoveries. "What has once been conceived cannot be taken back," Möbius complains as he realizes that his new comprehensive theory has fallen into the hands of the spiteful and power-mad Dr. von Zahnd.

The impetus for Dürrenmatt's play may be found in Robert Jungk's polemical history of modern atomic science, *Brighter than a Thousand Suns: A Personal History of the Atomic Scientists* (1958), on which Dürrenmatt wrote an essay in 1956, the year the original Swiss edition appeared. In his book, Jungk exposed the moral apathy and culpable insouciance of many scientists, who were eager to further research into the secrets of nuclear energy without regard for the human and environmental consequences. The heroes of Jungk's narrative are clearly those physicists such as James Franck and J. Robert Oppenheimer who finally saw the dangers of partisan misuse of science and spoke out against unbridled pursuit of progress in the realm of nuclear physics.

Dramatic Devices

The most striking critical innovation of Dürrenmatt's craft lies in equating destiny with chance in tragedy. By replacing the traditional inevitability of the tragic hero's fate with the accidental or coincidental, he creates situations that are often shockingly horrible but at the same time comic because of their grotesque irony. In *The Physicists* the outcome of events is inevitably disastrous but has humorous overtones, since chance rules from the beginning: The hapless Möbius, in his attempt to escape the moral consequences of his work in science, has stumbled into the one insane asylum whose director is mad enough to want to accept his apparent delusions and even cultivate them toward her own dark ends. At the same time, von Zahnd is rational enough to pretend that she is indifferent—a strategy that allows her to succeed in her evil schemes. As the antagonist, she eventually succeeds in obtaining from Möbius that which he set out to conceal, and thereby the traditional tragic conclusion is achieved (as in the case of Sophocles' *Oedipus Rex*) with the hero's attainment of the very opposite of what he intended. Paradoxes such as these (noble intentions leading to disaster, the apparent insanity of the "sane," the search for freedom in confinement and isolation from the world, and so on) represent the essence of Dürrenmatt's dramatic motivation.

Many critics have pointed out Dürrenmatt's conscious rejection of Bertolt Brecht's dramaturgy. Indeed, Dürrenmatt rejected the influential playwright's guiding principles: that humankind can be changed, and that the stage is a revolutionary tool for kindling such change. Dürrenmatt is intent on proving just the opposite—that individuals are victims of forces beyond their control. For Dürrenmatt, individual moral integrity is always what is at stake, not the success of social or political ideals; thus, the ending of *The Physicists* shows the tragic defeat of the ethically motivated but misguided hero, yet also renders futile the two competing global ideologies.

Dürrenmatt became well known for his peculiar brand of modern tragicomedy with the international success of *Der Besuch der alten Dame* (pr., pb. 1956; *The Visit*, 1958). In it the playwright introduces the character that some consider the prototype for the misshapen, embittered, and devious figure of Mathilde von Zahnd: Claire Zachanassien. Claire, like Dr. von Zahnd, has been wronged by men and the world, and is intent on exacting retribution by means of the power she has acquired. In the case of the bejewelled amputee Claire, the instrument of power is money; in Dr. von Zahnd's, it is knowledge. Both women regard the injustices they have suffered and the imperfections they see around them as grounds for the establishment of a new "justice" that is itself a perversion.

In many ways, *The Physicists* is a very traditional tragedy. It maintains the classical unities of action, time, and place; the entire play takes place inside one ward at "Les Cerisiers" within one twenty-four-hour period. The ending, Dürrenmatt's tragicomic innovations notwithstanding, follows the pattern of traditional Greek tragedy, with the hero's nullification of his own efforts. However, the spirit of the play, as a tragicomedy, is essentially parodistic even in disaster. Physics and humankind's faith in physics are parodied throughout the play, as are ideas and ideologies (communism as well as capitalism). Contemporary psychiatry is one of Dürrenmatt's obvious targets, and even classical culture becomes the object of visual parody, since the author's stage directions require numerous examples of Greco-Roman decor to suggest the irrelevance of traditional expressions of humankind's quest for order.

Critical Context

Dürrenmatt's interest in the dangers of uncontrolled scientific advancement was longstanding. As early as 1950 he had expressed his "scientophobia" in a comedy called "Der Erfinder" ("The Inventor"), written for the cabaret stage. A short story from the same period, "Der Tunnel" ("The Tunnel"), is also illustrative of the author's conviction that destruction and chaos loom just below the deceptively placid surface of everyday orderliness and conventional beliefs. In such early works, Dürrenmatt depicts a world in which technological growth is out of control and no one seems to recognize the danger. This plight is all the more disturbing in *The Physicists*, since science threatens to take on a more ominously powerful dimension than heretofore, transcending even the massive destructive capabilities of the atomic bomb.

Except for one lyric interlude—the starkly pessimistic "Song of Solomon" that Möbius recites to his children and former wife in the first act—Dürrenmatt's language is decidedly matter-of-fact. The calm, convicted tone of remarks by the psychiatrist von Zahnd and her murderous inmates contributes much to the grotesque effect Dürrenmatt intends, highlighting the extremes to which the various characters take logic and reason in the pursuit of power. In fact, *The Physicists* marks a turn away from the varied and sometimes lavish use of language that characterized the most productive period of Dürrenmatt's career, the decade of the 1950's: His style grew more controlled and colder in the intervening years. Dürrenmatt's "asceticism," as one critic has called it, did not appeal to a large audience. The playwright increasingly abandoned the realistic elements that made his grotesquerie so fascinating and his parody so effective. As illustrated especially in such plays as the extremely pessimistic "comedy" *Porträt eines Planeten* (pr. 1970; *Portrait of a Planet*, 1973), Dürrenmatt's art on the whole became more distant and more macabre, his characters more stiff, and these traits probably account for the limited critical and popular success of his later works.

Sources for Further Study

Crockett, Roger A. *Understanding Friedrich Dürrenmatt.* Columbia: University of South Carolina Press, 1998.

Murdoch, Brian. "Dürrenmatt's *Physicists* and the Tragic Tradition." *Modern Drama* 14 (December, 1970): 270-275.

Peppard, Murray B. *Friedrich Dürrenmatt.* New York: Twayne, 1969.

Tiusanen, Timo. *Dürrenmatt: A Study in Plays, Prose, Theory.* Princeton, N.J.: Princeton University Press, 1977.

Weimar, Karl S. "The Scientist and Society: A Study of Three Modern Plays." *Modern Language Quarterly* 27 (December, 1966): 431-448.

Whitten, Kenneth. *Dürrenmatt: Reinterpretation in Retrospect.* Indianapolis: Berg, 1990.

Mark R. McCulloh

THE PIANO LESSON

Author: August Wilson (1945-)
Type of plot: Family
Time of plot: The 1930's
Locale: Pittsburgh, Pennsylvania
First produced: 1987, at the Yale Repertory Theatre, New Haven, Connecticut
First published: 1990

Principal characters:
BOY WILLIE, a farmer from the South
BERNIECE, his sister, a maid
DOAKER, their uncle
LYMON, Boy Willie's friend from the South
MARETHA, Berniece's daughter
AVERY, a preacher
WINING BOY, a family friend
GRACE, Boy Willie's girlfriend

The Play

A play about family inheritance and legacy, *The Piano Lesson* revolves around a piano that has been in Berniece and Boy Willie's family for several generations. The play opens with Boy Willie and his friend Lymon driving from Mississippi to Pittsburgh, Pennsylvania, to sell watermelons. Boy Willie has another motive for going to Pittsburgh: He has his mind set on selling the family piano to raise enough money to buy a farm. Boy Willie believes that once he owns land, he can be the master of his own destiny. However, his sister Berniece disagrees; she refuses to sell the piano, although she hesitates to touch it. Avery, a self-anointed preacher and Berniece's boyfriend, is also interested in the piano. He wants Berniece to give the piano to him so that he can raise money to build his own church. Berniece, however, wants to keep the piano in the family.

Doaker, Berniece and Boy Willie's uncle, recounts the story behind the piano. It was originally owned by Joel Nolander. Robert Sutter, who owned Berniece and Boy Willie's great-grandparents as slaves, wanted to buy his wife, Ophelia, an anniversary present. Since he had no money, he traded Berniece and Boy Willie's great-grandmother and their grandfather for the piano. After a while, Ophelia missed having Berniece and Boy Willie's great-grandmother around. At Sutter's request, Berniece and Boy Willie's great-grandfather, a first-rate woodworker, went to Sutter's house and carved pictures of his wife and son on the piano. However, he did not stop there; he continued until the piano was covered with pictures of family members. Years later, Boy Charles, Berniece and Boy Willie's father, started to believe that the piano belonged to his family and that so long as Sutter kept the piano, he had the family. Boy

Charles and his friends managed to move the piano out of Sutter's house and hide it while Sutter was at a picnic. When Sutter found the piano missing, someone set Boy Charles's house on fire. When a mob found Boy Charles in a railroad boxcar in a train called the Yellow Dog, they set it afire as well. The fire killed everyone in the boxcar, including Berniece and Boy Willie's father and four hobos. The people who died in the boxcar became known as the Ghosts of the Yellow Dog.

Before Boy Willie and Lymon start for Pittsburgh, James Sutter, Robert Sutter's grandson, mysteriously falls into a well. Some people suspect it is not an accident, and Berniece starts to feel the presence of Sutter's ghost in her house. Boy Willie is greatly annoyed by Berniece's refusal to sell the piano. Acting childishly, he wants to cut the piano in half and sell his half. At Berniece's request, Avery tries to bless the house, but his blessing fails to get rid of Sutter's ghost. In panic, Berniece begins playing on the piano, chanting her ancestors' names for help. Sutter's ghost almost disappears.

At the end of the play, Berniece and Boy Willie reconcile. However, Boy Willie warns Berniece that if she does not continue to play on the piano, both he and Sutter's ghost will return.

Themes and Meanings

The Piano Lesson is about building one's future by establishing one's ontological and cultural relationship with the past. Berniece has spent her entire life trying to run away from her problems; after her husband died, she left the South for the North to look for a new beginning and to distance herself physically from what she does not want to reexperience emotionally. Not wanting to wake the piano's old spirits, she "shut the top on that piano" after her mother's death. In trying to avoid confronting the painful memories of the family's past, Berniece has uprooted herself from the family tradition and history, thereby exposing her vulnerability to that which she fears the most, making her susceptible to the frequent visits of Sutter's ghost.

Boy Willie represents the new generation of African Americans growing up in the South. He believes that the only way for African Americans to gain freedom, dignity, and respect is to stand up for what belongs to them: "If you got a piece of land you'll find everything else fall right into place. You can stand right up next to the white man and talk about the price of cotton . . . the weather, and anything else you want to talk about." Like many characters in August Wilson's plays, however, Boy Willie has a complexity that defies black-and-white, right-or-wrong analyses. He holds firmly onto what he believes and is not easily influenced by other people's opinions. However, his youthful energy and enthusiasm sometimes impugn the soundness of his judgment. In asking Berniece to cut the piano in half so that he can sell his half, he reveals his childish mentality. At the same time, he challenges his sister's religious beliefs and exhorts her that she "got to believe in it all"; she "can't go at nothing halfway." However, he seems only interested in the passages in the Bible that support and justify his vengeful spirit. His self-righteousness is also underlined in his not wanting to listen to people who disagree with him.

The Piano Lesson dramatizes the struggle of African Americans to reclaim their sense of history and identity. The question at issue is not whether the piano belongs to Berniece and Boy Willie but how to claim what belongs to them. As is demonstrated by Berniece's ambivalent feelings about the piano, the legitimacy of one's heritage cannot be upheld unless it is claimed. Berniece's fear to embrace that which belongs to her legitimizes the visit of Sutter's ghost—which, according to Doaker and Boy Willie, is looking for its piano. Berniece's fear also threatens her connections with her family history and her true identity. *The Piano Lesson* suggests that people cannot change history but can solicit its help in their attempts to establish meaning for the present and the future. To reclaim one's sense of history, one needs to collect enough courage to face the past, no matter how painful that process may be.

Dramatic Devices

Wilson's thematic accentuation of the continuity of history in *The Piano Lesson* takes on an epic scope that is emphasized in the characters' names. For example, Berniece is named after the great-grandmother who was traded for the piano, and Boy Willie is named after a great-grandfather named Willie Boy. Doaker and Wining Boy also remind the audience of the bards in Greco-Roman epics, whose responsibilities are to ensure that the past and the present are connected. Both Doaker and Wining Boy are storytellers. Doaker is down to earth and makes judgments mainly on empirical experience. Because of his strong ties to the past, Wining Boy enjoys reliving the past in his stories more than he is interested in keeping up with the present. His sense of humor provides a thematic as well as stylistic contrast to Doaker's seriousness. Both Doaker's and Wining Boy's stories are moving and mesmerizing. They are imbued in the richness, cadence, and rhythm of the African American vernacular tradition. Their stories provide historical information that makes possible fusions of the past and the present and of history and reality.

The epic scope of *The Piano Lesson* is also circumscribed by the presence of ghosts who are as much engaged in fighting for the possession of the piano as the living African Americans who are struggling to identify their relationship with history. *The Piano Lesson* is filled with ghost figures that reflect the influence of Magical Realism on Wilson's writing. Ghosts in the play, such as that of James Sutter, haunt, confuse, scare, and bedevil people to a point at which they begin to question the adequacy of their own sense of history. There are also ghosts with whom Wining Boy and Boy Willie believe they can communicate. Boy Willie believes that people can talk to the Ghosts of the Yellow Dog. He explains to his niece Maretha:

> They like the wind you can't see them. But sometimes you be in trouble they might be around to help. They say if you go where the Southern cross the Yellow Dog . . . you go to where them two railroads cross each other . . . and call out their names . . . they say they talk back to you.

The Piano Lesson starts with Doaker's recounting the history of the piano to Boy Willie and Lyman. It ends with Boy Willie's describing to Maretha the possibility of communicating spiritually with their ancestors. The continuum of the family history is delineated by legends and stories in which three generations of people find resonance.

Critical Context

August Wilson's voice is one of the most exciting and inspiring in modern American theater. His plays have won numerous prizes and awards, including two Pulitzer Prizes, seven New York Drama Critics Circle Awards, and a Tony Award. What distinguishes Wilson from his contemporaries is his sensitivity, sharpened by his awareness of and determination to celebrate African American culture. He has a sharp ear for a language that is as colorful as the African American experience itself, and his sense of humor is compassionate, mesmerizing, and entertaining at the same time.

Wilson's awareness of his social responsibility as an artist is reflected both in his efforts to historicize African American experience in the twentieth century and in his interest in using theater to record African American culture. Wilson once announced that he intended to write a play for every decade of the twentieth century, focusing each on a critical aspect of the black experience in the United States. Each of Wilson's full-length plays is set in a different era.

Each of Wilson's six long plays is also representative of the principal social concerns of its period. *Joe Turner's Come and Gone* (pr. 1986, pb. 1988) concerns the impact of black migration from the southern agrarian way of life to the large industrial cities of the North in search of freedom, dignity, and economic opportunities in the first decade of the twentieth century. *Ma Rainey's Black Bottom* (pr. 1984, pb. 1985) is about the aspirations of African American artists for control of their own destiny and autonomy during the 1920's. *The Piano Lesson*, set in the 1930's, concerns African Americans' attempts to make peace with their past. *Seven Guitars* (pr. 1995, pb. 1996) is about black musicians finding success and then seeing their dreams dashed, thanks to poverty, violence, and social injustice during the 1940's. *Fences* (pr., pb. 1985), set during the 1950's, is about the black struggle to survive in a society whose prejudice had prevented talented African Americans from achieving their dreams. *Two Trains Running* (pr. 1990, pb. 1992) centers on the black political struggles and entrepreneurial adventures during the 1960's.

Wilson's theater also provides African Americans with opportunities to reorient themselves toward the restoration of their African self-consciousness. Wilson's use of the African American vernacular tradition in his plays serves two purposes: It concretizes onstage the richness of black oral tradition, and it enables African American audiences to resituate themselves in history, to remind themselves of their current position in society, and to celebrate their cultural identity.

Sources for Further Study

Nadel, Alan, ed. *May All Your Fences Have Gates: Essays on the Drama of August Wilson*. Iowa City: University of Iowa Press, 1994.

Pereira, Kim. *August Wilson and the African-American Odyssey.* Urbana: University of Illinois Press, 1995.

Shannon, Sandra G. "Blues, History, and Dramaturgy: An Interview with August Wilson." *African American Review* 27, no. 4 (Winter, 1993): 539-559.

_______. *The Dramatic Vision of August Wilson.* Washington, D.C.: Howard University Press, 1995.

Wang, Qun. *An In-Depth Study of the Major Plays of African American Playwright August Wilson: Vernacularizing the Blues on Stage.* Lewiston, N.Y.: Edwin Mellen Press, 1999.

_______. "Towards the Poetization of the 'Field of Manners.'" *African American Review* 29 (Winter, 1995): 65-77.

Qun Wang

PICNIC

Author: William Inge (1913-1973)
Type of plot: Psychological
Time of plot: The early 1950's
Locale: A small town in Kansas
First produced: 1953, at the Music Box Theatre, New York City
First published: 1953

Principal characters:
HAL CARTER, a handsome drifter
MADGE OWENS, an attractive but vulnerable young woman
MILLIE OWENS, Madge's tomboy sister
FLO OWENS, the mother of Madge and Millie
ALAN SEYMOUR, Hal's rich friend and Madge's boyfriend
ROSEMARY SYDNEY, a spinster schoolteacher
HOWARD BEVANS, a businessman and bachelor
HELEN POTTS, a neighbor/confidante to the Owens family

The Play

Picnic begins on a bright "sunlit" stage revealing the porches of two small houses in a small Kansas town on the late summer morning of Labor Day. All the action of the play takes place within one twenty-four-hour period. This neighborhood, like the entire town, is poised for the last summer holiday of the season, culminating in the annual Labor Day picnic before the beginning of the school year. The houses are tidy but unremarkable, except that their occupants are all women, young and old, each of whom has been seared—or scarred—in one way or another by her experiences with men. In one house lives Flo Owens, whose husband abandoned her to rear her two daughters: Madge, the "prettiest girl in town," and Millie, a precocious, tomboyish teenager. A boarder, Rosemary Sydney, an old maid schoolteacher, also lives with them. Mrs. Potts, the friendly, harmlessly meddling neighbor in the next house, opens the play, speaking to Hal Carter, a strapping vagabond in cowboy boots, dungarees, and tee shirt.

She encourages him to let his metabolism digest the big breakfast he has eaten before he begins the chores he has contracted to do for his keep. As the first act proceeds within this matriarchal setting, each of the key characters is paraded before the audience. Flo, embittered by her years of living alone, broods over her daughters' welfare, looking for security in Madge's expected marriage to the stable and respectable Alan Seymour. She is wary of Hal's presence, but accepts him because he has been presented as Alan's former college buddy. Madge, a beautiful young woman, is the captive of a beauty that breeds resentment in her sister, fear in her mother, and adulation and lust in the young men of her town. Millie, a self-styled intellectual at age sixteen, smokes in secret and expresses disdain for her sister's beauty and femininity. Rosemary Sydney is, on the surface, prim but is inwardly a bawdy, frustrated woman whose longing for male companionship and marriage consumes her and compels her to grasp for attention from any man, whether Hal or businessman Howard Bevans.

Hal, vigorous and vital, signals early in the play what is absent in the Owens household; yet at the same time, Hal is also depicted as an unwelcome intruder into this small community—an appealing masculine specimen whose virility is a vivid contrast to the personalities and lifestyle of the two other prominent men in the play: Alan Seymour, his friend from college, and Howard Bevans, an aging businessman. While Hal is impulsive and uncouth, Alan is a cautious, unprepossessing young man destined for both goodness and greatness; he treats Madge with unadorned awe and reverence. To him, she is a goddess who deserves nothing but unalloyed tenderness and grace; he thinks of her not sexually but as the prototypical nice girl. Howard, on the other hand, is a bumbling but benevolent soul who prizes bachelorhood and independence.

As act 2 begins, picnic plans are evolving and the ensemble awaits departure time while the conversation turns on Hal's past, Millie's intellectualism, and Howard's noticing Rosemary's shapely legs—and Rosemary's drawing attention to Hal's. Meanwhile, Hal, much traveled and variously occupied since his college days with Alan, becomes the designated escort for Millie, though he secretly desires to be close to Madge. His outward bravado is eventually mitigated by his admission to Alan that he does not know how to act around women, a fact confirmed by his inability to divert the aggressive flirtation of Rosemary. When she tries to coerce him into dancing with her, Hal, embarrassed and perplexed, refuses and thereby incurs Rosemary's wrath. Humiliated, she accuses him of arrogance and chauvinism, rebuking him with the stinging charge that he came from the gutter and will return to it.

When Flo bursts in and surveys the scene, she forbids any more drinking and tells Millie to ride to the picnic with Alan, Mrs. Potts, and herself, while Madge is left to go with Rosemary and Howard. Rosemary, stunned by Hal's rejection and her sudden feelings of ineptitude, persuades Howard to take her driving "into sunset," thus skipping the picnic. Act 2 ends with Madge and Hal alone onstage, revealing their private, secret troubles—Hal his reform school past, Madge her weariness with being told that she is pretty—and frankly expressing their desire for each other. Madge abruptly kisses Hal, and he declares that they will not go to the picnic either.

Act 3 brings all the principals together to thrash out the implications of the various couplings that have occurred. Shortly after midnight, Howard and Rosemary return to the Owens residence, having made love. Coerced by circumstances in some ways beyond his control, Howard awkwardly tries to say good night, but Rosemary pleads with him to take her with him. He declines, but she persists in extracting his reluctant promise to return in the morning to take her off to get married. The scene shifts outside to the porch, where Hal and Madge have returned, suddenly very conscious of their predicament: how to explain to Alan, Flo, and Millie where they have been. As Hal attempts one more embrace, the curtain closes on a distraught Madge, unable to reconcile what she has done with the mundane activities and obligations she must face in the morning, and Hal, beating his fists together for the reckless bad faith with which he has treated the Owens home and his erstwhile friend Alan.

The sun rises on the doorstep in the play's last scene. Millie smokes a cigarette, prepared for the first day of school. One by one, the neighborhood residents saunter by, and there is a flutter of speculation among Flo, Mrs. Potts, and Millie over the previous night's events and what transpired between Madge and Hal. Into the midst of this comes Rosemary, bounding down the stairs, asking if anyone has seen Howard, with her immediate audience—including her sister schoolteachers who have come by to pick her up—unaware of what commitments were made in the night. A shivaree, or spontaneous wedding party, erupts when Howard arrives and Rosemary exults in her exit: "She got her a man."

Alan enters and, after pleasantries exchanged with Millie, confronts Madge, apologizing for Hal's behavior while completely exonerating Madge, and then promising that Hal will never bother her again. In his blind adoration of Madge, he is unable to see her as anything but chaste and victimized. Madge, noncommittal, expresses vague disappointment in what is happening to her. In the confusion of Howard and Rosemary's departure, Hal sneaks onto the scene and reports that he is urgently headed for a freight train to Tulsa to avoid the police whom Alan has called, accusing Hal of car theft. Alan spots Hal, and after brief fisticuffs between the two, he concedes that he has been bested by Hal; he recognizes that Madge will never be his and leaves. To Flo's dismay, Hal and Madge express their love for each other, and Hal begs Madge to come with him. As Hal flees, Madge runs to the house, emerging moments later with a packed suitcase, determined to follow Hal. Flo discerns that her daughter is following the same path that she herself had taken and pleads with her to stop. With the open approval of Mrs. Potts, Madge leaves, and the play ends with Flo wishing she had had the time to share with Madge her faltering motherly wisdom.

Themes and Meanings

In *Picnic*, William Inge has chronicled the angst of those who cannot articulate their own desperation because it remains to them a nameless gnawing in the soul. Much has been made of the legacy of the Kansas small-town life that Inge knew intimately and its influence on his work. This legacy is portrayed in *Picnic* as a smallness of ambition and desire, a predicament that the landscape itself perhaps perpetuates with its brooding, thundering skies and stark plains. These physical surroundings become emblematic, especially of the abandoned or disadvantaged women that Inge captured so evocatively, and they—not Hal or Alan—are the real center of the play. While in some sense Hal is the fulcrum of the play's thematic force, he is in the center only because Madge and Rosemary—and, in subtler ways, Mrs. Potts and Millie—inadvertently place him there by their own groping for identity and purpose.

For Madge, Hal is daring and adventure, in contrast with Alan's predictable safety and structure; to succumb to Hal is to break out of the routine and escape the foreordained. In this preference she shares the same spirit her mother Flo had manifested earlier, and with probably the same eventual disappointment awaiting her. Madge is weary of being told that she is pretty, of being venerated for a physical appearance she had no choice in assuming. Alan's infatuation with her beauty only reinforces her sense of longing for something or someone who will look past surface appearance and touch something unique within her. In Hal, she finds someone wild and unfettered; his overt masculinity and his animal-like appeal demand from her both pity and passion. What Alan cannot give her, she finds in—and returns to—Hal. Where Alan worships from afar, Hal indulges the flesh; he reigns as the epitome of manliness in a town beset by impotence and dry chastity.

Rosemary, ever the bridesmaid, finds in Hal a flickering reminder of her youth, a barren youth squandered in school teaching the children of others. When rebuffed by Hal, she inflicts on him the scorn she feels for herself and transfers her attention to the nice but ineffectual Howard. Her passion suffices for both, and after a night of promiscuity shocking for this small town, she bullies Howard into making her a "respectable" woman by marrying her. This theme of forced marriage is a familiar one to Inge's protagonists, and here it serves to accentuate the emptiness and futility of finding romance and true love within such a stifling environment. Mrs. Potts, herself a witness to the boredom and sterility of her neighbors' lives, openly endorses Madge's flight with Hal. Only in Millie does Inge offer the possibility of breaking the chain of wasted or contrived lives exemplified by Flo and Alan Seymour. Millie, forlorn and insecure in her own femininity, vows never to marry; her vision is to move to New York to write books that will shock people out of their senses. The Midwest is thus seen as first nurturing and then binding those who are reared within its boundaries. To move eastward or westward, to move out of the midwestern "center," is shown to be a man or woman's only hope for individuality or the possibility of love.

Dramatic Devices

Picnic, in common with all of Inge's plays, does not draw its strength from innovative staging or some imaginative reversal of the conventions of the theater. Inge's dramatic instrument was instead the steady, relentless, and well-focused depiction of the everyday as manifested in the small town of the Midwest. Just as his friend and fellow playwright Tennessee Williams evoked the South, Inge wrote to bring his native midwestern landscapes to life through the strong characterization of individual lives. The action and intrigue of one day in the waning summer of a small Kansas town are both the setting and substance of *Picnic*, a testimony to and a revelation of what Inge regarded as both "the sweetness of character" and the unarticulated tensions of the tortured midwestern soul.

The composition of *Picnic* began as a tableau, a series of character sketches of five women in small-town Kansas titled "Front Porch," which then evolved into a more developed play, *Summer Brave*, and finally into *Picnic*. Its evolution from these vignettes of characterization is clearly evident in the strong individualistic portrayal of the women in *Picnic*. Inge, as many critics have observed, had an uncanny insight into the psychological processes of the female mind, and he used that capability to create realistic dialogue, especially in the scenes that occur in the Owens household among an all-woman entourage. Madge, in particular, stands out as one only too trapped by her own beauty and the appearance of tranquillity of spirit.

The small midwestern town thus emerges in *Picnic* almost as a character itself; the ordinariness is palpable, the ever-present front porch is, in the morning, a symbol of gateways and pathways unexplored, of conversations destined to demarcate the premature endings, never the beginnings, of romance and adventure. These same porches at evening—shadowed and cloaked in diminishing sunlight—betray the final resting place of nostalgic glances back to what was not and never could have been, and the inevitable winter of discontent to follow. Only Madge's sudden, joyful decision to join Hal—against her mother's fervent protests—breaks the chilly atmosphere of sameness and safety. However, clearly Inge had an affection for these towns, referring to them in his other writings not as "flat," a pejorative stereotype of unrelenting dullness, but as "level," a place where a man or woman can get his bearings straight before embarking on a more ambitious task. This "levelness" is conveyed in *Picnic* by the barren stage, uncluttered by anything but the most homely of artifacts and images.

Critical Context

Picnic was Inge's second consecutive successful Broadway play, following on the heels of his debut work, *Come Back, Little Sheba* (pr., pb. 1950). *Picnic*, like each play in the quartet of Inge's well-received Broadway productions of the 1950's—also including *Bus Stop* (pr., pb. 1955) and *The Dark at the Top of the Stairs* (pr., pb. 1957)—is quintessentially a play about midwestern life—about its everydayness, its sense of sameness, directionlessness, and about the tension between men and women, loners all, who face their lives with a combination of resignation, despair, and lonely isolation. Robert Baird Shuman, speaking of this run of successes, suggested that "critics could do little but marvel at the success of a man who wrote modest plays about the most prosaic of people, but who had never experienced a box office failure."

That string of successes, however, ended at the close of the 1950's, as a series of Inge's plays, beginning with *A Loss of Roses* (pr. 1959, pb. 1960), was savaged by critics who found Inge not as effective a playwright when he left behind consideration of the midwestern malaise he knew so well. After the production of *The Dark at the Top of the Stairs*, it was only in his screenplay for the motion picture *Splendor in the Grass* (1961), an Academy Award winner for original screenplay, that Inge achieved critical success. In *Picnic*, however, Inge was at the peak of his talent; Robert Brustein saw it as a "satyr play glorifying the phallic male," and it was made into a highly popular film—as were each of the other three in the midwestern quartet of plays.

In the context of American theater, Inge's work may be compared with that of Eugene O'Neill or Tennessee Williams, whose regional settings parallel in power those of Inge's Midwest. However, Inge's own imaginative powers fall short of O'Neill and Williams in considering the larger themes of modern American life. If it can be said that great playwrights universalize the particular while good playwrights particularize the universal, Inge is decidedly a good playwright, one whose depiction of the longing of the human heart for meaningful companionship and a sense of destiny in *Picnic* is close to being the perfect metaphor for postwar listlessness and anxiety. At the time of its original staging, the urban, global village of the future was yet to arise, and Inge's small-town America only beginning to vanish. The increasing isolation of the rural, nonindustrial America from the metropolises and its effects on the inhabitants of small towns is mirrored no better than in the characters of *Picnic*. Without Inge it is quite likely that the reality of the American Midwest and the inner lives of its people would never have been brought to the attention of twentieth century theater audiences and filmgoers. For that achievement alone, Inge holds a special place in American drama.

Sources for Further Study

Armato, Philip M. "The Bum as Scapegoat in William Inge's *Picnic*." *Western American Literature* 10 (Winter, 1976): 273-282.

Brustein, Robert. "The Men-Taming Women of William Inge." *Harper's Magazine*, November, 1958, 53-57.

Diehl, Digby. "Interview with William Inge." In *Behind the Scenes: Theater and Film Interviews from the Transatlantic Review*, edited by Joseph McCrindle. New York: Holt, Rinehart, and Winston, 1971.

Gould, Jean. "William Inge." In *Modern American Playwrights*. New York: Dodd, Mead, 1966.

Leeson, Richard M. *William Inge: A Research and Production Sourcebook*. Westport, Conn.: Greenwood Press, 1994.

Lumley, Frederick. "William Inge." In *New Trends in Twentieth Century Drama: A Survey Since Ibsen and Shaw*. 4th rev. ed. New York: Oxford University Press, 1972.

McClure, Arthur F. *William Inge: A Bibliography*. New York: Garland, 1982.

Miller, Jordan Y. "William Inge." In *Reference Guide to American Literature*. 2d ed. Chicago: St. James, 1987.

Shuman, Robert Baird. *William Inge*. New York: Twayne, 1965.

Wolfson, Lester M. "Inge, O'Neill, and the Human Condition." *Southern Speech Journal* 20 (Summer, 1957): 225-226.

Bruce L. Edwards

PLENTY

Author: David Hare (1947-)
Type of plot: Social realism; allegory
Time of plot: 1944-1962
Locale: St. Benoit, France; London and Blackpool, England; and Brussels, Belgium
First produced: 1978, at the Lyttleton Theatre, London
First published: 1978

Principal characters:

RAYMOND BROCK, a British diplomat
SUSAN TRAHERNE, his wife, a British intelligence courier in France
ALICE PARK, Susan's friend, a radical feminist
LAZAR, a British intelligence agent and Susan's lover during World War II
SIR LEONARD DARWIN, Raymond's superior in the Foreign Service
MICK, a lower-class hustler
SIR ANDREW CHARLESON, the personnel chief of the British Foreign Service

The Play

Plenty begins in a room that has been stripped bare, like the prostrate, bloody, naked man who lies sleeping on a mattress. Susan sits smoking on a packing case as Alice enters and discusses the cold climate, which she relates to the "loveless English," thereby callously acknowledging the existence of Raymond. From their conversation the audience learns that there has been a fight between Susan and her husband Raymond and that Susan is leaving him and giving their house to Alice, who will use it as a home for unwed mothers.

The second scene shifts abruptly from 1962 London to 1943 France, where Susan and Lazar, two British undercover agents, have met at night in a field—Lazar has just parachuted into France and awaits a "drop" from an airplane. Despite the interference of the well-intentioned French Underground, the two secure the package. The distraught Susan loses her composure, declares that she does not want to die, like Tony, at Buchenwald, and embraces Lazar. Lazar asks her the French term for "mackerel sky," *un ciel pommele* (the phrase is repeated during their abortive reunion in scene 11); and while nothing romantic happens onstage, the excitement and vitality of this scene suggests the offstage sexual relationship that sustains Susan in the postwar years of torpor and mediocrity.

The following lengthy scene, which occurs in 1947 Brussels, introduces Sir Leonard Darwin, Raymond's superior in the British Foreign Service. Tony, with whom Susan has been touring Europe, has died abruptly, and it is Raymond's task to make the necessary arrangements. Since Tony has a wife back in England, Raymond's job is a bit complicated, and he has to make a conscious decision to lie. (Raymond's initial assistance leads to further concessions and the eventual ruination of his diplomatic career.) This scene also establishes Susan's distinction between "them," the "fools . . . who stayed behind," and "us," "those of us who went through this kind of war" in France. Susan's impatience and intolerance is at odds with Darwin's naïve, evolutionary optimism about European reconstruction: "Ideals. Marvellous. Marvellous time to be alive in Europe."

Scene 4 begins with a radio announcer's apt comments about a "reconstructed" musical selection and then dramatizes the extent to which Susan's obsession with the past dominates her life. As Raymond sleeps, a visual reminder of Scene 1, Susan and Alice, an aspiring writer, discuss Susan's problems with her amorous boss and the status of her affair with Raymond, who has been commuting from Brussels on weekends. Raymond wakes; as he speaks of "acclimatizing" and becoming rich, Susan cleans her gun (Alice says that she is "fondling" it), suggesting that she, like Darwin, "has slight problems of adjustment to the modern age." Susan's testiness and Raymond's resentment at her obscene criticisms of the Foreign Service result in a battle between people from different worlds. He asks, "But what other world do I have?" After a pause, Susan states, "I think of France more than I tell you." Even at this early stage of their relationship Raymond has learned that "when you [Susan] talk longingly about the war . . . some deception usually follows." Alice concludes the scene with a reference to "peace and plenty."

In scenes 5 and 6 Susan, having decided to have a child, secures the services of Mick, a hustling East Ender who cannot deal with being sexually used by a woman, particularly since his failure reflects on his manhood. Time again becomes the focus as Mick, the jazz "revivalist," declares that for him "it all stops in 1919," and Susan states, "England can't be like this forever." Scene 5 ends, fittingly, with Susan, who is about to start her affair with Mick, referring to the mackerel sky associated with Lazar. Susan's past also affects the end of scene 7, when, confronted by an angry Mick, she fires her revolver over his head.

The Suez Canal debacle is the focus of scene 7, which takes place in the Knightsbridge home featured in the first scene. At a dinner party the Brocks stage for Burmese guests and Darwin, Susan suffers another breakdown. She apparently cannot refrain from mentioning the Suez Canal "blunder or folly or fiasco," which she sees as the "death-rattle of the ruling class." Susan's disillusionment is shared, though not so hysterically, by Darwin, who resents being lied to by the government and declares that "when the English are the cowboys, then in truth I fear for the future of the globe." To change the subject, a guest is encouraged to describe Ingmar Bergman's film *Persona* (1967), which unfortunately features a woman "who despises her husband." The parallel prompts Susan's memories of "poor parachutists" and women who spent a single night with English resistance fighters. At the end of the scene Susan declares, "There is plenty."

After the interval, Raymond and Susan have returned from Iran for Darwin's funeral, five years later. While the intervening years have been relatively calm for the Brocks, Susan's inner peace has been achieved with pills. She will not return to Iran; the consequences of her decision are apparent in the following scene, in which she is interviewed on the BBC and then visits Sir Andrew Charleson at the Foreign Office. Sir Andrew and Susan discuss Raymond's career, which is proceeding at a "slowish" pace, in part because of his unwillingness to return to his post in Iran. When she realizes that Raymond has no future, she threatens to shoot herself and attempts to shift the blame for Raymond's fate to Sir Andrew.

The following scene, which occurs a year later at the Knightsbridge house, explains what led to the scene at the start of the play. As Susan begins to empty the house, Raymond asks, "Which is the braver? To live as I do? Or never, ever to face life like you?" When he threatens to have her committed, Susan sends Alice away and confronts Raymond. A month later, Susan and Lazar, who has heard the BBC interview and found her, are at Blackpool in a dingy hotel room, where both attempt to recapture what they had in France. To Susan's dismay, Lazar reveals that he "gave in. Always. All along the line," though he had hoped to regain the "edge" he had in France. The loveless encounter ends when Lazar leaves, opening the door.

The open door discloses "a French hillside in high summer" in 1944, after the armistice. The young Susan addresses a French farmer, who grumbles about his situation. Susan, however, has a different perspective: "We will improve our world." As she and her farmer friend walk down the hill, she affirms, "There will be days and days and days like this."

Themes and Meanings

In *Plenty*, David Hare's characters serve as figures in a political allegory detailing the post-World War II moral and psychological decline of England, as represented by various characters in the play. In the midst of postwar optimism and "plenty," both Susan and England are unable to adjust, to acclimate, to changing conditions. Susan may believe that there will be "days and days" of sunshine and promise, but her lucrative postwar advertising work is trivial. She wants to move on, to be productive, but she cannot get pregnant; her sterility reflects that of her generation and of England itself. Like England, she cannot accept her diminished power and control; her response is to withdraw through drugs and mental illness.

Raymond represents another England, as he lies battered and stripped at the beginning of the play. Though he has some reservations about English life (England looks a "trifle decadent" to him), he maintains his belief in privilege and property, and, like England, he resents the ingratitude and flight of those he has cared for paternalistically: "I've spent fifteen years of my life trying to help you. . . . I am waiting for . . . some sign that you have valued this kindness of mine." When Susan tells him that she is leaving, he threatens to have her committed, thereby binding her to him in a kind of "commonwealth" status. Although he jokes about Darwin being "God's joke . . . a modern Darwin who is in every aspect less advanced than the last," Raymond resembles his mentor, who has paternalistic notions about Europe. Darwin, as a representative of the old ruling class, believes in the empire but cannot reconcile himself to England's emulating the American "cowboys."

Darwin also feels betrayed by his government, which is epitomized by Sir Andrew, who symbolically "cuts less of a figure than Darwin but . . . has far more edge." The failure of English diplomacy is tied to the moral decay that accompanies a loss of power: "As our power declines, the fight among us for access to that power becomes a little more urgent, a little uglier perhaps." By having Darwin die in 1961, the year that England applied for membership of the Common Market, signaling its dependence on nations it had aided after the war, Hare ties Darwin's fate to England's.

Hare's *Plenty* dramatizes decline and the failure to reconstruct a nobler past, whether it be in jazz (Mick's reference to the post-1919 decline of jazz), in literature (Alice is reading F. Scott Fitzgerald's *The Last Tycoon*, 1941) in classical music (a piece called *Les Ossifies*, suggesting decay and calcification, must be the product of "reclamation"), or in personal relationships. Susan and Lazar want to reenact the "mackerel sky" love they shared in the war, but the reunion is spoiled because both have sold out and compromised: Susan has lied to make a living, and Lazar works in a corporate bureaucracy. When Susan says, "I want to believe in you. So tell me nothing," she tacitly acknowledges that time cannot be reclaimed or reconstructed in the decaying hotel room they share. Her realization undercuts the optimism of the final scene, in which her "days and days" reference becomes an ironic comment on her expectations and on England's.

Dramatic Devices

Although much of *Plenty* is staged realistically, the sets not only serve as backdrops for action but also express the state of the English nation. For example, the Knightsbridge home of the Brocks, which is "decorated with heavy velvet curtains, china objects and soft furniture" in scene 7, the occasion when the British seized the Suez Canal, is in scene 1 "stripped bare," much like Raymond and England. Similarly, the dark, "sparsely furnished and decaying room" where Lazar and Susan attempt to recapture their past is at once, because of its darkness, reminiscent of the dark, exciting night when they met in the second scene and indicative of the decay in their own lives. When Susan states, "I've stripped away everything," she means that she has discarded all trivial irrelevancies, but she also is "exposed," like Brock, and there is little left, except obsessive memories destroyed by reality. In fact, as Bert Cardullo has pointed out, in *Plenty* David Hare reverses the usual consolations of darkness and light. Susan's most exhilarating experience occurs in darkness, which makes her failure in the dark Blackpool hotel room even more ironic. Sunlight only reveals reality and her growing disillusionment and despair.

Similarly, Hare uses what Cardullo terms anticipatory darkness and sound to introduce all but two of the scenes; the darkness and sound become the promise that is destroyed when the house lights go up. While the sounds function to set the mood of a scene, they also serve occasionally as ironic commentary on what is to follow. In scene 7, for example, the music "from the dark" is "emphatic, triumphant," before the lights reveal that British victory has been achieved through diplomatic lies and "cowboy" behavior, actions that are hardly compatible with Aung's opening statement that "the English are the Greeks—ideas, civilization, intellect." The triumphant music sounds the "death-rattle of the ruling class."

The play does not begin in sound and darkness, because Hare wants the audience to see only the result of Susan's disillusionment: There is no promise at this point in her life. When the scene shifts from Blackpool to St. Benoit, there is again no sound; in scene 12 the "darkened areas of the room" of scene 11 disappear and are replaced by a French hillside in summer. Thus, the scenes are not divided but merged, suggesting that the failure of scene 11 is directly attributable to the naïve optimism of scene 12. Hare's stage directions are a bit ambiguous: There is a "fierce" green square. Despite the brilliant colors, ordinarily associated with life, the Frenchman in the scene has "an unnaturally gloomy air" as he comments on the status of the French ("the lowest of the low") and complains that "the harvest is not good again this year." Susan, however, ignores what the sunlight exposes—that there will not be "plenty"—and prefers to think that "we will improve our world."

Critical Context

Plenty is the logical succession to David Hare's earlier plays, which also chronicle the decline of English society. *Slag* (pr. 1970, pb. 1971), his first full-length play, was considered sexist by some critics; yet the play is as much about the boarding school as about the three women contending for power. Thus *Slag* is primarily critical of institutions. *Brassneck* (pr. 1973, pb. 1974), written with Howard Brenton, details the three-generation decline of a Midlands family. In the teleplay *Licking Hitler* (1978), the companion play to *Plenty*, Hare also examines a broad historical and geographical context and traces the British decline to the post-World War II years. In his later work for television and film, particularly in *Wetherby* (1985), a film he wrote and directed, Hare has used unusual protagonists, like Susan, who challenge audience empathy because they do not acclimate themselves to a society inimical to their values and beliefs. Hare's male characters either adapt and lose their integrity or resist and are crushed by the system. *Plenty* has won for Hare an international reputation, primarily because the film version, which Hare also wrote, was a success. Meryl Streep, who played Susan, enhanced Susan's complexity because her star appeal worked against the selfishness of Susan's stage character.

Susan can be seen as a descendant of John Osborne's Jimmy Porter, a railing misfit from the 1960's, when "angry young men" dominated the English stage. Hare can himself be linked with Terence Rattigan and Osborne, who also have used ideological conflict in their plays. Hare's anger, however, has lasted into the 1970's and 1980's, and his attention has remained focused on left-wing politics. Though he is a decidedly English writer, his later work has been more international in scope and has been favorably compared to Bertolt Brecht's in political stance and dramatic technique. He is, with Tom Stoppard, the most accomplished of contemporary English dramatists and certainly, because of his work in television and film, one of the most versatile.

Sources for Further Study

Brustein, Robert. "Theatre: *Plenty*." *The New Republic*, November 29, 1982, 24.
Bull, John. *New British Political Dramatists*. London: Macmillan, 1983.
Cardullo, Bert. "Hare's *Plenty*." *Explicator* 93, no. 2 (1985): 62-63.
Donesky, Finlay. *David Hare: Moral and Historical Perspectives*. Westport, Conn.: Greenwood Press, 1996.
Gale, Steven H. "David Hare's *Plenty*." In *Drama, Sex and Politics*, edited by James Redmond. Cambridge, England: Cambridge University Press, 1985.
Homden, Carol. *The Plays of David Hare*. Cambridge, England: Cambridge University Press, 1995.
Olivia, Judy Lee. "David Hare." In *British Playwrights, 1956-1995: A Research and Production Sourcebook*. Westport, Conn.: Greenwood Press, 1996.

Thomas L. Erskine

THE POLICE

Author: Sławomir Mrożek (1930-)
Type of plot: Absurdist
Time of plot: The mid-twentieth century
Locale: Unspecified
First produced: 1958, at the Teatr Dramatyczny, Warsaw, Poland
First published: Policja, 1958 (English translation, 1959)

Principal characters:
THE CHIEF OF POLICE
THE GENERAL
THE PRISONER, a former revolutionary, later the General's aide-de-camp
THE POLICE SERGEANT, an agent-provocateur
THE WIFE OF THE SERGEANT-PROVOCATEUR

The Play

Act 1 of *The Police* opens in the office of the Chief of Police in an unspecified monarchy. Much to the consternation of the Chief of Police, the Prisoner declares that after ten years in prison he has had a change of heart and will sign an oath of loyalty to the government. Ten years ago he had attempted to assassinate the General by throwing a bomb at him, but the bomb failed to explode. For ten years he has been interrogated and urged to renounce his antagonism toward the Infant King and the Regent. He has steadfastly refused, but now he has suddenly seen the light and will give in to the government's demands. He is tired of being the last prisoner in the country and eager to join the rest of the population in devoting all of his strength to the support of "the best political system in the world."

The Chief of Police is less than exhilarated by his last prisoner's sudden change of heart. He tries his best to trap the Prisoner into revealing that his newly discovered love for the government and the authorities is only a ruse to gain his freedom, but the former revolutionary is steadfast. He has observed the country and the populace from the window of his cell and admires their loyalty and the progress that has been made during the years of his imprisonment. More than that, he has begun to be weary of his adolescent rejection of law and order, which has left him free but aimless. He has become nostalgic for a sense of belonging, for "a joyful and calm conformity, an eager hope in the future, and the peace which flows from full submission to authority." He no longer wants to be the only remaining dark spot despoiling the otherwise perfect society which the Infant King and the Regent have created. Once he is reformed and released, prisons will no longer be necessary and can be turned into schools.

At this point, the Sergeant, in civilian clothes, enters the office, battered and limping. He has been making the rounds among the population, trying to provoke somebody into making disloyal remarks about the government to allow him to make an arrest, but has been treated roughly by an enthusiastically loyal populace. This is the last straw for the Prisoner: He demands to sign the oath of loyalty and to be released. The Chief of Police and the Sergeant are left to ponder a future without prisoners and prisons.

Act 2 takes place in the home of the Sergeant. The Chief of Police, in civilian disguise, comes to visit his subordinate but finds him gone, trying to provoke disloyalty even on his day off. The Wife of the Sergeant tells the Chief of Police how unhappy her husband is, not only because of his lack of success as agent-provocateur but also because he cannot wear his uniform in his line of duty. She herself is trying to assist him by spying on friends and neighbors, so far without success. Finally the Sergeant returns home and immediately changes into his uniform. He discovers that the Chief of Police has come to entrust him with a desperate mission, one that tests his loyalty to the utmost. After the Sergeant tells him of a recurrent dream in which he, in uniform, arrests his alter ego in civilian clothes, the Chief of Police assures him that his dreams will come true if he is willing to sacrifice himself for the future of the police force. Since there is no hope to provoke the people, who "have become wildly, cruelly, bestially loyal," into unpatriotic action or speech, the Sergeant himself will have to serve as a substitute revolutionary. Reluctantly he agrees to this unnatural proposition, shouts an invective against the Infant King and his uncle the Regent from his window, and is promptly arrested.

In act 3 the results of the Sergeant's devotion to duty are manifest. The police force has been granted funds for rebuilding the prison and for recruiting new personnel. The General himself has become interested in the Sergeant's case and will personally conduct the interrogation. Meanwhile, the policeman-turned-revolutionary is becoming increasingly confused about his identity. He has observed his country and his fellow citizens from the same cell window that was the vantage point of the former Prisoner, but he has arrived at different conclusions: The population looks sullen and dissatisfied to him, the railway system is atrocious, and the Infant King and the Regent are morons.

When the General arrives, he is accompanied by the former Prisoner, now his special assistant serving as an expert on subversive activity. The Prisoner/Aide devises a plan to goad the Sergeant into throwing the very bomb at the General which he himself had used ten years before; since the bomb failed to explode then, there is no danger for the general, but the act of throwing the bomb would convict the Sergeant of terrorism. The Sergeant needs little persuasion to throw the bomb; this time it does explode, but it fails to kill the General, who has taken cover in the toilet. While the General, the Prisoner/Aide, and the Chief of Police place one another under mutual arrest for failing in their respective duties, thus providing exciting investigative prospects for the police, the Sergeant, now completely turned revolutionary, shouts, "LONG LIVE FREEDOM!" at the top of his voice as the play comes to an end.

Themes and Meanings

The Police, like most of Sławomir Mrożek's other plays, is grounded in the playwright's actual experiences in communist Poland, where daily life was characterized by fear of prosecution for disloyalty and by an absurdly complicated bureaucracy. Mrożek regards life in Cold-War-era Poland as so absurd that his plays turn into grotesque, cartoonlike parodies. These nightmarish visions of his homeland led to Mrożek's exile in 1964, and his work was banned in Poland from 1968 until 1974. In the 1980's, this harsh stance of the Polish government softened significantly, and Mrożek's plays were once more widely performed.

The Police dramatizes a society, undefined but certainly recognizable as a parody of Poland, in which a totalitarian government, led by an Infant King and his uncle, the Regent, has managed to suppress all opposition. The last vestige of resistance, the Prisoner, feels out of place and strangely nostalgic for law and order. To be an anarchist revolutionary is a lonely, depressing existence, and the lack of support from the general population finally persuades the former rebel that conformity, even with a previously despised political system, is gratifying and comforting. There is a marked difference between the Prisoner's observations of his society from his cell window and those of the Sergeant in act 3. The perspective from a prison window is limited, and the interpretation of the scene depends heavily on whether one prefers existence inside the prison or the prison existence outside. The crematorium, a reminder of the infamous Nazi concentration camps in Poland during the Third Reich, is interpreted by the Prisoner as a sign of religious tolerance, by the Sergeant as a "non-productive investment." The faces of the people, seen from the perspective of the Prisoner, who wants to be released, are "full of happiness and satisfaction"; to the Sergeant they wear sour expressions.

A totally successful totalitarian state is unthinkable, since it defines itself by and gains its strength from opposition. When all opposition has been crushed or "reeducated," artificial enemies must be created. Once identified as a foe of the system and treated as such, the Sergeant no longer has a stake in supporting the party line. His eyes are opened to the cruel absurdity of the system, and he turns into a committed revolutionary. Even without such principled opposition, however, the totalitarian system will create enemies out of the inevitable internal power struggle among the politicians, the military, and the ideologues. The losers will without fail populate the prisons once more.

The Police analyzes the mechanisms of power and exposes the absurdities and inherent contradictions of totalitarian government. It points out the paranoia about opposition forces inherent in all totalitarian regimes and the paradoxical need for such opposition to guarantee the survival of the system. The play also shows how the lure of a higher standard of living can serve as a substitute for personal freedom; given such complacence, such a lack of popular support, the would-be rebel is reduced to absurdity. Finally, Mrożek outlines the bleakly ironic process whereby revolutionaries turn into the most ardent supporters of the system they formerly worked so hard to overthrow.

Dramatic Devices

The Police uses the techniques of the Theater of the Absurd. The play employs cartoonlike characters—Mrożek began his literary career as a newspaper cartoonist—and the cliché-ridden dialogue typical of the plays of Eugène Ionesco. Like many of Mrożek's early plays, *The Police* also exhibits the influence of Alfred Jarry, whose play *Ubu roi* (pr., pb. 1896; *Ubu the King*, 1951), set in Poland, is considered the prototype of the contemporary anti-illusionist theater. Mrożek works in this anti-illusionist vein by creating an unidentified country composed of grotesquely distorted real features of Polish society. In his production note he warns that "this play does not contain anything except what it actually contains. This means that it is not an allusion to anything, it is not a metaphor, and it should not be read as such." This caveat, while affording Mrożek a modicum of protection, is clearly duplicitous, for by his very prohibition Mrożek ensures that audiences will understand the parallels to life in Poland during the Cold War.

Thus the country is not named; indeed, it is ruled by an Infant King and his uncle, the Regent, who appear only as pictures in state offices. The characters do not have any personal names that might associate them with Poland but are identified only by their dramatic functions or their professions. The police officials have mustaches and wear jackboots, swords, and high, stiff collars. The Prisoner has a "pointed beard like those of nineteenth-century progressives." The result is a Kafkaesque no-man's land, at once nightmarish and ridiculous, run by a grotesque, menacing bureaucracy. Like many absurdist plays, *The Police* employs comic devices but is not ultimately a comedy: No harmony is created or restored at the end.

Critical Context

The Police served to establish Mrożek's reputation as a playwright in Poland and the rest of Europe. Based on this play and other, mostly shorter dramatic pieces of the 1950's and early 1960's, Mrożek became known as the leading exponent of the Polish Theater of the Absurd, though his subsequent exile in Paris helped to cement his stature as one of the international masters of the contemporary stage. His early plays, such as *The Police*, *Na pełnym mrozu* (pr., pb. 1961; *Out at Sea*, 1961), and *Strip-Tease* (pr., pb. 1961; *Striptease*, 1963), are thinly disguised metaphors for the playwright's nightmarish vision of his homeland.

In addition to their links with Alfred Jarry and the European absurdists, Mrożek's plays are firmly rooted in the Polish tradition of playwrights such as Stanisław Wyspiański, Stanisław Ignacy Witkiewicz, and Andrzej Trzebiński. The nostalgic longing for the past, expressed by the Prisoner in act 1 of *The Police*, is a continuation of the theme of trying to overcome the depressing reality of the present by a flight into an imaginary past, foreshadowed in Mrożek's very first dramatic attempt, a vignette titled *Profesor* (pr. 1956, pb. 1968; *The Professor*, 1977), and culminating in Arthur's attempt to reestablish the order of the past in *Tango* (pb. 1964, pr. 1965; *Tango*, 1968). The plays after *Tango* are less enigmatic and more directly political in nature, but they still concern themselves with the function of power and unproductive nostalgia for the past.

Sources for Further Study

Gerould, Daniel, ed. *Twentieth-Century Polish Avant-Garde Drama: Plays, Scenarios, Critical Documents*. Ithaca, N.Y.: Cornell University Press, 1977.

Kloscowicz, Jan. *Mrożek*. Translated by Christine Cankalski. Warsaw: Authors Agency and Czytelnik, 1980.

Kott, Jan. *Theatre Notebook, 1947-1967*. Translated by Bodesław Taborski. Garden City, N.Y.: Doubleday, 1968.

Miłosz, Czesław. *The History of Polish Literature*. New York: Macmillan, 1969.

Franz G. Blaha

THE POTTING SHED

Author: Graham Greene (1904-1991)
Type of plot: Mystery and detective
Time of plot: The 1950's
Locale: England
First produced: 1957, at the Bijou Theatre, New York City
First published: 1957

Principal characters:
John Callifer, a prominent author of rationalist tracts
Mrs. Callifer, his wife
James Callifer, their younger son
William Callifer, James's uncle, a priest
Anne Callifer, the Callifers' granddaughter
Mrs. Potter, the gardener's wife
Sara, James's former wife

The Play

The Potting Shed opens with the Callifer family gathering at the news that old Mr. Callifer, a once-prominent author of rationalist tracts, is about to die. The family, however, has been careful to exclude two of its members from the group, old Callifer's younger son James and James's uncle, William, who defected from the rationalist tradition by converting to Roman Catholicism and becoming a priest.

Callifer's granddaughter Anne, however, telegraphs James and invites him to the gathering. She also later brings in Mrs. Potter, the wife of the family's gardener, who explains the mystery lying at the heart of the play. An impish and outspoken thirteen-year-old, Anne functions as a puckish figure, arranging the necessary dramatic confrontations.

The central mystery of the play centers on the potting shed, a place filled with seeds and bulbs. Something happened there years ago that caused both James and his Uncle William to become family outcasts. James responds to Anne's telegram in the hope that he will discover from his dying father what took place in the potting shed that caused him, at age fourteen, to lose his ability to experience any deeply felt emotions. His only recollection is that of waking up in a sickbed and wondering why his parents have rejected him. James's mother, however, will not allow him to see his father before he dies, nor will she discuss the potting shed. When Anne invites Mrs. Potter to the house, however, the latter reveals to James that when he was a young boy he hanged himself in the potting shed. Mr. Potter cut him down and saw that he was dead. Then James's uncle arrived and through an apparent miracle brought him back to life.

Hearing this story, James finds his uncle to ask what happened that day in the shed. He discovers that William has become an alcoholic, ineffectual priest who has lost his faith but who nevertheless carries out the duties and rituals of his office. William explains to James that he loved him as a boy and that when he found him dead he prayed to God, "Take away my faith, but let him live." God answered the prayer, miraculously restoring James to life at the expense of William's faith. Since that day William, now a hollow man, has busied himself with the empty routines of the priesthood, serving a God in whom he can no longer believe.

James's self-knowledge is now complete. While he believed in nothing before, he now is totally committed to a belief in God and to a belief in the miracle of his own resurrection. The oppressive and godless humanism of his father, which drove him to commit suicide as a young boy, has now been overthrown by the power of love and rebirth.

The final irony of the play is Mrs. Callifer's admission that her husband was a fraudulent rationalist. After he discovered what happened in the potting shed, he became convinced that God may, in fact, exist. By this time, however, Mr. Callifer's reputation as a rationalist was well established. He realized that it was too late to recall all of his books and to begin rethinking the principles that shaped his life. His wife continued to protect his reputation by concealing her husband's conversion and by repudiating James and William. The play concludes on a positive note, as Anne tells of her dream in which she discovered a lion sleeping in the potting shed. When the lion awoke, it licked her hand.

Graham Greene wrote two versions of the third act of *The Potting Shed*, one for the American production in 1957 and another for the British production in 1958. In the American version, James explains his newly discovered faith to his divorced wife, Sara. He tells her that he can now love her because he loves God. He sees in his uncle's life without faith an ironic parallel to his own sterile relationship with Sara. A room from which faith has gone, he observes, is like a marriage from which love has gone. His uncle's self-sacrificing prayer to God has thus restored James to a life of feeling, love, and faith. In the British version, Greene has James describe his new faith to his mother instead of to Sara. His mother explains that the event in the potting shed brought a disturbing doubt into her and her husband's rational view of the world. "You mustn't mind our anger—you've spoilt our certainties," she declares. In both versions, James's relationship with Sara is left tentative. She expresses an apprehension about his new ardor even as she previously feared his belief in nothing.

Themes and Meanings

The central theme of *The Potting Shed* is that of rebirth. The potting shed is the symbolic location of James's resurrection from the dead. It is a place filled with bulbs and packets of seeds, emblems of new life. Ironically, the sterile and oppressive godless humanism of his father drove the young James to take his own life in this symbolic shed and to rise again, like Lazarus, a committed Christian.

Another theme embodied in the play derives from Graham Greene's obsessive concern with the devastation of childhood innocence. Old Mr. Callifer's lifelong dedication to obliterating belief in the supernatural undermined James's simple childhood faith and led him to his hopeless act of suicide. Callifer's books, *The Cosmic Fallacy* and *He Was a Man* (which argues that Jesus was a Palestinian religious leader but not God), with their sterile reasoning, are contrasted with the fertile seeds and bulbs of the potting shed and the simple faith of Mrs. Potter. The attempt by a sophisticated, intellectual adult to corrupt innocence is thus overcome by the force of a simple, instinctive faith in natural and spiritual rebirth.

It may seem somewhat contrived, however, for a priest to offer to sacrifice his faith to save his nephew's life. The bargain almost seems a parody of putting God on the spot rather than the plea of a desperate man who deeply loves his nephew. Furthermore, the significance of the miracle is attenuated by the fact that James's life is not spiritually renewed until many years later, when he finally learns from his uncle what happened in the potting shed.

The dramatic occurrence in the shed, however, has a powerful impact on James's family, even though he is unaware of that. Even as his father's rationalism ruined his childhood, James's resurrection has undermined his family's certainty that life has no supernatural bearings. His rebirth, in effect, has destroyed his father's life work of rooting out faith in God.

Dramatic Devices

A master of mystery and suspense, Graham Greene employs a detective-novel strategy to structure *The Potting Shed*. The first mystery the play introduces is why James and his uncle William are not invited to visit the dying Mr. Callifer. Why are these two members of the family treated as outcasts? This question is further complicated by the central mystery of the play, which centers upon the suppressed memory of what happened to James in the potting shed many years earlier. The element of mystery sustains the audience's curiosity as Anne Callifer, detective-like, helps to find the pieces of the puzzle for James to put together.

Having established the mystery in act 1, Greene gradually unfolds the details of what happened in the potting shed in act 2, first through the revelations of Mrs. Potter, who simply reports the physical details of the suicide and Mr. Potter's cutting the dead boy down, and then through Father William Callifer, who discloses his prayer to sacrifice his faith for the boy's life.

Although the audience never actually sees the potting shed, it remains throughout the play as a potent symbol of rebirth. All the characters are obsessed with the mystery of that small, seemingly ordinary shed, a place of symbolic and actual death and life. The potting shed finally yields the mystery of James's life and of his relationship to his parents and uncle at the conclusion of act 2.

In act 3, James's newly acquired knowledge makes him a complete person for the first time. He is like a man who has suffered amnesia for years and who suddenly regains his lost childhood. The seeds of self-knowledge, which lay dormant for years, have all at once come into blossom, and James is reborn for the second time, a true believer in the power of God and of love.

Critical Context

The Lazarus theme, which constitutes the central mystery in *The Potting Shed*, derives from Graham Greene's novel *The End of the Affair* (1951). In that novel, the hero, Bendrix, appears to be killed during a bomb raid. His married lover, Sarah, caught up in her love for Bendrix and her guilt over her adulterous affair, makes a bargain with God: She vows to give up her lover if God will restore his life. Bendrix does indeed come to life, and Sarah honors her vow.

The Potting Shed is an important work because of its skillful handling of a central theme in Greene's work—namely, the importance of doubt in the development of one's faith. In the light of the miracle in the potting shed, not only James but also his family and his former wife must reconsider the assumed certainties of their lives. The play also dramatizes a central irony found throughout Greene's works: the development of Christian faith in reaction to the influence of obsessive atheism or rationalism. Like Greene's novels, *The Potting Shed* takes a fundamental Roman Catholic belief, the resurrection of the body, and turns it into a human drama of the first order.

Sources for Further Study

Adler, Jacob H. "Graham Greene's Plays: Technique Versus Value." In *Graham Greene: Some Critical Considerations*, edited by Robert O. Evans. Lexington: University of Kentucky Press, 1963.

De Vitis, A. A. *Graham Greene*. New York: Twayne, 1986.

Duran, Leopoldo. *Graham Greene: An Intimate Portrait by His Closest Friend and Confidant*. San Francisco: Harper, 1994.

Greene, Graham, and A. F. Cassis. *Graham Greene: Man of Paradox*. Chicago: Loyola University Press, 1994.

Kelly, Richard. *Graham Greene*. New York: F. Ungar, 1984.

Meyers, Jeffrey, ed. *Graham Greene, a Revaluation: New Essays*. New York: St. Martin's Press, 1990.

Pendleton, Robert. *Graham Greene's Conradian Masterplot: The Arabesques of Influence*. New York: St. Martin's Press, 1996.

Richard Kelly

PRAVDA
A Fleet Street Comedy

Authors: Howard Brenton (1942-) and David Hare (1947-)
Type of plot: Comedy; political
Time of plot: The late twentieth century
Locale: England
First produced: 1985, at the National Theatre, London
First published: 1985

Principal characters:
LAMBERT LE ROUX, a wealthy South African businessman
ANDREW MAY, an idealistic newspaper editor
SIR STAMFORD FOLEY, a newspaper owner
REBECCA FOLEY, Sir Stamford's daughter, the wife of Andrew
MICHAEL QUINCE MP, a minor politician
EATON SYLVESTER, an aide-de-camp to Le Roux
ELLIOT FRUIT-NORTON, a liberal editor

The Play

Pravda, a two-act play, begins in an English garden in which Andrew May is painting. As Rebecca Foley enters and discusses her writing, the audience learns that Andrew has retreated to the countryside to escape the pressures of the newsroom and that Rebecca is nursing him back to health. When Andrew announces his intention to speak again to Le Roux and to return to the newspaper, Rebecca counters that she will leave him.

The next scene and the ones that follow precede the first scene and play out the events that led to Andrew's countryside retreat. In act 1, scene 2, Andrew is a low-level editor receiving an education in how to rewrite copy to make it either sensational or irrelevant. When the owner of the paper, Sir Stamford Foley, sells the paper to Lambert Le Roux so he can buy a racehorse, Andrew and Rebecca are brought together, the former editors are fired, and Andrew is made editor of *The Leicester Bystander.*

Act 1, scene 3 introduces Le Roux and his business manager, Eaton Sylvester, as they arrange to buy another English newspaper. It happens that the mother of Michael Quince MP owns 21 percent of the shares of *The Daily Victory*, and Le Roux persuades Quince that a sale would help Quince's career as a politician: "As a politician? Not even a politician, no longer a politician, with *The Daily Victory* behind you, a statesman."

The following scene dramatizes the struggle on the part of Elliot Fruit-Norton to maintain his position as editor in chief of *The Daily Victory* despite its sale to Le Roux, while Andrew unwittingly seals the paper's fate when he testifies to the board of trustees that Le Roux never interfered with the running of *The Bystander.* Thus, Andrew's naïve idealism enables the unscrupulous Le Roux to buy another paper. In the final scene of the first act, Fruit-Norton accepts the chairmanship of the National Greyhound Racetrack Inspection Board, while Andrew and Rebecca return from their wedding to see Le Roux fire many journalists at *The Daily Victory*. Clearly, Le Roux will exert a decisive influence on his papers despite Andrew's testimony. Amid all the firing and pressure to produce more nationalistic news, Andrew becomes the editor of *The Daily Victory*.

The first scene of the second act opens in the newsroom, where the editors are either promoting government bias or assigning investigative journalists to irrelevant topics. One reporter comments, "Funny, everyone used to be so frightened of investigative journalism." As Andrew announces that he has just won an award for quality journalism, Rebecca enters with the real news that she has received a confidential report from the Ministry of Defense concerning the danger of a plutonium spill. Andrew chooses to publish the leaked document, but he is fired by Le Roux before he can do so. Rebecca promises to publish elsewhere; Andrew promises revenge.

In the second and third scenes of act 2, Le Roux spells out to Sylvester his aggressive theories of strategy; meanwhile, all the editors and writers who have been fired by Le Roux form a "conspiracy" against him. In the scene between Le Roux and Sylvester, Le Roux announces that trust and loyalty have no place in his sense of values, and the audience is led to wonder whether Sylvester will remain loyal to Le Roux. In the next scene, act 2, scene 3, Sylvester meets with the conspirators and promises to give them scandalous information about Le Roux, stories having to do with bigamous marriages, murder, and extortion. Rebecca is highly suspicious. The conspirators do not know whether to trust Sylvester, but they decide to buy a newspaper with their pooled resources and publish exposés on Le Roux.

In act 2, scene 4, Le Roux (on a hunting expedition) and Andrew (on a walking tour) cross paths and discuss the campaign against Le Roux. Le Roux contends that no one will really care, but Andrew clings to his idealistic hope that the exposé will topple Le Roux. In a surprise development, a constable arrives to serve Andrew with libel papers: Sylvester has fooled the conspirators by selling them groundless scandals about Le Roux, who can now bankrupt the opposition by suing them for libel.

In the final scene, Andrew returns to the newspaper to become editor of Le Roux's recent purchase, *The Tide*. The former editor, whom Andrew has just replaced, tells him his first priority: "What was I doing one minute ago? When I was Editor. I'll show you the big tits competition. That's your first priority." The play closes with Le Roux's dark announcement, "Gentlemen. We have a new foreman. Welcome to the foundry of lies." At this point, the stage darkens.

Themes and Meanings

Pravda portrays falsification in the contemporary Western news media. The title invites a comparison between the falsehoods of Fleet Street (the center of English journalism) and those of Moscow. The authors do not suggest that English news media are actually as deceitful and propagandistic as the state-owned Press of the former Soviet

Union, but their satire shows that, given contemporary trends, an English newspaper can hardly communicate more truth than *Pravda*.

The play accounts for this falsification in several ways. Although Le Roux does more than any other character to undermine the integrity of the free press in *Pravda*, falsification by no means begins with him. In a scene before he buys his first newspaper, a woman seeks a correction from a newspaper that has falsely identified her as the mother of a drug dealer; the editor is too concerned with other matters to listen, and Andrew gives her a frank but reprehensible refusal: "I'll be honest. They don't look good on the page . . . if we apologize and correct, how can the readers know what is true and what is not? To print corrections is a kind of betrayal. Of a trust. It's a matter—finally—of journalistic ethics." The ironic point is that newspapers accept very little ethical responsibility and seek merely to maintain their own authority. Significantly, this scene occurs before Le Roux is introduced.

With the introduction of Le Roux, the audience witnesses the quick firing of a number of editors. The point is comically made (as Le Roux, in his abruptness, tries to fire people who do not work for him) that editors have little job security and so should not engage in controversy. Andrew's editor at *The Bystander* (the name of the paper makes comic reference to its policy of nonengagement) told him this explicitly before Le Roux purchased the paper, but Le Roux serves to accelerate this pattern. In the course of the play, Le Roux fires four editors, and one editor who attempts to resist Le Roux's effects hangs himself in despair. Le Roux cavalierly announces his desire to lower standards, saying "Good papers are no good. . . . All that writing. Why go to the trouble of producing good ones, when bad ones are so much easier? And they sell better too." Le Roux defends his activities by appealing to a realpolitik philosophy in which large breast contests, which make papers sell well, are more important than reporting on plutonium leaks, which do not enhance sales so much. Le Roux makes every newspaper he owns more an opiate of the masses (Karl Marx's term for organized religion) than a check on government, and his effectiveness in this campaign can be measured by the change in Andrew from a congenial editor to one who shouts "Stop all this chatter! Work! Work you bastards! Get to work!" By focusing on how one South African businessman influences the lives of a few individuals, the play warns of the possibility of Orwellian developments in English journalism.

Dramatic Devices

To account for the success of men such as Le Roux, *Pravda* directs the audience's attention to his personal appeal through several comic dramatic devices. Like John Milton's Satan, Le Roux is represented as exuberant and strong. Indeed, he is excessively strong. *Pravda* describes itself on its title page as a "comedy of excess," and a hallmark of this type of play is to give voice to generally understood but never stated facts of life.

Chronological inversion foregrounds the question of why anyone would be persuaded to work for a man such as Le Roux. In the first scene in the play, which is chronologically the penultimate scene, Le Roux has not yet been introduced, but Andrew claims he will go back to work for the yet-unnamed "him," much to Rebecca's displeasure. Rebecca refers to Le Roux at this point as a "Satan," and the audience must begin to wonder what attraction would cause Andrew to sacrifice his marriage. The play as a whole follows this scene, in effect answering the question of what draws Andrew to Le Roux, but the scene that follows chronologically is the one in which Andrew returns to Le Roux, apparently converted to Le Roux's viewpoint.

Le Roux's great cruelty is revealed when, after buying a newspaper, he signals the change of command by rapidly firing a good portion of the staff according to personal whim. These scenes play comically because Le Roux's methods are represented with accelerated directness, in contrast to the more subdued firing that occurs in the real world. One journalist who attempts to get out of the "line of fire" by going to the lavatory is told, "Use a public toilet. You're fired." Le Roux's cruelties have the compactness and suddenness of jokes, and this method, aligning the audience with Le Roux as it does, demonstrates through humor how most people wish to identify with authority. Comic presentation in this way points to the source of Le Roux's power, just as rhetorical sophistication suggests the appeal of Milton's Satan.

As Le Roux speaks his mind with cynical directness, so do other characters. Addressing the audience directly, Andrew reveals what he enjoys about his job: "I love it. The smell of hot type. . . . All my career. The world passing through a newsroom. Processed, bundled and delivered through your door." Like most of Le Roux's confessions, Andrew's is not very flattering. He likes the centrality of the newsroom but cares little about its relation to the world. He likes "processed" news, which the audience learns to understand as falsified news.

The world of the newspaper office and the world outside are connected by newspaper headlines (shouted by reporters) that emphasize the press's irrelevance and sensationalism: "HEADLESS MURDER CASE: WHOSE HEAD IS IT? . . . ROYAL HAIRDO: CUT OUT AND KEEP. . . . GAY BISHOP—MP'S PROTEST." These headlines characterize the consuming public as well as the press and confirm Le Roux's social views. Their popularity accounts for the success of his "realistic" philosophy.

Critical Context

Howard Brenton and David Hare, like many of the British dramatists after World War II who write on political themes, have been profoundly influenced by the writings of George Orwell. *Pravda* in many ways responds to the insights of Orwell's essay "Politics and the English Language," and the play demonstrates, less melodramatically than *Nineteen Eighty-Four* (1949), the ways in which a degraded language serves the general interests of those in power.

In this context, Brenton and Hare are accompanied by Trevor Griffiths and David Edgar, other playwrights who also work in avant-garde style in an attempt to radicalize audiences. Most of these writers began in the London fringe theaters (Hare founded and Brenton later joined the Portable Theatre), but Brenton and Hare succeeded more than the others at making inroads into the National Theater and the

Royal Shakespeare Company, ensuring large audiences for their plays. Some critics have wondered whether political playwrights who are subsidized by the government can bite the hand that feeds them; other critics have enjoyed the irony of playwrights who appear to do exactly that.

Despite the similarities in their careers, Brenton and Hare have developed in different ways, and each writer makes a different contribution to *Pravda*. Naïve, idealistic protagonists appear in many of Brenton's plays; Andrew May would appear to be a reincarnation of Jack Beaty, a well-meaning socialist who wakes up to find himself a modern-day Macbeth in *Thirteenth Night* (pr., pb. 1981). Many of Hare's plays present a knowing woman who cannot take advantage of her knowledge because of her status as a woman. Rebecca Foley in this way recalls heroines from many of Hare's plays, such as Susan Traherne of *Plenty* (pr., pb. 1978) or Anna Seaton of *Licking Hitler* (1978). Despite their stylistic differences, the two have collaborated before, on *Brassneck* (pr. 1973). Both writers are known for combining political themes with incisive wit.

Sources for Further Study

Boon, Richard. *Brenton the Playwright*. London: Methuen, 1991.

Bull, John. "David Hare: The State of the Nation." In *New British Political Dramatists*. London: Macmillan, 1983.

_______. "Howard Brenton: Portable Theatre and the Fringe." In *New British Political Dramatists*. London: Macmillan, 1983.

Donesky, Finlay. *David Hare: Moral and Historical Perspectives*. Westport, Conn.: Greenwood Press, 1996.

Kroll, Jack. Review in *Newsweek*, January 13, 1986, 64-65.

O'Connor, John. "Howard Brenton." In *British Playwrights, 1956-1995: A Research and Production Sourcebook*, edited by William M. Demastes. Westport, Conn.: Greenwood Press, 1996.

Wa, Duncan. *Six Contemporary Dramatists*. New York: St. Martin's Press, 1997.

Wilson, Ann, ed. *Howard Brenton: A Casebook*. New York: Garland, 1992.

Zeifman, Hersh, ed. *David Hare: A Casebook*. New York: Garland, 1994.

John Whalen-Bridge

THE PRICE

Author: Arthur Miller (1915-)
Type of plot: Melodrama
Time of plot: The 1960's
Locale: A brownstone in Manhattan, New York
First produced: 1968, at the Morosco Theatre, New York City
First published: 1968

Principal characters:
VICTOR FRANZ, a middle-aged police sergeant
ESTHER FRANZ, his wife
GREGORY SOLOMON, an eighty-nine-year-old furniture dealer
WALTER FRANZ, Victor's brother, a successful surgeon

The Play

The Price begins with Victor Franz's entrance into a room crowded with old furniture that is ugly but impressive. A nice-looking uniformed police sergeant, Victor steps meditatively, gazing at his deceased parents' furniture; various pieces attract him, before the phonograph draws him and he puts on a "laughing record." Two comedians' attempts to utter a sentence are interrupted by gales of laughter, and Victor himself chuckles and then begins to laugh hard.

Esther, his wife, enters, hears the laughter, and thinks that a party is occurring, and Victor worries that she has been drinking. While both wait for a furniture dealer, Victor tells her about his brother's refusal to take his calls regarding the furniture sale, and Esther cautions him to bargain with the appraiser. Money and class are important to Esther; she is upset about going to a film with Victor in uniform rather than a suit. Victor wonders whether the cause of her unhappiness is the departure of their son, Richard, to college. Esther does not deny this possible cause, but additional matters bother her, such as the absence of communication between Victor and his brother, Walter, and, more important, Victor's failure to retire from the force, return to college, and pursue the scientific career he had desired as a young man. Victor's indecision bewilders Esther, who all but calls him a failure. Before going to pick up his suit at the cleaners, however, she tries to cheer her husband by asking to see a fencing move (she has noticed his foil and mask).

As Victor playfully lunges at Esther with the foil, the furniture dealer, Gregory Solomon, enters. The courtly Russian Jew is nearly ninety and walks with a cane but is straight backed. To show her confidence in Victor, whose feelings she has hurt, Esther goes to pick up his suit and leaves the men to bargain. Solomon is pleased by the harp and several other pieces and would like to purchase them individually, but Victor insists that everything must be sold because the building is scheduled for demolition.

Believing that no deal can be made without trust, Solomon tries to win Victor's confidence, telling him stories about his varied past. Victor is suspicious and impatient, wanting only a price, and the old man is so upset that he rises to leave several times. Victor, Solomon says, must have used an old telephone book to contact him, since he had cleaned out his store two years earlier. Having overcome his fear that he will not live to finish selling the furniture, Solomon determines to make an offer, for he misses the work. As Solomon questions Victor about his family, while examining the furniture, both men perceive the difference between Solomon and Victor's father—the furniture dealer is resilient, while Mr. Franz was not. As Solomon remembers his family, he reflects on the indeterminacy of one's motives for past choices. Victor agrees, saying that he can no longer understand his motive to support his father and join the police force during the Depression, denying himself and his wife, while his brother, who was successful, sent only five dollars a month. As the eleven-hundred-dollar price is determined and Solomon begins to pay Victor, Walter appears unexpectedly, and the deal is suspended as act 1 ends.

Arthur Miller did not want *The Price* broken by an intermission, so the handshake closing act 1 is completed in act 2. After polite queries about each other's families, Victor tells Walter about Solomon's offer. Walter thinks the price too low but does not intervene, only asking for some of his mother's dresses. When Esther returns, however, Walter challenges Solomon's offer and promises to give his share to Victor and Esther. During the ensuing argument, Solomon begins to feel physically weak. As Walter attends the old man in a back room offstage, Esther, onstage, expresses pleasure at Walter's warmth and irritation with Victor for not responding to it. When Walter returns, he suggests another deal, keeping Solomon as appraiser but giving the furniture to the Salvation Army and claiming a charitable deduction—a twelve-thousand-dollar deal for Victor and Esther. Victor embraces neither the deal nor his brother, but he warms slightly to Walter's memory of their mother's admiration for Victor's fencing.

When Solomon again needs assistance, Walter leaves, and Esther again argues in his behalf. On Walter's return, Victor asks why Walter would not take his telephone calls, and Walter confesses that his nurse was trying to protect him, for he had had a mental breakdown. He explains his belief that much of his drive to succeed was a response to the sudden financial failure of his father, before therapy freed him. Buoyant, Walter offers Victor a job at his hospital as a liaison between scientists and the hospital board.

Solomon interrupts, offering $1,150 for the furniture; he also offers to do the appraisal if that is what is wanted. After Solomon leaves, Victor asks Walter what he really wants, denying that he has the education for the job Walter has offered. Walter angrily takes one of his mother's gowns and starts to leave, but Esther stops him and tries to get the brothers to discuss their real grievances. When they remain stubbornly silent, Esther describes how hurt Victor felt years before when Walter refused him a five-hundred-dollar loan to complete college. Walter, embarrassed, says that he recanted and offered the loan in a talk with his father, who refused it, insisting that Victor wanted to help him. Furthermore, Walter says that the loan was unnecessary since their father had had four thousand dollars that Victor did not know about. Stunned, Victor wants to know why his brother did not clarify the situation earlier, though Victor still believes that his sacrifice was necessary to show loyalty. Walter becomes angry and, after a few bitter words, flings his mother's gown into Victor's face and leaves. Accepting Victor's choice, Esther prepares to go to the movies after Solomon pays him. When they leave, Solomon is at first overwhelmed by his age and his task, but then he discovers the laughing record and puts it on, and *The Price* closes with laughter.

Themes and Meanings

The Price dramatizes two sides of a dilemma: to sacrifice ambitions and desires for a loved one and then lose oneself, or to not make the sacrifice, in which case one must struggle with feelings of guilt. Victor chose the first route, while Walter chose the second. Thus, Victor sacrificed his ambition, his desire to become a scientist, in order to help his father, and the result is that he is trapped in a job he despises and he feels lost, unable to make a decision about retirement and a new career. Walter, who fled his responsibility to a father crushed by the stock market crash of 1929, pursued a successful career as a doctor but is now tormented by guilt, so much so that he attempts to bribe Victor to alleviate it. At the end of the play, when Walter comments that he will not allow Victor to make him feel guilty again, it is clear that Walter actually has been tormenting himself.

Each brother envies the other. Victor envies Walter's successful career, while Walter envies Victor's generous spirit. Neither man, however, can return to his original choice and undo it. Victor understands this finality by the end of the play, while Walter is still trying to erase the years, his responsibility to his father, and his guilt. Gregory Solomon, whose wisdom lives up to his name, understands the problem with time and the irrevocability of past choices. He describes a recurring memory of a daughter who committed suicide. If he could talk to her again, what would he say? Furthermore, memory is fragmented; the whole of the past is impossible to recover. The past is, as Victor says at the end of act 1, like a dream. For each brother his past choice is as impossible to recover as is the protagonist-narrator's other path in Robert Frost's "The Road Not Taken" (1920).

Arthur Miller, in a production note, warns future actors and directors not to choose between Victor's ethic and Walter's. He says,

> As the world now operates, the qualities of both brothers are necessary to it; surely their respective psychologies and moral values conflict at the heart of the social dilemma. The production must therefore withhold judgment in favor of presenting both men in all their humanity and from their own viewpoints. Actually, each has merely proved to the other what the other has known but dared not face. At the end, demanding of one another what was forfeited to time, each is left touching the structure of his life.

Dramatic Devices

One of the most difficult tasks onstage is to move back in time. In *All My Sons* (pr., pb. 1947), Arthur Miller adopted a dramatic form used by Henrik Ibsen that ties progressive suspense to a discovery of a secret in the past. In *Death of a Salesman* (pr., pb. 1949), Miller used projected images in lighting, music associated with character and time, and Willy Loman's partially transparent house to establish past, present, and Willy's dreams. *The Price* does not use the special effects of *Death of a Salesman*, but Miller does adapt Ibsen's structure by using a room full of furniture as a portal to memory and fantasy for Walter, Victor, and Esther, and even for Solomon, though he is not a member of the family. The furniture thus enables an audience to see the characters both at the time they were making life-shaping decisions and nearly thirty years later, as they struggle with the consequences of those choices. The harp, with its cracked sounding board, is almost a stand-in for Victor and Walter's mother, and the worn easy chair represents their father.

Just as the props are entries to the past, so too are Gregory Solomon and Esther. They are indeed the furniture appraiser and Victor's wife, but they are also measures of response by Walter and Victor to their father and mother. Victor is kind to and protective of Solomon just as he was toward his father; Walter tries to get Esther's approval and favor just as he tried to win his mother's favor, competing with Victor. Walter's compliments on Esther's appearance and his fascination with his mother's elegant dresses and gowns are all of a piece. Walter thinks that Solomon is manipulating Victor just as their father did, while Victor resents Esther's snobbery and class consciousness in the same way he resented his mother's. Esther's failure to support Victor emotionally parallels his mother's failure to support his father when the family fortune collapsed.

Except for the absence of a catastrophe, *The Price* could almost be considered a tragedy rather than a melodrama, with Esther, Walter, Victor, and even Solomon experiencing recognition of their situations by play's end. *The Price*, however, is not without comedy. Solomon's decision to buy the furniture is almost as life-affirming as a romantic hero's decision to marry. His maneuvers to lower the price he pays Victor for the furniture are the moves of a comic rascal, and his repeated entrances break the tension between Walter and Victor in act 2 and are progressively more humorous. Though sorrow, guilt, and grief about past choices and their consequences dominate *The Price*, the play begins and ends with laughter—laughter in the face of life's difficulties.

Critical Context

Like many of Arthur Miller's other plays—*Death of a Salesman*, *All My Sons*, *A Memory of Two Mondays* (pr., pb. 1955), and *A View from the Bridge* (pr., pb. 1955)—*The Price* deals with the American dream of improving one's income, education, and social class. The four characters of *The Price* share this dream, but only Walter has achieved it. Solomon has built and lost several fortunes, while Victor and Esther have to be content with wage-earner prospects. Only a full scholarship to a prestigious university has rescued their son. *The Price*, however, is not an index of personal outcomes for its characters but a measure of the cost of pursuing the dream. The dilemma of Victor and Walter—choosing between their own ambitions and their father, who was broken in spirit by the Depression—is one many Americans share. Victor and Walter are not simply two parts of the same man, as Walter believes; they represent the contrary impulses in most Americans. The genesis of both impulses—selfishness and loyalty—is in the family, a family that Miller has observed acutely in all of his plays.

The goods of this world—its tape recorders, refrigerators, and Chevrolets—are important in *Death of a Salesman*, and they are in *The Price* as well; in the latter play, however, the harp, chiffoniers, divans, and dining-room table for twelve are decidedly upscale. Where Willy Loman was worried about objects being worn out before he could even pay for them, in *The Price* the furniture of the Franz family is imposingly solid and heavy with tradition. Such furniture is a challenge, Solomon observes, because it is not disposable and limits one's freedom to shop. Interestingly, Walter takes none of his family's possessions, while Victor only takes his foil, mask, and gauntlets. With these choices, Miller may be asking what is necessary, how much one needs. This issue has caused some critics to question the intensity of *The Price*, for Victor (and even Walter or Esther) is far from the hungers and appetites of a Willy Loman or a Joe Keller (in *All My Sons*). *The Price*, however, is clearer in its statement of its social dilemma than Miller's more famous plays.

Sources for Further Study

Bigsby, C. W. E., ed. *The Cambridge Companion to Arthur Miller.* Cambridge, England: Cambridge University Press, 1997.

Centola, Steve, ed. *The Achievement of Arthur Miller: New Essays*. Dallas: Contemporary Research, 1995.

Chaikin, Milton. "The Ending of Arthur Miller's *The Price*." *Studies in the Humanities* 8 (March, 1981): 40-44.

Cohn, Ruby. "The Articulate Victims of Arthur Miller." In *Dialogue in American Drama*. Bloomington: Indiana University Press, 1971.

Miller, Arthur. *Timebends: A Life*. New York: Grove Press, 1987.

Moss, Leonard. *Arthur Miller.* Rev. ed. Boston: G. K. Hall, 1980.

Nelson, Benjamin. "I Just Didn't Want Him to End Up on the Grass." In *Arthur Miller: Portrait of a Playwright*. New York: McKay, 1970.

Schlueter, June, and James K. Flanagan. *Arthur Miller.* New York: Ungar, 1987.

Schroeder, Patricia R. "Arthur Miller: Illuminating Process." In *The Presence of the Past in Modern American Drama*. Teaneck, N.J.: Fairleigh Dickinson University Press, 1989.

Weales, Gerald. "All About Talk: Arthur Miller's *The Price*." *Ohio Review* 13 (1972): 74-84.

Craig Barrow

PROOF

Author: David Auburn (1969-   )
Type of plot: Social realism
Time of plot: September, 1999, with flashbacks to September, 1995
Locale: Chicago, Illinois, at the home of Catherine's deceased father, Robert
First produced: 2000, at the Manhattan Theatre Club, New York City
First published: 2001

Principal characters:
ROBERT, a recently deceased, former professional mathematician
CATHERINE, a former primary caregiver and daughter of Robert
CLAIRE, a resident of New York, Catherine's sister and Robert's daughter
DR. HAROLD "HAL" DOBBS, a mathematician and Robert's former student

The Play

Proof revolves around a young woman, Catherine, and her reaction to her father's recent death, her sense of self, her connection with her sister, and a new relationship with one of her father's former students. On the night before her twenty-fifth birthday, Catherine prepares for her father's funeral and her newly arrived sister, who has her own plans for Catherine. Catherine also deals with Hal, a scholar who is searching through her father's numerous notebooks for new ideas and possible sparks of inspiration for new mathematical discoveries.

As the play opens, Catherine sits on the back porch and talks to Robert about her unknown plans for the future. Shortly, the audience realizes that Robert is a figment of Catherine's imagination, a phantom or ghost. Hal enters and Robert disappears. Hal's motives seem somewhat suspect to Catherine, who believes him to be completely self-serving. However, he convinces Catherine of his admiration for her late father, and she permits his continued search for her father's brilliance through his 103 notebooks upstairs. As their relationship develops throughout the play, Catherine simultaneously deals with her estranged sister, Claire. Learning that Claire finds Catherine to be mentally fragile and plans to move her to New York, Catherine resentfully struggles to ascertain whether she has inherited any aspects of her father's known insanity.

The work ends with the discovery of a proof that would be considered brilliant in the math world. The problem with its discovery is the murky identity of the author of the work. Catherine, claiming it hers, incites Hal's doubt and Claire's cynicism. Yet, once researched, Hal discovers not only that Catherine has inherited Robert's genius, but also that she has indeed made a serious revolutionary discovery. At the same time, Catherine confirms her suspicions that she not only has inherited her father's brilliance but also part of his mental illness. The play ends with Catherine agreeing to move with her sister to New York so that she will be close to family who will care for her. Yet, simultaneously, she is emotionally and psychologically satisfied in knowing that her work is indeed worthy and significant in a male-dominated field.

Themes and Meanings

Proof involves themes of identity and gender, family, and trust. The central character, Catherine, struggles with her identity in several ways. First, she exhibits the mathematic gifts of her father yet she wonders throughout the play how much like him she really is. Second, she readily gave up her education to care for her father, thus subsuming her focus on self and career to the role of caregiver. These decisions emphasize her ambivalence toward the clear gender bias in the fields of math and science. While she knows she has the ability to succeed in the field, she readily gives up her goal (a college education) for her father's care. Auburn is clearly indicating his recognition of professional gender discrepancies, that women are rare in the fields of math and science and that those biases are not always society-imposed but at times self-imposed.

Catherine illustrates the gender issue in the field of mathematics by pointing out the example of Sophie Germain, who had to reveal her mathematic discoveries through letters and under a male pseudonym in order for her thoughts to be taken seriously and finally recognized as a contribution to the field. Catherine further shows her own struggle with identity by hiding her original work, the revolutionary new proof, and by keeping it under lock and key until she finds someone whom she thinks she may be able to trust. However, once she finally reveals her work, she again struggles to establish her identity in a field that has traditionally been dominated by men and to overcome the doubts that those closest to her express regarding her abilities.

This play also illustrates a concern with family dynamics. Again, Catherine faces the problem of her father's death, of losing her purpose in her life—that is, taking care of her father. At the same time, she must deal with her sister Claire, from whom she has grown apart and who has plans to move her sister, with or without Catherine's agreement or cooperation. Claire clearly questions Catherine's state of mind and her ability to take care of herself, doubting Catherine's ability to survive on her own. The relationship between the two women is antagonistic at many points in the work.

The final theme Auburn explores in the work is that of trust. Catherine must face and work through the fact that neither her sister nor her lover, Hal, trusts her completely. Not only does their distrust of her lessen her self-image, but it also diminishes her diminished sense of identity—of knowing who she is and what she can accomplish in the academic arena. Catherine eventually accepts the lack of trust between Claire and her, but leaves Chicago strengthened upon learning that Hal finally believes her, her work, her genius, and her contribution to the field of mathematics.

Dramatic Devices

Auburn uses a variety of techniques to achieve his explorations of his themes. He begins the work *in medias res*, that is, after a crisis, the death of Catherine's father, but before the funeral and Catherine's subsequent proof of brilliance and move to New York. This technique invites the audience to search for the meaning in Catherine's behavior.

Auburn applies the device of stream-of-consciousness in order to convey the story of Catherine and her emotional, physical, and psychological development. By using stream-of-consciousness, Auburn forces the reader to flash back to moments in Catherine's past. The first act begins on the night before Catherine's twenty-fifth birthday and her father's funeral and ends on the day after the funeral and reception. However, at the beginning of act 2, Auburn reverts to a moment four years earlier, just before Catherine began pursuing a college career at Northwestern University and a few short months before her father's final descent into insanity. As the audience witnesses this scene, when Catherine leaves home and parts from Robert, they also recall Hal's presentation, four years later, of a heartfelt note of pride her father once wrote in a journal about Catherine. Auburn allows the reader to see the interaction between father and daughter that led up to the writing of that entry.

In act 2, scene 2, Auburn brings the play to the present, the day after the funeral, when Hal and Claire question Catherine's ability to have written a revolutionary new proof that Hal has just discovered. After three scenes of defense, Auburn flashes back to Catherine's realization of her father's insanity more than three years earlier, after she had left school to take care of him. Auburn makes sure the reader realizes that Robert could never have written the proof in the demented state to which he had fallen in those last years. The final proof of Catherine's abilities in the field of mathematics is realized in the last scene, a flash forward to the present, when she and Hal sit down to discuss her arrival at her work. While this narrative technique is troublesome to inattentive viewers, it is highly effective in keeping the audience searching for proof of both Catherine's brilliance and her sanity.

Further, Auburn employs the element of irony in the title and in the controversy of the work. A proof in mathematics is supposed to resolve a problem and provide absolute certainty of a conclusion to a problem. However, Auburn illustrates irony of human behavior upon the discovery of Catherine's proof; it casts an uncertain shadow on her identity as perceived by others and reflects uncertainty in those who find it. The mathematical proof of the play highlights the lack of trust and the surmounting doubt of each character in the play.

Critical Content

The winner of the 2001 Tony Award for best play and the Pulitzer Prize in drama, *Proof* is a significant text that explores character development, individual identity, and the importance of achieving one's potential. Catherine fights many barriers in achieving her own potential: She silently combats her family, who has wordlessly assigned her to the role of caretaker of her mentally ill father and to a subsequently reduced mental state. Assuming the traditional female role of caretaker, Catherine secretly explores her astounding gift for numbers by working on a revolutionary new discovery of her own in mathematics. However, instead of sharing her discovery with the world, she acquiesces to the male-dominated profession that doubts her abilities, allegedly because of her limited education, but in reality because she has never shown outward proof that she has inherited her father's gift for numbers. Not only does she face the barriers of family, but she also faces the stereotypes that society places on women and her own willingness to bow down to those limitations. Catherine finally shows her abilities and proves her talents as the play concludes, and the audience leaves the theater with an optimistic expectation that Catherine will be able to forge ahead and succeed in the field of mathematics.

Proof is significant for a number of reasons. First, it stresses the importance of being true to one's identity and of pursuing one's greatest potential, even in the face of almost hopeless odds in a biased society. Second, the play emphasizes the absurdity of discrimination: Even a person considered slightly "off" can contribute to society through a variety of avenues. Finally, the play illustrates the importance of trust and faith in helping all humans to achieve their identities and potentials through mutual and constant support.

Sources for Further Study

Brustein, Robert. "On Theater—Or, in the Heart or in the Head." *The New Republic* 224 (November 13, 2000): 28.

Congdon, Constance. "God Is in the Numbers." *American Theater* 17 (September, 2000): 72.

Flynn, Michael. "Science on Center Stage." *Bulletin of the Atomic Scientists* 57 (July/August, 2001): 9-10.

Gussow, Mel. "With Math, a Playwright Explores a Family in Stress." *New York Times*, May 29, 2000, p. E9.

Rockmore, Daniel. "Uncertainly Certain in Mathematics and Life." *Chronicle of Higher Education* 46 (June 23, 2000): B9.

Lisa A. Kirkpatrick Lundy

PURLIE VICTORIOUS

Author: Ossie Davis (1917-   )
Type of plot: Farce
Time of plot: The 1950's
Locale: Southern Georgia
First produced: 1961, at the Cort Theatre, New York City
First published: 1961

Principal characters:
PURLIE VICTORIOUS JUDSON, a self-ordained minister in his thirties
LUTIEBELLE GUSSIEMAE JENKINS, a pretty young housemaid from Alabama
MISSY JUDSON, Purlie's sister-in-law
STONEWALL JACKSON "OL' CAP'N COTCHIPEE" COTCHIPEE, the owner of the cotton plantation
GITLOW JUDSON, Purlie's older brother
CHARLIE COTCHIPEE, Ol' Cap'n Cotchipee's only son
IDELLA LANDY, Charlie Cotchipee's mammy

The Play

Purlie Victorious satirizes the old southern traditions and stereotypes. The play revolves around the attempt of the protagonist, Purlie, to buy back the Big Bethel Church (actually a barn that was used as a church) from Stonewall Jackson Cotchipee, commonly known as the Ol' Cap'n Cotchipee. The Ol' Cap'n is a firm believer in segregation. Purlie has returned to buy back the old barn and start his own church. His plan to obtain money by outwitting the old man is at the heart of this farce.

The money in question belonged to Purlie's deceased aunt, who had received a legacy of five hundred dollars from her mistress. The money is now in the custody of Ol' Cap'n. The Ol' Cap'n is unaware that Bee, Purlie's cousin and the lawful inheritor of the money, has recently died. Purlie plans to dupe Ol' Cap'n by having Lutiebelle impersonate Bee and claim her inheritance. Purlie's brother and sister-in-law doubt if Purlie can fool the old man.

The second scene shifts to the commissary office. Charlie Cotchipee, brought up by Idella Landy after his mother died in childbirth, is the awakened liberal, a believer in the rights of African Americans. He is nursing a broken nose as a result of a scuffle at the local bar, where he voiced his integrationist ideas publicly. His father berates his "Yankee propaganda." Going over the accounts, Charlie objects to the continuing practice at the commissary to sell spoiled flour, rotten beans, and tainted meat to the workers. The Ol' Cap'n, however, sees no need to change the tradition. When the son points out that every family owes them so much money that they would never be able to get out of debt, the Ol' Cap'n retorts, "It's the only way to keep them working." Gitlow, trusted by the old man, arrives to announce the arrival of "Cousin Bee." The Ol' Cap'n is so bent on convincing Charlie that his segregationist views are shared even by Gitlow that he does not pay attention to the news of Bee.

Act 2 brings Purlie and Lutiebelle, impersonating Cousin Bee, to visit the Ol' Cap'n. Purlie has coached Lutiebelle in the ways of educated ladies, but as a simple woman, she can barely keep her words straight without alluding to her mistress. In an effort to distract the sharp old man, Purlie presents him with the "Great White Father of the Year" award. The outrageous plan seems to be succeeding despite Lutiebelle's malapropisms and inaccuracies about Bee's family: The Ol' Cap'n is momentarily distracted by Purlie's award, which seems to vindicate his views on segregation. The money is about to exchange hands, but the ploy fails as Lutiebelle signs her own name on the receipt. Purlie manages to escape before he can be arrested by the sheriff.

Scene 2 of act 2 takes place two days later. Purlie returns to his brother's home and finds out that Gitlow left Lutiebelle at the Ol' Cap'n's house to help with the dinner, for the old man promised to send her five hundred dollars. Purlie is no stranger to the old man's lecherous habits and is furious. As Purlie is about to leave, a disheveled Lutiebelle arrives with a rolling pin still in her hand. Hearing of the old man's attempt to assault her, Purlie is beside himself and leaves to challenge the Ol' Cap'n.

Act 3 takes place on the same day. Purlie is still at large. He returns after a while, proclaiming that his enemy has been slain. No one believes him until he shows the Ol' Cap'n's bullwhip in his possession, because they know that the old man would never have willingly parted with his whip.

The rejoicing ends when Idella comes to warn Purlie that the Ol' Cap'n is coming with the sheriff looking for the thief who stole five hundred dollars and his bullwhip. Before Purlie can be arrested, Charlie is brought in by the sheriff as the suspected thief. Charlie confesses then that he obtained the deed to the church but registered it in Purlie's name. The old man is so shocked at the turn of events that he breathes his last breath standing up. As an acknowledgment of his contribution to the establishment of Purlie's church, Charlie is voted its first member. The epilogue shows the funeral of the Ol' Cap'n in the new church. The coffin holds the stiff body of the old man in standing position with the Confederate flag and his bullwhip beside him. In his oration, Purlie proclaims the dawn of a new day in the South.

Themes and Meanings

In *Purlie Victorious*, Ossie Davis turns to laughter as a means of overcoming racial bigotry. He uses stereotypes of both blacks and whites and racial clichés to make audiences laugh at the follies of all characters.

Ol' Cap'n Cotchipee owns all the land around the farm and though legal slavery is dead, he keeps economic slavery alive. Like the old plantation owners, he believes in perpetuating the myth of the shiftless, lazy, and carefree African American under a benevolent master. He makes it clear who the master is, and even trusted Gitlow is threatened with a whipping if he ever questions the Ol' Cap'n's orders. He is smitten by the beautiful Lutiebelle and, in the plantation tradition, considers it fair game to bed her. He has no patience with his son, who constantly reminds him that the Supreme Court has declared segregation illegal.

If the Ol' Cap'n is the old plantation owner incarnate, Purlie and his clan play up the traditional African American stereotypes, albeit to fool the old man. In Missy's words, Purlie has "the best second hand education." He understands his limitations in the conservative South but believes in his ability to outwit the old man. He threatens to beat the old man for molesting Lutiebelle but in the end maintains that nonviolence is the best way to uproot segregation. He believes in the beauty of blackness, and his praise of Lutiebelle, amusing as it is with its hyperboles, is an expression of his beliefs.

Gitlow, Perlie's brother, is the Uncle Tom figure. He is the Ol' Cap'n's supposed trusted worker, but he understands perfectly that his recently bestowed appointment as the Deputy for the Colored is not enough to save him from the wrath and whipping of the old man. He plays the game of appeasing the old man, enthusiastically supporting all that the Ol' Cap'n says about race relations and demeaning himself.

Missy seems to be the stereotype of the old "Aunty" figure—kind, genial, and ever giving—but the real Missy is no one's fool. She is a loving sister-in-law to Purlie but is clear-eyed enough to see through him. As she tells Lutiebelle, Purlie is "somebody else" every time she sees him. She is aware of her husband's Uncle Tom qualities and knows when to exercise her power over him and assist Purlie to claim the money.

Lutiebelle GussieMae Jenkins, the naïve, almost foolish young woman with a pompous name, is a caricature of the house slave. She cannot express a single idea without referring to Miz Emmylou, her mistress. Her portrayal reveals the lingering ill effects of the system of slavery and denigration of women, for Lutiebelle has no confidence in herself or pride in her beauty and ability. The dramatist emphasizes this sad outcome without resorting to long harangues on the stage.

In short, the play's characters, stereotypes though they may be, reveal a truth about African American lives and their subtle experiences with racism. Davis provides a lighthearted but true and poignant depiction of the way in which African Americans have survived the heritage of slavery.

Dramatic Devices

Ossie Davis uses structure, dialogue, and caricature as the primary means of conveying his satire on the southern segregationist way of life. All the three acts of the play, except for the last scene at the newly acquired church, are set on the plantation. The dialogue, the primary means of character development, uses dialect, black idiom, and malapropisms to enliven the scenes, and the ensuing laughter gently draws attention to the underlying unfairness of the world faced by African Americans. For instance, when the Ol' Cap'n is trying to establish that he is a caring man, he notes, "My ol' Confederate father told me on his deathbed: feed the Negras first—after the horses and cattle—and I've done it evah time!" He worries, "What's gonna become of 'em . . . afer I'm gone?" When Purlie questions Lutiebelle's attitude toward her race, she retorts, "Oh, I am a great one for race pride, sir, believe me—it's just that I don't need it much in my line of work."

Incongruity and exaggeration are perfect tools for showing the absurdity of the situation. All the characters are caricatures; hence they draw the audiences' attention to their idiosyncrasies. Davis uses contrast as an effective means of highlighting characters. The old man and his son Charlie hold contrary views about the rights of African Americans in the new South. Purlie and his brother Gitlow present another contrast: Gitlow is the Uncle Tom figure, while Purlie is the "New Negro" ready to claim his rightful place. Ida and Missy, the counterparts of the old house and field slaves, are reminders of the old system. Deceased Cousin Bee, who was struggling to educate herself, is the opposite of Lutiebelle, a bumbling, uneducated young woman who blindly reiterates what her mistress says. In portraying these characters, Davis laughs with the black characters, never at them.

Critical Context

Ossie Davis left Howard University to pursue a career as a dramatist. He turned to acting to make a living but kept his dramatist dream alive. His earlier one-act play, *Alice in Wonder* (pr. 1952), portrayed the insidious effects of McCarthyism. Later renamed as *The Big Deal* (pr. 1953), the play did not fare well. Encouraged by the unprecedented success of Lorraine Hansberry's *A Raisin in the Sun* (pr., pb. 1959), Davis turned to writing again and *Purlie Victorious* was the product. He mentions in his autobiography that he went looking for a hero and found an endearing fool.

Purlie Victorious was staged on the Cort Theatre in New York City on September 28, 1961. It was acclaimed in *The New York Times* by Howard Taubman and reviewed by several other local theater critics. Most reviewers commended Ossie Davis for his success in taking a racially charged issue and portraying the lives of African Americans in the South in a gentle, humorous tone. The success of *Purlie Victorious* established Davis's reputation and opened up the possibilities for other African American dramatists.

Despite the long run of more than 250 performances, *Purlie Victorious* was not a financial success. Davis appealed in vain to churches, socials, and fraternities for support. In 1963, the play was adapted for the screen under the name *Gone Are the Days*. In 1970 the musical *Purlie* (pr. 1970) was aggressively marketed to African American audiences. He published and produced two more plays: *Curtain Call, Mr. Aldridge, Sir* (pr. 1968, pb. 1970), a portrayal of Ira Aldridge, the famous Shakespearean actor, and *Escape to Freedom* (pr. 1976), the story of abolitionist Frederick Douglass as a young man, but none equaled the success of *Purlie Victorious*. *Purlie Victorious* has not been forgotten and continues to be a favorite on college campuses all across the United States.

Sources for Further Study

Abramson, Doris E. *Negro Playwrights in the American Theatre, 1925-1959*. New York: Columbia University Press, 1969.

Davis, Ossie. "Interview with Ossie Davis." Interview by Dwight E. Greer. *High Plains Literary Review* 9 (Spring, 1994): 74-80.
Davis, Ossie, and Ruby Dee. *With Ossie and Ruby: In This Life Together.* New York: William Morrow, 1988.
Funke, Lewis. *The Curtain Rises: The Story of Ossie Davis*. New York: Grosset and Dunlop, 1971.
Mitchell, Louis. "Ossie Davis." *Contemporary Dramatists*. 5th ed. Edited by K. A. Barney. London: St. James Press, 1993.
Taubman, Howard. "Ossie Davis Stars in His Play at Cort." *New York Times*, September 29, 1961, p. 29

Leela Kapai

THE QUARE FELLOW

Author: Brendan Behan (1923-1964)
Type of plot: Tragicomedy
Time of plot: The 1950's
Locale: Dublin, Ireland
First produced: 1954, at the Pike Theatre, Dublin, Ireland
First published: 1956

Principal characters:
DUNLAVIN, a prisoner
NEIGHBOUR, an older prisoner
REGAN, a prison guard
CRIMMIN, a young guard
HOLY HEALEY, a representative of the Justice Department
THE HANGMAN, the executioner
THE QUARE FELLOW, an anonymous condemned man

The Play

The Quare Fellow begins and ends in song, with a prisoner in solitary confinement plaintively chanting the jailhouse dirge "The Old Triangle." As a guard rouses prisoners in their cells, various of them begin talking, and one, an older man named Dunlavin, emerges polishing a chamber pot. He is tidying his cell, awaiting the visit of Holy Healey, a Justice Department representative who Dunlavin hopes will help him secure lodgings when he is eventually paroled.

The main topics of conversation are the imminent execution of a man who killed and mutilated his brother and a second murderer who has been granted a reprieve. Dunlavin is particularly repulsed by the thought that still another prisoner convicted of a sex crime will occupy a cell nearby. In Dunlavin's view, murder is a far more acceptable crime than sexual deviancy.

As the prisoners discuss the details of execution, the reprieved man and the new one enter, and talk centers again on the topic of acceptable crimes. Dunlavin and Neighbour soon begin reminiscing about women they knew during their brief freedom, until Warder Regan appears with rubbing alcohol to administer to the older convicts' aching legs. As the guard rubs him, Dunlavin sneaks repeated gulps from the spirits, until Healey arrives, dispensing platitudes as he chats with the prisoners.

In a brief exchange with Regan, Healey expresses pity for the men yet defends execution, while Regan condemns the practice. In his interview with Dunlavin, Healey, in spite of his humanitarian fulminations, avoids committing himself to aiding the man. Act 1 abruptly closes as the reprieved man attempts to hang himself and is cut down by the guards.

Act 2 again opens with verses from "The Old Triangle," as prisoners wander about the exercise yard, again discussing the impending execution. Neighbour and a now-drunk Dunlavin wager their rations of Sunday bacon on the chance of a reprieve for the condemned man. A British prisoner calls down into the yard and drops a note to be given to a friend outside to secure his bail. One man, who will be freed the next day, agrees to deliver the note. The prisoners soon direct their attention to the cook, who crosses the yard with a meal for the condemned man, and conversation now revolves around speculation about the contents of the meal.

After the prisoners are returned to their cells, the condemned man is brought to a side yard, while a work detail emerges to finish digging a grave. As the prisoners smoke cigarettes Regan has given them, they argue about the guard's temperament and reveal that, because of his concern and compassion, he is always chosen by the condemned to stay on watch for their final night on earth. Soon the prisoners begin arguing about law and order, as an embezzler vociferously favors harsh punishment to forestall the forces of chaos. Another young prisoner, who speaks alternately in Irish and English, expresses unusual compassion to the condemned man, wishing him "peace on the other side."

After Regan enters and commands the men back to their task, he and the young guard, Crimmin, discuss the execution procedures, and Regan tries to impress on Crimmin his duty to console the condemned man. After the prisoners exit, Crimmin and Regan meet the executioner, an otherwise abstemious British pub owner who drinks before each hanging. The act ends with Regan speaking out against capital punishment and encouraging Crimmin to attend to the condemned man, as "The Old Triangle" resumes.

Act 3, which is divided into two scenes, opens with an older guard, Donelly, assuring a young guard that a recent retirement may mean a promotion for each of them. Donelly reveals himself as an envious hypocrite, and he is chastised for laziness by the chief guard. Regan enters and soon finds himself in an argument with the chief over the condemned man's plight. Regan is an egalitarian, arguing that the man's death has as much meaning as anyone else's; bitterly, he suggests that hangings should be performed publicly for a citizenry barbaric enough to permit them in the first place. The drunken hangman and his assistant enter, and each man reveals his distaste for the impending ritual. The scene ends with the young prisoner singing in Irish for the condemned man to hear.

The final brief scene is a riot of conflicting voices, as prisoners jostle to discover the fate of the condemned man. Mickser, the prisoner being released that day, recounts the details of the death march in the language and cadences of a racetrack announcer. After the man is hanged offstage, the play ends with yet another verse from "The Old Triangle."

Themes and Meanings

There can be no question that a major theme in *The Quare Fellow* is the place of capital punishment in civilized society. Regan offers the clearest voice of opposition to what he regards as an utterly dehumanizing and futile exercise in legal revenge. In his view killing is killing, no matter on which side of the law it occurs.

In a compelling moment, he stands in the prison yard at night, staring up at the stars, wondering if punishments like this exist elsewhere in the universe. He wonders if somewhere there is another condemned man looking up at Earth for the last time. He wearily concludes his speculations by noting,

> Though I never saw them [condemned men] to bother much about things like that. It's nearly always letters to their wives or mothers, and then we don't send them—only throw them into the grave after them. What'd be the sense of broadcasting such distressful rubbish?

All the talk and speculation about the hanging reveal a curious irony surrounding the ritual. On one hand, there is great concern and empathy for the condemned man—special meals, an unlimited supply of cigarettes, a chance for religious penance (which the murderer does not allow his victim); on the other hand, there is the mechanical cruelty of the punishment itself. The incongruous shifts in tone and action underscore the horror of the ritual and its dubious moral justification.

The conversations reveal another major theme of Brendan Behan—hypocrisy. The embezzler, for example, is positively indignant that Regan does not enthusiastically support hangings. He threatens that he will report the guard to superiors and ironically complains that taxpayers are being cheated out of services by attitudes such as Regan's. Donelly is another study in smug self-satisfaction as he avoids his rounds while extolling his qualifications for advancement. When the young guard, unnerved by all the noise in the cells, says, "It's a hell of a job," Donelly answers, "We're in it for the three P's, boy, pay, promotion and pension, that's all that should bother civil servants like us."

Behan's primary concern throughout is affirming life itself. The lively banter of the inmates, in spite of its more ghoulish preoccupations, and the general tone of jocosity support such an affirmation. When the condemned man's dignity is denied him by the officials who choose to mark his passing with a number, and not even the correct number at that, the audience is led to share Behan's conviction that human life, however ignoble, amounts to something more than a mere cipher. The lament of "The Old Triangle" in the closing lines asserts both the plight of the confined and the indomitability of the human spirit in surviving the worst of circumstances.

Dramatic Devices

In an early version of the play, Brendan Behan had far more extensive and morally astringent dialogue between Healey and Regan; on the advice of various directors, however, he was persuaded to exclude some of this. Although he cooperated with the changes, Behan apparently had little desire to make the changes himself. Such reluctance has supported the criticism that he had

> a very limited knowledge of stagecraft and lacked the artistic discipline to sit down and mold his work into a finished form. . . . The play is loose and rambling in structure, lacks the unifying focus of a central character, and is weak in plot and climax, but it still succeeds.

The issue of a central character is a valid one. The play begins by centering on Dunlavin, who occupies the audience's attention throughout act 1 and through the first half of act 2. Then he recedes in importance, and Regan takes over as the moral conscience overseeing the ensuing atrocity. However important each of these figures may be, the one character—ironically, the one who never once appears onstage—who unifies all action and remains at the forefront of the audience's attention is the quare fellow himself, the condemned man.

By denying him a proper name and granting him no physical presence in the production, Behan dramatically comments upon the inhumanity of such a penal system. The condemned man is a figure of rumor and speculation; no one appears to know him. When some of the inmates discuss his crime, its seriousness is debated heatedly. When the young prisoner from Kerry speaks up, the audience learns that he once knew the man, spoke Irish with him, and is not afraid to proclaim, "I don't believe he is a bad man . . . and I'm sorry for him." The suggestion here is that to know a fellow human being is to confirm his humanity; the young man, by virtue of his acquaintance, along with Warder Regan, is quick to defend the condemned man against his more self-righteous critics.

The play is indeed loosely constructed, wandering among various characters and prison locales. Nevertheless, it would be incorrect to suggest that the work is not organized. Behan carefully constructed the production to grow in emotional and ethical intensity. As the prisoners joke and cajole and as the guards debate among themselves, the atmosphere of tension and horror gradually builds.

While some have asserted that the conclusion is anticlimactic, its elliptical presentation only accentuates the sense of atrocity. Instead of witnessing the actual death, the audience, like the prisoners craning at their cell windows, struggles to comprehend exactly what is taking place. The finality of the death is tellingly displayed when the convicts divide up the dead man's letters to sell to the tabloids for publication.

Also noteworthy is the play's language. Behan blends various dialects and languages—working-class colloquialisms, prison argot, educated speech, British accents, and untranslated Irish—suggesting the richness and diversity of humanity itself. Language is actually another of Behan's heroes, surrounding the reader with aural richness.

The Quare Fellow gains much of its energy from a shuttling between verbal precision and indirection. Euphemisms abound, as if the person or thing itself often cannot be confronted without discomfort. Thus the condemned man is "the quare fellow," and the executioner is "himself." Through it all, the audience sees men condemned by a system yet redeemed by language.

Critical Context

The Quare Fellow was Brendan Behan's first major literary success, and it made him an international celebrity. Begun in 1946 and titled "Casadh Sugain Eile" (the twisting of another rope), the play was intended as a one-act radio production.

The play originated in Behan's prison years (he was jailed at age sixteen and served an eight-year sentence for involvement with the Irish Republican Army) and is rooted firmly in lived experience. In Mountjoy Prison, the inmates referred to a condemned man as "the quare fellow," and one acquaintance of Behan, Bernard Kirwan, had been convicted of murdering his brother. The night before he died, Kirwan told Behan, "I will be praying for you in Heaven tonight." Many of the events surrounding this hanging found their way into the play.

The success of the play encouraged Behan's already outlandish personal proclivities. The week after the play opened, he appeared, clearly intoxicated, on British Broadcasting Corporation (BBC) television for a nearly unintelligible interview with Malcolm Muggeridge. Behan the person became as popular as Behan the writer; as his success grew, so did his physical dissipation.

The Quare Fellow encouraged Behan to move on to the greatest work of his short career, *The Borstal Boy* (1958), a gripping memoir of his years of incarceration. His later play *The Hostage* (pr., pb. 1958) was also an international success, elevating him in the minds of many to the ranks of one of Ireland's most outstanding twentieth century playwrights.

Like Sean O'Casey before him, Behan explored the lives of working-class people and the dubious glories of patriots. Behan's work reveals a keen ear for spoken language with all of its possibilities for subtlety, extravagance, wit, and pathos. His immediate subject in work after work is Ireland—its people, its troubles, its uniqueness—but as *The Quare Fellow* demonstrates, Behan also spoke to the human condition. It is as both Irish and world writer that Behan will be remembered.

Sources for Further Study

Boyle, Ted E., ed. *Brendan Behan*. New York: Twayne, 1969.

Hogan, Patrick Colm. "Class Heroism in *The Quare Fellow*." *Etudes Irlandais* 8 (December, 1983): 139-144.

Jeffs, Rae. *Brendan Behan: Man and Showman*. London: Hutchinson, 1965.

Kearney, Colbert. *The Writings of Brendan Behan*. London: Hutchinson, 1977.

McCann, Sean, ed. *The World of Brendan Behan*. New York: Twayne, 1966.

McMahon, Sean. "*The Quare Fellow*." *Eire-Ireland* 9, no. 4 (1969): 143-157.

Mikhail, E. H., ed. *Brendan Behan: Interviews and Recollections*. Totowa, N.J.: Barnes and Noble, 1982.

O'Connor, Ulick. *Brendan Behan*. Englewood Cliffs, N.J.: Prentice-Hall, 1970.

Witoszek, Walentyna. "The Funeral Comedy of Brendan Behan." *Etudes Irlandais* 11 (December, 1986): 83-91.

David W. Madden

A RAT'S MASS

Author: Adrienne Kennedy (1931-)
Type of plot: Surrealist
Time of plot: A summer evening
Locale: A house called "Rat's Chapel"
First produced: 1966, by the Theatre Company of Boston, Boston, Massachusetts
First published: 1968, in *New Black Playwrights*

Principal characters:
SISTER RAT "KAY," who has a rat's belly and a human head
BROTHER RAT "BLAKE," who has a rat's head and a human body
ROSEMARY, a white girl
JESUS,
JOSEPH,
MARY,
TWO WISE MEN, and
A SHEPHERD

The Play

A Rat's Mass is set in the rats' house, which is represented by two black chains forming an aisle, a red carpet runner, and candles. At the far left stand Jesus, Mary, Joseph, two Wise Men, and a Shepherd in procession formation. As the play opens, Brother Rat kneels, facing the audience, while Sister Rat stands at one end of the red aisle.

In his opening speech, Brother Rat mentions a "dying baby, Nazis, screaming girls and cursing boys, empty swings, a dark sun." He talks about death and announces that in his vision he sees Rosemary exalted at the top of a playground slide. As he speaks, he alternately kneels and stands, and the chains swing lightly. Sister Rat interrupts occasionally to remind Brother Rat that they have sworn—on Rosemary's Holy Communion book and on their father's Bible—to keep their secret forever. In this speech are embedded many of the play's dominant images— Nazis, playground equipment, death, gray cats, winter. At the end of Brother Rat's speech, the chains cease their swinging, and the procession of Holy Figures moves toward the center.

Sister reminisces bitterly about their childhood, when they lived in a "Holy Chapel" with their parents and everyone called them "the holiest children." Now she has been sent to live with relatives in Georgia, where she hides under the house and eats sunflower petals all day. Standing before her brother, she says, "I'm going to have a baby. I got our baby on the slide." She is frightened, asking why the War started. She wants to hang herself. Brother Rat begs her to stop sending him petals and to stop saying that she must go to the state hospital; he wants her to stop talking about her rat's belly, which is growing rounder.

Brother and Sister Rat join in a chant about the Nazis and the rats that have invaded their home. They lament that "every sister bleeds and every brother has made her bleed." They equate the Communion wine with blood, but the blood they see flooding the streets is Sister Rat's.

Once again, they remember their childhood before the War, and Rosemary, the pretty Roman Catholic girl with whom they were infatuated. They envied her because she went to catechism class and because she claimed to be a descendant of the Pope, Julius Caesar, and the Virgin Mary. Rosemary taught them Latin and told them stories of Italy—and while they were playing one evening, she forced them to perform an incestuous act on the slide while she watched. As they remember the end of their childhood, Brother and Sister Rat begin calling each other by their names, Blake and Kay.

Now Kay hopes that she and Blake can be married in the state hospital to which she will be sent. It becomes increasingly clear that she has suffered a mental breakdown, presumably because of her traumatic experience on the slide. Brother and sister mourn their lost childhood and speak with disbelief about what Rosemary has done to them. Throughout the scene, the Procession occasionally marches from one side of the stage to the other and the chains swing.

Rosemary comes down the aisle in her Holy Communion dress. Blake begs her for atonement and asks her to take them beyond the Nazis so that they can sail to the Capitol. Rosemary coldly suggests that he put a bullet in his head. The Procession announces that they are leaving Kay and Blake, who beg them to stay. The members of the Procession refuse and walk out.

Kay and Blake begin a dialogue that alternates between hope and despair, between envisioning a renewed springtime and lamenting a dying baby. In unison, they chant, "Now it is our rats' mass." The stage directions indicate that from this point on their voices resemble the sound of gnawing.

Blake attempts to come to terms with what has happened. He remembers how Rosemary persuaded him and his sister to obey her, and he agonizes over the gnawed sunflower petals that Kay sends him from the hospital. As he begs for atonement, he mingles in his plea the images of winter, yellow petals, bombs, dead babies, and his love for Rosemary. He is torn between his obsession with Rosemary and his duty to his sister, between his knowledge of what happened and his desire to pretend that "one of the boys playing horseshoes" was responsible, between wanting Rosemary's love and seeing Kay's blood everywhere.

Once again, Kay and Blake become Brother and Sister Rat, as Kay remonstrates with Blake for ignoring her while she was in the hospital. She remembers their happy childhood when they went to the movies. Now, she points out, the Germans and Caesar's army are after them, and they must hide. Rosemary agrees, saying that the Nazis are after the rats.

Resigned to their fate, Brother Rat and Sister Rat chant a lament for their dead baby, for the blood that has become a red aisle runner in the street. Suddenly, Rosemary announces that it is time for her wedding with Blake, that the Nazis have arrived, and that soon Brother Rat and Sister Rat will become headless. The Procession appears, carrying shotguns. Brother Rat and Sister Rat chant once more—an acknowledgment of their approaching destruction—and the Procession shoots until the rats fall. Only Rosemary remains.

Themes and Meanings

A Rat's Mass is a play about the negative aspects of the black experience, about prejudice and hatred and rejection, about being an outsider with no hope of ever belonging, and about the failure of traditional institutions to offer any solutions to the problem. Brother Rat and Sister Rat represent the black population, Rosemary the white society that subjugates and oppresses, and the Procession of holy figures the uncaring, impersonal church, which offers neither succor nor forgiveness.

For Brother and Sister Rat, the pain of living black in a white world is realized in their adoration of Rosemary, the white child who is all that they can never be—"a descendant of the Pope and Julius Caesar and the Virgin Mary." Rosemary is the source of their feelings of rejection ("Colored people are not Catholics, are they?"), the instigator of their sin ("Rosemary said if I loved her I would do what she said"), and the reminder of their guilt ("I will never atone you"). Clad in her white Communion dress, Rosemary is both the unattainable ideal and the avenging angel.

Dramatic Devices

A Rat's Mass makes its point through its structure—a parody of the Christian Mass—which metaphorically suggests that the traditional sources of acceptance and refuge, religion and the organized church, are ineffective and carry within themselves the seeds of bigotry, hatred, and destruction. Throughout the play, Brother Rat and Sister Rat abase themselves and mechanically speak lines that sound remarkably confessional; they beg for atonement and acceptance and ask to return to the purity and innocence of childhood. Again and again they kneel in supplication. Presiding coldly over this rats' mass is the white girl Rosemary in a Holy Communion dress that represents her membership among the elect—a dress whose whiteness ironically reminds Brother and Sister Rat of their blackness and of the innocence they have lost. In the background march the Holy Family, the Wise Men, and the shepherd. As a kind of Greek chorus, they reinforce the action of the play through their movements, marching across the stage and back to underscore their indifference to the despair evident in the rats' plaintive requests. The members of the procession speak only briefly—when Brother and Sister Rat decide that their only course is suicide—and then only to announce their departure. They return at the end of the play as the firing squad, pronouncing an ironic benediction to the mass by destroying the rats as Rosemary watches impassively.

Images of death and decay pervade the play. Brother Rat and Sister Rat are both plagued by hideous dreams of the Nazis coming to kill them, of gray cats and screaming children and blood and ambulances. In their nightmares, there are worms in Rosemary's hair and in the attic where they hide. Their private world is locked in eternal winter, with no hope of spring. Even innocuous playground equipment is imbued with guilty associations; Brother Rat and Sister Rat lost their innocence on the slide, and now "Rosemary will forever be atop the slide, exalted with worms in her hair." Sunflowers, generally a symbol of hope and life, become representations of Sister Rat's breakdown when she sends their gnawed petals instead of letters to her brother.

Perhaps what is most theatrical—and sometimes most frustrating to audiences—about *A Rat's Mass* is the surrealist quality of the play. The set, composed as it is of two black chains, a red aisle runner, and candles, evokes images of a Black Mass and forbidden rituals, creating inevitable unease in the audience. The main characters, who are described as "two pale Negro children," are part rat, part human, and as their despair mounts and their hope dies, they sound more and more like rats, less and less human. Adrienne Kennedy's choice of rats as representative of a maligned and mistreated minority is especially apt: Rats—unlike mice—evoke no sympathy, elicit only disgust and the desire to exterminate them, and conjure up images of filth and degradation, which are violently juxtaposed to the Holy Family and their entourage and Rosemary in her white dress.

Most startling of the visual images in the play is the finale in which the Holy Procession—composed of the familiar biblical figures who grace every Nativity scene ever displayed—guns down the fleeing Brother Rat and Sister Rat. This nightmarish ending provides strong reinforcement for one of the play's more pervasive ideas: that the organized church is responsible in large part for racism and hatred and indeed can be directly implicated in some of the deaths of oppressed peoples. The biblical characters so long held to be symbols of salvation and redemption become in this play the agents of destruction for a pair of innocent children, whose only fault is their color and their desire to emulate and be accepted by the dominant race and culture.

Critical Context

Like most of Adrienne Kennedy's plays, *A Rat's Mass* is a curious blend of monologue and dream vision, informed by highly evocative symbolism and incantatory dialogue, laced with references to mythical and historical figures. Neither her most ambitious nor her most important, the play nevertheless is a good example of the kind of work that has earned Kennedy the acclaim of theater critics, scholars, and audiences. Like her better-known plays, *A Rat's Mass* is concerned with the anguish of not belonging, with the pain of rejection.

Funnyhouse of a Negro (pr. 1962, pb. 1969), Kennedy's best-known play and an Obie winner, reveals the confusion in the mind of Sarah, a sensitive black girl who finally commits suicide to escape the anguish of being black. In this play, ineffective religion is personified in an impotent black Jesus who appears in Sarah's hallucinations but cannot help her because he, too, is black. In *The Owl Answers* (pr. 1963, pb. 1969), "SHE who is CLARA PASSMORE who is the VIRGIN MARY who is the BASTARD who is the OWL," the main character of multiple selves, searches for her roots and a place where she belongs. Unfortunately, she belongs nowhere. She is the illegitimate child of a black cook and a wealthy white man, and the play attempts to resolve her ambivalence about her heredity and her love/hate relationship with the forbidden white world.

Since the 1980's, Kennedy's career has branched out in two directions: She has taught as a visiting faculty member at various universities, and she has written for the juvenile stage. *A Lancashire Lad* (pr. 1980) is a musical that portrays a fictionalized version of Charlie Chaplin's boyhood, focusing on the pain and poverty of Chaplin's early years. A radical departure from the dense symbolism and surrealism of her earlier work, *A Lancashire Lad* tells Chaplin's story simply and eloquently. Another play for young people, *Black Children's Day* (pr. 1980), chronicles the lives of black people in the early days of Rhode Island. In the 1990's she wrote several new plays, including *The Alexander Plays* (pb. 1992), *The Ohio State Murders* (pr., pb. 1992), *June and Jean in Concert* (pr. 1995), and *Sleep Deprivation Chamber* (pb. 1996, with Adam Patrice Kennedy).

In the early twenty-first century critical commentary on Kennedy's work is growing. Even admirers of Kennedy's work, while they praise her for the compelling power and theatricality of her plays, admit that they often are baffled by her images and ideas. Hers is the agile and innovative mind that produces work that is loved or hated, but not often analyzed or ignored. What critics and reviewers have agreed on, however, is that Kennedy's work defies interpretation by traditional methods and instead demands to be approached creatively and with a knowledge of new critical techniques, and that her contribution to the avant-garde American theater is both valuable and substantial.

Sources for Further Study

Betsko, Kathleen, and Rachel Koenig. "Adrienne Kennedy." In *Interviews with Contemporary Women Playwrights*. New York: Beech Tree Books, 1987.

Blau, Herbert. "The American Dream in American Gothic: The Plays of Sam Shepard and Adrienne Kennedy." In *Modern Drama* 27 (1984): 520-539.

Bryant-Jackson, Paul K., and Lois More Overbeck, eds. *Intersecting Boundaries: The Theatre of Adrienne Kennedy*. Minneapolis: University of Minnesota Press, 1992.

Cohn, Ruby. *New American Dramatists, 1960-1980*. New York: Grove Press, 1982.

Diamond, Elm. "Adrienne Kennedy." In *Contemporary Dramatists*. 6th ed. Detroit: St. James, 1999.

Forte, Jean. "Realism, Narrative, and the Feminist Playwright." In *Feminist Theatre and Theory*, edited by Helen Keyssar. New York: St. Martin's Press, 1996.

Kintz, Linda. *The Subject's Tragedy: Political Poetics, Feminist Theory and Drama*. Ann Arbor: University of Michigan Press, 1992.

Tener, Robert. "Theatre of Identity: Adrienne Kennedy's Portrait of the Black Woman." *Studies in Black Literature* 6 (1975): 1-5.

E. D. Huntley

THE REAL THING

Author: Tom Stoppard (Tomas Straussler, 1937-)
Type of plot: Comedy
Time of plot: The early 1980's
Locale: England
First produced: 1982, at the Strand Theatre, London
First published: 1982

Principal characters:
HENRY, a dramatist
CHARLOTTE, an actor, Henry's first wife
DEBBIE, Henry and Charlotte's daughter
ANNIE, an actor and social activist, Henry's second wife
MAX, an actor, Annie's first husband
BILLY, an actor
BRODIE, a protester turned writer

The Play

As *The Real Thing* opens, the audience watches Max building a pyramidical house of cards. As he is about to add a pair of cards, a slamming door announces the return of his wife, Charlotte, and the cards collapse. With scalpel-like precision, Max begins to question Charlotte about her trip to Switzerland, finally revealing that he has discovered her passport in the recipe drawer and is now aware that many of her "trips," like this one, never really occurred. He congratulates her on the fine touches such as the Rembrandt placemats procured for her mother when she was supposed to have been in Amsterdam, for it is "those little touches that lift adultery out of the moral arena and make it a matter of style." They exchange acid remarks about the number of her lovers, with Max asking finally if her current lover is anyone they know; Charlotte responds that *he* is no longer anyone she knows.

Scene 2 reveals that what the audience has just seen was not "the real thing," but only a scene from a play Henry has written titled *House of Cards*. Charlotte, who is married in real life to Henry, not Max, is complaining about the part Henry has written for her in that play. Henry is too idealistic, too much a man of words to really know women or to portray believable characters in his works; he sacrifices reality for wit. At that moment Annie (married to Max) enters, fresh from her work on the Justice for Brodie campaign. Private Brodie, after meeting Annie on a train going to an anti-missile demonstration, became so genuinely committed that he assaulted two policemen and started a protest fire, using the wreath of the Unknown Soldier as kindling. For this "stupid piece of bravado and a punch up," Brodie was sentenced to six years, and Annie has taken up his cause.

Brodie, however, is not the only man on Annie's mind: She and Henry are having a real-life affair. Indeed, she urges Henry to make love to her on the carpet while Max and Charlotte are in the kitchen chopping turnips. Henry demurs, rejecting as a foolish, unnecessary risk what Annie regards as a concrete expression of genuine passion. They agree on a safer meeting later in Annie's car, only to find in scene 3 that such safety is illusory. In an altercation which mirrors the play-within-the-play in scene 1, Max confronts Annie with Henry's handkerchief, discovered in her car. She confesses that she loves Henry.

Scene 4 is reminiscent of scene 2, except that it is now Henry and Annie, married only fifteen days, who are talking, with Annie already protesting, much as Charlotte had, Henry's preoccupation with work and his ignoring of her. "You don't care enough to care," she tells him, teasing him with the story of an actor who sticks his tongue in her ear whenever he gets the chance. Henry is willing to grant other men "the odd crumb of ear wax from the rich man's table," for he is secure in the insularity of passion. He loves love, the way it "blurs the distinction between everyone who isn't one's lover."

Act 2 opens two years later. Henry, who loves sentimental pop music, is trying to like Annie's classical music. He is also writing superficial film scripts instead of "the real stuff" in order to meet the alimony payments due Charlotte. Though Annie will be acting in a production of John Ford's *'Tis Pity She's a Whore* (pr. c. 1629-1633) in Glasgow, she is really far more interested in performing in a play that Brodie has written about his experiences as a protester. Henry reads a section from Brodie's script in which Brodie, called Billy in the play, portrays his meeting with Annie on the train. Brodie's use of language, he complains, is horrendous. Words are sacred and deserve respect: "If you get the right ones in the right order, you can nudge the world a little or make a poem which children will speak for you when you are dead." Annie, by contrast, admires Brodie's real-life commitment and accuses Henry of wanting to keep Brodie in his place and keep writing a sacred preserve for the initiated only. She would like him to rewrite Brodie's play so it might be produced. He refuses, protesting that her concern must result from the fact that she fancies Brodie.

In two of the following scenes words from plays become real as Annie, now on her way to Glasgow, has a real-life actor named Billy approach her in much the same words as the fictional Billy in Brodie's play. Though Billy, like Henry, sees flaws in Brodie's play, he promises to perform in it for her sake, making a personal commitment that Henry would not. Later, rehearsing the incestuous love scene from *'Tis Pity She's a Whore*, Annie and Billy become lovers.

Meanwhile, as Henry visits his daughter, Debbie, Charlotte accuses him of always having used his romanticism about literature and people as an excuse for never really being involved with them beyond his own idea of them. He protests that it is not difficult to love people at their best; loving them at their worst qualifies as real love. That statement is put to the test as he discovers Annie's infidelity—through an accident similar to the one he had written about in *House of Cards*—and confronts her with it. Instead of playing the guilty wife, though, Annie declares that if she has had an affair, it must have been out of her need, and she asks Henry to consider that.

Henry does, acknowledging that, as Annie charges, the pain she has caused him is "the pain of letting go of something, some idea of me which was never true." At the same time, Annie reassures him of her love. Henry rewrites Brodie's play, which is subsequently performed on television with Billy playing Brodie. Brodie's play, however, is far from the real thing. Annie has broken off her affair with Billy, and now, after Brodie accuses Henry of ruining the play he put his life and guts into by making it clever, she confesses that Brodie had been on that train with no political motives whatsoever, and that all of his protests were designed simply in order to impress her. She then unceremoniously dismisses Brodie's crude sexual advance with a bowl of dip in the face. She appeals to Henry to look after her, and he responds that he is her chap. The play closes with Henry listening to "I'm a Believer" by the Monkees.

Themes and Meanings

The Real Thing is above all else a play about the thin line between language and life, ideals and reality. Like Tom Stoppard himself, Henry is a writer, and Stoppard admitted in an interview with Mel Gussow in *The New York Times Magazine* (January 1, 1984) that the play contains many self-referential jokes. As a writer, Henry recognizes that human fictions and the language which embodies them do indeed shape one's consciousness. If human love is talked about only as biology in boiler-room, four-letter language as Henry's daughter, Debbie, suggests, then the reality created by such perception will differ significantly from one in which human relationships are romanticized and idealized. Life and love do indeed often imitate people's fictions.

On the other hand, precisely because human fictions are neat, self-contained, and sometimes antiseptic, it is also possible for them to become a refuge from reality. This is what Charlotte means when she calls Henry virginal; in her view, he lives securely untouched in his world of words and romantic ideas, never making genuine contact with any human person. Women are initially attracted by his romantic attitude only to realize later, as she does, that it is a form of indifference. Indeed, *The Real Thing* may well be considered a debate between the creative and limiting powers of romantic language. Which is "the real thing"?

To this extent, Stoppard's work may also be viewed as a "testing-play" in the grand tradition of a work like William Shakespeare's *As You Like It* (pr. c. 1599-1600), in which Rosalind realizes that Orlando's traditional romantic rhetoric, learned by the book, must be tested by his acts. This is what Annie wants when she asks Henry to rewrite Brodie's play; she is in a sense testing his words about total commitment by requiring that he leave his safe preserve and descend, simply because it is important to her, into the soiled world of causes and compromise. Having failed to make such contact with his first wife, Henry finally recognizes Annie as a person in her own right apart from his picture of her, and he acts in terms of the needs of this real, contradictory woman, not his own. At the same time, his ability to act unselfishly is sustained by that very romanticism. The "real thing," then, exists neither wholly in words nor wholly in life but in the interplay between the two.

In a larger context, *The Real Thing* may also be viewed as a caustic attack on the vulgarization of language and the subsequent vulgarization of human life that follows from it. The artist who cares about words can never regard them simply as a means to an end; care about language fosters concern for truth and accuracy.

Dramatic Devices

As a play, *The Real Thing* actively involves the audience in the very themes and questions it raises. Stoppard accomplishes this through the daring device of presenting at opening curtain the play-within-the-play, *House of Cards*. It was not the real thing, the audience discovers in the second scene, only a play. However, as they watch that second scene, which reveals the love affair of Annie and Henry and their infidelity to their spouses, they see life imitating art, though this too is only a play, as Stoppard has made them consciously aware. Thus by calling attention to the very theatricality of the work, by dealing with the drama as a form of playing, Stoppard is inviting the audience to consider how art manipulates life. The lovers are caught by the very "stagy" device of a lost handkerchief (Shakespeare's *Othello* must surely come to mind), and Annie is questioned by Henry on her return from Glasgow much as was the unfaithful wife in *House of Cards*. The meeting in Brodie's play becomes a "real-life" pick-up as Annie journeys to Glasgow.

The play is clearly structured as a series of interreflecting mirrors representing the poles of art and reality. Furthermore, literary references from other plays which Stoppard incorporates into his own play expand the mirror images into art reflecting art reflecting life. The rehearsed words of love from *'Tis Pity She's a Whore* spark real passion in Billy and Annie. Where does a role end and life begin? Is there a real distinction? Similarly, at one point in the play Annie is rehearsing August Strindberg's *Fröken Julie* (pb. 1888; *Miss Julie*, 1912), a play about the seduction of a member of the lower classes (Brodie?) by an upper-class woman (Annie?); the entire second act may even be considered Annie's seduction of Henry from his ivory tower of idealism.

Henry's problem as a writer reflects his problems as a person. There is too much idealism as well as too much emphasis on style for its own sake in *House of Cards*. Charlotte thinks taking her role was a mistake, because Henry cannot write a real woman. He confesses to Annie, "I don't know how to write love. I try to write it properly, and it just comes out embarrassing." By the play's conclusion, he has learned not only to love a real woman but also to write love. His two worlds have come together.

Critical Context

Using the dialectical possibilities of theater to dramatize the play of ideas, Tom Stoppard has given his audiences witty debates on the place of humankind in an existentially absurd universe (*Rosencrantz and Guildenstern Are Dead*, pr. 1966, pb. 1967); on ethical relativity and moral absolutes (*Jumpers*, pr., pb. 1972); on art, politics, and the uses and abuses of history (*Travesties*, pr. 1974, pb. 1975); and on journalistic ethics (*Night and Day*, pr., pb. 1978). His political commitment and concern about the treatment of dissidents is also reflected in a work such as *Every Good Boy Deserves Favour* (pr. 1977, pb. 1978). However, except for *Night and Day*, which

Stoppard himself has called naturalistic, these plays might be classed as primarily dramas of ideas. With them Stoppard has won critical acclaim for his wit, verbal pyrotechnics, cleverness, and sense of theater as play. When the plays have been criticized, it is usually for lack of adequate, believable characterization, especially of women. Many have seen his characters as props on which to stick ideas—clever spokespersons for alternate sides of a debate, but not believable humans in their own right. In a 1979 interview with Mel Gussow (*The New York Times*, July 29), Stoppard said, "I'm not a playwright who is interested in character with a capital K and psychology with a capital S—I'm a playwright interested in ideas and forced to invent characters to express those ideas."

In *The Real Thing*, Stoppard displays all of his usual verbal and theatrical talents, but he also presents his audience with truly believable and moving characters. The debate on human love, art and life, role and inner person, and what constitutes "the real thing" is as sharply joined and as brilliantly stated as in any of the earlier plays. Beyond that, however, critics generally praised *The Real Thing* for its successful characterizations. Henry, the intellectual with a boyish quality, the skeptic who is also a believer who never loses his loving feeling, has been described as Stoppard's warmest character. Annie is independent, but also patient and loving, forgiving and forgiven, a fully realized woman. Only on the character of Brodie is there serious critical debate. Some blame Stoppard for placing the antinuclear argument in the mouth of a lout who lacks the verbal skills of Henry and hence is no fit antagonist for him. Perhaps they forget that Stoppard is dealing here not with one particular cause, but with the use of language only as a means in the service of any cause. Be that as it may, there is general agreement that *The Real Thing* enlarges Stoppard's stature as a playwright who can write brilliant plays of ideas and humanly believable characters as well.

Sources for Further Study

Bigsby, C. W. E. *Tom Stoppard*. Harlow, England: Longman, 1976.

Billington, Michael. *Stoppard the Playwright*. London: Methuen, 1988.

Cameron, Lloyd. *Tom Stoppard's "The Real Thing."* Glebe, Australia: Pascal Press, 1994.

Corballis, Richard. *Stoppard: The Mystery and the Clockwork*. London: Methuen, 1984.

________. "Tom Stoppard." In *British Playwrights, 1956-1995: A Research and Production Sourcebook*, edited by William W. Demastes. Westport, Conn.: Greenwood Press, 1996.

Delaney, Paul. *Tom Stoppard: The Moral Vision of the Major Plays*. London: Macmillan, 1990.

Rusinko, Susan. *Tom Stoppard*. Boston: Twayne, 1986.

Zeifman, Hersch. "Comedy of Ambush: Tom Stoppard's *The Real Thing*." *Modern Drama* 26 (June, 1983): 139-149.

Francis Gillen

RECKLESS

Author: Craig Lucas (1951-)
Type of plot: Dark comedy; satire
Time of plot: The 1980's
Locale: A series of towns throughout the United States, each called Springfield
First produced: 1983, the Production Company Theater, New York City; revised version 1988, at the Circle Repertory Theater, New York City
First published: 1983

Principal characters:

RACHEL, a housewife and mother
TOM, her husband
LLOYD, a physiotherapist
POOTY, Lloyd's wife, a deaf-mute and paraplegic
ROY, the head of a nonprofit agency called Hands Across America
TRISH, the budget director for Hands Across America
DOCTORS ONE THROUGH SIX, various psychiatrists Rachel visits for therapy
TIM TINKO, the host of a game show called *Your Mother or Your Wife*
TALK SHOW HOST, the host of the show on which Rachel appears
DR. HELEN CARRELL, a psychiatrist and a guest on a talk show
TOM JUNIOR, the older son of Rachel and Tom
MASKED ASSASSIN, the younger son of Rachel and Tom

The Play

The play begins on a snowy Christmas Eve. Rachel is having a "euphoria attack" as she looks out her bedroom window and anticipates the happiness that Christmas Day will bring to her family. She remembers thinking that as a child she "wanted to live in Alaska because it always snowed and Santa was up there, so it must always be Christmas." Her husband, Tom, is in bed watching television with the sound turned off and seems preoccupied and conflicted. Suddenly, in a fit of conscience, Tom tells his wife that he has taken a contract out on her life and that a professional killer is about to enter their home and murder her. At first, Rachel thinks Tom is kidding, but once convinced that he is telling the truth, she leaps out their bedroom window clad only in slippers and pajamas.

Rachel trudges to an Arco gas station and is rescued from her precarious predicament by Lloyd, a physiotherapist, who takes her home and introduces her to his wife, Pooty, a deaf-mute paraplegic confined to a wheelchair. The couple welcome Rachel (who tells them her name is Mary Ellen Sissle) and help her get a job at Hands Across America, a nonprofit humanitarian foundation, where Rachel meets Roy, the head of the foundation, and Trish, its budget director. When Rachel returns from her first day at work, she discovers that Pooty is neither a deaf-mute nor a paraplegic. Pooty pretends to be disabled because Lloyd (who escaped a bad marriage and changed his name to keep from paying child support) feels better about himself if he works with physically challenged people. Lloyd will later tell Rachel that in reality he walked out on his wife, who had multiple sclerosis, and his two children—one brain damaged—because he was too drunk to see his boy playing in the snow and he ran over him with a snowblower. He left his family destitute and with no hope for their future. Pooty tells Rachel that she met Tom at work and pretended to be disabled to get his attention and keep his interest. Now Pooty must continue to feign her conditions.

Bizarre events continue to occur, and Rachel is convinced she needs therapy. She seeks the counsel of a number of inept psychiatrists, none of whom does her any good. Eventually, Lloyd confesses to Rachel that he owes his former wife thirty-five thousand dollars, and suddenly Lloyd, Rachel, and Pooty appear on an Oedipal-like game show titled *Your Mother or Your Wife* (Rachel pretends to be Lloyd's wife, and Pooty pretends to be Lloyd's mother), hosted by Tim Tinko. On the show, the three dissemblers win one hundred thousand dollars, and the first act ends in ecstatic celebration.

However, Rachel soon discovers that Trish is embezzling money from the humanitarian organization. Rachel is still seeking therapy: She is trying to deal not only with her husband's betrayal, her bizarre life with Lloyd and Pooty, and the conflicts with her job, but also with a past that includes her mother being run over by a school bus, when Rachel was six, and her father dying of a heart attack the year that she married Tom.

Tom, the wayward husband, shows up at Lloyd and Pooty's house the following Christmas bringing Rachel a stuffed dog (rather than the real one she had always wanted) and a bottle of champagne, which he found on their front stoop. Tom was able to discover where Rachel was living after seeing her on the television program. He tells her he has been trying to find her and begs her to forgive him and return home. The audience is not certain if Tom really wants Rachel back or is more interested in getting his hands on some of her game-show winnings. While Rachel is preoccupied with Lloyd, Tom and Pooty drink the champagne and instantly die. Trish had poisoned the champagne and left it on the stoop so that no one would discover she had been embezzling, but the wrong people are killed.

Rachel and Lloyd, wearing a Santa Claus suit, are now fugitives, fleeing from the police, who think they poisoned Tom and Pooty. They begin journeying through the United States, stopping at towns named Springfield from Oregon to the Southeast. Lloyd will only drink champagne, but Rachel cares for him and encourages him to eat. Despite Rachel's attempts, Lloyd dies choking on a champagne cork in a seedy hotel room in Springfield.

Rachel, now mute, is in a homeless shelter, where she is treated by Doctor Six, who turns out to be the driver of the school bus that killed Rachel's mother. Doctor Six has free tickets to attend a talk show and she persuades Rachel to accompany her. The talk show guest, Dr. Helen Carrell, singles out Rachel and pulls her onstage. Suddenly, a masked assassin (the audience later learns he is Rachel's younger son) appears in the audience aiming a gun at Rachel but mortally wounding Dr. Carrell.

It is the Christmas season, sometime later. Rachel is now a psychologist in Alaska, and she is visited by a student from the University of Alaska, Tom Junior, her son. He claims he has just come for sleeping pills, but in truth, he has not been able to deal with his mother's earlier desertion and his father's death. Rachel agrees to treat him, and Tom Junior promises to return the next day.

Themes and Meanings

Reckless is an "antirealistic" play: It does not intend to portray slice-of-life realism but instead focuses attention on a fantasy dreamworld, where events occur that could never happen in real life. Some critics fault the play because of the improbability of the events. Probability, however, is not Craig Lucas's intention. In the first scene, Rachel says to her husband that the falling snow is a big white monster that is going to carry them away into a dream. The audience is unclear if the rest of the play might be that dream. As W. A. Henry wrote in his *Time* magazine review of the play, "Only Lucas . . . understand[s] how to make something beautiful out of a dream walking."

Reckless is a radical experiment. It takes the audience on a bizarre odyssey that emphasizes the ridiculousness and randomness of life. The play has two central themes: the need both to accept and cope with the "recklessness" of life and to appreciate that life is a journey of discovery. The play has been compared to such literary works as *The Wonderful Wizard of Oz* (1900), *Alice's Adventures in Wonderland* (1865), and the film *It's a Wonderful Life* (1946). It has the "dream" aspects of *The Wonderful Wizard of Oz* and *Alice's Adventures in Wonderland*, in which one lives a "black and white" existence until a cataclysmic event hurls the person on a journey to colorful Springfield (or Oz or Wonderland), where anything is possible.

The notion of discovering what one's life means is an important lesson in *It's a Wonderful Life*, and Rachel comes to learn that lesson as she seeks solace in Alaska and is able to help her son cope with his problems. Identity is an important motif in this play as almost every character is dissembling—pretending to be someone he or she is not. By the end of the play, Rachel has learned that it is safest to be herself. The play also attempts to define love, but seems to tout its dark side, illuminating the shadows that often encircle the human heart.

Reckless is an episodic play that takes the merriness out of Christmas and employs violence, death, and exaggeration to satirize the often irresponsible ways humans live their lives. Men murder their children, women desert their children, people appear and disappear, yet people continue to live their lives, oblivious, moving to another town—another Springfield. Rachel tries not to be oblivious and is forced, as a consequence, to seek professional help. Is it a mistake to care? Is it wrong to try to find oneself? These are some of the questions the play asks the audience to ponder. By the play's end, the plot has come full circle. Rachel has left the "Springfields," moved to Alaska, accepted Christmas, and helped her son do the same.

Dramatic Devices

The episodic structure of this play, composed of twenty-eight scenes, necessitates a simplicity in staging. Any attempt to literalize the many locales in the play would be a disaster, producing an excruciatingly slow pace. Since the play is nonrealistic, economy and suggestion are employed in casting and staging. There are multiple characters and multiple locales, but neither needs to be literal.

Although the play calls for a cast of at least twenty-one characters, Lucas suggests that the play can be performed with as few as seven actors. Since there is no need to maintain verisimilitude, actors may and usually do play more than one role. It works very well, for example, if the actor who plays Tom also plays Tom Junior at the end of the play. It also works well if the six doctors are played by the same actor. The actor who plays Roy often plays the Talk Show Host and Tim Tinko, while the actor who plays Trish usually plays Dr. Carrell. This kind of "doubling" reinforces for the audience the fact that this is nonrealistic theater and asks them to make connections among the various characters each actor plays. The various locales are not literally staged either. Blocks, chairs, stools, and lighting suggest Rachel's home, the Arco gas station, Lloyd and Pooty's home, the Christmas tree in their home, the Hands Across America organization, the game show, the various hotel rooms, and so on.

Critical Context

Lucas is a prolific writer. In addition to *Reckless* (which he adapted for film), he wrote several plays, including *Missing Persons* (pr. 1981, pb. 1995), *Stranger* (pr. 2000, pb. 2002), *Blue Window* (pr., pb. 1984), *God's Heart* (pr. 1993, pb. 1999), and *The Dying Gaul* (pr. 1998, pb. 1999). With Norman René he created *Marry Me a Little* (pr. 1980), a compilation of songs by Stephen Sondheim, and with composer/lyricist Craig Carnelia he wrote the musical play *Three Postcards* (pr. 1987, pb. 1988). His first motion-picture project was *Longtime Companion*, which dealt with the sociopolitical aspects of acquired immunodeficiency syndrome (AIDS). *Reckless* is an early work, but it shows Lucas's promise as a writer with a unique voice. He has been compared to playwrights Christopher Durang and Nicky Silver, who delve into the darker sides of life by employing irony and humor. Like Durang and Silver, Lucas is not content to mirror life as it is but is interested in expanding the boundaries of the traditional play, delving frequently into fantasy and fairy tale. He seeks out new domains and experiments with the imaginary rather than the documentary.

Some critics have argued that *Reckless* does not have a consistent tone. This mixed-genre play begins as a dark comedy, humorously satirizes a life's journey, and becomes a rather serious drama toward the end. *Reckless* creates a microcosm of death and violence in which characters commit a number of sins, yet humor is a tool many of them use for survival. Consistency is not required or necessary in this play. The audience laughs at the beginning and then wonders, by play's end, what was humorous. The laughter fosters empathy, its purpose to encourage members of the audience to examine their own lives.

Sources for Further Study

DiGaetani, John L., ed. "Craig Lucas." In *A Search for a Postmodern Theater: Interviews with Contemporary Playwrights*. New York: Greenwood Press, 1991.

Gould, Christopher, ed. *Anti-Naturalism*. New York: Broadway Play Publishers, 1989.

Henry, William A., III. "Beguiling Visions." *Time* 132 (October 31, 1988): 85.

Hopkins, Billy. "Craig Lucas." *BOMB* 28 (Summer, 1989): 56-59.

Lucas, Craig. "Equality in the Theater." *BOMB* 57 (Fall, 1996): 66-70.

Parks, Steve. "Exchanging Kisses and Swapping Souls." *Newsday*, March 12, 1993, 76.

Rich, Frank. "A Christmas Fable of People Who Learn to Know Themselves." *New York Times*, September 26, 1988, pp. C19, C22.

Spindle, Les. Review of *Reckless*. *Back Stage West*, October 29, 1998, 14.

Taitte, Lawson. Review of *Reckless*. *Dallas Morning News*, December 15, 1996, p. C1.

Vaughan, Peter. "Don't Take Lucas's Plays Too Seriously." *Minneapolis Star Tribune*, July 4, 1995, p. 7E.

Judy E. Yordon

RED ROSES FOR ME

Author: Sean O'Casey (John Casey, 1880-1964)
Type of plot: Expressionist
Time of plot: 1913
Locale: Dublin, Ireland
First produced: 1943, at the Olympia Theatre, Dublin, Ireland
First published: 1942

Principal characters:
MRS. BREYDON, a woman nearing fifty
AYAMONN BREYDON, her son, a railroad worker
SHEILA MORNEEN, Ayamonn's sweetheart
BRENNAN O'THE MOOR, the owner of a few old houses
ROORY O'BALACAUN, a zealous Irelander, Ayamonn's coworker
MULLCANNY, a mocker of sacred things
THE REVEREND E. CLINTON, the Protestant rector of St. Burnupus
INSPECTOR FINGLAS, a member of the Mounted Police and the rector's churchwarden
EEADA,
DYMPNA, and
FINOOLA, Mrs. Breydon's neighbors in the house
DOWZARD and
FOSTER, members of St. Burnupus's Select Vestry, and scabs during the strike

The Play

In act 1, Mrs. Breydon worries that her son is doing too much, with his "sketchin', readin', makin' songs, an' learnin' Shakespeare." She is worried about "this sorryful sthrike" threatened by railroad workers and about Ayamonn's "runnin' afther" Sheila Morneen. Ayamonn replies that the owners will accept the workers' demands and there will be no strike; he believes that Sheila's Roman Catholic faith and policeman father are not reasons enough to give her up. Eeada, Dympna, and Finoola interrupt, bringing a statue of the Blessed Virgin, their "Lady of Eblana," to ask for soap to clean it. Sheila arrives to urge the romantic Ayamonn to earn money for their marriage. Brennan brings a young carpenter, Sammy, to sing lyrics written by Ayamonn and set to music by Brennan. Roory O'Balacaun objects to the "foreign Minsthrel Show," as Sammy sings of Kaithleen ni Houlihan, who "carries a rich bunch of red roses for me." Roory calls the song indecent, and Mullcanny scoffs at Roory's bigoted prudery. Sheila leaves, swearing that she will not see Ayamonn again; he says, "Aw, to hell with her!" The statue then disappears, and Ayamonn tries to console his neighbors. Alone with Roory, Ayamonn slowly dons his work clothes. They sing a Fenian song of rebellion as they go to work.

In act 2, the next evening, Brennan explains that he took the statue to be repainted. Ayamonn defends Mullcanny's atheistic ways to Roory and Brennan: "I'll stand by any honest man seekin' th' truth, though his way isn't my way." Mullcanny calls Brennan and Roory a "pair of damned fools." Their quarreling is interrupted by Sheila, who says that Ayamonn can have a foreman's job, but only if he abandons the workers' cause. Ayamonn is furious. Mullcanny escapes a mob in the streets, with help from Mrs. Breydon. Breaking glass sends Brennan and Roory running, but Ayamonn takes a hurling stick into the street. Brennan, Roory, and Sheila accuse Mullcanny of causing trouble with his beliefs, but he retorts that people are merely "time's promoted reptiles." Ayamonn and his mother return, followed by Eeada, Dympna, and Finoola, who sing thanksgiving for the "miracle" of their statue's return. Mrs. Breydon is relieved that her flowers were not harmed by the stones. The Rector and two railwaymen announce that the strike will begin the next day, but that it has been "proclaimed" with a "warrant of warning" from the authorities. Ayamonn defiantly burns the warrant, frightening Sheila, who urges the Rector to forbid Ayamonn to go: "Show him God's against it!" The Rector will not, and Sheila, defeated, is left alone, weeping.

Act 3 is the next evening, on a bridge on the River Liffey. Eeada, Dympna, and Finoola sell cakes, apples, and violets, observing the dark sky over a city which has become "a graveyard where th' dead are all above th' ground." Brennan, with his melodeon, sings of love; pennies are tossed his way, but the loungers scoff at him for being a miser. Only Ayamonn appreciates Brennan's song, while Roory exclaims that songs should be about ancient Irish heroes. Ayamonn urges everyone, "Rouse yourselves; we hold a city in our hands!" He is inspired, his head "set in a streak of sunlight," looking like a heroic Irish poet of legend, whose head sang after it was cut off. Colors change from black and gray to bright green, scarlet, and bronze. The city is "in th' grip o' God!" exclaims Ayamonn. He leads a song swearing to build a new city out of Dublin: "Thy people shall build a brave city,/ Th' fairest an' finest that ever was seen!" Ayamonn joins Finoola in a dance on the bridge. In each other's arms, they hear the marching feet of police coming to attack the strikers, whom Ayamonn departs to lead.

Act 4 is the next day, full of sun and flowers, at St. Burnupus. Foster and Dowzard object to a daffodil cross made by Ayamonn as too popish, but the Rector decides to use it for the Easter service. Mrs. Breydon and Sheila ask the Rector to prevent Ayamonn from leading the strikers, but he again refuses. Ayamonn, at the head of the striking workers, is asked if his life is worth risking for a shilling; he explains that "to us [a shilling] is our Shechinah, showing us God's light is near." Mrs. Breydon and Sheila plead with him to stay at the church. The people call for Ayamonn to join them, and he does. Foster and Dowzard run from a crowd that is chasing them as scabs. They believe that Catholics have started a bloodbath attack on Protestants. Dowzard seizes the daffodil Celtic cross as they hear a bugle call sounding a charge. They hear rifle fire, and Foster throws the cross to the ground, then tramples it. Finoola, in great pain, reports that Ayamonn has been killed. The Rector picks up the broken cross of flowers and laments the death of his friend.

Mrs. Breydon, the Rector, and Sheila await the arrival of Ayamonn's body. Bagpipes play as he is borne into the church. Sheila lays crimson roses on his breast. She calls Inspector Finglas a "dusky-minded killer of more worthy men." He orders everyone to leave, but Brennan refuses. He bribes Samuel to open the church door, plays his melodeon, and sings farewell to Ayamonn.

Themes and Meanings

Red Roses for Me is about spiritual and intellectual freedom: how it is achieved and what it costs. Religious and political bigotry are products of poverty and deprivation. Desperate for something to believe in, some people trust in miracles wrought by statues. They are slaves of superstition, though they are open to instruction because they are sensitive to beauty. Poetic visionaries, such as Ayamonn, translate religious faith into political action.

To do that, Ayamonn must free himself from temptations to settle for less. He must resist his mother and his sweetheart, who want domestic security. He must defend freedom of intellectual inquiry from narrow-minded bigotry, even the right of atheist Mullcanny to study and teach the science of biological evolution against attacks by Ayamonn's own friends, Brennan O'The Moor and Roory O'Balacaun, a small-time Protestant capitalist and a zealous Irish-Catholic revolutionary. These two are bound to Ayamonn by friendship and social class, unlike the two bigoted Protestant vestrymen, Foster and Dowzard, and the police inspector, Finglas. These three lack the compassion to understand Ayamonn, so they help to cause his death, which is, ultimately, a ritual sacrifice. The Rector accepts that sacrifice, as do Ayamonn's mother, Brennan, and, eventually, Sheila. They understand what the Inspector and his kind never will: The workers' strike for a shilling is a sign of spiritual integrity. Money comforts the flesh, but it is also a symbol for freedom of spirit born of hope.

Hope is the fruit of vision, and vision is a function of art, as the play shows throughout, from the opening act, with its focus on Ayamonn's rehearsal for a Shakespearean play, through the spectacle of dance and song on the "bridge of dreams" in act 3, to the Christian rituals of prayer and song in the last act. All have meaning, however, only when they are properly addressed to the satisfaction of common needs and dreams. Humankind keeps progressing because people such as Ayamonn Breydon learn to put the welfare of others ahead of their own; it is he, ironically, who carries into darkness the red roses of his own song—now a tribute to his blood sacrifice.

Dramatic Devices

Red Roses for Me uses set design, props, costumes, makeup, lighting, songs, music, and dancing to create its expressionistic effects. The closed door to the Breydon flat in the first act is balanced by a church door in the last act; the opening of the Breydons' door to their neighbors is balanced by the opening of the church door for Brennan's farewell to dead Ayamonn. The bench of flowers in front of the Breydon window is echoed by the altar in the last act, where the Celtic cross of daffodils takes the place of the railroad signal, with its transverse arms, seen through the window in the first two acts. When Dowzard and Foster trample the cross of flowers near the play's end, gunshots are heard; their action expresses the "crucifixion" of the martyred hero, Ayamonn (whose name means "everyman").

The Shakespearean play that Ayamonn is rehearsing is set in the English Wars of the Roses, and the chair that Ayamonn plans to design as a prop for his production will be a throne with the Lancastrian red rose on it. Ayamonn says that Sheila is his rose, and she places red roses on his corpse at the end. Dublin itself becomes a rose in the third act, through the lighting around the city's skyline. This act blends the rhetoric of Ayamonn with choral song, solos, and dancing in a transfiguration of the characters as prophecies of what they can become.

Lighting creates a symmetry of silver lines identifying the church steeple with the scabbard the Inspector wears and the spike on his helmet. Ayamonn's head is caught in a ray of light as if it were separated from his body. When Ayamonn dances with Finoola, they move between golden light and violet shadow to make a metaphor of enriched life for all. They dance across what Ayamonn calls a "bridge of vision." Ayamonn lights a lantern before going to his work; in the last act, a lamplighter witnesses the beginning of Ayamonn's funeral procession. Clearly, Ayamonn's death does not bring an end to the light he has brought into his world.

Costumes, too, are symbolic in the play. Ayamonn sheds the costume of his Shakespearean role and puts on the clothing of a railroad worker, showing that he is committing himself to the world of work instead of the world of play. Most of the characters have unexpressive faces, aided by makeup, to show that they have lost their souls; when they are transfigured by Ayamonn's vision, they shine with spirit. Black and gray clothing contrast with flashy uniforms and gay Shakespearean costumes. Transfigured, the women in black show bright green and silver. The lounging men glow bronze, and in the end all wear gold sunbursts on their chests.

Critical Context

After Sean O'Casey had helped to save the Abbey Theatre from financial ruin with the success of his plays *Juno and the Paycock* (pr. 1924, pb. 1925) and *The Plough and the Stars* (pr., pb. 1926), his expressionist antiwar play *The Silver Tassie* (pb. 1928, pr. 1929) was rejected by the directors (including Lady Augusta Gregory and William Butler Yeats) of the theater. O'Casey refused to compromise and never again had one of his plays produced by the Abbey Theatre. He published plays from London and there had his next plays produced, including the anti-fascist propaganda plays *The Star Turns Red* (pr., pb. 1940) and *Oak Leaves and Lavender: Or, A World on Wallpaper* (pb. 1946, pr. 1947). These plays make blatant statements of sympathy for communism, and they lose dramatic force by their stridency.

The earlier, controversial *Within the Gates* (pb. 1933, pr. 1934), a political allegory, had been set in London's Hyde Park as a protest against the economic conditions of people living through the Great Depression. O'Casey set his political farce *Purple Dust* (pb. 1940, pr. 1944) back in Ireland; in this play, English exploitation of Irish resources is analyzed effectively through satire. O'Casey returned to his familiar settings, the workers' neighborhoods of Dublin where he was reared, for *Red Roses for Me*. The play was produced by an Irish theater, though not the Abbey, and it is generally held to be one of the most successful plays from the middle period of his career. In *Red Roses for Me*, O'Casey avoided blatant propaganda, employed the Irish speech rhythms of his great early plays, and drew upon his own experiences to produce a tribute to the human spirit wherever it rises above conditions of degradation.

Sources for Further Study

Esslinger, Pat M. "Sean O'Casey and the Lockout of 1913: *Materia Poetica* of the Two Red Plays." *Modern Drama* 6 (May, 1972): 53-63.

Goldstone, Herbert. *In Search of Community: The Achievement of Sean O'Casey*. Cork, Ireland: Mercier Press, 1972.

Hogan, Robert. *The Experiments of Sean O'Casey*. New York: St. Martin's Press, 1960.

Hogan, Robert, and Richard Burnham. *The Years of O'Casey, 1921-1926: A Documentary History*. Newark: University of Delaware Press, 1992.

Hunt, Hugh. *Sean O'Casey*. 2d ed. Minneapolis: Irish Books Media, 1998.

Kilroy, Thomas, ed. *Sean O'Casey: A Collection of Critical Essays*. Englewood Cliffs, N.J.: Prentice-Hall, 1975.

Kleiman, Carol. *Sean O'Casey's Bridge of Vision: Four Essays on Structure and Perspective*. Toronto, Ont.: University of Toronto Press, 1982.

Krause, David. *Sean O'Casey: The Man and His Work*. New York: Macmillan, 1960.

Rollins, Ronald Gene. *Sean O'Casey's Drama: Verisimilitude and Vision*. Tuscaloosa: University of Alabama Press, 1981.

Schrank, Bernice W. *Sean O'Casey: A Research and Production Handbook*. Westport, Conn.: Greenwood Press, 1996.

Smith, B. L. *O'Casey's Satiric Vision*. Kent, Ohio: Kent State University Press, 1978.

Templeton, Joan. "Sean O'Casey and Expressionism." *Modern Drama* 14 (May, 1971): 99-112.

Richard D. McGhee

THE REMOVALISTS

Author: David Williamson (1942-)
Type of plot: Social realism
Time of plot: The 1960's
Locale: Australia
First produced: 1971, at Café La Mama, Melbourne, Australia
First published: 1972

Principal characters:
SERGEANT DAN SIMMONDS and
CONSTABLE NEVILLE ROSS, policemen
KATE MASON, a suburban housewife (originally KATE LE PAGE)
FIONA CARTER, a young married woman, Kate's sister
KENNY CARTER, Fiona's husband
ROB (THE REMOVALIST), a furniture mover

The Play

Violence dominates *The Removalists* but does so in a way that borders on the comic and the absurd. Act 1 opens in a Melbourne police substation, which is described as "having an air of [decrepit] inefficiency." Ross, an enthusiastic rookie policeman, has just reported for his first day of duty, only to meet a jaded veteran, Sergeant Simmonds, who is to be his superior and mentor. At first, the dialogue appears aimless, but a pattern soon forms as the sergeant explains to his new assistant the essence of police work: to do as little as possible but always to maintain the delicate balance on which control rests. Wanting to respond in a pleasing manner, the young man tells Simmonds that "you've got to be trained for all eventualities in this rapidly changing world." To this Simmonds replies, "Nothing changes in this world, boy." The sergeant then relates, with obvious pleasure, a story about another idealistic rookie who made himself ridiculous when he mistook some innocent fun for a gang rape; this recollection is only one among several hints that brutality and violence surround the substation, indeed permeate all aspects of life.

Just as their exchange begins to seem tedious, two young women interrupt. Fiona, accompanied by her sister Kate, has come to the police station to report her husband, who beat her the previous night for not emptying the kitchen garbage. Simmonds handles the complaint with mock seriousness, stating pompously, "Yes. It's pretty terrifying when the family unit becomes a seat of violence." To prove his concern, he asks Fiona to expose her bruises, which he inspects, as the stage directions say, "slowly and lasciviously"; he then tells Ross to photograph the bruises for evidence. By now he has, through his lechery, created a sexual tension between himself and the victim's sister, who is enjoying the other woman's humiliation. In the hope that he might take advantage of Kate's apparent interest in him, Simmonds offers his and Ross's assistance to "the removalists"—furniture movers, that is—whom Fiona has engaged for the next evening. Reassured by their call on society's protectors, the women leave.

As the second act opens, Fiona and her husband exchange insults until Kate arrives, soon followed by one furniture mover. Before long the policemen, Simmonds and Ross, rush into the center of the room and unintentionally perform a sight gag or two; for one thing, Ross accidentally handcuffs himself. The action then alternates between comic scenes and the brutal onstage beating of Fiona's husband, Kenny, who has been handcuffed to a door. The wife beater, however, turns out to be likable, though crude and skilled in the art of the insult. At his best when verbally assaulting his sister-in-law, he takes special pleasure in recounting her alleged sexual promiscuity. The removalist adds his share of comedy, as he and Ross carry out furniture. Kate and the sergeant discuss his wife's "twenty-seven kidney fits," the private schooling of Kate's three children, and other mundane family matters.

The brutality that punctuates these and other exchanges begins with restraint—just a punch or two by the sergeant against handcuffed Kenny. The attacks then build gradually into a frenzy of brutality against the helpless man, while no one onstage displays concern or offers assistance. The audience cannot generate much sympathy, for the brutality, while real enough, remains—strange as it may seem—quite in keeping with the comic slice of life.

Once the sisters and the removalist leave the former husband and the policemen, the spirited Kenny, who has taken all the abuse in stride, finally loses control and starts insulting Ross. Going berserk, the young policeman throws himself at Kenny, now free of handcuffs. For the first time, Kenny shows fear; he runs into the kitchen, followed by Ross. Crashes and thuds from the kitchen fill the air, yet Simmonds stands, offering no help, only grinning to himself. Once Ross has spent his fury on Kenny, he enters alone, hysterical, and announces that he has killed him. While the two men debate how to handle their predicament, Kenny comes out of the kitchen, much to their relief. The reprieve, though, is short-lived, for the hapless victim soon dies from a concussion. At this point, Ross attacks Simmonds, screaming, "Hit me where it bruises. Go on Serg! You know how to bruise a man! Go on!" The final stage directions read: "*Ross advances on Simmonds, attacking him viciously. Simmonds fights back. As the play closes the fight almost takes on the air of a frenzied ritual of exorcism.*"

Themes and Meanings

The Removalists examines the nature of violence and in so doing proposes that senseless brutality is an unchanging force stemming from a basic flaw in humankind. Thus violence of one type or another invades all avenues of human experience.

From the outset, the embittered Sergeant Simmonds informs the idealistic rookie that nothing can be done to change matters beyond the station walls. His explanation for this state of affairs is a simple one: "The world is full of human beings." So violence is inevitable. Certainly, the action in *The Removalists* could have moved in a different direction. Without a clear motive, in some ways accidental, the murder of Kenny need not have taken place, and the inexplicable ritual of brutality in which the policemen engaged cannot have much logic behind it. Once the course is set, though, violence will have its way, whether in war, in domestic life, or in national affairs. Sometimes the violence is planned, but more often, as in *The Removalists*, it selects victims randomly.

Through handling the subject of violence in so outrageous a manner, the playwright poses indirectly some vital questions. Is there a way out of this violent "ritual of exorcism"? Or is the dilemma a hopeless one? Do humans relish violence vicariously—enacted in sports, on the screen or television, or read about in the newspaper? Should brutality be met with more of the same? Who are the victims? the victimizers? David Williamson's purpose in *The Removalists* is to raise these questions, not to answer them.

Dramatic Devices

In spite of its absurdist elements, *The Removalists* is a realistic play structurally. This quality heightens the action, so that what takes place—the senseless, fatal beating of a man—appears to be altogether natural within the course of events. Even the violent action occurs for the most part onstage. If the play had forsaken the dramatic devices of realistic setting, ordinary characters, comedy, and everyday language, it would have lost much of its impact as a modern allegory pointing up the ubiquity and consequences of violence.

The two locales, the police station and the couple's apartment, are both drab and colorless, and they serve effectively as backgrounds to lives that are just the same. However, all the characters emerge as individuals in their own right who show fear, longing, weakness, strength, foolish pride, and other qualities of everyday people. There is, for example, the removalist's inflated attitude toward his work, as he reminds everyone repeatedly that his time is important: After all, he has "ten thousand dollars worth of machinery tickin' over out there." Similarly, Sergeant Simmonds displays his hypocrisy over sexual matters, Kate her pretentiousness, and Ross his fear of discovering an evil force that will destroy his idealism.

The well-paced, sharply etched dialogue—complete with one-liners, obscenity, clever insults, and sexual innuendoes—helps to carry the theme, elaborate on it, and accent it. The playwright's major tool is language, and in this play it is appropriately colored by violent tones. Throughout, the characters threaten one another in the crudest and most brutal ways. For example, Kenny tells the removalist, "Look. Piss off or I'll spray the back of your throat with teeth"; later he threatens to "hammer the bastard." Simmonds warns Kenny that he will "crack" or "split" his "bloody skull." The language describing male-female relationships also verges on brutality. Women are consistently called "tarts," "bikes," and "bitches." The battered wife tells her husband: "Well, it hardly inspires confidence when you're made love to one minute and bashed up the next." Later, Kenny explains that in the past a man gained respect from his wife by beating her at least once a week. At another point, Kate asks Simmonds what he will do if she refuses to follow his orders: "Chain me to the bloody door and rape me?"

Had the dramatic devices of action, setting, character, comedy, and language been used differently, *The Removalists* could well have turned into a tedious and didactic work rather than what it is: one that expresses with power and conviction the dilemma created by the violent nature of human beings.

Critical Context

The Removalists is David Williamson's second play and his first successful one, and it demonstrates a firm hold on what constitutes effective drama, especially the delicate balance between comedy and seriousness. In the plays and television and film scripts that have followed, Williamson has continued to maintain and strengthen this keen understanding of theatrical convention. He has also retained the conviction that drama can carry ideas and provide entertainment at the same time. His later plays place believable characters in ordinary settings and provide them with forceful dialogue and action that makes subtle comments on human nature. *The Department* (pr. 1974, pb. 1975) examines bureaucracy, *The Club* (pr. 1977, pb. 1978) exposes corruption in professional sports, and *Travelling North* (pr. 1979, pb. 1980) looks at the process of aging. Human relationships are examined in *What If You Died Tomorrow* (pr. 1973, pb. 1974) and *The Perfectionist* (pr. 1982, pb. 1983), and *Emerald City* (pr., pb. 1987) takes up the consequences of fame.

An Australian writer, Williamson draws from his own experience and sets his plays firmly within the Australian context, remaining faithful to his country's geography, place names, cultural heritage, customs, and social mores. In particular, he makes full use of the Australian vernacular in dialogue. During an interview, Williamson noted that "of all the art forms, drama is the most parochial," explaining that plays come from a "particular tribe"; he added, however, "The very best of that tribal writing transcends the boundaries of that tribe." Certainly this has proven true with Williamson's work, for it not only has earned for him a place as Australia's most respected and popular dramatist but also has gained for him a wide audience abroad. For example, *The Removalists*, so acclaimed at home because of its pure Australianness, met with great success in Poland when performed there as a protest against the government's oppressive rule.

Sources for Further Study

Carroll, Dennis. "David Williamson." In *Australian Contemporary Drama*. Rev. ed. Sydney, Australia: Currency Press, 1995.

Fitzpatrick, Peter. *Williamson*. North Ryde, Australia: Methuen, 1987.

Holloway, Peter, ed. *Contemporary Australian Drama: Perspectives Since 1955*. Sydney, Australia: Currency Press, 1987.

Kiernan, Brian. "The Games People Play: The Development of David Williamson." *Southerly* 35 (1975): 315-329.

McCallum, John. "A New Map for Australia: The Plays of David Williamson." *Australian Literary Studies*, May, 1984.

Moe, Christian H. "David Williamson." In *Contemporary Dramatists*. 6th ed. Detroit: St. James, 1999.

Rees, Leslie. *The Making of Australian Drama*. Sydney, Australia: Angus & Robertson, 1973.

Williamson, David. Interview with Ray Willbanks. *Antipodes* 2 (Winter, 1988): 104-106.

Robert L. Ross

RESTLESS HEART

Author: Jean Anouilh (1910-1987)
Type of plot: Naturalistic
Time of plot: The 1930's
Locale: France
First produced: 1938, at the Théâtre des Mathurins, Paris
First published: La Sauvage, 1938 (English translation, 1957)

Principal characters:
Thérèse Tarde, a twenty-year-old violinist
Monsieur Tarde, her sixty-year-old father
Madame Tarde, her mother
Florent France, her wealthy fiancé
Gosta, Mme Tarde's lover
Hartmann, Florent's friend

The Play

Restless Heart opens near midnight in a rundown café. The stage is dominated by a bandstand, where Monsieur Tarde's small, third-rate orchestra is finishing a set. The group is tense as they await the arrival of Florent France, a world-famous and very wealthy pianist, who has asked Thérèse, his mistress, to marry him. Monsieur and Madame Tarde are anxious about telling Gosta, the pianist, the news. Although Gosta has been Madame Tarde's lover for thirteen years, he is in love with Thérèse. Because he has been drinking and has a terrible temper, they are afraid that he will ruin everything: Madame Tarde does not want to lose him, and Monsieur Tarde expects to take advantage of his daughter's good fortune.

Thérèse is "la sauvage." She accepts her sordid background, for it has determined who she is and what she understands of the world; she does not lie, and she does not pretend to be other than what she is. She loves Florent for his decency and goodness. He offers her marriage and happiness—a key thematic concept; however, she can accept his gift only by forgetting her past. Because Florent has always been wealthy and secure, he does not understand the effects of poverty upon the human soul. Florent's friend Hartmann does, and he functions as an observer and interpreter of both worlds. He comments on the actions of the play and interprets their significance for the audience.

Act 1 depicts Thérèse's sudden realization of the unbridgeable gap between her world and that of Florent, a recognition which has been suppressed by her love. Although it is the evening of her twentieth birthday and she is looking forward to Florent's arrival at the café, her parents and Gosta become embroiled in a series of arguments, all centering on her betrothal and their place in her new life. Her parents are coarse, loud, and greedy. Gosta is drunk and angry. Through it all, Thérèse remains in control, seemingly untouched by the conflict. As Florent will say of her background, "It could have made her lewd and cheap. It has merely decked her in strength and candour."

Florent and Hartmann's arrival has a dramatic impact on the group. The Tardes attempt to ingratiate themselves, Gosta leaves after threatening to fight Florent, and Thérèse is intimidated by Hartmann's probing evaluation of her. As her parents devise ways to get money from him, she feels ashamed for the first time. To show how little money means to him, Florent throws what he has on the floor. The Tardes "quiver with thwarted greed," and Thérèse, in order not to "act a lie," falls on her knees, saying "I belong to the same breed." Florent picks her up and holds her; the Tardes scramble to pick up the money, and Hartmann, who has watched the whole scene without moving, closes the act, saying, "You will have to tread very carefully, Florent."

Act 2 takes place six days later, in the library of Florent's country home. Although Thérèse has agreed to the marriage, she has spent the ensuing days trying to force Florent to break the engagement. She has brought her father, whom she encourages to drink and act crudely, she persuades a friend to write a letter to Florent warning him against the marriage, and she bribes Jeannette to come and reveal that she was Gosta's lover. Thus she forces the vulgarity and meanness of her background on Florent, who reacts with courtesy, generosity, and a sense of humor. Thérèse hates him for this complacency.

Hartmann understands what Thérèse is doing, and he encourages her to accept the "house of happiness where pain and sorrow have no place." She cannot, and in her final attempt to alienate Florent, she reveals her one secret, a self-induced abortion at the age of fourteen. Florent weeps for her. Thérèse is finally happy and agrees to the wedding. The act closes as she is "transfigured" in Florent's arms.

In act 3, Thérèse is in the library, being fitted for her wedding dress. She is different, as she listens without comment to the conversations of the girls working on her gown and the heartless responses of Marie, Florent's cousin. According to Hartmann, this smiling passive state, "which is a little bit like being dead," is the price Thérèse must pay for happiness.

The arrival of her father and Gosta, who has beaten her mother, shatters Thérèse's complacency, forcing her to realize that she can never deny or forget her past. She must leave Florent; she can never be happy as long as there is "a stray dog somewhere in the world." As she departs, Hartmann murmurs: "There she goes, small, and strong and lucid, to pit herself against all the sharp corners of the world."

Themes and Meanings

As one of Jean Anouilh's "black plays," *Restless Heart* pessimistically presents several of his key themes: the struggle to preserve a sense of personal purity in a degrading world, the rejection of material happiness, the conflict between idealism and compromise, the influence of one's past and family background, the complexity of parent-child relationships, and the unbridgeable gap between the rich and the poor.

Thérèse's search for happiness through love is problematic, because the ideal can never be realized, and finally she refuses to compromise. To accept the happiness offered by Florent, she would have to deny her past and see the world through the eyes of the rich. When she attempts to do so, she speaks of taming the black horse within; the result is the almost trancelike state she enters while her wedding gown is being fitted. She dreams not of the kindness of Florent but of a hard and cruel redeemer who would have had similar experiences and thus be able to understand her completely. She yearns to find "a white clearing at the farthest end of despair where one is almost happy."

These themes are dramatized onstage through the conflicts generated by three types of characters: what Anouilh terms the mediocre race, the compromisers, and the heroes. In *Restless Heart*, Monsieur Tarde typifies the mediocre race. Reduced by his hard life to a caricature of a parent, he is pathologically obsessed with money, viewing everything around him, including his daughter, in terms of the cost. He is both comic and cruel, humorous and heartless. His orchestra players are like so many chorus voices, living reminders of the ever-present mediocre reality from which the heroes are trying to break free.

The compromisers are clear-sighted and sensitive enough to understand both the sordid conditions of the poor and the mediocre and the plight of the heroes. Hartmann is a compromiser; he might have been a hero, but he likes the soft life that Florent offers. So he is the philosopher-friend, who maintains an ironic attitude about his own choices in life; some critics suggest that he is the voice of Anouilh.

For Anouilh, only the poor can produce heroes, who seek answers to metaphysical questions concerning the nature of happiness and who rebel against the society around them. Thérèse, in spite of the downward pull of her environment, has preserved deep inside a pure, clear spirit that remains untarnished. However, she can never succeed in her quest for happiness, for a soul mate. When she leaves the warmth and protection of Florent's home, she must fend for herself in a world that is cold and hostile.

Dramatic Devices

The dramaturgy of *Restless Heart*, an early Anouilh play, exhibits both the naturalism and beginnings of the theatricalism that came to be trademarks of Jean Anouilh's later, more mature plays. He utilizes set and language here to underscore the radical differences between the world of the poor and that of the wealthy. The rundown café of act 1 contrasts with the paneled library with a view of the grounds of acts 2 and 3. Anouilh also uses the nuances of language to indicate class differences. The Tardes use vulgarisms, clichés, and lower-class vocabulary to express themselves; Florent and his aunt, on the other hand, speak well. In accordance with her role, Thérèse uses more metaphors to express her feelings. Her intensity and complexity are thus reinforced by the nature of the language that she uses.

Structurally, each act builds to a climax, consisting of a dramatic image that reasserts visually what has been discussed in the act. The tableaux are effective devices for emphasizing the elements of theme. Act 1 closes with the Tardes on their knees, picking up the money Florent has thrown down to demonstrate how little it means to him. Thérèse is in his arms, while Hartmann watches and comments. At the end of act 2, Thérèse is again in Florent's arms, this time "transfigured" by his shedding a tear. The play ends with Thérèse's wedding dress lying on the couch, "a dazzling patch of whiteness in the gloom," as Hartmann describes her future.

The theatrical elements in *Restless Heart* reside in the use of music throughout and in the *commedia dell'arte* performance of Monsieur Tarde, as the comic buffoon, in act 2. These devices cut across the naturalism and reduce the tendency toward melodrama inherent in a play where the conflicts and characters are so clearly delineated and somewhat one-dimensional. The play opens with the off-key but spirited music of Tarde's orchestra; it closes with Florent's swelling Andante, executed beautifully and effortlessly. Madame Tarde sings a sexually suggestive song and gestures broadly to the lyrics in act 1; Thérèse repeats this in act 2, while she is trying to alienate Florent. The kind of music selected and the way in which it is played reflect the wide gap between Florent's world and Thérèse's.

Anouilh also uses lighting effectively to highlight the mood of each act and to underscore the differences between Florent, a child of light, and Thérèse's struggles with the darkness of her reality. Act 1 ends with soft lighting, suggestive of Thérèse's softening toward Florent's marriage proposal. In act 3, the light gradually fades, foreshadowing Thérèse's departure from the house of light, Florent's country estate, into the evening darkness.

Anouilh succeeds in reinforcing his philosophical arguments about the nature of happiness and reality through dramatic devices that are accessible to the audience and function to keep them emotionally as well as intellectually attuned to the characters' conflicts. With the comic bumbling of Monsieur Tarde, he also attempts to lighten the mood and quicken the tempo.

Critical Context

Jean Anouilh, with a career spanning more than fifty years, was one of France's most popular and successful dramatists. While there is one central theme running through his canon—the eternal conflict between idealism and reality—he arranged his plays in groups, according to the dominant tone, his maturing view of life, and forms that range from light comedy to tragedy.

The "black plays" are bitter and pessimistic. *Restless Heart*, which falls in this category, marked Anouilh's emergence as a precocious and promising young playwright. While the play is somewhat simplistic and heavy-handed, the absence of melodrama, the control of emotion, and the blend of the comic and tragic reveal Anouilh's increasing mastery of style as he moved away from naturalism toward theatricalism. In *Jézabel* (pb. 1946), *Le Voyageur sans bagage* (pr., pb. 1937; *Traveller Without Luggage*, 1959), and *L'orchestre* (pr. 1962, pb. 1970; *The Orchestra*, 1967), the central characters rebel against society not only because of past experiences that prevent their integration into society but also because of their increasingly romantic nature.

In the "pink plays," the characters escape ugly reality through fantasy and illusion. *Le Bal des voleurs* (pr., pb. 1938; *Thieves' Carnival*, 1952), the most famous work in this category, is a farcical depiction of love amid the various classes of society. *Léocadia* (pr. 1940; *Time Remembered*, 1952) is another play in this category. In the four "brilliant plays," written during the late 1940's and early 1950's, levity is balanced against the darkness of life. *L'Invitation au château* (pr. 1947; *Ring Round the Moon*, 1950) is an intricately plotted fairy tale with a happy ending, while in *Colombe* (pr. 1951; *Mademoiselle Colombe*, 1954) a corrupt society defeats the hero.

The "jarring plays," which are tragicomic in nature, depict middle-aged men striving to remain young while recognizing the absurdity of their desire. *L'Hurluberlu: Ou, Le Réactionnaire amoureux* (pr., pb. 1959; *The Fighting Cock*, 1960) and *Ornifle: Ou, Le Courant d'air* (pr. 1955, pb. 1956; *Ornifle*, 1970) reflect these characteristics. Anouilh's "costumed plays" reinterpret the actions of such historical and legendary characters as Antigone (*Antigone*, pr. 1944; English translation, 1946), Joan of Arc (*L'Alouette*, pr., pb. 1953; *The Lark*, 1955), Thomas à Becket (*Becket: Ou, L'Honneur de Dieu*, pr., pb. 1959; *Becket: Or, The Honor of God*, 1962), and Napoleon Bonaparte and Louis XVIII (*La foire d'empoigne*, pb. 1960, pr. 1962; *Catch as Catch Can*, 1967). In each of these works, Anouilh suggests that while the soul of human beings remains unchanged, the mask and costume vary to suit different eras.

Because Anouilh selected traditional and theatrical modes of dramatization rather than avant-garde or sociopolitical ones, critics did not credit him with profound contributions to twentieth century French theater. He has been called "a gifted stylist with a shallow point of view."

Sources for Further Study

Archer, Marguerite. *Jean Anouilh*. New York: Columbia University Press, 1971.

Della Fazia, Alba. *Jean Anouilh*. New York: Twayne, 1969.

Falb, Lewis W. *Jean Anouilh*. New York: F. Ungar, 1977.

Lenski, B. A. *Jean Anouilh: Stages in Rebellion*. Atlantic Highlands, N.J.: Humanities Press, 1975.

McIntyre, H. G. *The Theatre of Jean Anouilh*. Totowa, N.J.: Barnes & Noble, 1981.

Lori Hall Burghardt

THE RIDE ACROSS LAKE CONSTANCE

Author: Peter Handke (1942-)
Type of plot: Surrealist
Time of plot: Unspecified
Locale: A stage
First produced: 1971, at Berlin Schaübuhne am Halleschen Ufer
First published: *Der Ritt über den Bodensee*, 1971 (English translation, 1972)

Principal characters:
WOMAN WITH WHITE SCARF
EMIL JANNINGS
HEINRICH GEORGE
ELISABETH BERGNER
ERICH VON STROHEIM
HENNY PORTEN
ALICE and ELLEN KESSLER

The Play

The Ride Across Lake Constance violates many of the familiar conventions of the theater. This is immediately apparent in the play's treatment of its characters. In the printed text the characters are arbitrarily assigned the names of various celebrated German film actors. In performance, however, the stage directions explain that the actors should be called by their own names. "The actors are and play themselves at the same time," Peter Handke notes. Thus from the beginning the audience is invited to consider what it means to play a role, to act a part, rather than simply accepting the actor's function as a given.

The play opens with a woman in blackface, wearing a white scarf, moving around the objects onstage with a vacuum cleaner. Emil Jannings sits on a *fauteuil* (an upholstered armchair) with his eyes closed. When the sound of the vacuum cleaner stops, music from a record player becomes audible. The woman pulls off the drop cloths which have covered most of the furniture, including one under Jannings. She exits. The record player turns itself off. Jannings opens his eyes and speaks as if he were resuming a conversation, although it is never made clear what conversation this actually is. Heinrich George, hidden from view behind the screen, questions him; George then repeats his question as he steps out from behind the screen.

The two actors sustain a dialogue in which they pointedly test their means of communication with each other through language and gesture. They use their hands, facial expressions, and posture, as well as objects such as cigar boxes, cigars, and rings, to sustain this conversation. However, their attempts merely emphasize their inability to use ordinary signals smoothly. Jannings points to a cigar box on the floor as if asking George to pick it up. George misinterprets the gesture as pointing to a feature of the box and goes to look at it; Jannings then goes along with this new interpretation of his gesture, quickly finding something for George to notice on the box. Somewhat later, Jannings relates an experience which he had on a winter evening in the past; George questions not only the reality of the story, whether it was truth or fiction, but also how Jannings chose what sentences and expressions to use. The two end this dialogue with a series of clichés, making them more and more ridiculous. They wind up laughing at the expression "born winner," a variation they have generated from the expression "born loser."

The actors are joined by other actors designated as Elisabeth Bergner, Erich von Stroheim, and Henny Porten. The entrances of these three demonstrate the same kind of disorientation and disconnection of gesture and meaning. Each descends from the stairway, Bergner from one side, the other two from the other. In the sequence which follows, each of their ordinary gestures—offering a hand to kiss, bowing, standing in front of one another—is disrupted by a totally unexpected response by another character.

Porten has some trouble going down the stairs and descends repeatedly, each time misjudging the number of steps. Aided by von Stroheim, she finally arrives at the bottom. Bergner also descends into the room, stepping over the bodies of George and Jannings, who have thrown themselves in front of her. Bergner quickly sits and drinks a cup of tea, while George and Jannings get up and dust themselves off. She speaks as if asleep, then opens her eyes and asks a rapid series of formulaic questions, then tries to sit in several different *fauteuils*, rejecting them because each is too warm. Bergner asks Jannings if he is more powerful than George. He considers the question and begins to demand various items from George. George complies, egging him on to ask for more and more outlandish items. Jannings finally demands "the sun," and both, exhausted, stop the game.

Von Stroheim and Porten now join in the act. Von Stroheim manipulates Porten through his gestures, a manipulation that is ultimately ended when she is kicked across the room. It is, in fact, Jannings who kicks George, but the effect of the kick has been displaced. Porten then asks George if he is the salesman; George goes along with the identification and sells her a riding crop instead of the "tear-gas pistol" she has requested. She tries out the crop, making suggestive motions toward Jannings and George. Finally George asks von Stroheim if he and Porten belong together. His response, as he grabs her around the waist, is "Can't one tell just by looking at us?" George replies, "I guess so, now," implying that the appearance now signifies the relationship. Porten then asks if George and Jannings belong to each other. They look at each other as if discovering their relationship for the first time, then reply that they do, affirming this several times.

Von Stroheim and Porten inspect the room, which has several marked peculiarities, such as a magazine chained to the table and a drawer which will not open. Bergner goes to the mirror and begins to comb her hair and put on makeup. Her movements become more and more insecure; she panics, dropping things, walking around the room with awkward gestures, and calling for help in a direction where no one is present.

Porten helps her by guiding her around the room and showing her how to pick things up. Porten shows her how to speak as well, giving her model sentences until she is calm and can express herself easily. The two women become lighthearted and dance around the room, discovering the apparent simplicity of interpretation. Porten asks if certain postures and gestures have some other meaning: "Two people sit there, don't look at each other, and are silent. Are they angry with one another?" Bergner replies that these movements can be free of outward significance: "No they simply sit there, don't look at each other, and are silent!"

The two women are relieved at this discovery. Their joy spreads to the other characters when Bergner asks why the drawer is stuck, and von Stroheim replies "Let it be stuck!" George, Jannings, and von Stroheim dance, and sing about the drawer in unison. The men are now delighted with the objects in the room; they fondle and play with them. The women laugh, and the men imitate one another and show off for them. Finally, after this sequence of playfulness, all the characters seat themselves. They are calm but satisfied with their newly found linguistic independence.

This satisfaction, however, is short-lived. Slowly they begin to lapse back into their former difficulties. Porten tells von Stroheim that she has goose pimples, and he almost asks her if she is cold. He checks himself in time and asks her if she has goose pimples. Jannings shows them a pin, and they begin to refer to other uses of the word "pin" and other pins with which they had come into contact or heard about before, rather than only the pin in question. Bergner drops the pin and they all listen, but George ruins the effect by speaking too soon. Von Stroheim plays magician, conjuring rather ordinary objects from his pockets. They marvel at the reality of these objects, especially at a red piece of cloth which they inspect carefully.

In the next sequence von Stroheim, George, and Jannings play teaching games about the nature of language. Jannings concludes with a long speech on how language formulates reality. He points out that Bergner, as a woman, has learned to think of herself in terms of desirability. As if to illustrate this, Bergner asks a series of questions about herself. Jannings continues his speech, pointing out that the familiar song about the three-cornered hat has rendered him incapable of imagining a three-cornered hat. He ends his speech with a story about his having a bad day. When George fails to respond, Jannings prompts him, and George asks a series of questions about the way in which Jannings has defined his story. The two men end by betting on games involving George's putting cigars in boxes and spanking Porten. George loses both games.

Von Stroheim and Bergner play, self-consciously, the elements of a love scene. This is ended when Porten claps her hands. Jannings tries to begin a number of stories but is interrupted by the others and finally by the arrival of another character. Alice Kessler carries a suitcase and looks as though she has mistakenly come upon this performance. Alice speaks quite normally, and without any apparent self-consciousness. The other characters are quite disconcerted but attempt to play along. Alice speaks to each character in turn, and they are thrilled to be able to communicate with her. Her arrival is soon followed by the arrival of Ellen Kessler, who is dressed exactly like Alice and also carries a suitcase. Ellen imitates the movements and greeting of Alice exactly; the original five characters laugh as they repeat their replies to the two girls. Then Alice and Ellen begin to double their movements, running around the characters and manipulating them in unison. They then slow down, speed up, and begin to contradict one another's movements, disrupting one another's efforts to untie shoelaces, brush hair, and bring bottles and glasses to set before the characters.

Finally the two run off in opposite directions, return, and change directions, exiting into the wings. After a pause, Jannings and George get up and throw the suitcases, then the hats and gloves of the girls after them; the sound of the suitcases hitting the floor is delayed by several seconds, so that it sounds as though the hats and gloves are crashing down.

The characters turn back to one another. Bergner seems to have fallen asleep. Each comment is spoken a little too late, so that there are awkward pauses between sentences. The characters have resumed their states of disorientation. Hopelessly, they try to recall the moments of the play that took place earlier, the red cloth that von Stroheim conjured, and George's selling Porten the riding crop. Their recollections seem faint, and they become increasingly uneasy. Porten reaches for a cigar, and George asks if she is restless. She screams at his suggestion: "I only wanted to take a cigar!" She screams again. All the characters hunch up.

There is a high-pitched howling offstage. The woman with the scarf from the beginning of the play reenters with a huge doll which represents a child. The child begins to cry, but stops when George shuts a drawer in the chest. The woman quickly carries the child from one character to another; the child reaches for the women's breasts and between the men's legs. The child knocks things off the tables and begins to cry again. It stops when it reaches Bergner, and it is carried away. The characters attempt to move or to make sounds, but their feeble attempts die away. Bergner begins to wake up, and the other characters look at her. Von Stroheim gets up and goes to her. The other characters remain motionless. She opens her eyes, recognizes von Stroheim, and begins to smile.

Themes and Meanings

It is difficult to summarize effectively the events of *The Ride Across Lake Constance*, since Peter Handke intentionally shuns plot and causality as structures for the play. The title of the play does, however, suggest a story and a related moral. Michael Roloff's version of the story, which introduces the English translation, is as follows:

> It's a winter night. A man rides across Lake Constance without sparing his horse. When he arrives on the other side, his friends congratulate him profusely, saying: "What a surprise! How did you ever make it! The ice is no more than an inch thick!" The rider hesitates briefly, then drops off his horse. He is instantly dead.

The characters in the play expose themselves to dangers much like those of the man who has made the impossible ride across the lake. Handke's metaphoric Lake Constance is the interpretation of language and gesture; the perils of riding across Lake

Constance become the unforeseen dangers of ordinary communication. In both the story and the play, a true knowledge of the fragility of the "lake," or the connection between language and meaning, leads to fear, self-consciousness, and subsequent disorientation. Like the man who rides across Lake Constance, the characters are suddenly aware of their danger and subsequently experience various crises of inarticulateness. The events of the play enact these crises for the audience and lead the audience to question their own presuppositions about what words and gestures mean.

The play comments on several important aspects of language: its ability to define realities, to create relationships, and to define power. The standard forms and rules of language obsess the characters; they examine the relationship between language and the reality it is supposed to represent, especially the assumptions inherent in ordinary language, such as the cliché "born loser." Their dialogues draw attention to the verbal and gestural exchanges which take place between people in certain situations: formal introductions, economic transactions, sexual encounters. Handke is preoccupied with the power implicit in linguistic structures and interactions, defined through ordinary social roles.

The learning of the rules of language, as it is demonstrated in several instances in the play, is a dangerous process. The characters learn to use language through following certain models of speech and behavior, models which may ultimately enslave them. Language, Handke suggests, imposes its own ideas upon the unthinking speaker, defining a specific hierarchy of power and ultimately governing all modes of thought. The characters are enslaved by their own means of socialization: the language that they themselves have created and to which they have bound themselves. Awakened to this knowledge, they find themselves increasingly paralyzed with fear.

Dramatic Devices

Handke presents human activity in *The Ride Across Lake Constance* as inherently theatrical even without being directly representational. He shifts interest from certain traditional elements of drama—plot and characterization—to the events taking place on the stage itself. The play challenges the expectations of the audience even through its setting. Although the stage is furnished in the manner of a typical nineteenth century drawing room, it soon becomes apparent that the audience is not going to see the kind of play that usually takes place within such a stage setting; the setting thus parodies its own conventional theatrical use. Finally, as noted above, Handke gives the actors their own names as designations, so that they do not represent fictional people. Although they are costumed in suggestive ways—Jannings, for example, has on heavy makeup, and a bright red sash around his waist—these visual details do not contribute to a traditional role. The audience thus must reinterpret its expectations of theatrical convention and genre. In much the same way, the actions and phrases of the play seem to be familiar, but then they subvert their own familiarity.

The play includes a variety of dialogues and interactions that exaggerate and distort seemingly ordinary acts of language and gesture. The attempt to interpret these words and gestures becomes a series of discussions, questions, and word games, all of which lead to moments of real crisis for the actors and characters. Their fear, generated by the precariousness of this very act of interpretation, arises at many points of the play; it is especially overwhelming at the end. The doll-child's wailing suggests the frustration and terror that underlie human expression, and its destruction of the room suggests an inherent violence.

There is also, however, much lightheartedness in the play. The characters do experience moments of true revelation and elation. At one point they marvel at instances where language does reflect some reality. Von Stroheim tells them the story: "I was sitting by a lakeshore in the morning and the lake was sparkling. Suddenly I noticed: the lake is *sparkling*. It is really sparkling." Similarly, Porten tells of the time "when someone told me that his pockets were empty. 'My pockets are empty!' I didn't believe him and he turned his pockets inside out. They really were empty. Incredible!" The characters dance joyously over the discovery of how a drawer can simply be stuck, singing rounds in unison of "Oh, let the drawer be stuck, oh, oh, let the drawer be stuck!" Handke's play is carefully composed not only of perceptive and amusing dialogue, but of ingenious physical action; Handke makes frequent use not only of humorous "sight gags" such as the suitcases of the Kessler girls and the noises they make as they are thrown offstage, but also of striking visual sequences such as the gradual disorientation of Bergner as she views herself in the mirror. The events of the play are constantly surprising, revealing, and insightful. *The Ride Across Lake Constance* presents a complex metaphor about language and interpretation in ways that are both visually and verbally engaging.

Critical Context

The Ride Across Lake Constance follows several of Handke's dramatic works which have a similar direction and theatrical preoccupation. The *Sprechstücke* of 1966-1967 show Handke's fascination with the language of the theater. *Publikumsbeschimpfung* (pr., pb. 1966; *Offending the Audience*, 1969), *Selbstbezichtigung* (pr., pb. 1966; *Self-Accusation*, 1969), *Weissagung* (pr., pb. 1966; *Prophecy*, 1976), and *Hilferufe* (pr. 1967; *Calling for Help*, 1970) all shun the conventional plot and characterization of a more realistic stage; each of these pieces concentrates on making the audience self-conscious about their own relationship with the events of the stage, and aware of the subtleties of language.

Although these works primarily concentrate on language rather than on physical movement, like *The Ride Across Lake Constance* they also subvert theatrical conventions and expectations. *Kaspar* (pr., pb. 1968; English translation, 1969) shows more explicitly than the earlier *Sprechstücke* the dangers involved in the use of language. The audience witnesses the linguistic education of the central character, the clown Kaspar, as he progresses from one sentence to a range of verbal abilities. This education, however, alters him in more fundamental ways; as in *The Ride Across Lake Constance*, the learning of language becomes not only a complex, but also a politically dangerous process. *Das Mündel will Vormund sein* (pr., pb. 1969; *My Foot My Tutor*, 1970) and *Quodlibet* (pr. 1970; English translation, 1976) also precede *The Ride*

Across Lake Constance. These two plays focus on the interpretation and meaning of physical action and gesture as well as of language; *My Foot My Tutor*, for example, is a wordless play. In both these plays, Handke delves further into the exploration of the signs and words which constitute and define human activity and relationship. *The Ride Across Lake Constance* investigates the full range of this activity and articulates most clearly the problems and doubts with which Handke, as a dramatist, is most concerned.

Sources for Further Study

Firda, Richard A. *Peter Handke*. Boston: Twayne, 1993.

Gilbert, W. Stephen. "*The Ride Across Lake Constance*." *Plays and Players*, January, 1974, 48-49.

Hauptmann, Ira. "Aspects of Handke: A Play." *Partisan Review* 45, no. 3 (1978): 425-430.

Hays, Michael. "Peter Handke and the End of the 'Modern.'" *Modern Drama* 23 (January, 1981): 346-366.

Hern, Nicholas. *Peter Handke: Theatre and Anti-Theatre*. London: Wolfe, 1971.

Schlueter, June. *The Plays and Novels of Peter Handke*. Pittsburgh: University of Pittsburgh Press, 1981.

Josephine Lee

THE RIDE DOWN MT. MORGAN

Author: Arthur Miller (1915-   )
Type of plot: Tragicomedy
Time of plot: c. 1990
Locale: Elmira, New York
First produced: 1991, at Wyndham's Theatre, London
First published: 1991

Principal characters:
LYMAN FELT, an insurance executive
THEODORA "THEO" FELT, his wife
BESSIE, their daughter
TOM WILSON, their lawyer
FATHER, Lyman's father
LEAH FELT, Lyman's second wife

The Play

As *The Ride Down Mt. Morgan* opens, Lyman Felt is lying half-conscious in a hospital bed with a leg and an arm in casts. The night before the action begins, Lyman crashed his Porsche while driving down a treacherous stretch of Mount Morgan in the middle of an ice storm in upstate New York. While he has been unconscious, the hospital contacted his family in Manhattan and, as he awakens from what seems to be a dream about his father, he learns that his wife and daughter have just arrived. This does not make him happy; in fact, it seems to terrify him. He cries, "It can't happen, it mustn't happen!" He then slips out of the rear of the leg cast and moves across the stage, still in his hospital gown, while the empty cast remains in the bed. As he watches, the setting changes to the hospital waiting room, and he imagines a scene in which his wife, Theo, and his daughter Bessie meet Leah, his second wife, and all of them learn his secret: For the past nine years Lyman has been a bigamist, lying to and betraying everyone who loves him.

Throughout the rest of the play, Lyman moves in and out of the bed, back and forth between past and present, observing and imagining scene after scene—participating in some conversations, overhearing others—as events of his life are reenacted on the stage. Although the play consciously blurs the lines between reality and dream, fact and fantasy, tragedy and farce, the outlines of his story gradually emerge. Lyman is a rich, well-known insurance executive who heads a company that employs forty-two hundred people and is noted for its social responsibility. He is also a compulsive philanderer who may have betrayed his former business partner to the authorities in order to save his own neck. Nine years ago, at the age of fifty-four, he met a much younger woman, Leah, on a business trip to Elmira and they began an affair that led to her becoming pregnant. When she told him she was going to have an abortion, he promised to divorce his wife and marry her. Summarized this way, his story seems a cliché, the tale of a midlife crisis and a mistress. However, the play does not present this information chronologically, and long before these facts are revealed, the audience knows that Lyman's story does not end like most similar stories. Forced to choose between his wife and his mistress, he chose both. After promising Leah that he would leave his wife, he took Leah to Reno, where she thought he got his divorce, and they were married.

In fact, his divorce was a charade and, unbeknownst to either woman, he began to lead a double life, spending two weeks of each month with Theo in Manhattan and two weeks with Leah and their son Benjamin in Elmira. In the townhouse on East Seventy-fourth Street in Manhattan, he was a solid citizen, a doting father, and a newly attentive husband to Theo, who, like Lyman, is in her early sixties. In Elmira, he began a new life with Leah, who is in her thirties: They buy a ranch-style house, raise their own food, have sixty head of cattle, and begin to raise thoroughbred horses. Although he has always been afraid of flying, in Elmira he begins to pilot a private plane, to hunt, and to race sports cars.

Thus, the accident exposes him and raises the questions that the play explores: How could a man do this? How would he justify himself if his deception were exposed? How would the women react? Would either of them remain with him?

Themes and Meanings

In his introduction to the first edition of *The Portable Arthur Miller* (1971), Harold Clurman made an observation about Miller's plays that still holds. "All his ideas are parts of one Idea," he wrote, and that idea is that "[w]e are all part of one another; all responsible to one another." This idea appears in Miller's plays as a moral conflict between the visions of English poet John Donne and English naturalist Charles Darwin: Donne's view that existence means "no man is an island" and Darwin's belief that existence is fundamentally about "survival of the fittest." In play after play, Miller expresses this conflict through acts of betrayal—of a spouse, a parent or child, a sibling, a friend, a group, or a principle. At times the betrayal is primarily domestic—for example, in *Death of a Salesman* (pr., pb. 1949), *A View from the Bridge* (pr., pb. 1955), *The Price* (pr., pb. 1968), and *The Ride Down Mt. Morgan*. At other times it is social and political—such as *Incident at Vichy* (pr. 1964, pb. 1965). Most often it is both, as in *All My Sons* (pr., pb. 1947), *The Crucible* (pr., pb. 1953), or *After the Fall* (pr., pb. 1965).

Much of *The Ride Down Mt. Morgan* consists of conversations in which Lyman tries to justify his betrayals and charge the others with complicity; at times, he seems to make some convincing points against them. However, his rationalizations, his charges against Theo and Leah, his claims of having gone beyond guilt, and the play's frequent humor do not alter his status in the conflict that the play explores. Lyman's place on Miller's moral spectrum is clear in numerous instances: When he defends himself by claiming that "a man can be faithful to himself or to other people—but not to both" and "the first law of life is betrayal"; when he boasts that "what I wish I do!"; when Theo tells him that he seems like some kind of giant clam "[w]aiting on the bottom for whatever happens to fall from the ocean into your mouth"; when he claims that the only thing that matters is for a man to be true to himself and Leah answers "Even if he has to betray the whole world to do it?"; and, finally, when Miller gives Bessie the last word after Lyman begs her to help him know "what should I understand!" and Bessie answers, "There are other people." "Lie-man" wants to be excused because he did what was right for him, but the play does not support his defense.

Dramatic Devices

Because Miller is usually considered a realist concerned, above all, with moral, social, and political issues, his mastery of dramatic form is sometimes forgotten or underestimated. He once told an interviewer that he comes out of the tradition of the Greeks and playwright Henrik Ibsen, "where the past is the burden of man and it's got to be placed on the stage so that he can grapple with it. That's the way those plays are built. It's *now* grappling with *then*, it's the story of how the birds come home to roost. Every play." Certainly this is also the story of *The Ride Down Mt. Morgan*.

Still, if the essential subjects and concerns of Miller's plays have not changed much over the years, his dramatic techniques certainly have. Many of his plays—such as *All My Sons*, *The Crucible*, *A View from the Bridge*, *Incident at Vichy*, *The Price*, *The Last Yankee* (pb. 1991, pr. 1993), and *Broken Glass* (pr., pb. 1994)—are straightforward dramas in the realist tradition. However, throughout his career, Miller also has drawn on other traditions. *Death of a Salesman*, for example, was originally titled *The Inside of His Head*. This earlier title was "conceived half in laughter," Miller has explained, since "the inside of his head was a mass of contradictions." He went on to say, however, that the point he was making with this early title was expressed in the final play, explaining that the image in *Death of a Salesman* was imbued with the concept that nothing in life comes "next" but instead everything exists together and simultaneously within us. The means Miller chose to express this idea in *Death of a Salesman*—the flowing movement of the action from present to past, from "actual" to "remembered" events, from the exterior to the interior of lead character Willy Loman—are indebted not to Ibsen but to August Strindberg's dream plays and expressionism. The effect of *After the Fall* is crucially dependent on a similar movement in time, space, and the consciousness of Quentin. Miller again uses this technique in his play *Mr. Peter's Connections* (pr. 1998, pb. 1999).

The Ride Down Mt. Morgan also could have been called "The Inside of His Head," since, from the moment Lyman first walks out of his cast and imagines the scene in the waiting room, the audience is drawn into a theatrical space where the normal rules of realism, time, and setting are suspended. Not only does Lyman rise from his bed and return at will—sometimes suggesting that the scene is imaginary, sometimes that he is simply observing the action—but he occasionally takes on the role of director. For example, when he raises his hands and tells his wives and daughter "to lie down!" the three women "instantly de-animate." Then, "Lyman gestures, without actually touching them, and causes Leah and Theo to lie on the bed" next to one another. At other times the action seems outside his control.

Several times, scenes are run twice with slight variations. Later in the play, as he lies in bed, Leah and Theo appear "on either side of him, but on elevated platforms, like two stone deities," and they proceed to talk about their skills as cooks. Lyman's father appears and reappears—criticizing, challenging, threatening—dragging an ominous black cloth with which he eventually shrouds Lyman. Acting as a cross between the ghost of William Shakespeare's Hamlet and Willy Loman's brother Ben, he seems a projection of Lyman's deepest fears and insecurities. Because of the way the play causes its audience to doubt the reality of what they are seeing and hearing, the ending of the play, which suggests that either or both of the women may yet take Lyman back, gains an added level of ambiguity.

Critical Context

Arthur Miller's work spans nearly seven decades. While other playwrights have written as much, virtually no American playwright has enjoyed the longevity of such a career and few have had anything like Miller's international recognition. *Death of a Salesman* and *The Crucible* are now generally regarded as masterpieces of twentieth century American drama and literature; a half dozen more of his plays have grown in memory, outlasting initially critical reviews, and are performed regularly nationally and internationally. In the 1990's, he continued to write new one-act and full-length plays and continued to experiment with form and tone. Like a number of his plays from the late twentieth century, *The Ride Down Mt. Morgan* is clear evidence that Miller's imagination and invention have remained every bit as vital as his moral vision.

Sources for Further Study

Centola, Steve, ed. *The Achievement of Arthur Miller: New Essays*. Dallas, Tex.: Contemporary Research Press, 1995.

Corrigan, Robert W., ed. *Arthur Miller: A Collection of Critical Essays*. Englewood Cliffs, N.J.: Prentice-Hall, 1969.

Miller, Arthur. *The Portable Arthur Miller.* Rev. ed. Edited by C. W. E. Bigsby. New York: Penguin, 1995.

_______. *The Theater Essays of Arthur Miller.* New York: Viking, 1978.

Roudane, Matthew Charles, ed. *Conversations with Arthur Miller.* Jackson: University of Mississippi Press, 1987.

Bernard F. Rodgers, Jr.

THE RIMERS OF ELDRITCH

Author: Lanford Wilson (1937-   )
Type of plot: Social realism
Time of plot: The 1960's
Locale: Eldritch, a small town in the American Midwest
First produced: 1966, at La MaMa Experimental Theater Club, New York City
First published: 1967, in *The Rimers of Eldritch and Other Plays*

Principal characters:
ROBERT CONKLIN, an eighteen-year-old boy
EVA JACKSON, a crippled fourteen-year-old girl
NELLY WINDROD, a strong middle-aged woman
MARY WINDROD, Nelly's senile mother
SKELLY MANNOR, the town hermit, about sixty years old
CORA GROVES, the owner of the Hilltop Café

The Play

The Rimers of Eldritch begins in darkness. Two female voices are heard gossiping sympathetically about Cora Groves, who has taken a considerably younger man as her lover. As Martha and Wilma speak, a faint light begins to illuminate a middle-aged woman, Nelly, with her hand raised as if taking an oath. The gossip continues a few moments, then the lights are turned full on to indicate morning. Nelly swears, "I do," and the women, now seen on a raised platform suggestive of a porch, talk of "the trials that woman has to bear." The juxtaposition indicates that they are talking of Nelly, who is now being sworn in by the judge. The lights dim once again to evening, as the women's talk shifts to chastising the townspeople for allowing an unspecified character to terrorize them with his incoherent growling and illicit spying into their lives.

The unnamed character, whom the audience later learns is Skelly Mannor, is at the heart of the scandal for which Martha and Wilma believe the town must take responsibility. His murder forms the thematic and structural center of the play, and the audience is led to and from it via multiple points of view and rapid time shifts. Throughout the first act, the evidence of character is compiled. The audience learns that, with the lone exception of Cora, all consider Skelly a moral reprobate: accused of dog poisoning, bestiality (the town's boys bleat at him), and voyeurism (Patsy swears that he peeped at her as she changed clothes). In his sixties, he is old enough to have served as the town scapegoat for two generations, as the Skelly-baiting stories swapped by Peck Johnson and his son, Josh, attest. What finally triggers Skelly's death is less his actions than the explosive emotional interdependence in the claustrophobic town. For this reason, as well as the dramatic method used, the plot is best told through its characters.

Just as Nelly is about to begin her testimony in the opening scene, two other characters, Mary and Robert, speak in the grocery store where Robert works. Mary, Nelly's mother, is the principal "trial" Nelly must bear. Her grasp of facts is comically muddled in this conversation with Robert, but her later conversation with Martha and Wilma, in which she claims that her immunity to disease protects her from the town's wickedness, fully reveals her senility. She risks Nelly's anger by misrepresenting her daughter as physically abusive and guilty of killing her own father. After Nelly subsequently testifies that it was Mary who saw (in a dream) the attack on Eva Jackson and informed Nelly, Mary loses all credibility (and her hints to Robert in this first conversation that she knows that it was he who attacked Eva may be overlooked).

Robert appears an average teenage boy, just graduated from high school and undecided about his future plans. His indecisiveness is pointedly ignored by the townspeople (represented by Wilma), who believe that he will follow in the footsteps of Driver, his heroic older brother. So pronounced is this belief that Robert, much to his dismay, is often referred to as Driver Junior. The only difference the townspeople can discern between the two brothers is Robert's "unnatural" interest in a physically handicapped girl, Eva Jackson. She and Robert share long walks through the woods, for which she is reprimanded by her mother, who is as concerned for her daughter's health as for her virginity. With her love of autumn rime (frost) on pumpkins and the peaty smells of decay in the air, Eva's approach to life is shown to be more lyrical than that of the practical, marriage-minded teenagers Patsy and Lena.

Of nearly equal importance to these characters is the specter of Driver, the town hero, who died in an auto accident. His exploits at the local racetrack have raised him to legendary status in the eyes of all but Skelly, who insists to Robert near the end of the act that his beloved older brother had sadistic sexual tastes. "He beat Betty Atkins and did it by hand. Jacking all on her. I've seen him. I've seen him." Skelly's revelation to Robert is motivated by his belief that Robert is different from his brother, as he insists to both Robert and Eva, but each rejects his overtures of friendship. Skelly's inability to connect with them before his death is then dramatically echoed by Mary's litany of the pets buried in her backyard, the congregational singing of "I walk in the garden alone," and Cora's cries of "Oh God," closing the act. No one in this town can sustain a fruitful emotional relationship.

As in the first act, there are shifts in time and place in the second, which provides a development of the personal histories and relationships introduced in act 1. Act 2 opens on the Johnson porch, as Patsy informs her friend Lena of her impending marriage to Chuck. Patsy's only interest in marriage seems to be as an avenue of escape from the dereliction of Eldritch. Her interest in moving on is paralleled by the restlessness that drove Walter to leave Cora. (The audience now realizes that Cora's scream at the end of act 1 was a response to the discovery that he had left her.) Living on the outskirts of town, Cora physically and philosophically shares Skelly's outsider status. Having employed him for years, she is the only one to insist that Skelly would not have attacked Eva. In fact, she asserts throughout this act that Eva told her what really happened.

There are numerous court testimony scenes in this act, and Robert is now the primary witness. He insists that he and Eva were attacked by Skelly while on one of their walks and that Nelly shot Skelly before a rape could occur. However, the evidence becomes increasingly contradictory. Cora, now denounced as a harlot, maintains that Robert is lying. Senile Mary swears that she saw both Skelly and Robert beating Eva, but in a dream weeks before the event. Near the end of the act, Eva interrupts Robert's testimony with an ear-shattering scream and cries of "No!," but otherwise she remains mute throughout.

Her scream is in response to the false testimony of Robert, who is like his brother after all. The audience learns finally that Skelly had attempted to rescue Eva from a sexual attack but because of his bad reputation was mistaken by Nelly as the perpetrator. Following her daughter's scream, Evelyn asks aloud why God has burdened her with a crippled child, then answers with, "We love Him. We bless Him. Praise Him." The actors then freeze in a silent tableau as the audience hears Patsy and Walter offstage negotiating a sexual interaction. The play ends with Patsy swearing love to Walter and the townspeople slowly leaving the stage, a few at a time. Only Skelly's body remains onstage, where it fell before the final curtain.

Themes and Meanings

The Rimers of Eldritch is a play about the moral corruption at the core of an American small town that has lost its economic vitality. The old people, the marginally employable, and the few loyal families who have remained have become insular, even viciously so, because they have refused to relinquish a long-gone "glorious" past. So strong is the draw of the past—memories of full shops and bustling streets while the coal mine operated, and of Driver's more recent stock-car victories—that the town is unable to deal constructively with its present condition. Instead, it insists that unwelcome reminders of the present—the mentally deficient, physically handicapped, and morally ambivalent—should remain hidden from view or risk violent expulsion.

The rime, or hoarfrost, that Eva loves so well is symbolic of the town's double-edged attractiveness. Its values, rooted in an absolute belief in the law and religion (the judge and pastor are played by the same actor), make the town glisten in pristine righteousness. More than once Martha and Wilma claim that they are not judging the actions of others, but clearly that is not the case. The candy coating of the rime covers a meanness of spirit in the town; the underside of its all-American values is a corruption that leads to violence. The townspeople agree that they must take collective responsibility for this violence, but they continue to ignore its causes.

The difficulty some of the characters encounter in living up to the town's proclaimed values while trying to maintain a sense of their individuality forms the dramatic fulcrum of the play. For Robert, who is not an outsider by virtue of any apparent disability, the balancing act proves too challenging. The town's blind allegiance to the past encourages its inhabitants to see Robert as the heir to Driver's heroic legacy, yet they are equally blind to his ambivalence toward his brother's achievements and the memorial to them. (The rusting wreck of Driver's car remains in the middle of Church Street, where the tow chain, then the car's axle, broke on the journey into town after the fatal collision.) Only Robert's affection for the imperfect Eva and his snubbing of the girls his own age are suspicious.

What is remarkable about the townspeople's attitude toward Robert and Eva's relationship is how very natural it (and Cora's affair with Walter) is in comparison to the other sexual activity around town. From Patsy's impending marriage (because she is pregnant) to her sexual invitation to Walter, from Driver's sadism to Robert's rape attempt, from Peck Johnson's whipping of Patsy for her promiscuity to Evelyn's suspicions concerning her daughter's walks with Robert; from Skelly's alleged bestiality to his reminiscences (spoken to his dog) of a woodshed affair with Glenna Ann Reiley, rich daughter of a mine owner, the play is rife with illicit sexual activity. Indeed, the characters' twisted sexuality forms the very stuff of moral decadence, tying the town's inhabitants to one another in emotionally unfulfilling unions.

Through both the nature of the cords that bind this community together and Robert's failed attempt to break with that past and become an individual, the situation leading to Skelly's death is constructed. The town believes that it has purified itself of sin by accepting responsibility for Skelly's scapegoating, but it has learned nothing about itself. According to Lanford Wilson, America's small towns exist in a perpetual autumn. As the end of the play demonstrates, Patsy and Walter, as the new generation, will continue the moral decay beneath the shimmering rime.

Dramatic Devices

Because of the importance of the autumnal metaphor (not to mention the pun) to the play's theme, Lanford Wilson utilizes the dramatic techniques of poetic realism. The audience is given an early clue to his break from naturalism by the stage design. Although Wilson does not specify a bare stage or platforms of varying heights and sizes (such as those used at the play's premiere), he does recommend that nothing more realistic than suggestions of "American Gothic motifs" be used. With such an evocative stage in mind, Wilson specified in his stage directions that particular attention be paid to the lighting: "A scene continues—sometimes two or more in separate areas of the stage simultaneously—until the lights dim on the scene and focus attention elsewhere." The insistence of well-timed lighting is important for underscoring a sense of the simultaneity of place, as well as of past, present, and future.

As lyrical as the stage appears, the characters are convincingly realistic. Deftly, Wilson reveals the townspeople's distinct personalities through their everyday gossip and domestic exchanges, as well as through their responses to the crisis of Skelly's death. For all of their individuality, however, Wilson also has them operate as a group protagonist against the evil they think they see in Skelly. From the bleatings of the teenage boys to the ruin of his property to the pastor's insistence on collective responsibility, the townspeople close ranks and function as a single unit.

The collage of overlapping and contrapuntal dialogue aptly conveys the story and combines the lyricism of the staging with the realism of the characterization. Language is always the central technique in Wilson's plays, and particularly in this one. The gossip, speculations, and reminiscences merge to form a smooth, if kaleidoscopic, narrative of the circumstances of Skelly's death, an investigation that also serves as the dramatic impetus of the play. As the town gossip and scenes of domestic tranquillity are continually crosscut with court testimony and the sermons and singing of a church service, the basis for the town's values becomes apparent. This technique also shows, however, that the formation of those values has created the violent situation. The repetition of an entire scene in act 1, in which Skelly insists to Eva that she should tell Robert that he is not like the others, dramatically reiterates the inevitability of disaster in a town so tied to its past.

This kind of repetition, with some variation, can be seen in both acts. Whereas act 1 opens with the gossiping of Martha and Wilma and the court testimony of Nelly, act 2 opens with the gossiping of Patsy and Lena and Robert's testimony. Life in Eldritch continues for the younger generation as it did for the older—with the significant difference that the guilt of the younger is even more manifest. Martha and Wilma only talk about and judge Cora's affair with Walter; Patsy physically involves herself with him. Nelly may have pulled the trigger on Skelly, but Robert attempted rape and lied about it. The younger generation, as the distorted mirroring of acts shows, is even more implicated in the evil of the town than were its elders, and the sense that another sacrificial lamb will be needed is made dramatically, as well as thematically, apparent.

As language-based as the play is, Wilson's characteristic "talkiness" never becomes burdensome. Because of the rapid shifts in time and place and between characters, *The Rimers of Eldritch* moves forward with an almost cinematic speed. With the impeccable timing of a professional acting and stage crew, the transitions are seamless, creating a bedrock of horrific violence just below the uncracked surface of small-town virtue.

Critical Context

The Rimers of Eldritch takes its place among several Wilson plays in which he explores the often violent consequences that attend a relationship to one's own or to a collective past. All too often, the victims are socially marginal individuals: the physically or mentally handicapped, homosexuals, drug dealers, prostitutes, and various hustlers. Such a theme is evident in Wilson's first major success, *The Madness of Lady Bright* (pr. 1964, pb. 1967), a one-act play in which an aging drag queen tries to come to terms with the ravages of time on his body and his friendships (his calls to old friends are met with disconnected numbers). Only "Dial-A-Prayer" offers a human, though taped, contact which can momentarily stave off the collected detritus of the past. In *The Gingham Dog* (pr. 1968, pb. 1969), a middle-class interracial couple, locked into their separate historical racial identities, divorce because they cannot accommodate the changes in each other that the Civil Rights movement has prompted.

Two other notable plays offer group protagonists, but in these later plays the group is a society of misfits rather than a society against them. *Balm in Gilead* (pr., pb. 1965) depicts a motley crew of urban misfits, two of whom fall in love. The hope of this union is cut short, however, when Joe is stabbed to death for trying to leave drug dealing; Darlene's only recourse then is prostitution on the streets. *The Hot l Baltimore* (pr., pb. 1973), perhaps Wilson's best-known play, gathers the inhabitants of a Baltimore hotel together on the eve of its demolition. As with *The Rimers of Eldritch* and

Balm in Gilead, its story is told through the interwoven biographies—the pasts and the dreams—of the inhabitants. *Burn This* (pr. 1987), a contemporary love story about the ambivalence of commitment, is perhaps closest to *The Rimers of Eldritch* in its seamless interweaving of technique and story. As Wilson has said himself of this play, "it's convoluted in exactly the same way those early plays are. But this isn't circles, it's mirrors and landscapes."

With *Burn This* Wilson demonstrated that his early plays were not merely exercises in dramatic technique, as some feared, but preparations for the perfecting of his elliptical and oblique delving into social relations and the pulls of the past. His work with the trilogy of Talley plays—*5th of July* (pr., pb. 1978), *Talley's Folly* (pr., pb. 1979), and *Talley and Son* (pr. 1981)—has brought him recognition on Broadway in addition to a Pulitzer Prize. While some may bemoan the trilogy's "well-made" structure, which has undercut Wilson's lyricism, others praise the intensification of action and concentration of character conflict. Whatever the merit of each criticism, as David Savran has noted, "Wilson remains a skilled writer of romantic fictions, providing audiences with a modicum of self-examination and thereby facilitating their return to a world less poised and graceful than his own."

Sources for Further Study

Bigsby, C. W. E. Introduction to *Beyond Broadway*. Vol. 3 in *A Critical Introduction to Twentieth-Century American Drama*. New York: Cambridge University Press, 1985.

Brockett, Oscar G. "Theatre and Drama Since 1960." In *Modern Theatre: Realism and Naturalism to the Present*. Boston: Allyn and Bacon, 1982.

Busby, Mark. *Lanford Wilson*. Boise, Idaho: Boise State University Press, 1987.

Dean, Anne. *Discovery and Imagination: The Urban Plays of Lanford Wilson*. Rutherford, N.J.: Fairleigh Dickinson University Press, 1995.

DiGaetani, John L. "Lanford Wilson." In *A Search for Postmodern Theatre: Interviews with Contemporary Playwrights*. New York: Greenwood Press, 1991.

Kane, Leslie. "The Agony of Isolation in the Drama of Anton Chekhov and Lanford Wilson." *West Virginia University Philological Papers* 31 (1986): 20-25.

Marranca, Bonnie, and Gautam Dasgupta. "Lanford Wilson." In *American Playwrights: A Critical Survey*. New York: Drama Book Specialists, 1981.

Savran, David. "Lanford Wilson." In *In Their Own Words: Contemporary American Playwrights*. New York: Theatre Communications Group, 1988.

Schvey, Henry I. "Images of the Past in the Plays of Lanford Wilson." In *Essays on Contemporary American Drama*, edited by Hedwig Bock. Munich: M. Hueber, 1981.

Lynda Goldstein

RISE AND FALL OF THE CITY OF MAHAGONNY

Author: Bertolt Brecht (1898-1956)
Type of plot: Opera; epic theater
Time of plot: The mid-nineteenth century
Locale: The mythical American West during the gold rush
First produced: 1930, at the Leipzig Opera House, Leipzig, Germany
First published: *Aufstieg und Fall der Stadt Mahagonny*, 1929 (English translation, 1957)

Principal characters:
PAUL ACKERMANN (also known as JIM MACINTYRE, MAHONEY, or MALLORY),
JACOB SCHMIDT (also known as JACK O'BRIEN),
HEINRICH MERG (also known as BANK ACCOUNT BILL), and
JOSEPH LETTNER (also known as ALASKA WOLF JOE), lumberjacks
LEOCADIA BEGBICK,
TRINITY MOSES, and
WILLY (FATTY) THE BOOKKEEPER, outlaws
JENNY, a prostitute

The Play

At the beginning of *Rise and Fall of the City of Mahagonny*, an old truck carrying three fugitives from the law, Leocadia Begbick, Trinity Moses, and Willy (also known as Fatty) the Bookkeeper, breaks down in the middle of a desert in the American West. Although they intended to become rich by prospecting for gold, presumably on the West Coast, they decide that it would be simpler and more lucrative to build a city and lure rich prospectors into their town with liquor and women. Mahagonny, which is erected in a couple of weeks, attracts Jenny Smith from Oklahoma and six other prostitutes. Eventually, men from big cities begin arriving at the "city of nets" to experience what they have heard to be a paradise.

Among the new arrivals are four lumberjacks from Alaska: Paul Ackermann, the main character (also known as Jim MacIntyre, Jim Mahoney, or Jim Mallory in some versions), and his three friends Jacob Schmidt (Jack O'Brien), Heinrich Merg (Bank Account Bill), and Joseph Lettner (Alaska Wolf Joe). They meet Leocadia Begbick, who introduces them to her "girls"; Paul decides to take Jenny after Jacob finds her too expensive. Soon, however, the city finds itself in a crisis: Inflation and the rising crime rate cause people to leave in alarming numbers. Even Paul considers moving on, because he does not feel completely satisfied with his new life. He senses that something is missing, but his friends persuade him to stay.

In the next scene, the four men, along with others, are drinking and smoking in front of the Hotel of the Rich Men. Signs surround them forbidding them to sing obscene songs and make noise. Again, Paul expresses his misgivings about staying in the city, because it is too quiet and boring. News of an approaching hurricane, however, disturbs their daydreams and frightens the town's inhabitants. Only Paul relishes the upcoming storm, because it will bring some change, even if it is in the form of destruction, into his monotonous life. Begbick senses the danger in his attitude and warns, "Fierce is the hurricane/ Fiercer still is the typhoon/ But the worst of all is man." Taking advantage of the situation, Paul invites the people of Mahagonny to do whatever they wish. An arrow on a large map visible in the background marks the hurricane's course toward Mahagonny. Just as the city's destruction seems inevitable, the storm unexpectedly moves around the city, leaving it unharmed.

After this miraculous turn of events, the city's population decides to continue its hedonistic lifestyle. A male chorus sings of the city's delights:

> First, don't forget the joys of eating
> Second, comes the sexual act,
> Third, go and watch the boxers fighting
> Fourth comes drinking as per pact,
> But mainly get it through your head
> That nothing is prohibited.

Some of the subsequent scenes portray the folly of such an extravagant lifestyle. Jacob gorges himself to death. The scene titled "Love" depicts Begbick's women for sale but also portrays a tender moment between Paul and Jenny in which they voice their feelings for each other through a touching poem about flying cranes. At the boxing ring, Joseph challenges Trinity Moses to a fight despite Willy the Bookkeeper's warnings that it would be murder. Joe is, predictably, killed.

Later, at Begbick's, Paul treats everyone to drinks, but when Begbick demands to be paid, he discovers that he has no money left. Jenny and Heinrich refuse to lend him money, and he is arrested. In the courtroom, Begbick serves as the judge, Willy the Bookkeeper is the defense lawyer, and Trinity Moses, who is selling tickets to the two trials, is the prosecutor. During the first trial, Begbick acquits an accused murderer, because he has bribed her. The ostensible reason for the acquittal is the absence of an injured party. When Paul begs Heinrich for a hundred dollars so that he can do the same, his "friend" refuses him. Not surprisingly, Paul is found guilty of seducing Jenny (who testifies against him), of singing forbidden songs, of disturbing the peace during the night of the hurricane, and of being an accessory to Joe's death, because he encouraged him to fight. Moreover, he is condemned to death "because of his lack of money, which is the greatest crime on earth."

In the background of the execution scene, the audience sees the peaceful city of Mahagonny; the electric chair is in the foreground. Several people, including Jenny and Heinrich, have gathered to watch Paul's execution. Although many of the spectators do not wish to see Paul killed, they are not willing to pay for his release. Paul takes leave of Jenny and Heinrich and reminds all present of God's existence. Begbick commands him to sit on the electric chair, and Jenny and four men put on a play about God in Mahagonny. It will not matter, they conclude, if God sends them to Hell, because they are already there. The skit forces Paul to realize his mistake: He came to Mahagonny thinking that money could buy happiness, but he discovers that he has neither friends nor freedom.

After Paul's execution, Mahagonny experiences its own gradual destruction: Chaos, inflation, and a growing animosity among the townfolk signal the demise of the city of paradise. Marching demonstrators bear placards demanding chaos and the "fight of all against all"; other posters proclaim the need for the just distribution of goods, love, and the continuation of the golden age. Another parade of people bears Paul's corpse and a poster saying "For Justice." In this final scene of chaos, no salvation appears forthcoming: It concludes with everyone proclaiming that they cannot be helped.

Themes and Meanings

Most critics agree that Bertolt Brecht's *Rise and Fall of the City of Mahagonny* serves as a satire of capitalist society. (It is well known that Brecht had begun reading Karl Marx's writings during the time he was working on this play.) Brecht appears to be particularly critical of capitalist society's obsession with money, its shallowness, and its hypocrisy, which are most evident in a contemporary urban setting. People's greed and selfishness ultimately lead to their dehumanization and alienation from fellow human beings.

Brecht's criticism is aimed at the rich and the arrogant who believe that money can buy pleasure. In his play, he demonstrates how money brings only unhappiness and loneliness; the "friends" Paul buys—Jenny, Heinrich, and the men for whom he buys drinks—abandon him when he needs them. Although Jenny and Heinrich proclaim their loyalty toward Paul, they refuse to pay for his release from prison.

Kurt Weill, Brecht's collaborator and the composer of his songs, claimed that Mahagonny was an international city and that the American names suggest not America per se but a mythical America. Nevertheless, some interpreters have viewed the play as a critique of American society; they point to the American location, the whiskey, the poker table, the song about the moon of Alabama, and the electric chair as proof that Brecht deliberately wished to criticize American urban life. Some have even interpreted Mahagonny as a metaphor for Las Vegas. Others have perceived the play as a critique of the chaotic and immoral Weimar Republic, particularly Berlin of the 1920's with its rampant prostitution, unstable government, political corruption, and economic crises.

In his notes on the play, Brecht himself claimed that it was intended to have a provocative effect. By exposing the ills of society, it would cause people to become aware of a need for change and would incite social reform. He points out, for example, that the glutton stuffing himself to death brings to mind the starvation of others.

Several critics have observed the biblical references in the play. They view the approaching hurricane as alluding to the biblical theme of divine retribution and the destruction of Sodom and Gomorrah. What is typically Brechtian, however, is the inversion of this theme: Mahagonny is spared, and Paul's reminder of God's existence falls on deaf ears. People, not God, destroy themselves and their cities. Some have even interpreted Paul as a modern-day Job or a Christ figure. His request for water before his execution supports the latter hypothesis. Moreover, as the people of Mahagonny carry his corpse through the streets, they speak of getting vinegar for the dead man, an allusion to an event that occurred when Christ was on the cross. However, Paul, unlike Christ, does not prove to be a powerful leader. Again, Brecht could be saying that there is no place for a Christ figure in contemporary society because he, like God, no longer exercises any power over humankind. This attitude is consistent with the Marxist perspective Brecht espoused, which claims that the afterlife is an illusion, that God does not exist, and that human beings have only the here and now. In summary, the biblical references can be understood as ironic: They are meaningless remnants of an older civilization, obsolete in contemporary society.

Dramatic Devices

In *Rise and Fall of the City of Mahagonny*, Bertolt Brecht combines opera with elements from his epic theater, cabaret, and vaudeville. In his notes on the work, he dubbed it a "culinary opera" that both gives pleasure and educates. It not only embraces a "hedonistic approach" but also provokes the audience to question accepted conventions and to become aware of "the irrationality of the operatic form." In particular, he observes that "the irrationality of opera lies in the fact that rational elements are employed, solid reality is aimed at, but at the same time it is all washed out by the music. A dying man is real. If at the same time he sings, we are translated to the sphere of the irrational."

Brecht produced an opera "with innovations" by employing some of the techniques of his epic theater. One significant innovation is the "separation of elements" of the opera. Instead of creating a *Gesamtkunstwerk* (integrated work of art) in which the music, words, and setting are fused together, a technique that draws in the audience and makes them part of the musical production, he separated the various elements. Consequently, he makes the spectators aware of the opera as a contrived work of art. The distance achieved between the production and the spectators allows them to observe and reflect upon the message of the artwork.

Brecht's text and Weill's music most clearly demonstrate the didactic role of the epic opera. The playwright claimed that "the text had to be neither moralizing nor sentimental, but to put morality and sentimentality on view." Brecht undercuts the tender love scene between Paul and Jenny, for example, by Jenny's refusal to help her former lover when he is condemned to die. As a result, he both presents a traditional romantic theme and exposes the hypocrisy of such sentimentality. The spectator both enjoys the touching scene and becomes aware of its artificiality.

This "jolt" into an awareness of the illusory quality of the artwork and the contrasting harsh reality constitutes Brecht's *Verfremdungseffekt*, or alienation effect. Brecht's favorite description of the theatergoer was that he left his brain, along with his hat, at the check-in room. The alienation effect, on the other hand, causes the audience to reflect on the work's social message and consequently on the injustices of the real world and incites them to change it.

Similarly, Weill's music does not lull the spectator into complacency but offers ironic commentary on the action. The trite texts, often jarring music, and harsh voices underline the banality of the emotions and ideas presented and allow the audience to gain critical insight into conventional behavior and platitudes. Weill employed elements from popular music—cabaret, operetta, and especially American jazz—to achieve self-irony and parody. For example, the song in which Jenny explains her failure to help Paul when he is condemned is the same one he sang when he proclaimed the new law of hedonism in Mahagonny:

> Your life in this world's what you make it
> And no one will carry you through.
> If there's got to be kicks, then I'll give them
> And the kicked one, believe me, will be you.

The repetition of the song under much different circumstances gives an ironic twist to its original meaning: The egoistic attitude implicit in the song brings about Paul's doom, not his happiness.

Other elements in the opera, including the use of placards and projections, serve as didactic tools and ironic commentary on the scenes. The posters with conflicting messages that are carried by the demonstrators at the conclusion not only portray the chaos in Mahagonny ("For the just distribution of goods" and "For the unjust distribution of goods") but also comment ironically on one another ("For love" and "For the venality of love"). Furthermore, the projection of a peaceful Mahagonny contrasts sharply with the execution scene (with electric chair) in the foreground.

Critical Context

The epic opera's predecessor, the *Songspiel Mahagonny* (unpublished until 1963; the little mahagonny), was produced at the Chamber Music Festival in Baden-Baden, Germany, in 1927 and caused an uproar that foreshadowed the even more scandalous effect *Rise and Fall of the City of Mahagonny* generated in Leipzig. The latter was actually a continuation and expansion of the former. Hissing, whistling, and fighting broke out during the work's premiere, and the police were summoned. During subsequent performances, the lights were kept on, and the police were stationed along the walls of the theater to prevent similar riots. Lotte Lenya, Bertolt Brecht's main actor, commented that the audience believed that the dramatic work was simply communist propaganda, not the traditional opera that they expected. Despite the scandal, the work was a success, and the premiere performance was considered a historical moment in the German theater.

Some critics consider this work, which was written at the same time as *Die Dreigroschenoper* (pr. 1928, pb. 1929; *The Threepenny Opera*, 1949), the quintessential expression of Brecht's thought during what Klaus Schuhmann calls his "transitional period" (1926-1929). During these years, Brecht read Marx and was in the process of committing himself to communism. In particular, Marx's dictum that it was more important to change the world than merely to interpret it exercised a great influence on Brecht's attitude toward the role of dramatic works, according to Fritz Sternberg. Because Brecht had little confidence in the political effect of opera, however, he soon turned to other dramatic forms, such as the ballet-cantata *Die Sieben Todsünden der Kleinbürger* (pr. 1933; *The Seven Deadly Sins*, 1961), in which the "culinary" aspect was deemphasized and the didactic element could be stressed. As Brecht himself stated, the epic opera was supposed to be "fun," to be enjoyable, even as it made jabs at capitalism.

Others point out that *Rise and Fall of the City of Mahagonny* represents a significant experiment in the operatic form rather than an important stage in Brecht's ideological development. While working on this musical play, Brecht devised the main traits of his epic theater and integrated these principles into his "epic opera." The techniques he used in it to produce the alienation effect were developed further in his later plays.

Sources for Further Study

Bentley, Eric. *Bentley on Brecht*. New York: Applause, 1999.

Brecht, Bertolt. *Bertolt Brecht Journals, 1934-1955*. New York: Routledge, 1995.

Casabro, Tony. *Bertold Brecht's Art of Dissemblance*. Brookline, Mass.: Longwood Academic, 1990.

Cotterill, Rowland. "In Defence of Mahagonny." In *Culture and Society in the Weimar Republic*, edited by Keith Sullivant. Totowa, N.J.: Rowman and Littlefield, 1977.

Ozsvath, Zsuzsanna. "Brecht's *Rise and Fall of the City of Mahagonny* and *The Good Woman of Setzuan*." *University of Hartford Studies in Literature: A Journal of Interdisciplinary Criticism* 13 (1981): 178-186.

Parmalee, Patty Lee. "1927-29, Studying Marx: Mahagonny and the Learning Plays." In *Brecht's America*. Columbus: University of Ohio Press, 1981.

Margarete Landwehr

THE RIVER NIGER

Author: Joseph A. Walker (1935-)
Type of plot: Domestic realism
Time of plot: 1973
Locale: Harlem, New York City
First produced: 1972, at St. Mark's Playhouse, New York City
First published: 1973

Principal characters:

JOHN WILLIAMS, a house painter and poet in his fifties
MATTIE WILLIAMS, John's wife, in her fifties
GRANDMA WILHEMINA GENEVA BROWN, Mattie's eighty-two-year-old mother
DR. DUDLEY STANTON, John's friend in his fifties
JEFF WILLIAMS, John and Mattie's twenty-five-year-old son
ANN VANDERGUILD, Jeff's black South African, twenty-two-year-old girlfriend
MO, a twenty-two-year-old black gang leader and friend of Jeff
GAIL, a twenty-one-year-old woman in love with Mo
CHIPS, a sexually perverted young fool,
AL, a homosexual, and
SKEETER, a drug addict, all part of "Mo's Men"

The Play

The play begins on the eve of the homecoming of Jeff Williams, who is returning from military service. The first scene of the play, however, shows the aging patriarch John Williams at work on the poem that provides the title and central symbol of the play. "I am the River Niger—hear my waters," are the first words uttered by John, whose personal search for a "battlefield" in which he can distinguish himself as an "African warrior" is the underpinning that provides pattern for the play. He finds that battlefield in a heroic gesture that ends the play.

From the point of departure to the point of arrival in this journey of affirmation, several things happen. It is suspected early in the play, and confirmed by the end, that Mattie Williams, mother to Jeff and wife of John, is seriously ill with cancer. Jeff's homecoming has him entering a new phase in his life in which he makes the difficult transition from adolescence to adulthood. To make that transition, Jeff must confront his father, who experiences his own crisis as he tries to make a success of his failures and to accept his wife's illness and his son's independence.

These intimate, internal struggles are paralleled by the social struggle represented by Jeff's old gang. Formerly, under Jeff's leadership, the gang was involved in community building, but in his absence it has adopted the tactics of armed revolution, and its members have degenerated into unprincipled behavior and infighting.

Upon his arrival, Jeff is first greeted by Ann, his girlfriend, to whom he later proposes. She is accepted by Mattie and John but is looked upon suspiciously by Grandma, who fears that Ann will hinder Jeff's progress in life, just as John's wife and family did to him. John, a highly intelligent man, had to give up college to work three jobs in order to support his wife, child, and some of his wife's family. His sacrifices result in a lack of satisfaction with his life, with which he copes by drinking. When, at the end of act 2, Jeff discloses that he did not graduate from navigation school and refuses to put on his uniform because he no longer believes in his country, John, a proud man, is overwhelmed and abruptly leaves the house, not to return for six days.

Throughout the play the audience also learns about the activities of the gang now under Mo's leadership. The perversions and bickering of Chips, Skeeter, and Al are depicted through their interactions with each other and the members of Jeff's family. However, the most pressing problems for the gang are its confrontations with police and the suspicions of the presence of an informer in the group. Mo seeks Jeff's help to root out the traitor, something Jeff hesitates to do because he does not want to get his family involved and because he does not believe in the revolutionary jargon and actions of his misguided childhood friends. His plans are to attend law school—something his father began to do in his youth—and change the unequal system from within.

When Jeff refuses to participate in the gang's efforts, Ann offers to help. She reveals that her father has been imprisoned for nine years after taking responsibility for the revolutionary activity of his sons in South Africa, who were operating a press that printed antigovernment material. Fearing for Ann's safety, Jeff reconsiders and becomes involved. The police informer, however, provokes a police raid on the Williams house, which leads to the heroism and subsequent death of John Williams.

At the start of act 3, John returns after a six day "bender" with an acceptance of his son's perspective and his wife's illness. He also has completed his magnum opus, "The River Niger," a poem about the grandeur and symbolic importance of the African river, which is presented in life-affirming, masculine terms. He enters into an explosive situation, however, as the informer is about to be exposed and the police surround the house. When the informer is discovered as Al, there is an armed clash and exchange of gunfire between John and Al. John dies, sacrificing himself to save his son and the others from arrest by taking responsibility for the gang's killing months before of Buckley, an abusive and corrupt narcotics officer, and for the possession of illegal firearms. John dies content that he has found his "battlefield," and the lance, so to speak, is handed over to Jeff, who is about to confront the police as the play ends.

Themes and Meanings

A three-act domestic drama set in Harlem in 1973, *The River Niger* reveals the personal struggles of house painter-poet John Williams and his family and provides references to and commentary on the social and political issues of the time that surround the affirmation of African American identity on its own terms, as opposed to the terms imposed by the dominant white majority or emanating from a compromising, integrationist solution.

The domestic tragedy of *The River Niger* is also a tragedy with wider, social implications. An examination of personal as well as communal values is experienced by the characters who question the meaning of their lives, which includes the reality of being black in the United States. In Grandma Wilhemina Geneva Brown's comments about not considering herself as black—and therefore as superior to blacks—a complex, historical viewpoint on race emerges. The one black person she truly admires is her husband, Ben Brown, who died defending his land against a white poacher.

John Williams and his lifelong friend Dudley Stanton, a doctor of Jamaican descent, bandy statements that refer to blackness in a humorous, good-natured way, exploring perception and prejudice, insight and cliché. In the completion of his poem and the killing of the police informer that results in his own death, John reaches a clear achievement as his past failures are reconciled and his status as an "African warrior," an authentic, worthy black man, is confirmed.

Jeff and his friends discuss the contemporary, politically aware, and active young black man and his role in defending and furthering the interests of the black "family." Jeff, like his father, is a man of words, of knowledge and philosophy. The solution for change that he proposes is based on principle informed by reasoned argument. His refusal to put on his military uniform because he no longer believes in his country—a move that deeply upsets his proud father—and his refusal to become involved in the violent agenda of his friends are examples of the logic and firmness of his resolve. This resolve, combined with his caring for the women in his life, portrays him as a positive male role model who contrasts with his gang-member friends, who are confused but well-meaning; Mo, Chips, and Skeeter put their faith in a rhetoric of revolution that they do not quite understand and that exposes Jeff's family, and by extension every black family, to avoidable peril.

Joseph Walker dedicated *The River Niger* to "highly underrated black daddies everywhere," and in the play, as in most of Walker's work, women are essentially presented in supporting roles; the focus of the play is on the struggles of the male characters in a male-dominated world.

Dramatic Devices

The River Niger is a domestic drama presented with a high degree of social realism. Depicting a "brownstone on One Hundred Thirty-third between Lenox and Seventh," the stage is made up of a cross-section of a house, with a living room and kitchen, as well as stairs going up to the bedrooms, and front and back doors. The characters' daily lives are presented in intimate detail. The audience sees and hears them dealing with groceries, discussing relationships, drinking, smoking marijuana, expressing sexual desire, and engaging in self-evaluation in the frank yet poetic manner that characterized the work of such contemporaries as Arthur Miller, Eugene O'Neill, and Tennessee Williams.

Dialogue and action are used to render the character of African American experience and to provoke thought and discussion on pressing social and political issues of the day. The play raises these issues in terms of how they affect the characters and not simply philosophically or dogmatically. The dramatic confrontations that marked the Civil Rights movement in the 1960's are alluded to in the conflicts that engage the characters. The real-life violence experienced by American society at the time finds an echo in the play's physical action, overtly presented in the armed confrontation between Al and John and implicitly presented by blaring sirens and cops with bullhorns offstage. This effectively conveys a world beyond the theater.

In terms of pacing, the play stays fairly close to the classic unities of time and place, and the development of the intrigues and their resolution happen in a realistic fashion. Nonetheless, *The River Niger* has a highly poetic quality that is present not only in the fact that John Williams is a poet and reads his poetry; there are also many moments of poetry from the other characters as they come to poignant realizations stated in a simple yet eloquent fashion. These poetic moments are underscored by the recurrence of a bass line played by an offstage musician that provides an atavistic musical counterpoint to the lyricism of the play's language.

Critical Context

One of eight plays written by Joseph A. Walker, *The River Niger* is considered by most critics to be his best. Indeed, in the season it was first produced, it won the Obie Award for Best American Play and received the Tony Award for best play. It also earned for its author the Dramatists Guild Award and a Guggenheim Fellowship.

Along with these distinctions, *The River Niger* holds a central place in Walker's oeuvre in that it elaborates his favorite themes and treats them in an artistically superior fashion. Most of his other works for the theater, like *The Harangues* (pr. 1969), *Ododo* (pr. 1971, pb. 1972), *The Lion Is a Soul Brother* (pr. 1976), and *District Line* (pr. 1984), deal with the predicaments and perspectives of African American men but have been criticized for artistic shortcomings and questionable portraits of race. Yet, the quality of the depiction of family ties, friendship, and values in *The River Niger* raises the play and its themes to a transcendent plane. Black audiences can recognize themselves in it, but the play also provides a portrayal of universal feelings.

The play is, ultimately, a success and an important theatrical achievement in that it documents the struggles of a black family at a turning point in recent history and presaged the arrival of a mature black theater.

Sources for Further Study

Clurman, Harold. "Theatre: *The River Niger*." *Nation* 215 (December 25, 1972): 668.

Kauffmann, Stanley. "Theater: *The River Niger*." *The New Republic* 169 (September 29, 1973): 22-33.

Lee, Dorothy. "Three Black Plays: Alienation and Paths to Recovery." *Modern Drama* 19 (December, 1976): 397-404.

Oliver, Edith. "Black River." *The New Yorker* 48 (December 16, 1972): 86-87.

Paul Serralheiro

THE ROAD

Author: Wole Soyinka (1934-)
Type of plot: Postcolonial; psychological
Time of plot: The 1960's
Locale: Nigeria, West Africa
First produced: 1965, at the Commonwealth Arts Festival, London
First published: 1965

Principal characters:
PROFESSOR, the proprietor of a drivers' haven; formerly a Sunday school teacher and lay reader
MURANO, a personal servant to Professor
KOTONU, a truck driver
SAMSON, a passenger tout and driver's mate to Kotonu
SALUBI, a driver trainee
CHIEF-IN-TOWN, a politician
SAY TOKYO KID, a driver, the captain of a group of thugs
PARTICULARS JOE, a policeman

The Play

Professor, the protagonist of *The Road*, searches for the Word, or Logos, the inward rational principle of language, consciousness, and the natural universe. As the proprietor of the Aksident Store, Professor also dedicates his life to the knowledge and propagation of death, which the Word symbolizes: "The Word may be found companion not to life, but death." Life is the field of activity, while death, as represented by the Word, is an absolute stasis in which all activity has its unified source. Pursuing the Word can involve the fear of death, which for the Yorubas (the people to which Wole Soyinka belongs) is not considered to be the cessation of life. Professor tries to cheat the illusion of death and embrace the Word, but he ends up only cheating himself.

Death is a constant companion on the road, the synecdoche for the industrial states of Europeanized Africa. The characters in *The Road* live in ignorance of the true interplay between life and death. Professor's most intimate medium in his quest for the enigmatic Word is Murano, who is accidentally run over by the truck driver Kotonu during the annual Drivers' Festival. Murano had been masquerading as the god Ogun, the Yoruba god of carvers, metal, engineering, technology, war, and fire. Ogun symbolizes the creative-destructive principle. Murano dies in a phase known to the Yorubas as *agemo* and is therefore in a state of suspension: "Agemo, the mere phase, includes the passage of transition from the human to the divine essence." Murano is a dramatic embodiment of the Word: He is mute, arrested in time, and vanishes during daylight; the Word is silent, eternal, and to most people hidden by the darkness of ignorance.

When Murano is killed, just before the play opens, Kotonu and his tout Samson hide his body in their truck to avoid the frenzied worshipers. Professor discovers Murano and engages him in his former occupation as wine-tapper and companion who might reveal the secrets of freedom from incarnate bondage. As Professor explains, Murano walks with a limp because "when a man has one leg in each world, his legs are never the same." Murano has one foot on the Word, and the Professor hopes to find rehabilitation in this connection.

Professor's following consists of a group of drivers and truck-park layabouts who congregate every evening for "communion service," in which they share palm wine tapped and delivered by Murano. Kotonu asks Professor whether Murano is the "god apparent," since he was killed in possession by Ogun. Professor thinks that by holding a god captive he can anticipate and cheat the final confrontation with death.

Kotonu, after killing Murano and witnessing an accident at the broken bridge, abandons the road and becomes manager of the Aksident Store. An ambiguous figure, Professor stocks the store from the abundant sacrifice of wrecks and road victims, forging licenses and removing traffic signs to keep his business flourishing. His rationale of reverent purpose—the search for the Word—belies his affinity to the gang of layabouts, whose consciousness of death lacks only his style of spiritual exploitation. Wole Soyinka satirizes Professor by showing how his search leads down the perverse road of madness and megalomania.

The Road consists of two parts, with a series of five major mimes in which one of the characters is in a state of possession. In the opening mime, Samson sits on Professor's chair, placed on top of a table in the presence of Salubi, a would-be chauffeur, and pretends to be an "African Millionaire" flinging bribes to a line of police. Their hilarious fantasy is suddenly disrupted by Professor, returning from a road vigil, carrying his usual bundle of newspapers and a road sign newly removed to guarantee his success. Salubi dives under the table in panic, but Samson, although petrified with fear, continues his imposing act and manages to confuse Professor, who thinks that he has found a kindred spirit. The irony is that they are really antithetical spirits. By virtue of his willingness to accept fate as it comes, Samson appears to have greater affinity for the Word than does Professor, who searches for the Word on bits of newspaper instead of within the self.

In a subsequent scene, Samson imitates Professor in his former churchgoing days, when during service he would bow at every mention of the name Jesus Christ. This distracting mannerism, together with his habit of shaking his head in disapproval and taking notes on the bishop's grammatical errors, held priority in the interest of the congregation over the actual sermon. Finally, the bishop thought that he would teach Professor a lesson by using Jesus Christ in every other sentence, prompting him to rise, bow, and sit like a marionette. The congregation was hushed, for they knew that this was the final duel. Professor clinched victory by taking and holding one last bow. His move was applauded, as Samson recalls, by a thunderous noise from outside that sent everyone running: The church wall adjacent to the window had collapsed under the weight of the exuberant spectators.

Each of the three remaining imitation/possession scenes involves death, and Professor is the prophet of death. Soyinka uses the chorus to re-create the original atmosphere of the scenes imitated, as with organ music in the bowing scene and the layabouts' dirging in the subsequent scenes. At the end of the first part of the play, Murano mistakes the requiem for the departed souls of the bridge accident for the evensong that usually summons him to serve the palm wine "communion." This simple confusion of time illustrates Murano's nontemporal condition.

Part 2 opens with Samson and Kotonu reenacting the bridge accident for Professor. Just as they approach the bridge, an overcrowded truck passes them and plunges through the rotten planks of the bridge. The violent screech of Kotonu's brakes is heard in the theater as they pull up to peer down the chasm. Although Professor sees the accident as a sacrifice to a thirsty river goddess, he considers it largely wasted. Professor criticizes the accident, as he does the layabouts for fighting at political rallies for money, because in both cases death lacks the dedication to the understanding he considers necessary for redemption. He thus claims to have the sole key to salvation. Death itself is not sufficient, for clearly death is not literally equivalent to the Word. Ironically, while the Professor initiates his followers into the cult of the Word, the process of redemption seems to occur without him during the scenes of possession.

The cathartic reenactments of *The Road* are dramatizations of cultural transcendence. The Driver's Festival is the most intense enactment of the play. It occurs when the tailgate of the truck serving as the store falls, ejecting Kotonu and the grotesque mask worn by Murano at the time of his death. Instantly the stage is flooded by celebrators searching for their lost god, the masquerader who has just been run down by Kotonu. Samson and Kotonu frantically hide the body of Murano in the back of the truck. Kotonu then deceives the other drivers by donning the mask, which is still soaked with the dead man's blood.

Samson also undergoes possession by the dead, precipitated by policeman Particular Joe's hunt for Murano's killers. Particular Joe gropes around the back of the store truck with his hands and is about to discover the mask when Samson distracts him by donning the uniform of Sergeant Burma, the former Aksident Store manager, who was recently killed in a road accident himself. Samson then imitates Sergeant Burma, while the layabouts sing a dirge. Reenactment thus takes Kotonu and Samson toward the Word's boundlessness, melting their identities with the fate of the dead men and terrifying them into hysterically ripping off the mask and uniform.

Finally, Murano's reenactment occurs at the evening "communion," when he is forced by Professor to wear the mask. Murano dances to the rhythm of *agemo* in the ritual of Egungun, as he did as the masquerader before his death. In the previous reenactments, only the possessed were frightened; now, everyone is frightened, except Professor, of an impending death. Even though the Word is manifested through possession, Professor is never really possessed. His vicarious attempt to penetrate the mystery of death culminates, with apparently no spiritual rebirth, in his own accidental death at the hand of Say Tokyo Kid, the skeptical ringleader of the layabouts.

Themes and Meanings

The Road combines the psychic themes of tragedy and myth with the grim reality of death, symbolized by the spider's web. Murano prods the web several times to draw attention to the parallel between the spider and the road as sources of sudden death. Professor's quest for the Word is rendered ambiguous by the incongruous juxtaposition of his constant rhetoric about revelations through the mystical Word and his collection of spare parts for the Aksident Store. This search for spare parts is the commercial aspect of Professor's quest for the essence of death.

Wole Soyinka's satire extends from Professor's attempt to discover the Word by means of destruction to all manner of institutionalized corruption, such as the would-be millionaire policeman parodied by Samson and Salubi in the first play-within-a-play. Although Professor was expelled from the church because of drunkenness, his role as a seeker of the Word gives him a certain profundity. Always the proprietor of the Aksident Store, Professor nevertheless has a mystical side that makes him appear a man possessed. And yet he is baffled by the possession of others. There are five scenes in which relative boundaries dissolve through reenactment; the Professor is confused in one and merely witness to the rest, while Samson actively partakes in all. Soyinka could be satirizing the academic professional obsessed with relative as opposed to universal truth, with conventional as opposed to natural law.

In trying to exploit Murano, Professor encroaches on the power of the god Ogun, with fatal consequences. What he fails to understand is that the Word cannot be experienced indirectly through a medium such as Murano. Professor's fear of death represents a fear of letting go, of nonattachment: "I must hope, even now. I cannot yet believe that death's revelation must be total, or not at all." Unable to grasp the Word by making an imaginative leap through an expansion of consciousness, Professor meets with death accidentally at the hands of Say Tokyo Kid instead of symbolically at the hands of Ogun himself, thus rendering the outcome of his quest ambiguous. In his parting advice, he tells his followers always to be prepared for death. Although he imparts no eternal wisdom to the drivers, his failure to communicate his knowledge may indicate that one must discover for oneself the essence of the Word and death. Ironically, however, Samson and Kotonu approach understanding of this essence through their reenactments without even trying. This effortlessness suggests that the Word, or infinity, can be experienced by transcending the intellect and senses in a state in which the finite ego, as it were, ceases to exist.

Dramatic Devices

Wole Soyinka's condensation of time and space began with the play-within-the-play of *A Dance of the Forests* (pr. 1960, pb. 1963) and the periodic flashbacks of *The Strong Breed* (pb. 1963, pr. 1964) and reaches its greatest originality in *The Road*. The characters of this play revive the past through an intensity of recall that dissolves the boundaries of time and personality and allows them to dramatize their mental images instantaneously. Soyinka's paradigm is the communication between the Word and the masquerader at the moment of his possession by the spirit for whom he is dancing.

The difference between Murano's possession by Ogun and the possession of the other characters by the past incidents that they relive is one of intensity and depth. Murano transcends into the pure energy of the Word at the source of thought, while the others dive to deeper levels of thought that are purged in the process of being dramatized.

In his essay "The Fourth Stage" (1976), Soyinka explains that in addition to the three worlds commonly recognized in African metaphysics—those of the unborn, the living, and the ancestors—there is a less understood fourth space, "the dark continuum of transition, where occurs the inter-transmutation of essence-ideal and materiality." The characters of *The Road* enter this transitional space while being possessed or reenacting events from the past. In this experience of transcending the boundaries of space, time, and causality, the characters momentarily cross over the gulf between the human and the divine, the finite and the infinite, in their transition toward an experience of primal reality. Making this highly subjective experience accessible to the audience is Soyinka's dramaturgical feat.

Soyinka symbolizes this experience with the enigmatic Word. Ultimately, the Word represents the unity of name and form, sound and meaning, that is found in the fourth space. The approach toward the Word that occurs in the play's reenactments is accompanied by the chorus, which re-creates not only the original atmosphere of the scene imitated but also the atmosphere of ritual transition across the abyss. Sound, therefore, functions as an important transitional device, although the sound of the Word is never actually manifested and its meaning cannot be discovered on the printed page. Another transitional device is the road itself. Soyinka uses it as a middle ground, a no-man's-land, full of corruption and impending death. Similarly, Professor's Victorian outfit, his threadbare top hat and tails, represents a middle state, belonging neither to European nor to African culture. Thus, *The Road* teaches that the Word's ultimate meaning exists beyond the range of ordinary waking consciousness and requires a transition toward higher states, of which Soyinka provides a glimpse.

Critical Context

Wole Soyinka, who received the Nobel Prize in Literature for 1986, is considered a "difficult" or literary as opposed to a popular dramatist. *The Road*, even though it falls within the traditional framework of his other plays, defies narrow classification. It ranges in mood from the near tragic to the absurdly comic, and it contains grim realism, abstract symbolism, caustic satire, and religious and mystical speculation. As an example of ritual theater, *The Road* presents a microcosm of the "cosmic" human condition. As Soyinka says of ritual theater in *Myth, Literature, and the African World* (1976), "powerful natural or cosmic influences are internalized within the protagonists." Since the stage for Soyinka is "brought into being by a communal presence," the ritual aspect of the play draws the audience into participating in the cathartic process.

Soyinka distinguishes European from African literature on the basis of their different relations to the audience and to reality. Whereas the European literary experience consists of a series of literary ideologies, such as realism, naturalism, and absurdism, the African literary experience concerns mainly the discovery and understanding of timeless truth and the preservation of the moral fiber of society. For Soyinka, African literature does not have an independent existence as an ideological entity. *The Road*, like Soyinka's other plays, employs ritual devices within a folkloric framework in order to engage the audience in the cathartic process. Ideally, this process has the effect of raising collective consciousness and thereby bringing the community into harmony with the laws of nature. In his visionary projection of society, Soyinka's satire extends well beyond the road. His absolute standard includes the Christian God and Yoruba deities, such as Ogun and the spirits of timber and the graveyard. The characters (and through them the audience) apprehend these deities not merely as abstract concepts but as real forces open to direct experience on the basis of expanded awareness. For Soyinka, crossing the transitional gulf cannot be separated from the African cultural context.

Sources for Further Study

Adelugba, Dapo, ed. *Before Our Very Eyes: Tribute to Wole Soyinka, Winner of the Nobel Prize for Literature*. Ibadan, Nigeria: Spectrum Books, 1987.

Bossler, Gregory. "Writers and Their Work: Wole Soyinka." *Dramatist* 2 (January/February, 2000): 9.

Gates, Louis, Jr., and Kwame Appiah, eds. *Critical Perspectives, Past and Present*. New York: Harper Trade, 1994.

Gibbs, James, Ketu H. Katrak, and Henry Louis Gates, Jr. *Wole Soyinka: A Bibliography of Primary and Secondary Sources*. Westport, Conn.: Greenwood Press, 1986.

Jones, Eldred Durosimi. *The Writing of Wole Soyinka*. 3d ed. Portsmouth, N.H.: Heinemann, 1988.

Maja-Pearce, Adewale. *Wole Soyinka: An Appraisal*. Oxford, England: Heinemann, 1991.

Moore, Gerald. *Wole Soyinka*. 2d ed. London: Evans Brothers, 1978.

Ogunba, Oyin. *The Movement of Transition: A Study of the Plays of Wole Soyinka*. Ibadan, Nigeria: Ibadan University Press, 1975.

Okagbue, Osita. "Wole Soyinka." In *Contemporary Dramatists*. 6th ed. Detroit: St. James, 1999.

Sekoni, Ropo. "Metaphor as Basis of Form in Soyinka's Drama." *Research in African Literatures* 14 (Spring, 1983): 45-57.

Soyinka, Wole. *Myth, Literature, and the African World*. Cambridge, England: Cambridge University Press, 1990.

Wright, Derek. *Wole Soyinka: A Life, Work, and Criticism*. Indianapolis: Macmillan, 1992.

William S. Haney II

THE ROAD TO MECCA

Author: Athol Fugard (1932-)
Type of plot: Problem play; psychological
Time of plot: 1974
Locale: South Africa
First produced: 1984, at the Yale Repertory Theatre, New Haven, Connecticut
First published: 1985

Principal characters:
MISS HELEN, an elderly woman
ELSA BARLOW, a teacher in her thirties
MARIUS BYLEVELD, a pastor

The Play

The Road to Mecca takes place in the town of New Bethesda, in the heart of South Africa's arid Karoo. The year is 1974, and the setting is the home of Miss Helen, an elderly widow whose work as an artist has led to her increasing estrangement from her neighbors. The play opens as Miss Helen's young friend Elsa Barlow, a teacher from Cape Town, arrives unexpectedly for a visit. The older woman, her appearance unkempt and her small house in need of a thorough cleaning, is flustered by the surprise visit, and the two quarrel as Miss Helen fusses over her guest. Their initial unease dissipates, however, when Elsa delights her friend by playfully pretending to leave and arrive again.

Elsa's visit to Miss Helen was prompted by a disturbing letter she has received from the older woman, but Miss Helen refuses to discuss the topic. Miss Helen also brushes off Elsa's inquiry regarding burns on her hands and a burn mark on the window near one of her lamps. The pair talk instead about village gossip and about Elsa, who has angered her superiors by teaching her nonwhite students to question South Africa's repressive society. She is still troubled by her encounter with a black woman and her child to whom she gave a ride during her drive to New Bethesda. Elsa has also broken off her affair with her boyfriend, who is, she now confesses, a married man.

The two also discuss Miss Helen's work, an elaborate cement sculpture garden consisting of owls, camels, dozens of Wise Men, and other figures, all facing east—toward Mecca, as Miss Helen explains. She began the sculptures following her husband's death fifteen years earlier, and they have become a vital source of creative expression as well as a source of conflict with her more conventional neighbors, who regard her work—and undeniable eccentricity—with suspicion. It was her sculptures that led to Miss Helen's friendship with Elsa, who had stopped, intrigued, years earlier and offered the older woman the only praise and admiration her work had received. Miss Helen's creative spirit is also on view inside her small house, where the walls are all hung with mirrors and bits of glass that catch and reflect the lamplight.

Now, Miss Helen confides, she seems to have reached a barricade on her "road to Mecca," and she fears an unnamed darkness that has entered her and caused the loss of her creative energy.

Miss Helen admits that she has no visitors besides Elsa; the local pastor, Marius Byleveld; and a young black woman who helps her with the house. Elsa is appalled to learn that Marius is making arrangements for Miss Helen to enter a home for the elderly and that he is expected that evening to obtain her signature on an admittance form. When Miss Helen insists that she can still live on her own, Elsa urges her to tell the pastor that she wants to stay put. Act 1 ends as Marius arrives.

Act 2 opens as Elsa retreats to a corner of the room to grade papers and listen as Miss Helen and Marius talk. When Marius's gentle persuasions confuse Miss Helen, she pleads with Elsa for help, and the younger woman confronts the pastor, accusing him of bullying Miss Helen into entering the home. Elsa learns, to her dismay, that her friend has lied to her about the burns she noticed earlier; they are the result of a fire that would certainly have killed Miss Helen if a passing neighbor had not come to her rescue. Elsa angrily berates Miss Helen for betraying her trust, then, realizing that she has hurt her friend deeply, explains to Marius that the older woman's independent spirit has been an inspiration and a challenge to her in her own life.

Marius insists that his only concern is for Miss Helen's welfare, but Elsa accuses him—and the other townspeople—of resenting Miss Helen's refusal to conform to their expectations. Marius acknowledges that at the heart of his concern is Miss Helen's withdrawal from the church, and he condemns her statues as little more than idolatry. Miss Helen responds with a deeply felt explanation of what her work means to her, beginning with her own loss of faith many years before her husband's death. Beneath its conventional surface, she tells him, her married life had been an empty lie, a fact brought home to her on the night of her husband's death. Terrified that her own life was now effectively over as well, she had drawn courage from the light of a small candle and had resolved to fill her life with light, both figuratively through her work and literally through the candles and mirrors in her home. Her confusion over entering the home for the aged had been the result of her growing realization that her creative inspiration has left her—and with it, her ability to keep her own darkness at bay. As Miss Helen speaks, Elsa lights the dozens of candles throughout the room until it glows and sparkles from their flames.

As he listens to her, Marius at last realizes that Miss Helen has taken a spiritual path far different from his own, and he voices his own sense of loss at the distance that now separates them. It is clear from his words that Marius has long loved Miss Helen and that his concern for her welfare is genuine. After Marius leaves, Miss Helen blows out her candles one by one. Elsa admits that she is jealous of the depth of feeling between Miss Helen and Marius, and she refers again to the woman and child she met on the road. She confesses that she has recently had an abortion and feels now that she has put an end to the first real consequence her life has had. She begins to cry, and Miss Helen comforts her.

As the two make plans to ensure that Miss Helen will, indeed, be able to manage on her own, the older woman admits that she knows now that her work as an artist has come to an end and she must face the darkness in herself that she had so feared. It will be, she says, the last phase of her apprenticeship. The play ends as the two women reaffirm their friendship and trust in each other.

Themes and Meanings

The Road to Mecca is an examination of the dual themes of artistic creativity and the often lonely place of the artist in society. In the character of Miss Helen, Athol Fugard has created an example of an artist driven purely by a need to create. Lacking encouragement, recognition, or any other social reward, Miss Helen persists in her work out of a profound need for self-expression, a need so fundamental that she is willing to risk censure and ridicule from her neighbors as well as the isolation that accompanies them. The play never addresses the question of the actual merits—or lack thereof—of Miss Helen's sculptures, and it is clear that for Fugard's purposes the issue has no meaning. The world's evaluation of Miss Helen's work as "good" or "bad" is unrelated to the crucial fulfillment and meaning it brings to her life.

As she explains to Marius, Miss Helen's life with her husband was an empty denial of her true creative spirit; his death was a liberating moment that offered her the chance to pursue a path utterly out of step with the small community in which she lives. That art itself can be perceived as a dangerous threat to those within society who adhere strictly to its conventions is evident in the protests and bannings that have been directed at many works of art over the years, from Édouard Manet's *Luncheon on the Grass* (1863) and Igor Stravinsky's *The Rite of Spring* (1931) to Martin Scorsese's film *The Last Temptation of Christ* (1988) and Salman Rushdie's *The Satanic Verses* (1988). Scarcely a field of artistic endeavor has not produced works that anger those who disagree with their premise. Miss Helen's case may seem insignificant by comparison, yet her neighbors manifest the same mistrust and suspicion that lie at the heart of every reaction against those who break dramatically with the status quo. Her sculptures do not conform to what her neighbors consider to be art, and her life—tied as it is so inextricably to her work—has broken with the town's expectations of respectable widowhood. Convincing Miss Helen to enter a home for the aged will draw her permanently back within the boundaries of an acceptable lifestyle—and effectively put an end to her journey along her personal "road to Mecca."

Fugard refuses to offer up a dramatic conflict as uncomplicated as the quiet struggle between Miss Helen and pastor Marius Byleveld at first seems to be. Although Miss Helen's other neighbors may have seized upon the retirement-home plan as a means of suppressing a creative spirit whose freedom disturbs them, Marius's motives are far more complex. He, too, is frightened by Miss Helen's departure from the conventions of village life, but his fear has a deeper source: the possibility of losing the radiant woman he loves to the very thing within her that gives her inner light. Set up in the play's first act as the potential villain of the piece, Marius emerges by its close as a decent man deeply concerned for Miss Helen's welfare and alone in the knowledge that the qualities that drew him to her have now created an unbridgeable gulf between them. It is a poignant situation, and one expressive of the difficult and lonely life that is sometimes the artist's only path toward his—or her—particular vision.

Dramatic Devices

The Road to Mecca is a play in which the characters embody three quite different responses to the inner need for expression and meaning in life. Miss Helen has listened fearlessly to the call of her artistic creativity and followed it despite societal pressure. Elsa, too, longs for an expressive inner life and draws strength and encouragement from her friend's example, but she remains frightened by the thought of trusting herself completely to that path. For Marius, social convention and a lifetime of disappointed hopes have taken their toll, leaving him unable to break free of his moorings and join the woman he loves on her journey. As the play unfolds, the conversations and conflicts among the three characters serve to explicate their positions and the effects their choices have had on their relationships and their lives.

The play's plot turns on whether Miss Helen will agree to enter the home for the aged, giving in, in effect, to her mounting fears that her creativity has left her. The home becomes a symbol of all the restrictions on her independence that Miss Helen has battled for so many years, and her eventual refusal to sign the admittance form represents her recognition that her inner journey has simply taken a new turn.

Dominating the play's atmosphere is a sense of the vast Karoo desert, which surrounds the small village of New Bethesda, a landscape that can be seen as symbolic of the barrenness of the soul and spirit in an unexamined or unfulfilled inner life. Miss Helen's sculptures stand in the mind's eye amid the desolation like flowers sprung miraculously from the arid land—a vivid symbol of the play's suggestion that art is indeed a miracle and one well worth the sacrifices it may demand.

A central image in the play is the contrast between light and darkness, with light representing life, hope, and creativity and darkness suggesting inward emptiness and death. Miss Helen's life has been lived first in the darkness of a loveless marriage and then in the light of her own creativity. Now a new darkness looms on the horizon as she enters old age and draws nearer to death, and her final acceptance of its approach represents her realization that in trusting completely her inner sense of direction, she has found the key to overcoming not the darkness itself but her fear of it. For Marius, left bereft years earlier by the death of the wife he loved, Miss Helen has become a source of light, and his loss of her to her "road to Mecca" leaves him in darkness. Elsa is floundering in darkness as the play opens but has begun, by its close, to move into the light by at last facing the decisions and mistakes she has made. The climactic scenes in which Elsa lights the lamps and candles as Miss Helen explains the importance of her work makes the image concrete: The flames mirror the import of Miss Helen's words.

Critical Context

Although *The Road to Mecca* is less overtly concerned with the turbulent history of South Africa than most of Fugard's earlier plays, it is no less personal than his autobiographical drama *"MASTER HAROLD" . . . and the Boys* (pr., pb. 1982). The road of the artist and the personal sacrifices it entails are well known to the playwright, who has had many of his plays banned in his own country. Miss Helen's refusal to bend to society's wishes or to abandon work that her neighbors find unsettling has direct parallels in Fugard's own life, for his wrenching dramatic attacks on apartheid have angered many of his fellow countrymen.

If *The Road to Mecca* is allegorically about Fugard's life, it is also specifically about the life of the woman who inspired it: Helen Martins, an eccentric woman whose unusual sculptures intrigued Fugard during a visit to New Bethesda. The circumstances of the play, if not the precise incidents that make up its plot, were suggested by Martins's life and work and by her friendship with a young social worker. As Fugard explains in "A Note on Miss Helen," his foreword to the play,

> as a writer I couldn't help responding to this very eccentric character in this strange little community—a community which was in a sense hostile to her life and her work because it was a deviation from what the townspeople considered to be the way a life should be lived. . . .

Viewed from a broader perspective, however, *The Road to Mecca* can be placed within the context of Fugard's earlier, more directly political works. Although the examinations of apartheid seen in such plays as *The Blood Knot* (pr. 1961, pb. 1963), *Sizwe Bansi Is Dead* (pr., pb. 1972), and *"MASTER HAROLD" . . . and the Boys* are not present here, the play's story of the deep human need for freedom and the dangers to the spirit when that need is ignored or crushed certainly is a commentary on South Africa's repressive social system. It is a mark of Fugard's skill as a playwright that he has found in the life of a "very eccentric character" both a personal artistic statement and a moving testament to the essential, transforming power of freedom.

Sources for Further Study

Fugard, Athol. "A Note on Miss Helen." In *The Road to Mecca*. New York: Theatre Communications Group, 1985.

_______. *Notebooks, 1960-1977*. New York: Knopf, 1984.

Gray, Stephen, ed. *Athol Fugard*. London: Methuen, 1991.

Hauptfleisch, Temple. *Athol Fugard: A Source Guide*. Johannesburg: Donker, 1982.

Henry, W. A. "*The Road to Mecca*." *Time*, June 15, 1987, 70.

King, Kimball, and Albert Ertheim. *Athol Fugard: A Casebook*. New York: Garland, 1997.

Vandenbroucke, Russell. *Truth the Hand Can Touch: The Theatre of Athol Fugard*. New York: Theatre Communications Group, 1985.

Walder, Dennis. *Athol Fugard*. New York: Twayne, 1985.

Janet E. Lorenz

ROMULUS THE GREAT
An Historical Comedy Without Historic Basis

Author: Friedrich Dürrenmatt (1921-1990)
Type of plot: History
Time of plot: March 15-16, 476 C.E.
Locale: Villa of Emperor Romulus in Campania
First produced: 1949, at the Stadttheater, Basel, Switzerland
First published: Romulus der Grosse, 1958 (English translation, 1961)

Principal characters:
ROMULUS AUGUSTUS, the emperor of the Western Roman Empire
JULIA, his wife
REA, his daughter
EMILIAN, a Roman patrician
ZENO THE ISAURIAN, the emperor of the Eastern Roman Empire
SPURIUS TITUS MAMMA, captain of the cavalry
CAESAR RUPF, a manufacturer of trousers
ODOAKER, a Teutonic chieftain

The Play

As *Romulus the Great* opens, Spurius Titus Mamma arrives totally exhausted and wounded at the emperor's villa, which seems deserted except for a flock of chickens. He brings news that the Roman Empire is collapsing, but the chamberlains refuse to let him see the emperor without an appointment, which is impossible to arrange with any speed. As the cavalry officer runs out in frustration, Emperor Romulus appears onstage to discover that the minister of finance has fled with the empty imperial cashbox; the empire is bankrupt, but the imperturbable Romulus directs his full attention to his breakfast, whose centerpiece is an egg freshly laid by one of his chickens, each of which is named for a historical leader.

The minister of state enters, extremely agitated about the cavalry officer's news, but Romulus suggests that the officer rest from his long ride before reporting any news to him. At the breakfast table, Romulus's wife, Julia, and daughter Rea become more and more upset as it becomes clear that the Germans (Teutons) have conquered Pavia. Emperor Zeno enters, pleading for sanctuary. As bad news continues to arrive, Romulus makes wry jokes, indicating his detached attitude.

Caesar Rupf, a wealthy manufacturer of trousers, enters and offers to pay the invading Teutonic chief to evacuate Italy, on condition that trousers become obligatory dress and that the emperor's daughter become his wife. Julia is in favor of the marriage, but Romulus refuses. At the end of the act, the cavalry officer tries to deliver his message but is turned away by Romulus, who tells him that he is sacrificing himself needlessly since the country is already doomed. "Emperor, you're a disgrace to Rome!" cries the officer.

Act 2, which takes place that afternoon, finds everything in disarray. The minister of state is having the archives burned so they will not fall into enemy hands, Zeno keeps stepping on eggs, and the cavalry officer keeps up a litany about being "tired, so tired, . . . dead tired." Into this chaos comes Emilian, Rea's fiancé, who has just spent three years in a Teutonic prison. Rea appears, practicing her tragic verses, and meets a changed Emilian, who orders her to get a knife. Frightened, she runs off. When Emilian hears about Caesar Rupf's proposal, he asks Rea to become Rupf's wife in order to save Rome, and out of love for Emilian she agrees. Romulus, however, again refuses the marriage. When he leaves, Emilian voices the final word, "Down with the Emperor!"

That night (act 3) as Romulus is in his bedroom, Julia comes to say good-bye before escaping to Sicily. In the resulting conversation, Romulus reveals that he became emperor in order to destroy the empire by doing nothing, and she indignantly calls him a traitor. After she leaves, Rea enters and tries to persuade her father to agree to the marriage, but he convinces her that her love for Emilian is too important to sacrifice.

After she has left, Emilian, Zeno and his chamberlains, the ministers of war and state, and the cook step out of hiding places, one by one, wearing black cloaks and carrying daggers. As the conspirators demand an accounting, Romulus directs himself to Emilian, the only one to whom he believes he owes an accounting because he has suffered so much as a victim of Romulus's refusal to defend himself and the empire. To Emilian, Romulus explains his judgment against Rome, which chose violence and tyranny over humaneness and truth. Romulus sees the arrival of the Teutons as just punishment and calmly challenges the would-be assassins to kill him if they believe him wrong. A cry that the Teutons are coming scatters the group, and Romulus orders that the Teutons be allowed to enter.

The last act opens on the next morning. Romulus calmly receives the news that his wife and daughter, Emilian, his ministers, and the cook have drowned on their raft-crossing to Sicily. Composed, he fully expects the Teutons to kill him. In the person of the Teutonic leader Odoaker, however, he finds a man like himself, a chicken breeder and antihero. Far from planning to execute Romulus, Odoaker had hoped to subject himself and his people to Rome in order to contain the warlike tendencies of people such as his nephew, Theodoric. Both Romulus and Odoaker have failed. Powerless before the blind fate that nullified their plans, each must accept his fate: Romulus will go into retirement, and Odoaker will rule as benevolently as possible until his nephew assassinates him. In the final scene, Odoaker is proclaimed king of Italy.

Themes and Meanings

Romulus the Great is a provocative play, using a satirical tone to portray the central character's defeat by blind chance. While the fall of Rome is certainly material for a Greek-style tragedy, and Friedrich Dürrenmatt used much of the form of such a tragedy, including a messenger heralding the imminent invasion, this tragedy is presented with the trappings of the ridiculous. Greek tragedy itself is mocked when Rea recites verses from this literature as her world crumbles around her.

Dürrenmatt saw the world as hostile, often impossibly confusing to human beings who attempt to make sense of it and do the right thing. This play is subtitled *An Historical Comedy Without Historic Basis* because of the liberties the author took with historical fact, but each liberty has a purpose in that it breaks through illusion by setting opposites together. Historical scholars view the empire as a great and noble enterprise; Dürrenmatt's play sets an ironic reality against the audience's perception of the tradition and ideals of Rome. The audience is thus forced to see the ridiculous within the tragic; pathos is invariably undercut with irony.

The emperor as pacifist, as well as Rome's judge, is the focus of the action. The plot revolves around the view that Rome (and Western civilization) has betrayed its values, becoming a destructive rather than constructive force, and deserves to be destroyed. The glorious past of the empire has been reduced to a series of busts of past emperors, which are displayed in the villa until they are sold by Romulus, one by one, to pay his debts.

Particularly sharp criticism is leveled against mindless social conventions and against excessive nationalism and militarism. Zeno's recitation of Byzantine formulas when he requests asylum parodies the conventions, which are certainly also criticized in the character of Julia and her motivations for wishing to be empress. As the empire breaks down, many of the characters indulge in heroic posturing, mouthing words about sacrificing themselves for their country and resisting the enemy at any price, even after defeat is obvious.

The problem of justice is a central theme in all Dürrenmatt's work. Romulus's offer of his own life is a necessary consequence and just atonement for the suffering his decision has caused. Emilian represents this suffering and therefore is the one person to whom Romulus must explain his actions. The conflict between Romulus's position and Emilian's is presented but not resolved, because such a resolution is impossible.

The conclusion demonstrates an incomprehensible reality. Both Odoaker and Romulus are pacifists and believed in their course of action, but both failed. Fate in the form of blind chance defeats them, and their good intentions are neutralized: The invading Teutons will take over and repeat the mistakes of the Roman Empire. A world order governed by blind chance is shown to be triumphant, and the acceptance of the indignities this order hands out is revealed as the only heroism possible.

Dramatic Devices

The play is carefully constructed so that each act works up to a final moment. The character of Romulus is to be revealed slowly, as Friedrich Dürrenmatt himself indicated, so that he appears to be a disgrace to Rome at the end of act 1 and so that Emilian's demand that he be removed is understandable at the end of act 2. Only in act 3 does the audience clearly perceive Romulus's purpose in sitting in judgment over the Roman Empire. At this moment the fool gains a type of dignity, and the farce becomes more serious. At this moment, too, his firmness of purpose, totally lacking in consideration of others, becomes apparent. A man who seemed to be a cynical joker, witty in the face of danger, is revealed to be dangerous in his determined and blind focus on one purpose. Act 4 shows history's punishment of him. Ignoring his hopes and wishes, fate refuses Romulus a sacrificial death and imposes instead the comedy of retirement.

Romulus the Great combines tragic and comic elements in a form that has come to be called tragicomedy. Clearly, the tone of the play includes farcical elements, among them a cast of secondary characters with humorous names. The central character's chicken breeding makes him seem an utter fool, as he worries about which hen has laid an egg that morning while the Empire is falling to invaders. In keeping with this tone, it is the chicken Odoaker who lays eggs, and Romulus, the Julians, and Orestes, his commander-in-chief, lay nothing. The image of the cook chasing and beheading Romulus, Orestes, and Romulus's predecessor for dinner completes this farcical scene. The fact that chickens are wandering everywhere in the rundown villa, so that the characters are continuously in danger of stepping on an egg if they do not tread carefully, confronts the audience with the nature of the do-nothing emperor. When Odoaker arrives and confesses to sharing Romulus's passion for chicken breeding, this shared interest confirms a shared antiheroic character. The great contrast between the expected and reality as presented in the drama is the main source of comic, even grotesque, elements.

Tragedy is leavened with comedy throughout the play, even in the parody of Greek tragedy itself. In act 3, the assassination attempt, a staple of tragic drama, begins to unravel as Romulus steps on the fingers of the minister of state, who is hiding under his bed, and the man cuts himself with his dagger accidentally. Then Zeno is discovered in the closet when Romulus goes there for a bandage. One by one, the other members of the party come out of hiding, as the scene reaches a climax in Romulus's justification and then quickly dissolves as a cry that the Teutons are coming scatters everyone except the exhausted Spurius Titus, who, at last, has fallen asleep.

Critical Context

For Friedrich Dürrenmatt, drama was an attempt to represent reality onstage. While specific political ideologies and dramatic theory were not areas of concern to Dürrenmatt insofar as they were purely abstract, his dramas reveal a perspective very much in line with literature written in German since 1950, characterized first of all by a radical pessimism and feelings of disillusion, nihilism, and isolation. Many postwar dramatists believed that the possibility of writing classical tragedy had been destroyed by the historical events they had just witnessed. Dürrenmatt himself wrote that in the twentieth century individuals could no longer be held accountable and there should be no more individual guilt and atonement. In the modern world, power is wielded by anonymous bureaucrats, leaving comedy as the only dramatic form possible.

Romulus the Great was Dürrenmatt's first dramatic success; although often referred to as a comedy, it has the form of a consistent tragicomedy. In subsequent dramas, such as *Der Besuch der alten Dame* (pr., pb. 1956; *The Visit*, 1958) and *Die Physiker* (pr., pb. 1962; *The Physicists*, 1963), Dürrenmatt continued the practice of infusing a serious subject with a comic tone, presenting an incomprehensible world in which the individual is carried along by events outside his control.

Romulus the Great, revised several times, is deliberately provocative and shows a style and tone that are associated with all Dürrenmatt's subsequent work. He used grotesque exaggeration, including parody and farce, and his heroes are determinedly unheroic, making decisions in a world that cannot be understood. The major themes of sacrificial death, the desire for justice, and blind chance, as well as minor elements such as the tendency of his characters to dine well (as Romulus does), reappear in later works. Much of Dürrenmatt's view of reality was already demonstrated in this work, as was his skill as a practical dramatist. His plays can be read and enjoyed, but the real test is their success onstage. To judge by the number of performances and audience response, *Romulus the Great* and several of his subsequent dramas have passed the test.

Sources for Further Study

Crockett, Roger A. *Understanding Friedrich Dürrenmatt*. Columbia: University of South Carolina Press, 1998.

Daviau, Donald G. "*Romulus der Grosse:* A Traitor for Our Time?" *Germanic Review* 104 (1979): 104-109.

Diller, Edward. "Friedrich Dürrenmatt's Theological Concept of History." *German Quarterly* 40 (1967): 363-371.

Jenny, Urs. *Dürrenmatt: A Study of His Plays*. London: Eyre Methuen, 1978.

Peppard, Murray B. *Friedrich Dürrenmatt*. New York: Twayne, 1969.

Tiusanen, Timo. *Dürrenmatt: A Study in Plays, Prose, Theory*. Princeton, N.J.: Princeton University Press, 1977.

Whitten, Kenneth. *Dürrenmatt: Reinterpretation in Retrospect*. Indianapolis: Berg, 1990.

Susan L. Piepke

THE ROSE TATTOO

Author: Tennessee Williams (1911-1983)
Type of plot: Social realism
Time of plot: 1950
Locale: Sicilian immigrant village on the Gulf Coast
First produced: 1950, at the Erlanger Theatre, Chicago, Illinois
First published: 1951

Principal characters:
SERAFINA DELLE ROSE, a Sicilian woman
ROSA DELLE ROSE, her teenage daughter
ASSUNTA, an old woman
ESTELLE HOHENGARTEN, a neighborhood woman
ALVARO MANGIACAVALLO, a young man
FATHER DE LEO, the neighborhood priest
JACK HUNTER, a young sailor and Rosa's boyfriend
MISS YORKE, a schoolteacher
FLORA and
BESSIE, customers
THE STREGA, a witch

The Play

The Rose Tattoo is a three-act play set in a Sicilian immigrant village on the Gulf Coast of the United States. The play opens at dusk and Serafina Delle Rose, the main character, is sitting in her living room, waiting for her husband, Rosario, to return; she is pregnant. A sign reveals that she is a seamstress, and Estelle Hohengarten arrives with a piece of rose-colored silk she wants made into a man's shirt. During the course of act 1 the audience learns that Rosario is a truck driver who is engaged in smuggling to earn enough money to pay off his truck. Serafina reveals to Assunta that on the night she conceived her son, she awakened to feel needle pricks on her breast and saw there a rose tattoo, exactly like Rosario's tattoo. The tattoo disappeared, but she knew she had conceived. Later, the neighborhood women and Father de Leo come to tell Serafina that Rosario has been killed. In defiance of the Church's strictures, Serafina decides to cremate Rosario and to keep his ashes. The trauma causes her to miscarry.

Scene 4 opens in June, three years later, with Serafina besieged by women who have paid her to sew graduation dresses for their daughters. Serafina is disheveled and disoriented, and Rosa is locked up in the house naked because Serafina learned that she met a sailor named Jack at a high school dance. Miss Yorke, one of Rosa's teachers, arrives and persuades Serafina to let Rosa attend the graduation ceremony.

While Rosa is gone, two customers, Flora and Bessie, arrive on their way to an American Legion convention. During a confrontation about their morals, they reveal to Serafina that Rosario was engaged in a long-term affair with Estelle Hohengarten.

Serafina chases them out of the house with a broom. Rosa arrives with Jack and cleans up Serafina so she can meet him, and Serafina makes Jack swear on his knees before the shrine to Mary that he will respect Rosa's purity.

Serafina fears that the story about Rosario may be true and asks Father de Leo about the rumor, but he refuses to answer. Alvaro's appearance and his fight with the salesman reveal his overtly emotional nature and his similarities to Rosario. Serafina gives him the rose-colored silk shirt to wear, which she made unwittingly for Rosario. Their attraction is obvious, and it is not surprising that Serafina invites him to come back.

Later that night, Serafina's appearance echoes her look in act 1, and when Alvaro enters with a box of chocolates, he reveals that he too has a rose tattooed on his chest. During the course of the evening Serafina telephones Estelle Hohengarten, who confirms her affair with Rosario, prompting Serafina to smash the ash urn on the floor. Eventually, after pretending to leave, Alvaro returns by the back door and goes to bed with Serafina. Meanwhile, Rosa's return with Jack reveals that she wanted to have sex with him, but he could not break his oath. Their plans to run away together are Rosa's idea, prompted by her strong desire to experience sex with Jack.

During the final confrontation between Serafina and Rosa, prompted by Alvaro's behavior upon seeing Rosa on the couch, Serafina is initially duplicitous about Alvaro, pretending she does not know who he is or why he is there. After some argument, Serafina runs him out of the house. Rosa realizes Serafina is lying about her relationship with Alvaro and makes her intention to go with Jack clear. Serafina eventually admits to the relationship with Alvaro and tells Rosa to go to Jack, which she does. Assunta arrives, and Serafina reveals that she has just felt the burning on her breast of the rose tattoo, meaning she has again conceived. She runs to join Alvaro.

Themes and Meanings

The Rose Tattoo concerns itself with several of Tennessee Williams's major themes, especially the importance of sex as the vital key to all human relations, and the ability of women to see this reality much more clearly than men. Serafina is the most obvious bearer of this message, as she revels in her pregnancy early in the play and on more than one occasion brags about the rich sexual life she and Rosario share. In fact, whenever she speaks of Rosario, her speech is in terms of their unquenchable sexual desire for each other. When Rosario is killed and the object of her desire is removed, Serafina completely disintegrates, both physically and mentally, and becomes almost inhuman in her slatternly appearance and bizarre behavior. Her connection with Rosario is so strong that she defies the Roman Catholic Church and keeps his ashes in a kind of shrine, equating them with the statue of the Virgin Mary. Rosario becomes a kind of god to her, and she speaks of how she holds him in her arms in her dreams and memories, which are more important to her than anything in the world of the living.

Serafina also attempts to control her daughter Rosa's sexuality, locking her in the house naked so she cannot leave to meet Jack, her sailor boyfriend. The fact that Rosa is kept naked calls attention to her entry into the world of adult sexual desire. Serafina also makes Jack kneel before a statue of Mary to pledge that he will respect Rosa's purity. Later it becomes clear that Rosa is more than willing to be seduced by Jack, while he is restrained by his pledge before the Virgin Mary. Rosa realizes the power of sexuality, while Jack is restrained by societal and religious mores.

Alvaro is the lone man who seems to realize the importance of sex in the life of Serafina, and he makes his desire to seduce her abundantly plain. She is alternately attracted to and repelled by him, eventually succumbing to the lure of his similarity to Rosario. After symbolically killing Rosario by dispersing his ashes, Serafina gives herself to Alvaro ecstatically, her cries of bliss heard by Rosa in the yard. When Serafina finally realizes that Rosa's desire for Jack is sincere, she sends her to him with her blessing. Notably, there is no talk of marriage; Serafina realizes that desire itself is the end and blesses Rosa's entry into the adult world as a keeper of desire, even as she welcomes a pregnancy to underline her reentry into the world of the living.

Dramatic Devices

The most important devices used by Williams in *The Rose Tattoo* are multiple instances of symbolism, especially rose symbolism. The rose comes up over and over in the play, in the names of the major characters (Rosario, Rosa, and Delle Rose), the tattoos on both Rosario and Alvaro, the color of the silk shirt, the rose oil both Alvaro and Rosario use in their hair, and in many other instances. In fact, at times the symbolism becomes so pervasive and overt it ceases to function effectively as symbolism and becomes a distraction. However, the sexual symbolism of the rose and its connotations as a romantic flower do support the theme of the play, which revolves around the vitality and necessity of healthy sexual relationships without shame or guilt.

Other symbols employed by Williams include the moody lighting, especially naturalistic lighting such as truck headlights sweeping across Serafina's house or the earthy atmosphere of her Sicilian neighborhood. The Strega (witch), with her evil eye and her goat that prompts comical chases through the yard, reinforces the ethnic origins and beliefs of the characters, even as they bedevil those who produce the play onstage. Several bits of comical action, including the slapstick set piece with Flora and Bessie, two characters described by Williams as "clowns," tend to be heavy-handed and less than amusing, but they are clearly intended by Williams to symbolize the joyous celebration of life and vitality that Serafina represents.

Finally, the dressmaker dummies in Serafina's house not only provide realism regarding her profession as a seamstress but also symbolize the lackluster neighborhood women who do not embrace the life-giving power of sexuality as Serafina does. Ultimately, Serafina both begins and ends the play filled with new life, having rediscovered the power and joy to be found in a full embrace of her sexual nature. The dummies with their empty insides provide a final contrast to Serafina's being, filled with love and life.

Critical Context

Written only a few years after *The Glass Menagerie* (pr. 1944, pb. 1945) and *A Streetcar Named Desire* (pr., pb. 1947), the two plays that are arguably Williams's masterworks, *The Rose Tattoo* represented a new direction for Williams, while still focusing on his core themes. Like Blanche DuBois in *A Streetcar Named Desire* and to a lesser extent Amanda Wingfield in *The Glass Menagerie*, Serafina Delle Rose is a southern woman whose life is largely defined and described by her interactions with men. However, Serafina has many important differences. As a Sicilian, Serafina represents a notion popular in Williams's oeuvre and in American culture in the early twentieth century: Members of ethnic minorities are more "earthy" and in touch with the vital forces of nature. Certainly Serafina embraces her need for sex and her desire for Rosario with a vehemence and lack of shame that the furtive and flirtatious Blanche would envy. Nevertheless, though Williams's affection for the Sicilian characters is readily apparent in the play, the underlying cultural ethnocentrism is sometimes startling and offensive to modern readers.

In addition to her ethnic background, Serafina is Catholic and working class. Unlike Amanda and Blanche, she has no glorified past on which to look back with longing. However, the fact that Rosario was a "baron" is a point of some pride for her, a point that echoes the destructive glorification of the past to which Williams returns as a theme again and again. The neighborhood women and their constant gossipy interference in Serafina's life recall the gossip that proved so destructive to Blanche, and serve as such a concern for Amanda. The fact that many people are highly judgmental and careless about whom they hurt with their talk is also a constant theme of Williams. Serafina, however, deals more honestly and directly with the neighborhood snoops than either Blanche or Amanda, though they still manage to do their destructive work.

Overall, Serafina Delle Rose and her daughter Rosa denote a more positive look at the themes Williams treats in all his major works. Beset by gossip and tormented by those who are less sensitive, less honest, and uncomprehending of their honest embrace of sexuality, both Serafina and Rosa refuse to be cowed and destroyed, driven into madness or despair. In defiance of those around them who do not understand, they move forward at the end of the play, with a hopeful feeling for their futures.

Sources for Further Study

Bigsby, C. W. E. *Tennessee Williams, Arthur Miller, Edward Albee*. Vol. 2 in *A Critical Introduction to Twentieth-Century American Drama*. Cambridge, England: Cambridge University Press, 1984.

Bloom, Harold, ed. *Modern Critical Views: Tennessee Williams*. New York: Chelsea House, 1987.

Devlin, Albert J., ed. *Conversations with Tennessee Williams*. Jackson: Mississippi University Press, 1986.

Spoto, Donald. *The Kindness of Strangers: The Life of Tennessee Williams*. Boston: Little, Brown, 1985.

Williams, Edwina Dakin. *Tennessee Williams: A Tribute*. Edited by Jac Tharpe. Jackson: Mississippi University Press, 1977.

Vicki A. Sanders

THE ROVER
Or, The Banished Cavaliers

Author: Aphra Behn (1640-1689)
Type of plot: Comedy of manners
Time of plot: 1642-1660
Locale: Naples and Madrid
First produced: Part I, 1677, Dorset Garden, London; Part II, 1681, Dorset Garden, London
First published: 1677 (Part I); 1681 (Part II)

Principal characters:
WILLMORE THE ROVER, an Englishman
BELVILE, an English colonel
BLUNT, a country fool
DON PEDRO, the brother of Florinda and Hellena
FLORINDA, the sister of Hellena and Don Pedro, in love with Belvile
HELLENA, the sister of Florinda and Don Pedro, in love with Willmore the Rover
DON ANTONIO, a nobleman
ANGELICA BIANCA, a courtesan
LUCETTA, a prostitute
BEAUMOND, the English ambassador's nephew
NICHOLAS FETHERFOOL, an English squire
ARIADNE, the daughter-in-law to the English ambassador
LA NUCHE, a courtesan
SHIFT and
HUNT, exiled cavaliers
DON CARLO, a nobleman
PETRONELLA, a bawdy woman

The Play

Set in Naples during the annual carnival, Part I of *The Rover* begins with a conversation between two sisters. Hellena's family plans for her to become a nun, but she is clearly more interested in men than in God. Her sister, Florinda, is in love with the English colonel Belvile, a cavalier, who saved her life during the Siege of Pamplona. Her brother, however, wants her to marry the wealthy Don Antonio, while her father wants her to marry the ancient Don Vincentio. Defying their brother, the two unhappy sisters, disguised, attend the carnival, where they encounter three Englishmen: Belvile, Willmore, and Blunt. Hellena is reunited with Belvile, and Willmore the Rover is immediately attracted to Hellena, who is disguised as a gypsy. Blunt, a foolish character who is paying for the other Englishmen's trip, falls under the spell of Lucetta, who plans to steal his money.

Both Don Pedro and Don Antonio are attracted to the famous courtesan Angelica Bianca. While the two noblemen fight over her, Willmore seduces Angelica, who reluctantly falls in love with him. Willmore, however, quickly turns his attention back to Hellena, who insists on marriage before pleasure. At Lucetta's house, Blunt is deceived and robbed before falling through a trapdoor into a sewer. After inadvertently disrupting Florinda and Belvile's romantic plans, Willmore wounds Don Antonio outside Angelica's house. Soldiers then seize Belvile, whom they mistake for Willmore. The wounded Don Antonio asks Belvile to fight Don Pedro in his place. The next morning, Belvile, disguised as Antonio, defeats Don Pedro and wins the hand of Florinda. Before the marriage can take place, however, Willmore reveals Belvile's true identity, causing Don Pedro to flee with Florinda. Disguised as a man, Hellena pursues Willmore, while Angelica, angry at the Rover's betrayal, seeks revenge.

Florinda escapes from her brother's house but is almost raped by Blunt and then by her brother, neither of whom knows her real identity. Once Belvile and Florinda finally marry, Angelica threatens to shoot Willmore but is thwarted by Don Antonio. Realizing that Hellena is exceedingly wealthy, Willmore agrees to marry her.

Part II takes place in Madrid. Willmore and Beaumond are attracted to the courtesan La Nuche, who loves Willmore in spite of his poverty. Shift and Hunt, also exiled cavaliers, plan to marry two rich, but deformed, Mexican sisters. The sisters—one a giant, the other a dwarf—hope to be changed to normal proportions by a mountebank. Fetherfool and Blunt also hope to marry the women for their money. Ariadne, who is supposed to marry her cousin Beaumond, falls in love with Willmore, who disguises himself as the mountebank in hopes of swindling the two deformed sisters. Later that night, Willmore, La Nuche, Beaumond, and Ariadne meet in a garden, where the darkness causes great confusion. Not knowing each other's identity, Willmore and Beaumond fight. Ariadne discovers Beaumond's indifference toward her and continues her pursuit of Willmore despite his refusal to marry.

Meanwhile, in a darkened bedroom, Don Carlo and Fetherfool mistake each other for La Nuche. Hoping to escape Don Carlo's anger, Fetherfool climbs out a window and is left naked in the street. Ariadne, fooled by Beaumond, is led to the mountebank's home, where Fetherfool steals a pearl necklace from the Mexican giant while Blunt pursues the bawdy Petronella, who has stolen a casket of jewels from La Nuche. In the end, Shift and Hunt marry the Mexican giant and dwarf, Beaumond and Ariadne agree to marry, and Willmore seeks "Love and Gallantry" with La Nuche.

Themes and Meanings

Typical of comedies written after the Restoration, *The Rover* explores issues of love, courtship, and marriage. Like her contemporaries, Aphra Behn treats these issues with a certain degree of bawdy, detached cynicism. Her characters are predominantly self-serving, and her plays never melt into the kind of sentimentality that distinguishes the drama of the later eighteenth century. Similar to other Restoration gallants, Willmore is an attractive, witty, free-spirited protagonist, who falls in love capriciously and desires sex without marriage. He does not, however, treat women as disdainfully as other gallants, such as Horner, the protagonist in William Wycherley's *The Country Wife* (pr., pb. 1675). More important, Behn avoids her contemporaries' practice of reducing women either to virginal commodities or to corrupt whores. The female characters in *The Rover* are complex, intelligent women whose value is not compromised by the sexual desire they share with the male characters. Behn's satire is not directed toward women but rather toward hypocritical social conventions that reduce romance to competition and women to possessions.

This theme is introduced in the first scene of Part I. Destined for a convent and an arranged marriage, Hellena and Florinda have no sexual autonomy and are trapped in roles that have been assigned to them by their male relatives. The carnival represents an opportunity for the women to escape these roles. Once they are disguised, Florinda can actively seek Belvile, and Hellena can search for the romance she desires. Behn makes it clear, however, that the sisters have not escaped the dangers of masculine hegemony. Without the protections of name and social standing, Florinda is almost raped. In the end, Hellena wins the Rover, but the audience must question his commitment to their marriage, a suspicion borne out in Part II, when Willmore nonchalantly mentions Hellena's death as he seeks new romance in Madrid. Even Angelica, the prostitute who controls men through her beauty, becomes a victim. Seduced and abandoned by Willmore, she ends the play bitter and powerless. Her pathetic attempt to seek revenge on Willmore casts a dark shadow on the play's otherwise comic ending and calls attention to the perilous world in which the female characters live.

In Part II, Behn develops her feminist themes more strongly. In their dialogue, Willmore and La Nuche savage the values of their society by equating marriage for money with prostitution. Willmore, true to his convictions, becomes disgusted when La Nuche shows more interest in Beaumond's money than in his love. In the context of the play, however, La Nuche's decision is understandable. Like the other women, she must use her sexuality to survive. The fickle Willmore is likely to abandon her as quickly as he did Angelica. Ariadne at first resists the loveless marriage that has been arranged for her. After experiencing the confusion and danger of loving Willmore, however, she agrees to marry Beaumond, not out of love, but because she has given up on love. Exhausted and bewildered, she accepts Beaumond in an effort to avoid the crushing masculine forces that humiliate Angelica and marginalize Hellena. La Nuche and Willmore avoid the hypocrisy of marriage, but there is little hope for their future. Willmore will continue to rove, and La Nuche may once again face the imperatives that drove her to prostitution.

In the end, Behn's plays send complicated messages. Willmore remains a witty and tenacious hero. Because of her intelligence, courage, and adventurous spirit, La Nuche becomes a heroine. Their union, as Behn scholar Heidi Hutner argues, expresses a "cultural longing for a prelapsarian golden age in which the sexes love mutually and women are desiring subjects rather than passive objects." At the same time, however, Willmore is far from innocent. However attractive he may be, he willingly participates in a culture that demeans and endangers women.

Dramatic Devices

The Rover plays contain many characteristics of Restoration drama. Like other playwrights, Behn presented engaging protagonists, scintillating dialogue, intrigue, and farce. Lucetta's trickery, which leaves Blunt naked and filthy in Part I, and Fetherfool's attempt to disguise himself as a clock in Part II, illustrate the kind of slapstick comedy that is as funny for a modern audience as it was for Behn's theatergoers. To quicken the pace of her plays and to create a visually stunning performance, Behn took full advantage of movable scenery, which was an innovation in the late seventeenth century. Scenery, painted on large shutters, was quickly moved offstage to reveal new characters and a new location. Thus, in Part I, the action can move, for example, instantly from the street to Blunt's apartment.

Behn also utilized the intimacy of the proscenium stage, which allowed the actors to perform only a few feet from the audience. Much of the plays' exposition and comedy are contained within the asides that the characters share with the audience but conceal from one another.

Critical Context

The Rover plays are among the most widely read of Behn's large body of literary works. Part I was tremendously successful during the seventeenth century and was frequently revived throughout the eighteenth century. Behn's artistry becomes particularly apparent when her plays are viewed in comparison with their source, Thomas Killigrew's long closet drama *Thomas: Or, The Wanderer* (wr. 1654, pb. 1664). Not only did Behn shorten Killigrew's drama, which would never have been successful onstage, but she also changed its tone. Killigrew's humor depends upon a vulgarity that is entirely absent from Behn's plays. Behn eliminated Killigrew's misogyny and transformed his female caricatures into complex, fully developed characters.

Equally important, Behn used this drama to explore ideas related to gender and culture that are found throughout her works. Depicting the way in which society inhibits and ultimately perverts desire, *The Rover* shares much with Behn's poem "The Golden Age" (1684), her novel *Oronooko: Or, The History of the Royal Slave* (1688), and many of her other plays. *The Rover* also presents the virtues, however ambiguous, of cavaliers like Willmore, Belvile, and Beaumond, who remained loyal to the Stuart family during the Interregnum period. In this way, the plays belong to what Robert Markley has labeled Behn's "Tory Comedies." These plays, which also include *The Roundheads: Or, The Good Old Cause* (pr. 1681, pb. 1682) and *The City Heiress: Or, Sir Timothy Treat-All* (pr., pb. 1682), celebrate natural aristocracy and uninhibited sexuality while ridiculing the "Puritan ideology of self-denial."

Ultimately, *The Rover* plays are difficult to characterize. They are both derivative and highly original. More important, they are wonderfully enjoyable comedies that never lose their ability to raise important and disturbing questions. For readers of Restoration drama, they remain as eclectic and delightful as their protagonists.

Sources for Further Study

Duffy, Maureen. *The Passionate Shepherdess: Aphra Behn, 1640-1689*. London: Jonathan Cape, 1977.

Gallagher, Catherine. "Who Was That Masked Woman? The Prostitute and the Playwright in the Comedies of Aphra Behn." In *Rereading Aphra Behn: History, Theory, and Criticism*, edited by Heidi Hutner. Charlottesville: University of Virginia Press, 1993.

Hutner, Heidi. "Revisioning the Female Body: Aphra Behn's *The Rover*, Parts I and II." In *Rereading Aphra Behn: History, Theory, and Criticism*, edited by Heidi Hutner. Charlottesville: University of Virginia Press, 1993.

Link, Frederick M. *Aphra Behn*. New York: Twayne Publishers, 1968.

Markley, Robert. " 'Be Impudent, Be Saucy, Forward, Bold, Touzing, and Leud': The Politics of Masculine Sexuality and Feminine Desire in Behn's Tory Comedies." In *Cultural Readings of Restoration and Eighteenth-Century English Theatre*, edited by J. Douglas Canfield and Deborah C. Payne. Athens: University of Georgia Press, 1995.

Todd, Janet. *The Secret Life of Aphra Behn*. New Brunswick, N.J.: Rutgers University Press, 1997.

Christopher D. Johnson

THE ROYAL HUNT OF THE SUN

Author: Peter Shaffer (1926-)
Type of plot: History; allegory
Time of plot: June, 1529, to August, 1533
Locale: Southern Ecuador; northwestern Peru; Trujillo, Spain
First produced: 1964, at the Festival Theatre, Chichester, England
First published: 1964

Principal characters:

FRANCISCO PIZARRO, the commander of the expedition to the Inca empire
HERNANDO DE SOTO, his second-in-command
MARTIN RUIZ, his page, later a soldier of Spain
MIGUEL ESTETE, the royal veedor, or overseer for King Carlos V
PEDRO DE TRUJILLO, the master of horse
FRAY VINCENTE DE VALVERDE, the Dominican chaplain
FRAY MARCOS DE NIZZA, a Franciscan friar
ATAHUALLPA, the Sovereign Inca of Peru
VILLAC UMU, the high priest of Peru
FELIPILLO, an Indian boy, Pizarro's interpreter
CHALLCUCHIMA, an Incan general

The Play

The Royal Hunt of the Sun begins in darkness with old Martin, a wealthy soldier of Spain, serving as chorus and providing exposition. His function is to provide an eyewitness account of how the aging Francisco Pizarro, with a scruffy expeditionary army of 167, conquered an empire of 24 million Incans. "This story is about ruin," he says. "Ruin and gold." It is also a story of vaulting ambition and colonial greed. The mature Martin Ruiz rues the day he first set eyes upon Pizarro.

The action then shifts back in time some forty years to Trujillo, in Spain, where Pizarro is recruiting soldiers for his Peruvian expedition. Young Martin, a boy of fifteen, well schooled in the codes of chivalry and an idealistic advocate of his king and Roman Catholicism, is enlisted, along with others: Diego, who becomes master of horse; Salinas, the blacksmith; Rodas, the tailor; and the Chavez brothers, Juan and Pedro.

The second scene introduces Valverde, the Dominican chaplain; his associate, the Franciscan de Nizza; Pedro de Candia, a cavalier from Venice, in charge of weapons; and the arrogant Miguel Estete, overseer in the name of King Carlos V, who threatens to challenge Pizarro's authority in the New World. The expedition departs into the forest at the end of the scene.

Scene 3 introduces the god-king Atahuallpa, Sovereign Inca of Peru; Villac Umu, his high priest; and Challcuchima, his general. Atahuallpa believes that the White God is coming to bless him. This naïve belief will be his undoing.

Thereafter, the action continues to alternate between the Incan court, fortified high in the mountains, and the approaching Spanish army. After six weeks, the army passes through the forest and arrives at the border of the Incan Empire, finding a road fifteen feet wide. The army is there met by the Incan general Challcuchima, who brings commands that the Spaniards should visit the god-king at Cajamarca, a month's march up the mountains. Scene 8 contains "The Mime of the Great Ascent" high in the Andes. After they arrive, the Sovereign Inca demands to see their god, whom he believes to be Pizarro. Valverde, angered by his blasphemy, orders Pizarro to attack. Act 1 ends with "The Mime of the Great Massacre." The Indians are massacred, and Atahuallpa is taken hostage, as Pizarro crowns himself.

Act 2 is titled "The Kill," and here the conflict is brought down to a personal level between Pizarro and the captive Atahuallpa, who still has the power and authority to crush Pizarro and his meager invading army, vastly outnumbered by the native people. Communication is at first complicated by Felipillo, the treacherous Indian interpreter, who lusts after the Inca's wife. Having learned enough of the Incan language to recognize Felipillo's deceit, young Martin advises Pizarro. The tactful and honest Martin from that point forward becomes the interpreter and is therefore "privy to everything that passed between them during the next months."

Pizarro, a cynic mainly interested in plunder, promises to set Atahuallpa free if the Inca will fill with gold a room twenty-two feet long by seventeen feet wide, and Atahuallpa commands that the gold be gathered from across his empire. He is trusting and does not entertain thoughts of Spanish treachery. During the time required to accumulate this treasure, Atahuallpa debates the nature of divinity with the churchmen and the nature of kingship with Pizarro.

The Spaniards put pressure on Pizarro to kill the Inca, but he would rather not. In conversation with his second-in-command, De Soto, Pizarro realizes that his reputation as conqueror will be assured only if he murders his Incan counterpart. Atahuallpa calmly believes that because of his divinity he cannot be killed. He tells the sixty-three-year-old Pizarro: "You will die soon and you do not believe in your god. That is why you tremble and keep no word. Believe in me."

Finally, Pizarro allows a Spanish court to accuse Atahuallpa "of usurping the throne and killing his brother; of idolatry and having more than one wife." The god-king is found guilty and murdered; thus he fails the ultimate test of his divinity. Curiously, Pizarro seems to want to believe in Atahuallpa's divinity and is devastated by this demonstration of the Inca's mortality.

Themes and Meanings

The play can be read in several ways, and the possible interpretations are not necessarily exclusive. It represents a quest on at least three levels: the quest for gold by a greedy colonial power, Pizarro's personal quest for fame and reputation, and the quest for faith and meaning in an apparently random and haphazard world. Because of these layers of symbolic meaning, the play demands to be considered as an allegory. It is more than simply a historical drama.

Like Peter Shaffer's play *Equus* (pr., pb. 1973), *The Royal Hunt of the Sun* reveals the playwright's fascination with the ancient world and its religions. This fascination, which is more clearly articulated in *Equus* by Martin Dysart, is dramatized in *The Royal Hunt of the Sun* and commented upon by Martin Ruiz, who mediates the action for the audience much as Dysart does in *Equus*. The suggestion in both instances is that modern humankind has lost something of value as a consequence of distancing itself from the primitive. Pizarro wants desperately to believe in Atahuallpa. The Inca believes in himself and his power, but his power has never been tested by cynical nonbelievers such as the Spaniards. Atahuallpa is a perfect icon of honesty and trust, while the Spaniards are dishonest and deceptive. In the end Pizarro cannot deny his own nature and conditioning, but he is still seeking some means of transcendence.

Martin Ruiz and Pizarro are both middle-aged men undergoing a crisis of faith. They are modern men who sense that organized religion cannot provide for their spiritual needs and yearn for a release through primitive, ritualistic worship. Clearly, Atahuallpa is a noble figure, godlike in his serenity in the face of danger and treachery that he cannot quite comprehend. Marcos de Nizza, the spiritual leader of the expeditionary force, by contrast seems politically compromised and morally bankrupt.

The play also criticizes European civilization, which is more greed-centered than God-centered. The conquistadores invade Peru in the name of Christianity, but their true motive is clearly greed and, in the case of Pizarro, ambition for fame. The themes of the play as announced by Martin are "ruin and gold," and the play can easily be read as an indictment of colonial exploitation.

The Incas live in a peaceful and prosperous, well-structured and decently governed society. The implication is that their civilization may in fact be superior to the civilization represented by the invading Spaniards, who are clearly interested only in plunder. What is ruined is as much the decadent Spaniards as the Inca empire they leave wasted behind them. As the older Martin gives evidence, the ill-gotten gains of plunder and colonial exploitation have not provided much spiritual comfort. The play sets in clear contrast Martin's youthful idealism and his later conscience-ridden cynicism. Miguel Estete is the perfect allegorical representative of the king of Spain—vain, arrogant, and utterly lacking in compassion or human understanding. Old Martin summarizes the fate of Peru: "We gave her greed, hunger and the Cross; three gifts for the civilized life." The Spaniards turned "the family groups that sang on the terraces" into slaves, leaving in their wake "a silent country, frozen in avarice." Martin goes on to speak of the ruin and fall of Spain, "gorged with gold, distended; now dying."

Shaffer therefore invites the spectator to judge a civilization by the quality of its religion, and Christianity is clearly found wanting. Both Martin and Pizarro have rejected organized religion; Pizarro, in particular, finds primitive worship as a possible alternative to atheism, which affords no potential for spiritual expression. Martin's mistake was to idolize Pizarro as a chivalric hero. Actually, Pizarro has only contempt for the ideals of chivalry. The chivalric knight owes his allegiance to his God and to his king; Pizarro, however, is a cynic and an atheist, so he essentially betrays the false image that Martin has romantically fabricated.

Shaffer's characters reveal a schizophrenic split between the actual and the ideal. Martin perfectly captures this split by being presented on one hand as a hopeful and trusting young idealist and on the other as an older and disillusioned cynic who has witnessed and understood the death of idealism and hope through the fate of Pizarro. Pizarro yearns for transcendence. He shifts his faith from Christianity to the Incan sun god, and when Atahuallpa dies, so does his faith and his final hope, and so, too, does Martin's faith in Pizarro.

Dramatic Devices

Peter Shaffer is arguably one of the most purely theatrical playwrights of his generation, skilled in constructing a distinctive theater of spectacle. His characters are mythic figures set within the framework of ritual drama, as evidenced especially in *The Royal Hunt of the Sun* and *Equus*, both plays structured around central quest figures. In *The Royal Hunt of the Sun* Pizarro describes his mission as "God-hunting," and the Inca represents for him a primitive god in whom he wishes to believe. Like Dysart in *Equus*, however, Pizarro is fated to kill the god. Both Dysart and Pizarro are cynics—"figures of despair," in the words of one critic—and neither one succeeds in achieving his spiritual goal.

Parallels between these two plays abound, despite the fact that *Equus* is set in contemporary England and *The Royal Hunt of the Sun* in sixteenth century Peru. Both plays are structured in two acts subdivided into multiple scenes. As Barbara Lounsberry has noted, the action of both plays follows a similar four-stage development: the god free, the god chained, the god sacrificed, and the sacrificer chained. In *Equus* the action is placed within a psychological contest, while in *The Royal Hunt of the Sun* the action is historical and the outcome determined by the "facts" of the historic conflict.

The historical Inca is a man trying to be a god, and so is *Equus*'s Alan Strang, the disturbed boy who mutilates horses. They are both younger than their adversaries, Pizarro and Dysart, and the conflict in both instances on the larger scale is between innocence and experience. Just as Atahuallpa trusts Pizarro, Alan trusts Dysart, the doctor who will cure him by killing his spiritual potential. Dysart understands what he is doing to his patient, unlike Pizarro, who knows that he is only a cog in the colonial machinery of imperial Spain but who seems somehow to believe in the serene transcendence of his adversary.

The larger conflicts of the two plays are essentially the same. The main conflict is that between the civilized and primitive worlds, with the suggestion that the primitive is bound to lose against the deviousness and treachery of the civilized. Pizarro is in conflict both with the Sovereign Inca and with himself. Christianity is in conflict with paganism.

The larger quest of a "hunt" for God gives the play an allegorical design, and the characters are to an extent locked into allegorical functions. The challenge is to make these symbolic characters believable as authentic human types, and Shaffer meets that challenge. Estete, for example, serves the king of Spain and has made the state his god. Martin Ruiz demonstrates how innocence is transformed by experience. As a young boy, Martin is a trusting idealist who believes devoutly in "the rules of Chivalry." Pizarro's actions destroy the ideal, leaving the older Martin with nothing to believe in. In the end, Martin is nearly as cynical as Pizarro, whom he has come to hate for showing him the way of the world and destroying his chivalric illusions. Chivalry, for Martin, is a failed religion.

The playwright's second challenge was to translate symbolic action into effective theatrical terms, and in this regard Shaffer had the help of director John Dexter. *The Royal Hunt of the Sun* depends upon abstract spectacle and a flexible, abstract design that will advance the play. Two key actions are presented in mime—the ascent of Pizarro's army into the Andes mountains and the massacre of the Incas. As with the final spectacle of *Equus*, the massacre of the Indians would be repugnant if represented in literal and naturalistic terms. Instead, the effect is of a purely imagined theatrical spectacle that will by nature resist being translated into another medium, such as the cinema. Some have argued that Shaffer's success as a playwright is attributable mainly to the imaginative stagecraft of Dexter; this is an overstatement, perhaps, but Shaffer himself has acknowledged his debt to Dexter in the preface to the *Equus* text. First and foremost, *The Royal Hunt of the Sun* is an exquisitely designed piece of theater that can be perfectly realized only on the stage, and in this it shares a strong kinship with *Equus*.

Critical Context

As already noted, *The Royal Hunt of the Sun* is more than a history play, but the sketched historical background comes from William H. Prescott's *History of the Conquest of Peru* (1886), which was Peter Shaffer's main inspiration for the play. The playwright made some minor alterations for symbolic reasons. Prescott supposes Atahuallpa to have been about thirty years old, for example, while Shaffer makes him the same age as Jesus Christ at the time of the Crucifixion. Moreover, the historical Pizarro lived longer than Shaffer's play suggests. He was murdered in 1541, at the age of about seventy.

Shaffer's play was praised by some reviewers as a masterpiece, condemned by others as being merely a "showy fraud." Robert Brustein, for example, found it pretentious and mundane and objected to its "sentimental sermonizing." Certainly *The Royal Hunt of the Sun*, like *Equus*, had its detractors, but the vitality of its spectacle was generally recognized.

Shaffer takes on large themes and therefore opens himself up for criticism as being pretentious. Shaffer himself described the play as being "about a man's search for immortality," hardly a modest theme. He has admitted that the play was written to create spectacle and to make magic, "if the world isn't too debased to convey the kind of excitement I believed could still be created out of 'total' theatre." His intention was to create "an experience that was *entirely and only theatrical*."

The play has epic magnitude. It anticipates the historical and chronological dexterity of *Amadeus* (pr. 1979, pb. 1980). It foreshadows the theme and abstract conflict of *Equus*. It also anticipates the personal conflicts of *Shrivings* (pr. 1970, pb. 1973), *Equus*, and *Amadeus* and the intense concern for fame and reputation that dements the narrator of *Amadeus*. Dennis Klein convincingly defends the play's grandiose themes, heroic characters, and formidable *mise en scène*, pointing out that the play was intended, after all, for the stage and not for the printed page. If the language may at times seem overblown, it is nevertheless consistently poetic. It was selected for inclusion in the anthology *Best Plays of the Sixties*, edited by Stanley Richards in 1970.

Sources for Further Study

Cooke, Virginia, and Malcolm Page. *File on Shaffer.* London: Methuen, 1987.

Dean, Joan F. "Peter Shaffer's Recurrent Character Type." *Modern Drama* 21 (September, 1978): 297-308.

Glenn, Jules. "Twins in Disguise: A Psychoanalytic Essay on *Sleuth* and *The Royal Hunt of the Sun*." *Psychoanalytic Quarterly* 43, no. 2 (1974): 288-302.

Kerensky, Oleg. "Peter Shaffer." In *The New British Drama: Fourteen Playwrights Since Osborne and Pinter.* London: Hamilton, 1977.

Klein, Dennis A. *Peter and Anthony Shaffer: A Reference Guide*. Boston: G. K. Hall, 1982.

_______. *Peter Shaffer.* Rev. ed. New York: Twayne, 1993.

Lounsberry, Barbara. "God-Hunting: The Chaos of Worship in Peter Shaffer's *Equus* and *Royal Hunt of the Sun*." *Modern Drama* 21 (March, 1978): 13-28.

MacMurraugh-Kavanagh, M. K. *Peter Shaffer: Theatre and Drama*. Basingstoke, England: Macmillan, 1998.

Pennel, Charles A. "The Plays of Peter Shaffer: Experiment in Convention." *Kansas Quarterly* 3, no. 2 (1971): 100-109.

Plunka, Gene A. *Peter Shaffer: Roles, Rites, and Rituals*. Teaneck, N.J.: Fairleigh Dickinson University Press, 1988.

Stern, Carol Simpson. "Peter Shaffer." In *Contemporary Dramatists*. 6th ed. Detroit: St. James, 1999.

Taylor, John Russell. *Peter Shaffer.* Harlow, England: Longman, 1974.

James M. Welsh

THE RULING CLASS
A Baroque Comedy

Author: Peter Barnes (1931-)
Type of plot: Satire
Time of plot: The late twentieth century
Locale: England
First produced: 1968, at the Nottingham Playhouse, Nottingham, England
First published: 1969

Principal characters:
JACK, THE FOURTEENTH EARL OF GURNEY, an insane English nobleman
SIR CHARLES GURNEY, his uncle
LADY CLAIRE GURNEY, Sir Charles's wife
DINSDALE GURNEY, Jack's dim-witted cousin
DANIEL TUCKER, the family butler
DR. PAUL HERDER, a psychiatrist
GRACE SHELLEY, the mistress of Sir Charles and the wife of Jack

The Play

The Ruling Class begins with three sharp raps of a gavel. At a banqueting table, the thirteenth earl of Gurney offers a toast to England and to the ruling class. In a parody of John of Gaunt's apostrophe to "this England" in *Richard II* (pr. c. 1595-1596), the earl eulogizes England's class structure. While the British national anthem plays, the scene shifts to his lordship's bedroom, where he is preparing to indulge in one of his diversions—hanging himself. Dressed in a three-cornered hat, a ballet skirt, long underwear, and a sword, he steps off a stool. After dangling for a few seconds, he regains his balance on the stool and delivers a soliloquy that betrays his madness. He tries it again but accidentally kicks over the stool. The thirteenth earl is dead.

Following this prologue, act 1 begins. After a funeral scene, the action moves to Gurney Manor. Sir Charles, Lady Claire, Dinsdale Gurney, and Bishop Lampton are discussing the disposal of the estate. Matthew Peake, a desiccated and deferential solicitor, enters and reads the will. Tucker, the butler, is left twenty thousand pounds; after a pause, he begins singing and dancing. Virtually everything else is left to the earl's insane son, Jack. While the others shout angrily, Tucker reenters, smoking a cigar. He picks up a large vase, drops it (thereby getting everyone's attention), and announces Jack, the fourteenth earl of Gurney.

The new earl is dressed as a monk and speaks softly and gently. He says that he has returned to take his proper place in the world. After asking that all pray with him, he declares himself to be the Son of Man, the God of Love, the Naz. In the next scene Dr. Herder, proprietor of a mental institution, tells Sir Charles that his nephew is a paranoid schizophrenic but not dangerous. Because his parents had "sent him away, alone, into a primitive community of licensed bullies and pederasts" (that is, public school), he has withdrawn from reality and become the Prince of Peace. He can speak only of love and of sharing with his fellow man.

Sir Charles is appalled. Not only is his nephew mad, but he is also a "Bolshie." Moreover, he sleeps on a cross and refuses to answer to the name Jack—to any name of God, yes; but to Jack, no. Because the will stated that no contesting of it was permitted, however, nothing can be done—unless there were to be an heir. Since Jack believes himself to be married to the Lady of the Camellias, Sir Charles decides to use his mistress to play that part. Perhaps Grace can captivate Jack, marry him, and produce an heir. Then Sir Charles can have him committed. He will then be able to do as he wishes with the estate. Tucker tries to warn Jack, but Jack will not hear of it and leaves. Tucker, quite drunk, then states that he is the only true Englishman at Gurney Manor and that he is also a communist.

When Grace is introduced to Jack, he is immediately taken with her. The two are married by the bishop and retire to the nuptial chambers. The next morning Grace tells Sir Charles that although Jack is "wonky," there was nothing wrong with his maleness. In the next scene Grace is nine months pregnant. Dr. Herder, who has learned of the plan, is determined to cure Jack by confronting him with another messiah. While Grace is having her baby (a boy), Dr. Herder challenges Jack with Mr. McKyle, a "High Voltage Messiah." Jack retreats to his cross but is forced to come down and face McKyle. Overcome, he admits to being simply Jack. Act 1 ends on this note.

In the first scene of act 2, the potential fifteenth earl of Gurney is being christened. Sir Charles is ready to commit the fourteenth earl, but he is stopped by Dr. Herder, who declares Jack now to be stable. In several scenes Jack wrestles with his old personality and tries to force it into his subconscious. He is learning how to be cunning. Tested by Kelso Truscott, the Master of the Court of Protection, he is declared to be sane. In a frightening soliloquy Jack betrays the torment within him. He now believes that he is no longer the Messiah; instead, he has become God Almighty, the God of Justice. His distorted personality becomes the Moral Avenger of 1888, Jack the Ripper.

Jack and Grace are visited by two Tory ladies who wish him to speak to a party gathering. He learns that there is no death penalty in modern England. He and the ladies discuss the immoral times, and he suggests that the answer is to bring back fear, which will restore law and order. Jack breaks into song, a paraphrase of "Dry Bones." In his version the bones are being broken on the rack, and the words have been transmuted from connected to disconnected bones.

Shortly thereafter, Lady Claire comes to Jack and attempts to seduce him. The scene shifts to the London of 1888. Jack, now the Avenging God, becomes the Keeper of Morals. He murders Claire with a knife. When the police investigate, Tucker is adjudged guilty, especially after he is discovered to be a communist. Clearly, Jack could not have done it. Before he is carried away, Tucker exclaims,

> You Gurneys don't draw the line at murder. (*Suddenly exploding with rage and fear.*) Upper-class excrement, you wanna' do me dirt 'cause I know too much. I know one per-cent of the population owns half the property in England. That vomity "one per cent" needs kosher killing, hung up so the blue blood drains out slow and easy.

After this outburst Jack is lauded by the policemen as a model of noblesse oblige. Shortly afterward, Dr. Herder accosts Jack. The two verbally spar, then fence with walking sticks. Herder realizes that, although Jack has killed Claire, he is normal, according to his peers.

Jack is now ready to take his seat in the House of Lords. Sir Charles challenges him, but Jack wins. He is now the head of the Gurney clan, and Sir Charles is put out to pasture. Even Dinsdale supports Jack instead of his father. Following a quick scene of Jack enduring terrible internal turmoil, the scene shifts to the House of Lords. After his installation, Jack speaks to the lords of the need to restore order through fear and intimidation. Moldering corpses and bloated, goitered lords applaud his ideas for restoring "normalcy." In the last scene, Jack is alone amid the dummies. Grace enters, singing of her love for him. He kisses her passionately. As the lights fade, he reaches into the pocket of his parliamentary robes. A scream of fear and agony is heard.

Themes and Meanings

The Ruling Class is first and foremost a scathing indictment of the English aristocracy and the insanity of a world dominated by a class whose only qualification is an accident of birth. The play is also a look into the worlds of fantasy and of the subconscious. It may also be construed as a statement by Peter Barnes about his interpretation of the ruling order of the universe.

The very phrase "the ruling class" has a connotation in Great Britain that those not familiar with the country cannot understand. From the medieval period to the present day, British politics and society have been either dominated or strongly influenced by the principle of deferring to one's "betters." One was born into a particular class, and one usually remained in it. Status was determined by who was born where and in what order. From the opening scene of *The Ruling Class* to the last scene, it is clear that Barnes finds all of this to be absurd. He is appalled that a tiny part of the population owns a grossly disproportionate share of the wealth and power in his country. His intent, then, was to satirize this situation as savagely as he could. In this he succeeded.

The fourteenth earl of Gurney symbolizes all that is wrong with the system. Because of primogeniture, this benevolently mad individual inherits great wealth and power. Indeed, according to Barnes, the earl typifies the insane decadence created by the power of generations past. The humorous paradox provided to this grotesque caricature is Tucker, the closet communist butler. This juxtaposition provides not only comic comparisons but also critical statements about who is insane and who is not and about who deserves status and who does not.

In Great Britain, aristocracy-bashing has long been popular. In 1909 David Lloyd George, then Chancellor of the Exchequer and leader of a movement to control the political power of the House of Lords, said in a speech, "They have no qualifications—at least, they need not have any. . . . They need not be sound either in body, or in mind. They only require a certificate of birth—just to prove that they are the first of the litter. You would not choose a spaniel on these principles. . . ." Barnes was only one in a long line who exploited this issue; however, he did it better than most.

At another level, *The Ruling Class* is a dual look at the mind and the universe. It is patently obvious that both the thirteenth and the fourteenth earls are quite mad. The questions that arise from such a situation deal with the causes of the insanity. Are they insane from inbreeding or from decadence? Is that insanity a trait of the ruling class in general? If they are insane, why are they not institutionalized? Are wealth and power all that are required if one is to be labeled eccentric instead of mad? Intertwined with that theme is the theme of the ruling order of the universe. The juxtaposition of the God of Love in act 1 and the God of the Law of the Old Testament in act 2 roughly parallels Barnes's view of the ruling class. The fourteenth earl is cured of his benevolence and thus becomes acceptable to his peers. This ironic symbolism reveals Barnes's opinion about British aristocrats. He damns them for their emphasis on the status quo regardless of humanity or truth.

Dramatic Devices

> The aim is to create, by means of soliloquy, rhetoric, formalized ritual, slapstick, songs and dances, a comic theatre of contrasting moods and opposites, where everything is simultaneously tragic and ridiculous. And we hope never to consent to the deadly servitude of naturalism or lose our hunger for true size, weight and texture.

The above statement by Peter Barnes appeared in the original program notes for *The Ruling Class* in 1968. Without question, Barnes meant what he wrote. The thematic devices he listed are certainly utilized to the fullest possible extent in his play. Barnes preferred using ludicrous or slapstick backdrops to enunciate his points, while using dialogue twists and shifts to keep the playgoer's attention throughout. Indeed, the playgoer's senses are visually and verbally assaulted so that, by the end of the play, a veritable collage of images has been implanted in the mind.

An example may be seen in the first five minutes of the play. The thirteenth earl of Gurney is something of an eccentric: After a hard day as a judge, he likes to indulge himself with a kinky diversion, hanging himself for a moment or two. In this first scene, the earl has shed his clothes down to his long underwear. After donning a sword and scabbard, a ballet tutu, and a three-cornered cocked hat, he slips his head into a noose, steps off a stool, dangles, then regains his footing. After this bizarre scene, the earl delivers a brief soliloquy about himself and his class. The lightning-quick imagery created by Barnes in this speech sets the tone for the whole play. After this speech is delivered, the earl reinserts his head into the noose, saying, "Just time for a quick one." He then accidentally kicks over the stool, thus ending his life and setting the stage for the play itself. The scene, with its bizarre humor and farce, its outrageous props, actions, and rhetoric, serves to introduce the playgoer to the various messages of the play.

While Barnes is not able to maintain the pace set by the prologue over the course of the entire play, various images do stand out as effective and memorable. The fourteenth earl has a messianic complex and believes himself to be the representative of the God of Love. If he is to function in society, his peers consider that he must be cured. It simply will not do to have a peer of the realm literally hanging on a cross. In a confrontation with another "messiah," the earl is "cured," and he gives up his cross. He then, however, became a representative of the God of Justice and Retribution, who is acceptable to the Conservative House of Lords. Instead of Jack the Messiah, he becomes Jack the Ripper. This theme of retribution is followed with a scene late in act 2, set in the House of Lords. As the fourteenth earl speaks of the necessity of floggings and hangings, cobwebs, skeletons, and goitered freaks applaud his pronouncements.

Barnes utilizes dramatic devices liberally and with effect to create a memorable and entertaining satirical comedy. Familiar lines from William Shakespeare are quoted and misquoted; snatches of familiar songs, such as "Dry Bones," are injected, although with slightly changed lyrics. Parody and slapstick are intertwined with invective. While the message is often acerbic, the play is never overpowered by the propaganda, in large measure because of the vivid images created by the stagecraft of the playwright.

Critical Context

The Ruling Class is but one of several plays by Peter Barnes that convey similar themes. The power of the ruling class, the abuse of authority, the lack of humanity and concern for the lower classes, and the role of God in the modern world are all concerns of the playwright. Barnes's own background helped determine this attitude. He was born to a working-class East End (Cockney) family that operated an amusement stall at a seaside resort. As a child, he witnessed the Great Depression, World War II, and the struggles of the immediate postwar era. His first efforts at playwriting were social commentaries but were not successes. *The Ruling Class* was a major success, winning for him the John Whiting Award and the 1969 Most Promising Playwright Award. After that time he wrote numerous plays with similar themes, but none was as successful as this play.

While some detractors dismissed *The Ruling Class* as shallow, most critics agreed that it was an excellent play, consistently amusing and penetratingly satirical. Barnes was an admirer of Ben Jonson, the seventeenth century English satirist; *The Ruling Class* was definitely influenced by Jonson's style. Theater critic Harold Hobson, in his preface to the published edition of the play (1969), deemed it one of the four most important theatrical events in British theater since 1945. He put *The Ruling Class* in the same category as Samuel Beckett's *En attendant Godot* (pb. 1952; *Waiting for Godot*, 1954), John Osborne's *Look Back in Anger* (pr. 1956), and Harold Pinter's *The Birthday Party* (pr. 1958). In sum, *The Ruling Class* is a rare combination of humor, satire, message, and style that remains fresh and enjoyable.

Sources for Further Study

Barnes, Philip, ed. "Peter Barnes." In *A Companion to Post-War British Theater.* Totowa, N.J.: Barnes & Noble, 1986.

Blumenfeld, Yorick. "The London Show." *Atlantic* 224 (August, 1969): 99-101.

Bull, John. "Peter Barnes." In *Contemporary Dramatists*. 6th ed. Detroit: St. James, 1999.

Dukore, Bernard F. *Barnestorm: The Plays of Peter Barnes*. New York: Garland, 1995.

_______. *The Theatre of Peter Barnes*. Exeter, N.H.: Heinemann, 1981.

Inveso, Marybeth. *The Gothic Impulse*. Ann Arbor: University of Michigan Press, 1991.

Kalem, T. E. "The Hangman God." *Time*, February 15, 1971, 60-61.

William S. Brockington, Jr.

SAND MOUNTAIN

Author: Romulus Linney (1930-)
Type of plot: Realism; comedy
Time of plot: The late nineteenth century
Locale: Southern Appalachian Mountains
First produced: 1985, at the Philadelphia Festival for New Plays, Philadelphia, Pennsylvania
First published: 1985

Principal characters:

Sand Mountain Matchmaking
REBECCA TULL, a young widow
CLINK WILLIAMS,
SLATE FOLEY, and
RADLEY NOLLINS, her suitors
LOTTIE STILES, a wise old woman
VESTER STILES, her grandson
SAM BEAN, the successful suitor

Why the Lord Come to Sand Mountain
SANG PICKER, a mountain woman, the narrator
THE LORD, a mountain traveler
SAINT PETER, The Lord's traveling companion
JACK, an older man
JEAN, his young wife
FOURTEEN CHILDREN, played by one actor
PROSPER VALLEY FARMER, a greedy man

The Play

Sand Mountain is the collective title for two one-act plays, *Sand Mountain Matchmaking* and *Why the Lord Come to Sand Mountain*. These plays share a common locale (Sand Mountain) and are designed to be performed by the same cast; they also relate thematically.

Sand Mountain Matchmaking is a light curtain raiser, running about thirty minutes in performance. Rebecca Tull, a nubile young widow, sits in a chair through nearly the entire play interviewing a series of suitors, each of whom dances in to a strain of mountain music. She rejects three, who represent all the known marriageable men in the district, and then is advised by a wise old mountain woman to use a charm, a spell: Each suitor must be told, "A man's horn is times three the size of his nose." Somewhat reluctantly, Rebecca repeats this sentence to each undesirable suitor; each then leaves in a huff. At that point, Sam Bean enters, having been attracted by word of a young woman brazen enough to say such a thing to her suitors. In a somewhat longer scene, Rebecca and Sam find that they have much in common, and the play ends with the clear implication that Rebecca has found the appropriate husband.

Why the Lord Come to Sand Mountain is a somewhat longer work which, although containing much effective comedy, aspires to more profundity. It is narrated by the Sang Picker, a mountain woman who gathers ginseng root and comments upon the folkways of her fellow denizens of Sand Mountain. In her opening monologue, she establishes that her people like tall tales, especially those with a biblical foundation, and then launches into the story of why Jesus and Saint Peter once visited Sand Mountain. As she begins to tell it, the other actors enter and perform it.

The Lord and Saint Peter are thoroughly human mountain men who journey into the neighborhood seeking Sand Mountain. The Sang Picker directs them. Despite a gathering thunderstorm, The Lord rejects an invitation to spend the night with the Prosper Valley Farmer—a well-fed bourgeois. Instead, The Lord pushes on to the mountain shack of Jack and Jean, an older husband and young wife, and their fourteen children. The couple, though deeply impoverished—and currently drunk—take the two men in and share with them their meal: soup and cornbread. The fourteen children, played by one actor, fight over even this simple fare until The Lord calms them by telling them stories. Saint Peter, exasperated by these events and baffled by The Lord's insistence upon visiting these poor people, when much better accommodations were available in Prosper Valley, also lapses into the background. The Lord, Jack, and Jean are left to drink mountain brandy (miraculously renewed in the jug each time they drink from it) and exchange tall tales—an art at which The Lord matches the mountaineers, story for story.

At first, the stories are merely humorous exaggerations, but Jack and Jean begin to act them out with exuberance. Eventually, Jean asks somewhat timidly if they might tell "Jesus Tales," a mountain tradition of apocryphal stories of Jesus' miracles and Saint Peter's well-meaning stupidity. Several of these stories ensue, building up to one last story: The Lord requests that Jack and Jean tell the story of Joseph the Carpenter. This one is acted out in full by Jack, Jean, and Fourteen Children and forms the crux of the play.

"Joseph the Carpenter" begins with Joseph, a man eighty-nine years of age, considering marriage with Mary, a girl of fourteen. Joseph is skeptical, but Mary insists that she wants to marry only him. In another quick scene, Mary, now married to Joseph for over a year, tells him that she is pregnant, yet still a virgin. Comical in his disbelief, Joseph nevertheless promises not to deny parentage of the baby. Later still, Jesus is portrayed as a rebellious young boy, torn between Mary's conviction of his divine mission and Joseph's earthy insistence on unpretentious hard work. Finally, in a climactic scene, the young Jesus strikes his father, who then hovers on the edge of death. In an extraordinarily effective *coup de théâtre*, The Lord (who up to this point has been watching the portrayal) enters the action to speak the words of the young Jesus, and the reason for The Lord's visit to Sand Mountain suddenly becomes clear: Jesus needs, through these simple mountain folk so like Joseph and Mary, to revisit his own childhood, both to say good-bye to his earthly father and to seek forgiveness for a youthful indiscretion.

On this poignant note, everyone goes to sleep for the night, but the play has a comic denouement: The Lord gives his hosts a gift the next morning by decreeing that what they first begin that day will last all day; they begin pulling clothes from a washtub and end up with a sumptuous wardrobe. The Prosper Valley Farmer, supported by Saint Peter, demands equal treatment, and Jesus reluctantly pronounces the same decree. The Farmer, however, leading the other Prosper Valley citizenry, decides that before beginning to pull coins from their purses they should all step into the woods and urinate—a process that will then continue all day. The Sang Picker offers a summary comment, and the play ends.

Themes and Meanings

Sand Mountain Matchmaking is largely without thematic content. The play is lightly comic throughout, with each character a well-sketched caricature of a mountain type—never condescendingly quaint, but nevertheless heartily and effectively two-dimensional. The phallic ribaldry of the spell that drives away unwanted suitors and attracts the right one continues to function throughout the major scene between Rebecca and Sam, ensuring plenty of laughs but not much thoughtfulness. Rebecca's independence of spirit is attractive, but the play can hardly be described as a tract for women's rights. In short, the work exists as light entertainment, without serious thematic pretensions.

It is an entirely appropriate preparation, however, for the more complex play which is to follow. Precisely by introducing mountain folkways and vocabulary in a lightly comic vein, Romulus Linney warms up his audience for the more challenging material of *Why the Lord Come to Sand Mountain.* Religiously conservative audiences might take offense at a Jesus portrayed convivially drinking brandy, telling tall tales, committing youthful indiscretions, and, ultimately, seeking human forgiveness. Linney prepares his audience by emphasizing the warmth, love, and playfulness of the people he is portraying.

Why the Lord Come to Sand Mountain brings the audience to the heart of Linney's thematic concept. Above all, the play portrays with honesty and integrity the downhome people with whom Jesus presumably would have elected to spend his time had he been born in North Carolina instead of Judaea. At the same time, by emphasizing the earthly humanity of Jesus, Linney forces his audience to reconsider a fundamental aspect of the Christian message: Blessed are the poor, the hungry, and the meek. Even God, having become flesh and lived with humanity, experiences pain, sorrow, and love. The Lord brings it all into focus at the moment that his reasons for visiting Sand Mountain suddenly become clear.

These religious musings do not burden the play, nor do they turn it into a sermon. Saint Peter, ever the foil for both humor and meaning in the play, asks The Lord at the end of "Joseph the Carpenter" what might be the point of the story, since "none of that really happened." Jean, with The Lord's clear approval, repeats a theme introduced earlier: "Hit ain't the ending whut's important. Hit's the beginning." The daily new beginning to find meaning in life is more important than any ultimate truth actually found.

Dramatic Devices

Sand Mountain Matchmaking is full of presentational devices that, while removing the action from a realistic context, add to its comic delight. The musical phrases that introduce each character invite dance steps with each entrance. The blocking suggested in the stage directions keeps Rebecca and each of her suitors in two chairs facing the audience during most of the play. Romulus Linney describes his work as "a formal interview play" and asks that "business and movement . . . be kept to a minimum."

Similarly, the structure of *Why the Lord Come to Sand Mountain* is carefully calculated to hold the audience at a distance until the last possible moment, when the play's thematic complexity comes into focus with a single theatrical stroke. The Sang Picker narrates the story of The Lord coming to Sand Mountain; within that tale, Jack and Jean act out the story of Joseph the carpenter; within that play, Jesus suddenly begins to play himself, thus charging the play-within-a-play-within-a-play with spiraling layers of meaning.

Linney calls for long journeys to be suggested by the actors' circling of the stage. Actors sit with their backs to the audience until, on cue, they turn to join in the action. The passage of an entire night is accomplished by the seated actors simply dropping their heads in a few moments of "sleep." These presentational devices combine to establish the play as fantasy and to keep the audience from empathic involvement until the critical moment.

Perhaps most interesting are the several ways that these apparently dissimilar plays are linked into a single theatrical event. Since much depends upon a warm acceptance of the uneducated mountain people as salt-of-the-earth humanity, Linney introduces them in a comic vein and only gradually moves into greater depth of character development. Thus, the lightness of the first play effectively prepares the audience for the complexity of the second, just as the comic elements in the second play lead up to and away from its moment of emotional purgation. Unfamiliar vocabulary and sentence structures are introduced in a comic mode in the first play and then are used with greater power in the second. The reappearance of actors in similar roles in the second play effectively reinforces both its seriousness and the distancing quality of role-playing. In short, these two plays are linked in ways that cause them to reinforce each other and to build effectively to a single climactic moment. Although either could be performed separately, the impact of each would be lessened by this separation. There is meaningful artistry in their juxtaposition.

Critical Context

Romulus Linney's plays have not been performed very often or very effectively in New York, and thus he has been described in *The New York Times* as "perhaps the most underrated, underrecognized American playwright today." However, his plays have been produced with notable frequency at regional professional theaters and in amateur theaters around the United States, and his aficionados rapidly increased by the end of the twentieth century. *Sand Mountain* is typical of one genre of Linney's work, for he lived for a number of years in North Carolina and has written several plays centered upon Appalachian people, their humor, and their religion. Perhaps the best known of these is *Holy Ghosts* (pr. 1971, pb. 1977), which spellbindingly portrays a storefront church full of snake handlers and develops its audience's sympathetic appreciation of the sincerity of their mutual love and caring despite the bizarre lack of sophistication in their theology. Also depicting rural southerners, *A Woman Without a Name* (pr. 1985) portrays a nearly illiterate woman whose process of self-education and liberation turns upon the destruction of all of her children, indomitable will clashing excruciatingly with maternal love. His *Mountain Memory: A Play About Appalachian Life* (pb. 1997) chronicles the lives of an Appalachian family between 1776 and 1995 as they experience changing times, constantly struggling to hold onto their land and their dignity in the face of great evil and temptation.

Other Linney plays include his first, *The Sorrows of Frederick* (pb. 1966, pr. 1967), based on the life of Frederick the Great, *The Love Suicide at Schofield Barracks* (pr. 1972, pb. 1973), offering a postwar look at the same location in which James Jones's *From Here to Eternity* (1951) is set, *Childe Byron* (pr. 1977, pb. 1981), depicting a conversation between a deceased Lord Byron and his daughter Ada, and *Two* (pr. 1990, pb. 1993), winner of the National Critics Award. He is the recipient of the 1999 Award of Merit Medal for Drama from the American Academy and Institute of Arts and Letters, as well as two Obie Awards—one in 1980 and the other in 1992 for Sustained Excellence in Playwriting.

Sources for Further Study

DiGaetani, John. "Romulus Linney." In *A Search for a Postmodern Theater: Interviews with Contemporary Playwrights*. New York: Greenwood Press, 1991.

Linney, Romulus. Interview with Don B. Wilmeth. *Studies in American Drama* 2 (1987): 71-84.

Moe, Christian H. "Romulus Linney." In *Contemporary Dramatists*. 6th ed. Detroit: St. James, 1999.

Schlatter, James F. "Story-teller in the Wilderness: The American Imagination of Romulus Linney." *Southern Quarterly: A Journal of the Arts in the South* (Winter, 1994): 63-75.

Tedford, Harold. "Romulus Linney on 'Sublime Gossip.'" *Southern Theatre* 38 (Spring, 1997): 26-32.

Wilmeth, Don B. "Romulus Linney." In *Speaking on Stage: Interviews with Contemporary American Playwrights*. Tuscaloosa: University of Alabama Press, 1996.

Philip G. Hill

THE SATIN SLIPPER
Or, The Worst Is Not the Surest

Author: Paul Claudel (1868-1955)
Type of plot: Problem play
Time of plot: Near the end of the sixteenth century
Locale: Spain, Italy, Czechoslovakia, Africa, Central America, South America, and the Balearic Islands
First produced: 1943, at the Comédie-Francaise, Paris
First published: Le Soulier de satin: Ou, Le Pire n'est pas toujours sûr, 1928-1929 (English translation, 1931)

Principal characters:

DON RODRIGO, a Spanish nobleman who loves Doña Prouheze
DOÑA PROUHEZE, a Spanish noblewoman
DON PELAGIO, a Spanish judge, Prouheze's first husband
CAMILLO, Prouheze's second husband
THE GUARDIAN ANGEL, who watches over Prouheze
DOÑA MUSICA, Prouheze's sister
DOÑA SEVENSWORDS, the daughter of Prouheze and Camillo
DOÑA HONORIA, Rodrigo's mother
A JESUIT PRIEST, Rodrigo's brother
DAIBUTSU, a Japanese painter who works for Rodrigo

The Play

The Satin Slipper contains fifty-two scenes, divided into four separate days. As the first day begins, a dying Jesuit priest prays that his brother Rodrigo will someday accept God. In the next scene, Pelagio asks his friend Balthazar to accompany Prouheze to the African city of Mogador, where Pelagio and Prouheze will represent the interests of the king of Spain. Pelagio plans to leave for Mogador after his wife's departure from Spain. His arranged marriage with the younger Prouheze has made neither of them truly happy. Camillo, a disreputable character who also loves Prouheze, will direct the Spanish soldiers in Mogador. Although she wishes to be faithful to her marriage vows, Prouheze clearly loves Rodrigo and not Pelagio or Camillo. As she prepares to leave for Africa, she takes off her satin slipper and places it on a statue of the Virgin Mary, whose protection she seeks. The king of Spain appoints Rodrigo his Viceroy for the West Indies and Panama. Rodrigo, however, does not wish to accept this position. In a vain attempt to escape from Spain, he is badly wounded; Prouheze herself barely escapes abduction and death at the hands of brigands. Paul Claudel then introduces the first of many supernatural elements in this play: Prouheze's Guardian Angel assures her that Rodrigo still lives and will someday see her again.

As the second day begins, Doña Honoria fears for the life of her son Rodrigo. Both she and Pelagio realize that Rodrigo and Prouheze love each other deeply. Honoria convinces Pelagio, however, that he should not travel to Africa with his wife. Honoria argues that the harsh life in Mogador will contribute to Prouheze's spiritual growth, and she affirms that it will be necessary to separate Prouheze from Rodrigo in order to save the souls of these two lovers. Prouheze leaves for Mogador, whence she will never return. After his physical recovery, Rodrigo travels to Mogador on an official mission for the king of Spain. In the fortress of Mogador, Camillo hands Rodrigo a note in which Prouheze has written the four words "I stay, you go." Respecting Prouheze's wishes, Rodrigo sails for the New World. In the final scene of the second day, the Moon, a symbolic character, explains the rationale for Prouheze's decision. According to the Moon, Prouheze reasoned thus: "There is for ever someone from God's side forbidding him [Rodrigo] my bodily presence because he would have loved it too well. Ah, I want to give him much more!" She has sacrificed sexual pleasure so that Rodrigo can attain salvation.

Ten years pass between the actions of the second and third days. Rodrigo has become a ruthlessly efficient colonial administrator who exploits the native communities of the New World in order to enrich the king of Spain. In Mogador, Camillo has physically and emotionally abused Prouheze, who had married him after Pelagio's death. Prouheze has a dream in which her Guardian Angel reveals to her that she will soon die. This end to her physical suffering will result in her own salvation and in the spiritual conversion of Rodrigo. Near the end of the third day, Rodrigo returns to Mogador. The dying Prouheze speaks to the unbelieving Rodrigo of the extraordinary spiritual joy she has experienced in Mogador. As the third day ends, Prouheze, dressed entirely in black, is carried onto a funeral barge. Her death changes Rodrigo's view of the world.

The action of the fourth day takes place at sea near the Balearic Islands. Most of the characters in the fourth day do not understand Rodrigo's metamorphosis. Once an amoral colonial administrator, Rodrigo now distributes large religious pictures painted by his Japanese servant Daibutsu. Rodrigo proclaims openly his commitment to Roman Catholicism. He learns that Doña Sevenswords, the daughter of Prouheze and Camillo, wishes to undertake a crusade against Mogador in order to avenge her mother's death; Rodrigo, however, is no longer interested in war.

The king of Spain concludes mistakenly that the Spanish armada has defeated the British navy. Against the advice of his counselors, he proposes to name Rodrigo Viceroy of England. Rodrigo is willing to accept this appointment only if the king agrees to free the Americas from Spanish colonial domination. Rodrigo no longer believes that Europeans have any right to impose their will on the inhabitants of the New World. After he leaves the king's presence, Rodrigo is arrested on the charge of treason. Sold into slavery, he is bought by an elderly nun who plans to use him as a servant in her convent. Like Prouheze, Rodrigo will end his days in the service of God.

Themes and Meanings

The plot of *The Satin Slipper* is so exceedingly complicated that John O'Connor felt the need to include a ten-page summary with his English translation, on which Paul Claudel himself collaborated. Fortunately, readers can appreciate the basic themes of this play even if they do not remember all of its intricate subplots.

Love, spiritual growth, and the search for happiness through religion are the major themes of *The Satin Slipper.* Claudel reminds his readers that God often works in unexpected ways. Published versions of this play open with a Portuguese proverb, "God writes straight with crooked lines," followed by Saint Augustine's remark that "even sins" play a role in Divine Providence.

The complex evolution of Prouheze and Rodrigo is quite extraordinary. In the very first scene of this play, Rodrigo's brother, a dying Jesuit, laments that his brother "has turned his back" on God in order "to conquer and possess" Prouheze. The Jesuit priest senses that God will somehow transform the physical desires of Prouheze and Rodrigo into a longing for spiritual values "in the deprivation of each other's presence through the daily play of circumstance." Spectators may attribute these fortuitous circumstances either to mere chance or to Divine Providence.

Several images of love and spiritual belief are presented in *The Satin Slipper.* These include the basic amorality of Camillo, who associates love with domination and frequently beats his wife, Prouheze. Camillo converts from Roman Catholicism to Islam, for reasons that are never explained. His abuse of Prouheze demonstrates that Camillo learned no moral lessons from either the Bible or the Koran.

Prouheze and Rodrigo respond to love and God in more complicated ways. At first, Claudel describes Prouheze as a frustrated wife in an arranged marriage. Her physical attraction to the younger Rodrigo and not to Pelagio, an elderly judge, seems very understandable. Rodrigo's desire to sleep with his beloved Prouheze seems perfectly normal. Their physical desire for each other will gradually evolve into a more spiritual longing. During the third day of this play, Prouheze's Guardian Angel compares Prouheze and Rodrigo to souls in Purgatory who are "going up to Heaven." Only Prouheze, whose life has been enriched by the spiritual values she discovers in her solitude and suffering in Mogador, can lead Rodrigo to salvation. She alone can persuade Rodrigo to renounce wealth and political power in order to grow spiritually and thus to attain salvation. Shortly before she dies, Prouheze tells her beloved Rodrigo: "Be generous in thy turn, as I have done canst not thou do likewise? Strip thyself! Cast off everything, give all to get all!"

When he traveled to Mogador in the third day of this play, Rodrigo hoped that Prouheze would satisfy him both physically and emotionally. Prouheze's final remarks to him, and especially her courageous acceptance of death, transform the egotistical Rodrigo into a sympathetic and altruistic individual. Rodrigo's insistence that the teachings of Christ require Christians to end their colonial domination of other people offends the king of Spain and his counselors. Rodrigo, however, must end his political career in order to remain faithful to his religious beliefs.

Dramatic Devices

Although the original version of *The Satin Slipper* is generally considered to be Paul Claudel's most profound play, this very lengthy version has never been staged, for a very practical reason: A complete performance of the 1928-1929 version of *The Satin Slipper* would require two very long evenings. Only Claudel himself believed that its full dramatic power could be effectively communicated to theatergoers under such conditions. Fortunately, the eminent French actor Jean-Louis Barrault proposed in 1942 a solution that satisfied both Claudel and the directors of the Comédie-Française. Barrault assisted Claudel in revising *The Satin Slipper*. The stage version is approximately half as long as the original version. The most significant change proposed by Barrault was to reduce the eleven scenes in the fourth day into a two-scene epilogue. Music by the eminent French composer Arthur Honegger added to the solemnity of this religious drama. Since its initial run of more than fifty performances during the 1943-1944 theatrical season at the Comédie-Française, the Barrault-Claudel version of *The Satin Slipper* has been performed frequently both in France and in many other countries.

The stage version of *The Satin Slipper* downplays the epic and historical sweep of the original version and transforms Claudel's play into a fairly intimate drama that conveys to spectators the growing influence of spiritual and moral values on Rodrigo and Prouheze. Through creative uses of recurring musical themes for each key character, muted lighting for the appearances onstage of Saint James, Prouheze's Guardian Angel, and the Moon, and set designs that draw attention to the eternal flow of the oceans during Rodrigo's and Prouheze's voyages of self-discovery, the 1943 version of *The Satin Slipper* suggests quite subtly but effectively how spiritual values become meaningful to the lovers. The artificiality and social injustices in both Spain and its many colonies serve only to alienate Rodrigo and Prouheze from their compatriots who accept the existing unjust social order. When one recalls that *The Satin Slipper* was revised and first performed in occupied Paris, the moral and political implications of this powerful spiritual play become rather clear to sensitive spectators and readers. One can readily imagine why Parisian theatergoers responded so favorably to the early performances of *The Satin Slipper*.

Critical Context

From 1890, when *Tête d'or* (English translation, 1919) was published, until his death in 1955, Paul Claudel remained a very active writer. His plays and lyric poems are still held in the highest esteem. Although he was born and died in France, Claudel spent most of his adult life in other countries. Between 1893 and 1935, he was a member of the French diplomatic corps. Thus, he wrote his lyric and dramatic masterpieces far from his native land. He integrated diverse cultural traditions into his own spiritual and aesthetic perception of the human condition. The very history of the composition, publication, and performance of *The Satin Slipper* suggests the importance of cultural diversity for Claudel. It was during his service as the French ambassador to Japan that he completed *The Satin Slipper*, which was first published while he was the French ambassador to the United States. The play was first performed eight years after his retirement from the diplomatic corps.

Critics were somewhat reserved in their praise of the play's original version. Claudel was quite displeased when several influential French Catholic writers, including François Mauriac and Gabriel Marcel, suggested that *The Satin Slipper* would interest only Roman Catholics. Claudel rejected such restrictive interpretations of his dramatic masterpieces. In his 1964 book on critical reactions to *The Satin Slipper*, Pierre Brunel noted that many of the most enthusiastic admirers of this play have been non-Catholics and even nonbelievers. Although *The Satin Slipper* clearly contains overt references to the Catholic traditions Claudel knew so well, it is nevertheless a work of universal significance. Sensitive readers and spectators from diverse cultures can appreciate the psychological depth and keen moral insights in this dramatic exploration of the meaning of love, personal growth, and self-sacrifice.

Sources for Further Study

Caranfi, Angelo. *Claudel: Beauty and Grace*. Lewisburg, Pa.: Bucknell University Press, 1989.

Chiari, Joseph. *The Poetic Drama of Paul Claudel*. New York: P. J. Kenedy and Sons, 1954.

Fowlie, Wallace. *Claudel*. London: Bowes and Bowes, 1957.

Freilich, Joan. *Paul Claudel's "Le Soulier de satin": A Stylistic, Structuralist, and Psychoanalytic Interpretation*. Toronto, Ont.: University of Toronto Press, 1973.

Ince, W. N. "The Unity of Claudel's *Le Soulier de satin*." *Symposium* 22 (1968): 35-53.

Killiam, Marie-Therese. *The Art Criticism of Paul Claudel*. New York: Lang, 1990.

Paliyenko, Adrianna M. *Mis-Reading the Creative Impulse: The Poetic Subject in Rimbaud and Claudel, Restaged*. Carbondale: Southern Illinois University Press, 1997.

Waters, Harold A. *Paul Claudel*. New York: Twayne, 1970.

Wood, Michael. "The Theme of the Prison in *Le Soulier de satin*." *French Studies* 22 (1968): 225-238.

Edmund J. Campion

SAVED

Author: Edward Bond (1934-)
Type of plot: Naturalistic
Time of plot: The early 1960's
Locale: South London, England
First produced: 1965, at the Royal Court Theatre, London
First published: 1966

Principal characters:
PAM, a twenty-three-year-old working-class woman
LEN, a twenty-one-year-old laborer, in love with Pam
FRED, a twenty-one-year-old laborer, the father of Pam's illegitimate baby
MARY, Pam's mother
HARRY, Pam's father, a laborer

The Play

The play begins in the living room of the home in which Pam lives with her father and mother. Having just met Len, she has brought him home with her, and they are preparing to engage in sexual intercourse. Harry, getting ready for work, enters the room as they are settling themselves on the couch, but he says nothing and leaves immediately, allowing them to continue, rather jokingly, with the sexual act. After this encounter, Len moves in as a lodger and becomes seriously interested in Pam, but she is attracted to Fred, another, tougher young man.

In the next scene, Pam is taking care of a baby she has had with Fred. She is still living with her parents, and Len continues to board with them; he takes care of Pam—as much as she will let him, since she now despises him. Fred pays no attention to her. Mary and Harry seem to take the situation without comment, which is consistent with the fact that they do not speak to each other. Len acts as a go-between for Pam and the elusive Fred, but he has little success in getting Fred to visit her. He has even less success in pleasing Pam, who wants him to move out of her parents' home and leave her alone. The baby, offstage much of the time, cries incessantly and is ignored by Pam.

The central scene of the play occurs in the local park, where Pam confronts Fred, begging him to visit her more often. In the ensuing quarrel she walks off, leaving the baby in its carriage for Fred to take care of, or not, as he pleases. Mocked by a gang of friends, Fred threatens to abandon the baby. Slowly at first, and then with increasing enthusiasm, the young men torment the baby. At first, Fred resists their suggestions that he join in, but as the attack on the child goes beyond pinching to punching and to throwing burning matches into the carriage, Fred gets involved. Stones are thrown at the child, and when the gang members, including Fred, flee, there is no doubt that the baby has been killed.

Fred goes to jail for the killing, having refused to name any of the other men. Pam waits faithfully for him, still trying to get Len out of the house; Len, in turn, still tries to help Pam as much as she will allow. She is sure that Fred will come to her on his release from prison. Though he is pressured to leave in order to make room for Fred, Len refuses to do so, and Pam's parents show no inclination to evict him. On the day Fred is freed, Len accompanies Pam to meet him at a cafe near the prison, but they are not the only ones to greet the former convict. The young men who helped Fred in the murder are also on hand, as is a young girl with whom Fred was involved before the killing. Pam begs him to come with her, but he and his friends jeer at her and leave. She blames Len for failing to persuade Fred.

Things grow worse at home. Harry accuses Mary of having an affair with Len; in response, Mary smashes a hot teapot over her husband's head. Pam is so hysterical about Fred's refusal to join her and Len's refusal to leave that Len is advised to keep to his room. Harry does not seem to be really upset about Len and his wife, and the two men console each other for the difficult, unhappy situation they are in, but neither of them wants to leave. Pam has no success in convincing Fred either to come to her or to take her away from the family home.

The last scene is innocently quiet. The play has come full circle, back to the family living room, where Harry is working on his football pools, Mary is clearing up the table, Pam is reading the *Radio Times*, and the ever-patient Len is fixing a chair. It is a tour de force of theatrical restraint, since aside from one brief request for a hammer, made by Len to Pam (she ignores him), nothing is said. Harry finishes his lottery entry and seals the envelope. Mary and Pam sit, saying nothing, on the couch. Len fixes the chair, crouching beside it, his head lying sideways on the seat. All seems well.

Themes and Meanings

Saved aims to expose the brutalized nature of modern capitalist society. On the surface it may appear to be an unremittingly realistic representation of urban gang violence and the meaningless, unfeeling nature of life in working-class Great Britain, but its intention goes beyond the simple depiction of emotional squalor among the laborers. Edward Bond, like a latter-day George Bernard Shaw, likes to surround his plays with explicit statements of meaning. His central thesis is the belief that capitalism debases, not only materially but also in every other way that affects the lives of human beings and their ability to live with one another.

Written in the 1960's, *Saved* may seem even more stunningly apt in the early twenty-first century in its representation of urban decay, manifested not so much in the physical surroundings as in the way in which people live. However, it is important to remember, if the meaning Bond imposes on the work is to be understood, that the play does not explore a problem which is explainable simply in terms of unemployment or drugs and criminal violence. Bond's characters in *Saved* are not out of work; they are enmeshed in gratuitous indifference at the best, and even more gratuitous violence at the worst, even though they are steadily employed. The capitalist system has deprived them of the capacity to live in a civilized manner. Indeed, their animal instincts have been nurtured by the system for the sake of profit—for example, through television entertainment, which provides a steady stream of violent images. As Bond sees it, capitalism uses violence, instilling it into society as a consumer commodity, available to all at a low price.

The idea that capitalism debases a society totally, depriving the working classes of their right to live in a just society and dragging them down into animality, is what the play is representing in the horrifying conduct played out in the park. The violence of the ruling classes, in the guise of law and order, breeds an answering violence in the victims. At its worst, it erupts in bestial, unreasoning acts, expressions of a kind of mad, caged-animal ferocity. Treated like dogs, human beings become dogs, but hardly of the lap-dog variety.

Dramatic Devices

Saved is an almost perfect example of the naturalist play, in which human conduct as it is played out in real life, particularly among the least fortunate members of a society, is explored relentlessly and usually without comment, and in which the forces of heredity and environment act upon characters powerless to resist. The naturalistic play is, however, more than simple documentary. It is Bond's intention to lay blame for the reprehensible conduct of his characters on the place that they, through no fault of their own, inhabit in a capitalist society. He has, on many occasions, been accused of gratuitous brutality and sensationalism, but he belongs to a quite important movement in the theater that began in the work of Émile Zola and Henrik Ibsen, who used drama not simply to entertain but also to attack social inequities.

Bond deliberately wanted to upset his audience; in *Saved*, therefore, he put as much sordid, dreary reality on the stage as he could, attempting to reproduce, with little artistic shaping, the desultory banality of working-class language, relationships, and conduct. The sets are kept as rudimentary as possible, and what constitutes "set" is tasteless and ugly. There is a deliberate flatness in the speech patterns, which are often regionally accurate but confined to boring incoherence. No attempt is made to make the conversations interesting; clichés pervade the supposed witty badinage of the play's young men and women, who clearly possess extremely limited imagination. There is no attempt to make the characters look better than they might be in real life; it could be argued that Bond is determined to make them look their worst.

Consistent with this determination to avoid artistic enhancement is Bond's de-emphasis on plot and structure. The play is made up of thirteen short scenes with seemingly arbitrary jumps in time and consequence, presented without explanation, rather awkwardly plodding through the dreary day-to-day life of south London griminess. Only the murder scene has any deliberate theatrical shape. There is a constant sense that things simply happen, as they do in real life. Time means nothing. Pam meets Fred in the park; he flirts for a moment with her. Two scenes later, without any further connection shown between them, Pam is taking care of a baby she claims to be Fred's child. After the murder, Fred spends what must have been some considerable time in prison, but there is no attempt to convey a sense of time having passed. The narrative is virtually shapeless. One thing is depicted as the same as any other; nothing really means anything, and the killing of the child is commented upon as nothing much more than an inconvenience. Life grinds on.

Critical Context

Saved is the high point (or the low point, depending upon one's point of view) in Edward Bond's long and prolific career of using the theater to make the British public squirm. It certainly is the play that caused him and his supporters the most public difficulty, since it was seen by many, including some theater critics, as having gone too far in exposing the emotional and moral vacuum at the heart of English working-class life. However, Bond had his supporters, including the late Sir Laurence Olivier, the most prominent British actor of the time. Olivier and others not only asserted Bond's right to artistic freedom but also defended the theatrical quality of his work and the validity of his attack on the meaninglessness of many aspects of contemporary urban life. Bond gained renewed attention in 2001 with the New York revival of *Saved.* Critic Charles Isherwood, writing in *Variety* noted "The play's clear-eyed observation of the interplay between need and neglect, and how people are warped by them, is as pertinent and powerful today as it was in 1965."

Bond has continued to be an artistic gadfly. In 1971, he rewrote, or at least reinterpreted, William Shakespeare's *King Lear* (pr. c. 1605-1606). He stripped the play of all vestiges of heroism and tragic exultation, claiming that the modern world had no place for sublime action but needed to see the vicious scramble for power as it really was. In his adaptation, Lear is simply a nasty thug—no better than his daughters—who learns that violence will not work and that he must accept moral responsibility for what happened. A very formidable play, *Lear* (pr. 1971) adamantly rejects Shakespeare's ending as pure sentimentality. Subsequently, Bond wrote *Bingo: Scenes of Money and Death* (pr. 1973), in which he suggests that in his retirement to Stratford, Shakespeare descended to participation in money-grubbing land deals, supporting and conspiring in small-town real estate speculation.

Artistically, Bond's work can be quite uneven. For every play of the power of *Saved*, there are several others that have failed badly. His plays of the mid-1980's, including *The War Plays: A Trilogy* (pb. 1985), well-meaning examinations of the aftermath of nuclear war, are somewhat limited as works of art. In the late twentieth century, he brought forth such plays as *Lulu: A Monster Tragedy* (pr., pb. 1992), *Coffee* (pb. 1995, pr. 1996), *Eleven Vests* (pr., pb. 1997), *The Crime of the Twenty-first Century* (pb. 1999, pr. 2000), and, as the twenty-first century began, *The Children* (pr., pb. 2000) and *Have I None* (pr., pb. 2000).

Despite his inconsistencies, failures, and public disdain, Bond has maintained his role as one of the leading figures in a group of politically engaged British playwrights that includes David Hare and Howard Brenton. This group carries on the tradition of attacking the hypocrisies and dishonesties of British life—a tradition that began after World War II in the work of John Osborne, Arnold Wesker, and John Arden.

Sources for Further Study

Bond, Edwin. *Edwin Bond Letters*. Edited by Ian Stuart. London: Harwood, 1994.

Cohn, Ruby. "Edward Bond." In *Contemporary Dramatists*. 6th ed. Detroit: St. James, 1999.

Coult, Tony. *The Plays of Edward Bond*. London: Methuen, 1977.

Hay, Malcolm, and Phillip Roberts. *Edward Bond: A Companion to the Plays*. London: Eyre Methuen, 1978.

Mangan, Michael. *Edward Bond*. London: British Council, 1998.

Robert, Philip, ed. *Bond on File*. London: Methuen, 1985.

Scharine, R. *The Plays of Edward Bond*. Lewisburg, Pa.: Bucknell University Press, 1976.

Spencer, Jenny S. *Dramatic Strategies in the Plays of Edward Bond*. Cambridge, England: Cambridge University Press, 1996.

Trussler, Simon. *Edward Bond*. Harlow, England: Longman, 1976.

Charles Pullen

SCENES FROM AMERICAN LIFE

Author: A. R. Gurney, Jr. (1930-)
Type of plot: Satire
Time of plot: From the 1930's to the near future
Locale: Buffalo, New York
First produced: 1970, at Tanglewood, Lenox, Massachusetts
First published: 1970

Principal characters:
FATHER, a well-to-do white American
MOTHER, his wife
SNOOZER, their son

The Play

Scenes from American Life is a collection of nearly forty short scenes connected by scraps of period music, each scene showing a glimpse of life in upper-middle-class Buffalo over the course of about fifty years. A few of the characters appear in more than one scene, but most do not. Most of the characters are not even named; each is instantly recognizable, however, by his or her type.

The play begins in the early 1930's, with the entrance of a maid carrying a tray of martinis. She is followed by a group of guests, including a Godfather and Godmother, and finally by Father, the Bishop, and Mother, who carries a doll dressed in an elaborate christening gown. As Father and the Bishop talk about the new son who has just been christened, Mother worries that the child has no suitable nickname.

This first scene sets the tone for those that will follow. Conversation during the party turns to the Depression (which affects other people, but not these), the high-quality bootleg gin smuggled in for the event, the baby's sterling silver presents, proper manners, and the Bible. These are well-to-do white Anglo-Saxon Protestants (WASPs), with nothing more pressing on their minds than getting through this party. As the scene ends with the baby's tipsy Godmother spilling her drink on the child, Mother finds the perfect nickname for him: Snoozer, "because he sleeps through everything."

The next scene, which lasts only about a minute, occurs in or just before the 1970's, with a Speaker explaining to an audience the history behind the name Buffalo. He and Snoozer, the Speaker says, have discovered that the name is not from the animal, but from the French *beau fleuve*, meaning "beautiful river." As great ships once floated into Buffalo's port, he explains, the city now should float a new bond issue to build a stadium of which the city can be proud.

With the third scene, the play returns to the 1930's, this time presenting a Mother (but not Snoozer's mother) chastising her child's nurse for entertaining a man in her room. After a dialogue in which the Mother speaks sternly to the nurse about responsibility and morality, the nurse is dismissed, and the Mother turns to the telephone, where she makes arrangements for a secret meeting with her lover.

In this manner the play progresses. The characters survive World War II, the Korean War, and the Vietnam War apparently unscathed. They play tennis, undergo analysis to deal with drinking problems, take dancing lessons, throw parties, discuss their stock portfolios, wonder whether perhaps Jews should (some day) be admitted to their club; date acceptable people, marry unhappily, and, rarely and briefly, ponder the emptiness of it all. One young woman is offered two choices by her parents: a college education or a coming-out party. A grandfather tries to cure his grandson's stuttering by offering him money. A grandmother explains to her grandchildren the roles servants and "darkies" play in the world. The values of responsibility, tradition, and concern for the family are passed down from generation to generation.

Several of the scenes occur in the not-too-distant future, what must have been intended as the mid-1980's. The United States in this future is a police state in which no one crosses state lines without a travel permit, people out after curfew are subject to questioning, once-safe neighborhoods have been fortified with electrical fences, and young people who are able flee to Canada to begin new lives. Snoozer's club has had its license revoked because of its resistance activities, and Snoozer himself has been killed under mysterious circumstances, probably by the authorities.

In the final scene, the family that opened the play returns. On the Sunday before Labor Day, in a year during the 1960's, Mother, Father, Snoozer, his wife Esther, and his sister Sibby and her fiancé Ray walk from the summer house down to the lake after dinner. This year, they comment on the pollution in Lake Erie and remember evenings when they could see fish jumping. Next year, they resolve, they will install a pool so the children can swim.

The family reenacts the annual family ritual: Having collected the summer's tennis balls, they take turns tossing them into the canoe. The first to toss a ball that stays in the boat wins first choice of dates for use of the house the following summer. Ray appears to win but is disqualified for stepping over a line that only the family can see; Snoozer is the victor. Then the boat, which seems easily repairable to Ray but hopelessly old and decrepit to the others, is doused with kerosene, lit, and set adrift. The group sings sadly, a red glow from the fire visible on their faces, as the boat burns and drifts away. As the song ends, they stand watching, and the glow fades until they are left in darkness at the play's conclusion.

Themes and Meanings

Scenes from American Life is a play about wealthy and tradition-bound WASP society in Buffalo, New York, and how this society responds to changes in the country over a period of about fifty years. Ultimately, it is about the decline and fall of elitist American society as the nation changes and becomes more egalitarian, WASP children grow up and take Roman Catholic spouses, and Jews join the country club.

Although the inhabitants of A. R. Gurney's Buffalo have their obvious flaws, the playwright's portrait of them is nostalgic and affectionate. In the poignantly comic scene in which the daughter is asked to choose between college and a coming-out party, Gurney's sympathy clearly lies with the daughter, but he does not make the mother out to be a villain. The daughter struggles to explain why she would like to go to college, but, like many young people, her reasons are not clear even to her. In the end, she is not strongly independent enough to overcome her family's wishes. The mother is only trying to provide the best for her daughter; she sincerely does not understand why a young woman would want to go to college. She may be foolish, but she is not evil.

In fact, the inhabitants of Gurney's Buffalo do attempt, in the face of a changing world, to come to grips with serious issues, to help make things better for those less fortunate. However, they are so out of touch, Gurney shows, that their attempts to show concern reveal them at their most pathetic. A minister explains that the Bible requires generosity but must not be taken literally when it says that the rich should sell their possessions and give all to the poor. An old lady announces that she is donating one of her homes to be a summer camp for black children, a place for them to learn swimming, tennis, and croquet. "It is my firm belief," she explains, "that if colored children can spend their summers in the country, they will cease throwing fire bombs from their cars, and detention areas will no longer be necessary." These people may be well-meaning, but there is much that they fail to understand. Gurney has observed,

> What seems to obsess me is the contrast between the world and the values I was immersed in when I was young and the nature of the contemporary world. The kind of protected, genteel, in many ways warm, civilized, and fundamentally innocent world in which I was nurtured didn't seem in any way to prepare me for the late twentieth century. I tend to write about people who are operating under these old assumptions, but are confronting an entirely different system of values.

The outcome of this particular brand of elitism, the scenes in the future seem to predict, is the destruction of the society. Several critics have found these scenes to be the weakest in the play, protesting that Gurney does not make it clear whether these people deserve the fate that is handed them. Are all wealthy and powerful groups destined eventually to lose the power they hold as the world changes? Or has this society begun to fade because of particular sins? Is this a cautionary tale? Gurney does not make this clear.

Dramatic Devices

Scenes from American Life is a picture of an entire social class, not of specific individuals or families, and A. R. Gurney emphasizes this universality through the device of having each of his actors play several parts. In the course of the play's nearly forty scenes, more than one hundred different characters speak, and several others ad-lib in the background. Gurney's script calls for a much smaller cast—four men and four women, each appearing in several scenes. To weaken individual identities further, Gurney insists that the roles be distributed so that, for example, an actor playing a father in one scene plays the father in another. The only repeating characters are Snoozer's father and mother, who are played by the same actors in the play's first and last scenes.

Gurney uses set and costume to advance his message that his view of WASP society is not limited to specific people or times. His prescribed set is a stark and simple one, with no drawing-room walls or background landscapes that might become familiar and seem to refer to specific places. Instead, a nearly bare stage with different levels or focal points, and simple chairs or other props carried in and out by the actors, enable the setting to shift quickly from a living room to a church to a car to a ski lift, smoothly and without interruption for set changes. The play covers many people and many moments, and each individual scene must flow smoothly into the next so that the audience will not have a chance to consider any one moment at length.

Similarly, the actors wear simple costumes, with nothing to distinguish one from another. Accessories and props are used to help place a scene in a particular time, but for all intents and purposes the costumes help make the actors absolutely interchangeable.

The only indispensable object in a production of *Scenes from American Life* is the piano that remains prominently in the center of the stage throughout the play. The pianist playing a medley of tunes is the first thing the audience sees and hears as the play begins, and the last thing it sees at the end. In between, the pianist plays music that places each scene in its proper time period and also helps set the tone for the action. In the first scene, for example, the pianist plays "You Must Have Been a Beautiful Baby" as the christening party begins, a fanfare to celebrate the gift of a large check, and "Rockabye Baby" to accompany the singing guests as the scene ends.

Often the music adds a note of satiric gaiety when the dialogue turns serious, or of patriotic sentiment when the characters demonstrate their misplaced concerns, or of pomposity and solemnity as a minister condones selfishness. The piano is used, then, to mark a change in scene abruptly, and often to undercut what the characters are saying. The pianist, unifier and evaluator of all that occurs onstage, is the only performer who maintains the same role throughout the play.

Critical Context

Scenes from American Life is one play among several in which A. R. Gurney takes a satirical look at upper-middle-class WASP society. It was his first full-length play, and the first to be taken seriously by critics. Many of his earlier, shorter works, most notably *The David Show* (pr. 1966, pb. 1968) and *The Golden Fleece* (pb. 1967, pr. 1968), also use humor and satire to expose the banalities of modern life in the United States.

Scenes from American Life shows the tensions within families in several scenes; this is a theme to which Gurney has returned throughout his career. *Children* (pr., pb. 1974), an adaptation of a short story by John Cheever (with whose work that of Gurney has often been compared), follows one WASP family through a long weekend, presenting an image of upper-middle-class society that is less satirical but no less critical than that presented in *Scenes from American Life*.

Gurney's fascination with unusual staging devices has stayed with him, as has the theme of the decline and fall of elitist society. *The Dining Room* (pr., pb. 1982) presents a series of vignettes occurring over three generations in one family dining room, again with a small cast playing multiple roles. *Sweet Sue* (pr. 1986, pb. 1987) has each character played by two actors, echoing the breaking down of individual personality with which Gurney experimented in *Scenes from American Life*. *The Perfect Party* (pr. 1985) uses qualities of the farce to tell the story of a professor trying to be the perfect host, within one of Gurney's recurring settings: academia. His plays of the 1990's include *The Old Boy* (pr. 1991, pb. 1992), *Later Life* (pr. 1993, pb. 1994), *Sylvia* (pr. 1995, pb. 1996), *Far East* (pr. 1998, pb. 1999), and *Ancestral Voices* (pr. 1999, pb. 2000).

With more than three dozen plays, musicals, script adaptations, and novels, Gurney has established a reputation as the chronicler of a society passing into extinction. In 1986, he asserted to an interviewer that he did not "have too much more to say about the subject." Whatever other directions his work takes, he remains an important critic of American WASP society—important because he has written of its fallen idols with affection and wit.

Sources for Further Study

Barnes, Clive. "*Scenes from American Life* at the Forum." *New York Times*, March 26, 1971, p. 33.

Gottfried, Martin. Review in *New York Theatre Critics' Reviews* 32 (June 13, 1971): 271.

Gurney, A. R., Jr. "The Dinner Party." *American Heritage* 39 (September/October, 1988): 69-71.

Hughes, Catharine. "New York." *Plays and Players* 18 (June, 1971): 30-32.

Oliver, Edith. Review in *The New Yorker*, April 3, 1971, 95-97.

Strachen, Alan. "A. R. Gurney." In *Contemporary Dramatists*. 6th ed. Detroit: St. James, 1999.

Cynthia A. Bily

THE SCREENS

Author: Jean Genet (1910-1986)
Type of plot: Existential; epic theater
Time of plot: The twentieth century
Locale: Algeria
First produced: 1961, at the Schlosspark State Theatre, Berlin, Germany
First published: Les Paravents, 1961 (English translation, 1962)

Principal characters:
SAÏD, a poor man who becomes a thief and a traitor
LEILA, his wife, a remarkably ugly woman
THE MOTHER, his mother
WARDA and
KADIDJA, prostitutes
SIR HAROLD and
MR. BLANKENSEE, European administrators

The Play

The Screens, an epic drama that normally lasts five hours and contains ninety-eight characters, is divided into seventeen scenes or tableaux. The number seventeen probably symbolizes the return of the seventeen-year locust cycle, since Jean Genet, perhaps the twentieth century's most pessimistic writer, viewed human time in exactly the same way that scientists view the cycles of nature. The first three scenes introduce the major characters: Saïd, Leila, and the Mother.

Scene 1 shows the hero of the play, Saïd, on his way to his marriage to the ugliest woman in that part of the Arab world, Leila. By using the names Saïd (which means both "mister" and "fortunate or lucky" in Arabic) and Leila (in Persian mythology, a woman renowned for her beauty—the counterpart to Juliet), Genet immediately activates a level of irony that the casual reader might overlook.

Saïd, a thoroughly unheroic character, seems to be marrying her simply because it is the conventional thing to do and she is the only partner he can afford. After they are married, she is so repulsive that he spends what little money he has in one of the many local bordellos in the area. His marriage so alienates him from his fellow Arabs that he decides to leave for France. First, however, he steals a coat from a friend, Taleb, and is sent to prison. Leila, deeply in love with him and demanding masochistic punishment at all times, also becomes a thief and follows him to prison so that she can continue to be humiliated by her husband. She is so ugly that Saïd insists that she wear a cloth bag over her face, with three holes for breathing and vision. Saïd so brutalizes her throughout the play that by the last act she has only one eye left. After scene 10, Saïd makes few appearances, but he does return in the last two acts to assume an increasingly important symbolic role.

As Saïd progresses from the role of outcast to thief to prisoner and finally to traitor, he also moves, on a symbolic level, to heroic dimensions in Genet's inverted value system. The further he descends into his abjection, the greater he becomes in the eyes of both the women in the Algerian villages and the revolutionary Arab activists. Both groups adopt him as their emblem because they see the only hope of victory in men such as Saïd who deliberately choose violence and evil for their own sake.

The next important character is Saïd's mother, known as "the Mother" throughout the remainder of the play. She dedicates herself unrelentingly to helping her son reach his heroic status. She is as cruel to Leila as is her son, though she and Leila do work together to help him attain his emerging heroic reputation. She also serves the role of nostalgically recalling her son's childhood and mourns the untimely death of her husband.

Rather than a chronological series of actions, the play consists of scenes that depict the gradually growing consciousness within certain groups of the apocalyptic end of the French presence and power in Algeria. Scenes 4 and 10 show the colonials, Sir Harold and Mr. Blankensee, blithely ignoring the inevitability of their expulsion by the Arab rebels. Mr. Blankensee distracts himself by tending his rose garden, while Sir Harold promises to sacrifice even his own son for the sake of the family legacy.

The most important scenes, however, take place in or just outside the many bordellos depicted in the play. The most colorful and honest characters in the play are the magnificent prostitutes Warda and Kadidja. Both the French soldiers and the Arab men, as they emerge from behind the many screens onstage, are constantly buttoning up their trousers as they pick up their weapons of war. Besides the Dead, the prostitutes are the only members of the cast who understand what drives men to perform deeds of violence and cruelty; they articulate the connection between sex and aggression, power and self-destruction.

The scenes shift without any discernible motivation; Genet celebrates the confusion and suggests that, except for the first five or six scenes and the last two, they could be arranged randomly. The themes are so insistent and compelling that any arrangement would serve to reveal them. Besides the bordello, recurring settings include fields, the prison, the cemetery, the village square, and, most important, the final scene in the Underworld or the land of the Dead.

If the arrangement of the first sixteen scenes seems random and arbitrary, the last scene is a masterpiece of organization. It is the longest scene by far in the play, and it is divided into three levels of three sections. Genet seems to be suggesting the nine circles of the Underworld of Dante's *Inferno* (c. 1320). The first three levels depict the underworld and, consistent with Genet's ironic intent, rest on the highest part of the stage, which is bathed in light. The next two represent the prison and the grocery shop, while the last four show the brothel, the village square, the interior of a house, and the ground floor of the stage itself. Everyone in the play is dead; all are waiting for the return and apotheosis of the hero, Saïd. The story of Saïd has become "a song"—that is, he has moved into the realm of myth and legend within what the venerable Ommu calls the "esthetics of decease." All the assembled dead await the wisdom of Saïd as he passes from life to the Land of the Dead. His final pronouncement on the entire enterprise is, "To the old gal, to the soldiers, to all of you, I say shit."

In some ways the play's conclusion is ambiguous. The audience never knows whether Saïd is actually dead; the irony is that there is virtually no difference between life and death in any case.

Themes and Meanings

The respected drama critic Harold Clurman characterized *The Screens* as "epic nihilism," while the distinguished scholar Raymond Federman called it the "theatre of hate." Ostensibly, it concerns the historical exodus of the French colonials after 130 years of relentless exploitation of generations of Arabs in Algeria, and the bitter recriminations that resulted. The conflict nearly tore France apart as politicians attempted, unsuccessfully, to disengage France from the viper's tangle of cultural, religious, political, and economic complications of its Algerian involvement. Jean Genet, while utilizing the historical time and place, is much more concerned with venting his hatred on the French colonials. His hatred spills over into the victims, the Arabs, also. His real target, however, is civilization itself, particularly modern civilization. One critic referred to *The Screens* as an "acid bath of loathing."

Genet was undoubtedly influenced by the earlier French playwright Antonin Artaud and his concept of the Theater of Cruelty. Genet certainly subscribed to Artaud's idea that the modern theater should seek to shock its audience into the realization that not only is the world a cruel and vicious place but indeed the world is "nothing." For Genet, experience is process, and the process can be viewed only through a series of perceptions that form themselves into images; these images humanity mistakes for reality. The truth of experience is that there is no truth, merely illusions that groups of desperate people agree to call "truth" and "reality." For Genet, there are two kinds of people: those who live in illusions or fictions and do not know it and those who recognize the fictiveness of their fictions and discard the possibility of establishing any kind of objective truth.

This particular play embodies that principle more than any of Genet's other plays because it is about "screens"—that is, the settings or props that create the illusions of reality. Since this play is a vividly modernistic work, its form not only is an extension of its content but also *is* its content, since that is what life is: illusion based on nothing more than the human imagination and its infinite permutations. The major project of the play is to demonstrate the dynamics of this fictive process and to reiterate its major theme that life is no more than an aimless dialogue between light and dark and, therefore, nothing. For Genet, discussions of right and wrong, morality and immorality, and other seeming dichotomies are patently absurd, since everything can be reduced to mere phenomenological fluctuations. The primary image that recurs more consistently than any other in the play is the image of emptiness, and the emerging metaphor that finally dominates the play is that of cosmic emptiness. Indeed, at the conclusion of this epic, the stage is totally empty.

Dramatic Devices

Jean Genet's directions at the beginning of the play are absolutely specific. All the characters, except Saïd, must wear garish makeup, false noses, and huge hairpieces, especially the prostitutes. If possible, most of them should wear masks, and no face should present anything even close to conventional beauty.

He specifies that the stage should be open-air and that there should be "an extremely varied set of stages, levels, surfaces." Screens should be constantly moved on and offstage to establish the appropriate *mise en scène*. He insists, however, that there must be at least one "real object" on the stage, in contrast to the objects drawn in *trompe l'oeil* on each screen. He suggests a rock pile or wheelbarrow or other such objects so that the audience may determine what is "really" there and what only "appears" to be there.

The major dramatic devices become the major content of the play, since Genet perceives the world as nothing more than a stage with ever-changing perspectives. The actors use the screens as barriers to protect them from violent reality. They also draw on the screens, temporarily creating their own reality. Finally, the Dead burst through the screens to destroy their function and to establish once and for all that the only reality is the fact of death itself. The fact of death, that all life leads to a meaningless death, justifies Genet's claim that life is nothing.

Critical Context

The Screens was the last play written by Jean Genet, and in many ways it is the culminating statement of this important playwright. Genet never repeated himself thematically, although his characters and situations are unmistakable products of his unique sensibility. Each of his plays is a major development of certain key concerns that do, however, surface in all of his plays. In his two earliest plays, *Les Bonnes* (pr. 1947, pb. 1948; *The Maids*, 1954) and *Haute Surveillance* (pr., pb. 1949; *Deathwatch*, 1954), he explored the possibility of the canonization of evil in the former and the ritual switching of roles in the latter. In perhaps his most famous play, *Le Balcon* (pb. 1956, pr. 1960; *The Balcony*, 1957), he entertained notions of the world as a vast bordello run by Madame Irma, a demonic version of the imagination, in which humanity might view itself in a bizarre hall of mirrors, thus reversing the terms of the so-called civilized world. In *Les Nègres* (pb. 1958; *The Blacks*, 1960), Genet plays off the American minstrel show in an outrageous role reversal by actual black actors with their faces painted white in order to mock and satirize the white power structure.

The Screens, then, was a fitting culmination and summation of all these themes; the specific Algerian historical setting serves as an accurate representation of the violent and arbitrary nature of reality. Present, however, in all Genet's plays is his penchant to lyricize whatever he finds or creates, since, as an artist, the creation of "the Song" is the only freedom that he possesses. There is a compelling magnificence to the "abyss that is existence," and Genet, perhaps better than any other modern artist, registers the terror of that recognition while simultaneously celebrating the grandeur of annihilation.

Sources for Further Study

Brooks, Peter, and Joseph Halpern, eds. *Genet: A Collection of Critical Essays*. Englewood Cliffs, N.J.: Prentice-Hall, 1979.

Coe, Richard N. *The Vision of Jean Genet*. New York: Grove Press, 1968.

Hammerbeck, David. Review of *Los Bliombos/The Screens*. *Theatre Journal* 50 (December, 1998): 525-529.

Knapp, Bettina L. *Jean Genet.* Rev. ed. Boston: Twayne, 1989.

McMahon, Joseph H. *The Imagination of Jean Genet*. New Haven, Conn.: Yale University Press, 1963.

Parham, Sidney F. Review of *The Screens*. *Theatre Journal* 42 (May, 1990): 249-251.

Thody, Philip. *Jean Genet: A Study of His Novels and Plays*. New York: Stein and Day, 1968.

Webb, Richard C. *Jean Genet and His Critics: An Annotated Bibliography, 1943-1980*. Metuchen, N.J.: Scarecrow Press, 1982.

White, Edmund. *Genet: A Biography.* New York: Random House, 1994.

Patrick Meanor

THE SEARCH FOR SIGNS OF INTELLIGENT LIFE IN THE UNIVERSE

Author: Jane Wagner (1935-)
Type of plot: Women's; comedy
Time of plot: 1970-1985
Locale: Los Angeles and New York
First produced: 1985, at the Plymouth Theatre, New York City
First published: 1986

Principal characters:
LILY, the actor performing the play
TRUDY, a bag lady
CHRISSY, an unemployed young woman
PAUL, a divorced man
KATE, a wealthy socialite
AGNUS ANGST, a teenage punk artist
JANET BEASLEY, her mother
LUD, her grandfather
MARIE, her grandmother
TINA and
BRANDY, prostitutes
LYN, a professional woman
MARGE, Lyn's friend, the owner of a plant store
EDIE, Lyn's friend, a lesbian writer

The Play

The Search for Signs of Intelligent Life in the Universe begins on the corner of "Walk, Don't Walk" somewhere in New York City, although the playwright describes no realistic set in which to place the play's action. Trudy, the bag lady whose monologues lead the spectators through the play's events, speaks directly to the audience about her pending encounter with aliens from outer space. Trudy once worked as a designer and creative consultant for Howard Johnson's and Nabisco, but when she found herself suggesting that the cracker company pitch the concept of munching to the Third World, she went off the deep end.

As a result, she began having what she calls "time-space continuum shifts." Her umbrella hat works as a satellite dish and picks up signals that transmit snatches of people's lives. Her unusual gift allows Trudy to channel the mosaic of lives that make up Jane Wagner's play. When Trudy hears a "sizzling sound like white noise," the other characters are zapped into being, and the performer transforms in front of the audience.

Part 1 of the play is episodic and briefly introduces various characters who are eventually woven into the more linear story in part 2. Trudy's umbrella hat first tunes in to the performer, Lily, who welcomes the audience. Lily admits that she worries quite a bit, about philosophical issues such as whether there is a "cosmic scheme of things" and mundane issues such as reflective flea collars, soap operas, and Andy Warhol.

Trudy beams out of Lily to continue her discussion of the search for signs of intelligent life, which she is conducting with her "space chums." Her antennae next pick up Chrissy, a young woman exercising in an aerobics class, who complains about her inability to find and hold a job. "All my life I've always wanted to be somebody," she says. "But I see now I should have been more specific." Chrissy attends a number of personal growth seminars to open herself to change and to avoid her suicidal tendencies, but she is branded a "classic 'false hope' case."

Also an athlete, Paul is distressed by his recent divorce. In the story Trudy transmits, he admits that he had an affair when his wife was pregnant, with a woman named Marge. Marge owned a plant store, and when Paul slept with her in the room above it, Marge asked him to donate his sperm to her lesbian friends who wanted to have a child. Paul agreed; now he confides that he has been haunted ever since by the thought of his "secret kid."

Watching television one day, Paul sees a child prodigy playing the violin in a concert and notices a resemblance to himself. He tries to find Marge, to ask her questions, but when he returns to the plant store, he finds that Marge is dead. Paul is left ruminating over whether the young violinist is his son.

Next Trudy listens to Kate, an urbane woman waiting in a beauty salon for a bad haircut to be corrected. Kate's hairdresser, Bucci, has cut her hair short on one side and long on the other. She complains that she is dying of boredom and is not even excited by an affair she is having. She plans a visit to Los Angeles for plastic surgery on her fingertip, which she sliced in a "dreadful Cuisinart accident." She dreads going to the theater that evening to see "this actress/comedy thing"; the reference is to Wagner's play and Lily Tomlin's performance at the Plymouth.

Several times, Trudy visualizes a skinny punk kid with hair the color of Froot Loops. In her next trance, she finds the young woman, Agnus Angst, complaining on a pay phone at an International House of Pancakes that her stepmother and father locked her out of the house. Agnus's real mother, Janet, is a lesbian performance artist who lost custody to her "bio-businessman" father. Her father is angry because Agnus spit into a petri dish of bioplasm at his lab. Agnus screams that people are "specks" and exits with her chains clanging.

She returns to Marie and Lud, her grandparents; they are vaguely embarrassed by their granddaughter, whose reflective flea-collar necklace makes her glow in the dark like a poltergeist. Agnus leaves the house shouting that they do not understand her.

Trudy tunes into Agnus's performance at the Un-Club, where the girl announces, "I'm getting my act together; throwing it in your FACE." She performs a kind of punk rap song about her anger at the unacceptability of the air and the corruption of the world. Her rant ends with a quote from G. Gordon Liddy: "The trick is not to mind it." Agnus attempts his solution, but as she holds her hand over a lit candle, she ends part 1 by screaming, "I MIND IT!!"

Trudy initiates the more cohesive story line of part 2 by describing the aliens' philosophy that "everything is part of everything," an axiom that is loosely based on the "Quantum Inseparability Principle." The theory proves true in Wagner's play, as the characters from part 1 are found as references in the lives of those in part 2. For example, two prostitutes, Tina and Brandy, are taken for a ride by a journalist who wants to write about their lives. They drive past Agnus Angst, who has become a runaway. Tina relates her life history and her survival philosophy, revealing in the process that she supported Bucci, Kate's hairdresser from part 1, while he worked on his beauty-school degree.

Trudy takes her "space chums" to Howard Johnson's, where they continue to reflect on the origins and meaning of intelligent life on this planet. Trudy speculates that language developed "because of our deep inner need to complain," a proposition borne out by many of the characters she transmits. After she describes her dialogue with the aliens, Trudy's static white noise sends the audience to Los Angeles in 1985, as Lyn sorts through her possessions for a garage sale.

When Lyn finds her journal, Wagner's play is propelled into an extended reminiscence on the hopes and failures of liberal and feminist sentiments from 1970 to 1985. The journal's year marks each segment and allows Wagner to comment on social movements and issues such as consciousness raising, lesbianism, pacificism, feminism, and upwardly mobile professionalism.

Lyn's friend Marge is the plant-store owner with whom Paul had an affair in part 1, and Edie and Pam are the lesbian couple whose son Ivan is, in fact, the child prodigy fathered by Paul's sperm. Conversations among Lyn, Marge, and Edie, and Lyn's reminiscences, make up the bulk of part 2. Her journal relates that Lyn married Bob, a sensitive man who wore drawstring Indian cotton pants and Birkenstock sandals and carried the same shoulder bag as Lyn. Although Lyn and Bob set out to have an egalitarian relationship, Lyn found herself shouldering most of the child-rearing work, while Bob attended personal growth seminars and sensitivity training.

Lyn eventually became a "super-mother," working at a high-powered public relations job in which she hired, then fired, Chrissy as her secretary. Bob eventually had an affair with a younger woman, and his relationship with Lyn ended.

The journal relates that Marge became an alcoholic and eventually committed suicide, while sardonic Edie and her lover, Pam, took their son to New York to play an important concert at Carnegie Hall. Kate, the bored socialite from part 1, reappears to say that she saw the Carnegie Hall concert and that she found a suicide note on her trip to Los Angeles. Since the note refers to "false hopes," it was probably written by Chrissy. Kate redeems Chrissy's death by finding her suicide note full of feeling and, ironically, of life.

As a result, Kate realizes her own inability to feel. After the concert, she joins Brandy and Tina in talking to Trudy on a street corner; when it begins to rain, she takes the umbrella hat Trudy offers. Kate, then, joins the human community and suggests that hope is not at all false.

Trudy ends the play with a thank-you note from her alien friends. Their last visit on Earth was to a performance of a play, which Trudy calls a "goose bump experience." Because she had not told them to watch the stage, the aliens watched the audience. They said, "Trudy, the play was soup . . . the audience . . . art." Trudy says that maybe someday "we'll do something so magnificent everyone in the universe will get goose bumps."

Themes and Meanings

The Search for Signs of Intelligent Life in the Universe takes up themes of the interconnectedness of people and of people's methods for finding meaning in lives that sometimes seem absurd. Since the panoply of characters whose thoughts Trudy transmits exemplifies a range of race, class, and even gender, the play suggests that a common search for meaning links humanity at its core.

The play's allusions to the performance of the play itself allow Jane Wagner to suggest that the ritual of attending and performing theater creates a site for such linkages to occur. The play's theatricality, and the fact that all of its characters are performed by the same actor (Lily Tomlin in the first production), stresses universal human connections.

The play is feminist in tone, particularly in part 2, which focuses on a moment in American history through the lens of contemporary feminism. Wagner's humor, however, gives the play a bittersweet irony and optimism and avoids didacticism. Her perspective centers on women's experience, but her aim is toward the universal. Trudy's good humor and eccentric observations about reality provide Wagner's commentary on life's absurdities and balance the bleaker alienation of characters such as Agnus Angst, Kate, Chrissy, and Marge. Trudy is a Cassandra-like visionary, of the sort "who has flashes of insight but can't get anyone to listen to 'em 'cause their insights make 'em sound so *crazy*!"

Although Marge and Chrissy commit suicide, their pain, as well as Agnus Angst's, seems to come from the depth of their feeling and sensitivity to their surroundings. That Kate is redeemed by reading Chrissy's suicide note suggests that it is through feeling, rather than bitter aloofness, that people connect with their world and themselves.

Lyn's journey through the feminist and human potential movements into the 1980's preoccupation with upward mobility, overachievement, and money also allows Wagner to comment on the changing tides of American values. Her optimism, however, prevails, as Lyn's trek through her own history ends on a note of affection and connection to the people who formed her. At the garage sale, she decides to sell everything but her autographed copy of *Ms.* magazine and the "Whales Save Us" tee shirt that Bob was wearing when they met. Underneath the 1980's ambitions, Wagner sees a nostalgia for and perhaps a commitment to a more collective past.

Trudy's final monologue suggests that the search for signs of intelligent life is eternal: "All this searching! All these trances, all this data, and all we *really* know is how *little* we know about what it *all* means." Wagner proposes that life's mystery is in fact its beauty, and that rather than trying to find meaning, people should revel in living fully. As Trudy says, "The moment you are most in awe of all there is about life that you don't understand, you are closer to understanding it all than at any other time."

Dramatic Devices

The Search for Signs of Intelligent Life in the Universe was produced as a one-woman show on Broadway. The focus on the single performer, who transforms quickly and completely into each of the characters Trudy transmits, heightens the play's theme of human interconnectedness. The text requires a tour-de-force performance, since the actor must impersonate characters of various race, gender, class, and even national regions.

Particularly in part 1, the play's story line is nonlinear. Characters are introduced in different surroundings, such as the beauty salon where Kate waits for Bucci, the aerobics studio where Chrissy works out, and the Un-Club where Agnus Angst performs. Since the play is presented on a bare stage, with only one black step unit as a seat for the actor and no props, sound effects are crucial in establishing time, place, and mood. Transitions between sections and characters are marked by the white noise that emanates from Trudy's imaginary umbrella hat, an electric, dissonant sound not unlike that made by a television tuned in to a station that is off the air.

Agnus Angst is characterized by sounds of heavy chains dragging at her feet and of zippers being yanked and closed on her multi-zippered jump suit. (The actor performing each role never changes her costume, which is a plain black blouse and black slacks.) During Lyn's journal reminiscences, many musical cues are added in production to evoke the 1970's and early 1980's. The early women's movement is characterized by Helen Reddy's anthem "I Am Woman"; Lyn's experimentation with lesbianism is backed by Chris Williamson's "Sweet Woman"; Bob's construction of his never-completed flotation tank is accompanied by New Age music. Other, more documentary, sound bites evoke the historic events to which Lyn reacts, such as Geraldine Ferraro's acceptance of the Democratic Party's nomination for vice president in 1984. Lighting, too, is used to advantage in distinguishing shifting moods and time periods.

Wagner's text reveals its theme by subtly interconnecting characters who at first seem unrelated. Agnus Angst's mother, Janet, is referred to as a friend of Lyn and her set; Bucci, Kate's hairdresser, was put through beauty school by Tina, the prostitute; Lyn hires Chrissy as her assistant; Kate finds Chrissy's suicide note; and Paul sleeps with Marge and donates the sperm that allows Ivan, Edie and Pam's son, to be conceived. Wagner weaves these characters and events effortlessly into a mosaic of human lives that evokes people's transcendent connection.

Critical Context

The Search for Signs of Intelligent Life in the Universe is notable for its deviation from the traditional form and content of mainstream American drama. Most commercially and critically successful plays are family dramas written in the psychological realism genre. They concern traditional family relationships, and female characters are seldom central. Their stories are linear, proceeding from exposition, through crisis, resolution, and denouement in an Aristotelian fashion. The actors never break through the imagined "fourth wall" to talk to the audience, and the audience appreciates the drama by identifying with its characters.

The Search for Signs of Intelligent Life in the Universe breaks many of these rules. Trudy, the narrator, speaks directly to the audience, inviting them to become participants in the search for meaning. Because of the humor in Jane Wagner's play, the performance often resembles a stand-up comedy routine, in which much of the dialogue is one-liners. The play circles in and out of its events in a nonlinear fashion, and there is no crisis propelling its action.

The play's focus on women's issues through female characters also made it an important document in twentieth century dramatic literature. Wagner's frank, gentle, humorous treatment of contemporary American feminism also reinvigorates the one-woman-show convention of feminist theater, by adding an element of presentation that allows for cogent social commentary. The actor's transformations must be complete, vital, and varied, but the audience should always be aware that the performer is commenting on her roles. Wagner is careful to introduce Lily (Tomlin), for whom the performance was written, as a character in the play and implies that the performer is present beneath each of the other characters. Because of its commercial success and feminist implications, *The Search for Signs of Intelligent Life in the Universe* is an important addition to the canon of American drama.

Sources for Further Study

Gill, Brendan. Review in *The New Yorker*, October 7, 1985, 109.
Henry, William A. Review in *Time*, October 7, 1985, 68.
Merrill, Lisa. Review in *Women and Performance* 10, no. 1 (1986): 97-99.
Rafferty, Tim. Review in *The New Yorker* 67 (October 7, 1991): 102.
Raven, Arlene. "Crossing Over." In *Crossing Over: Feminism and Art of Social Concern*. Ann Arbor: University of Michigan Research Press, 1988.
Vilanch, Bruce. "Earth to Lily." *Interview* 18 (May, 1988): 52-59.

Jill Dolan

SEASCAPE

Author: Edward Albee (1928-)
Type of plot: Comedy
Time of plot: The late twentieth century
Locale: A beach on the East Coast of the United States
First produced: 1975, at the Shubert Theatre, New York City
First published: 1975

Principal characters:
NANCY, a well-to-do middle-aged woman, impulsive, with a zest for living
CHARLIE, her husband, a rather phlegmatic middle-aged man
LESLIE and
SARAH, married sea creatures at an advanced stage of evolution

The Play

On a bright sunlit beach, picnic finished, Nancy paints while Charlie relaxes on a blanket. A jet airplane approaches, continuing loudly overhead and then fading away. Nancy comments on the noise of airplanes; Charlie predicts their crash into the dunes one day. He doubts that they do any good.

Relaxing again, the couple begins what appears to be an ongoing discussion. Retired and well-off, they ponder how they will spend the days ahead now that their careers and children are behind them. With nothing to tie them to any one place, Nancy suggests that they spend the time traveling around the world from beach to beach. At first barely listening, Charlie finally asserts that he does not want to *do* anything; he has earned a little rest. Is that what their life together adds up to, Nancy wonders, to end as they began, infants with pacifiers, milk, and sleep? Nancy, it seems, will not settle for retirement farms; life is not over for her.

Again the sound of the jet intrudes, becoming deafening as it crosses overhead. The dialogue that follows is exactly like that at the opening. After a bit, as Nancy begins to paint, Charles shares a memory of how, when he was twelve or thirteen, he liked to find a protected cove near his family's summer place; taking two large stones to weight himself down, he would sink to the bottom to sit on the sand long enough to stop feeling like an intruder. Excitedly, Nancy urges him to try it now, to go down to the edge of the beach and "be young again," but Charlie firmly refuses. They should still be having a good life, Nancy feels, rather than being content with memories of the good life they have had.

The climax of act 1 occurs when two sea creatures, Leslie and Sarah, appear atop the dune. Suddenly Charlie, sensing something behind him, turns; he is aghast and immediately defensive. Nancy, however, is fascinated with what they see: human-sized green lizards with humanoid arms and legs and large saurian tails. When Leslie picks up a large stick and brandishes it overhead, Charlie thinks that the end is near, but at this moment another jet crosses overhead, louder and lower than before. Frozen with fear, the amphibians dive behind the sand dune. While they are out of sight, Charlie decides that the only possible explanation for what they have just seen is that he and Nancy are dead, casualties of the spoiled liver paste they ate for lunch. When the lizards reappear, Nancy rolls onto her back, assuming the position of submission that she has seen in animals, and begs Charlie to follow suit. Hesitating only a moment, Charlie assumes the position, too. "Now, Charlie, smile! And mean it!" she urges as act 1 ends.

When act 2 opens, neither couple has moved. The sea creatures now begin to sniff, touch, and poke the humans while discussing the situation—in English. Guardedly, Leslie addresses Charlie but gets no response. Sarah greets Nancy, who, eager for this new experience, responds warmly. After introductions, the couples begin to compare their lifestyles: eating habits, handshakes, terms for various parts of the body, what frightens them. The discussion serves to educate the sea creatures about life on land.

Soon the conversation turns to their families. Sarah, who has had hundreds of children she has never seen after laying her eggs, is startled to learn that humans usually bear one child at a time and care for it for about eighteen years. When Sarah wants to know why the children stay so long, Nancy explains that humans love their offspring. The sea creatures do not know what love means; it becomes apparent that they have no concept of emotions.

When the lizards notice seagulls flying overhead, Leslie, cautious of the unknown, becomes wary, but Nancy, attempting to ease tensions, jokes that it makes little difference because, according to Charlie, they are all dead anyway. Her husband has trouble accepting what he cannot explain. Leslie, on the other hand, refuses to believe that they are dead; he disagrees with Charlie's theory of existence—that life could be an illusion.

Again the jet intrudes. Once again Leslie and Sarah, terrified, rush half out of sight while Charlie and Nancy engage in the familiar refrain about the noise and uselessness. Now, however, Nancy and Charlie are moved to compassion because of Leslie and Sarah's fear. They explain about airplanes and about machines that go under the water. When Nancy mentions her husband's youthful excursions underwater, Charlie, increasingly uneasy, finally explodes by asking Leslie why he and Sarah came up to a place to which they were not accustomed. Sarah relates their growing sense of no longer belonging, of a feeling that they had changed somehow. Understanding, Charlie and Nancy describe the evolutionary process eons ago that brought them up to earth and left Leslie and Sarah to develop in the sea. Nancy explains how creatures adapted and changed—an idea Leslie rejects.

Charlie adds that this is an ongoing process: Mutate or perish. There are advantages in being human, Nancy points out. Humans use tools, make art, and are aware of their mortality. These are the things that separate humans from brute beasts, Charlie explains.

The act and the play climax when Charlie pushes the sea couple into an emotional experience by asking Sarah what she would do if Leslie went away and she knew he would never be back. He presses her until, understanding the full impact of the question, Sarah begins to cry. Angry at seeing his mate cry for the first time, Leslie strikes Charlie, then begins to choke him. Suddenly he releases him. The ferocity of the confrontation and his awakened emotions have made Leslie realize how dangerous earth is; he thinks that they must return below. As they are about to depart, Nancy reminds the couple that they will have to return to land sooner or later, that they have no choice. Reluctantly, Leslie and Sarah realize that, indeed, this is true. Nancy volunteers to help them to adjust now; Charlie shyly agrees. "All right. Begin," Leslie responds.

Themes and Meanings

Seascape concerns the necessity for individuals to examine their lives in order to live life fully. All four characters in Edward Albee's play are at crossroads; they need to make choices, but choices based on a consciousness of mortality. Albee explores animal nature and human nature in a juxtaposition of these apparent opposites. This opposition forms the dramatic tension of the play. Charlie is content to remain passive, while Nancy urges activity and involvement; Leslie is wary of the unknown, while Sarah is receptive to new ideas; the emotional development of the humans is more advanced than that of the sea creatures. Act 1 presents numerous examples of the differences between Charlie and Nancy: their proposed retirement plans, their past life together. Even their encounter with Leslie and Sarah points up their different responses to new experiences: Charlie is afraid and defensive; Nancy is awestruck, open, and welcoming. The necessity of exploring and questioning relationships and values becomes the focal point of *Seascape*.

Both couples have experienced what Albert Camus calls "absurdity," a feeling of alienation. Sarah and Leslie no longer seem to belong in their underwater home. Nancy and Charlie are experiencing the changes retirement brings. All have been moved to question their existence. In act 2, after preliminary comparisons of their lives, the discussion of alienation begins to draw the couples together. The second act, then, becomes a process of education and evolution in the understanding and awareness of the parallels between the couples' different but related worlds. As a result, they grow toward an interconnection born of sharing and love. Both couples make the decision to take the next step in the cycle of life.

The play highlights the evolutionary process in human life, the process of moving from one level of consciousness to another. Progress, only possible when people become dissatisfied with their present lives, is necessary for growth to self-knowledge. Nancy, who accepts flux as a part of life, is the instrumental force in moving the other three to an awareness and acceptance of this concept.

At the heart of this process is communication, as it is in many of Albee's plays: Communicating honestly opens people up, raising their consciousness. In act 1, authentic communication in which there is honest sharing does not exist between Nancy and Charlie. Nancy essentially tries to revive Charlie's lifeless spirit; however, having "turned off" life, relationships, and experience, Charlie turns a deaf ear to her attempt at communication. *Seascape* asserts that there are discoveries still to be made about life and living, but those wonders are experienced only through active participation, through climbing "the glaciers and the crags," as Nancy suggests. The world may be precarious and absurd, but one can achieve transcendence through self-awareness. The death of one level of consciousness leads to the birth of a higher level.

Seascape confronts the reader or theatergoer with his or her own passivity and urges an optimistic existentialist view: Loving and sharing produce awareness and responsibility, belonging and community.

Dramatic Devices

Seascape is set at the conjunction of land, water, and air: arid sand where human life is lived, teeming ocean where human life once lived, and space above, a new frontier for human life—or death. The setting symbolizes the themes of the play, depicting the union of sand and sea—the former suggestive of death in life, the latter of both life and death. The title of the play not only alludes to the physical setting but also conveys the idea of escape, which is the route the play refutes. Escape into the water—death—was Charlie's youthful activity; death by withdrawal from life is his present inclination. Each time the jet flies over, the amphibians retreat seaward; finally, after their emotional awakening, they turn once again toward the sea. Ultimately, however, they choose a different escape: from the sea to life on land.

The recurring jet frames four sections of this play, which is similar in structure to many of Edward Albee's other plays—that is, contrasting ideas and worlds are brought together for examination. Outsiders arrive in the domain of others, resulting in a confrontation that produces maturation, education, and growth to self-knowledge for the less sophisticated visitors. In the first segment, Charlie and Nancy discuss their present problem: what to do in retirement. The second is an exploration of their past, Charlie's underwater jaunts, and their sexual relationship. Sarah and Leslie are introduced in the third section, and the contrasts between the two couples are developed. The last segment brings them all into harmony and moves them to another, higher plane in their "evolution."

The sound of the jet, which becomes louder with each passing, may suggest the terrifying part of life, or perhaps the destructive forces in the world. Possibly it represents the passing of the human spirit into a higher realm of consciousness. All four characters react to the noise of the jet with either annoyance or fear. Fear of the unknown and an uneasiness with the present are characteristics of both couples. They are reluctant to move out into unknown paths.

Albee's style in *Seascape* is to combine humor with a serious subject. There is humor and wit in the lizards' examination of human life and in the exchanges between husband and wife in act 1. The similarity between the two couples' feelings of alienation is amusing, as is their defensive behavior in their initial face-to-face encounter. The overall feeling of lightheartedness, the simplicity of the story, the compelling sea creatures, and the idyllic seaside setting all contribute to the rather cheerful mood. Beneath the amusing conversations, however, Albee communicates a serious message.

Although not all scholars agree, Albee insists that his play is realistic. The jet, introduced early in the play, provides an element of realism; it helps to set the time and place in reality rather than fantasy. The audience becomes comfortable in this familiar world and is willing to accept Sarah and Leslie as "real" when they are finally introduced. According to photographs and reviews of the initial production, effective lizard costumes aided this leap of faith as well.

Critical Context

Seascape continues Edward Albee's exploration of human relationships. *The Zoo Story* (pr. 1959, pb. 1960), his first play; *Who's Afraid of Virginia Woolf?* (pr., pb. 1962), his first full-length play; and *A Delicate Balance* (pr., pb. 1966), his first Pulitzer Prize-winning play, are all concerned with the relationships that define people's lives, focusing particularly on the difficulty of communicating honestly. *Marriage Play* (pr. 1987, pb. 1995) carries the examination of relationships into a failed marriage, with more violent and harsh overtones than *Who's Afraid of Virginia Woolf? Three Tall Women*, his 1991 play (pb. 1994), continued his exploration with relationships, this time with an autobiographical bent. The play examines the life of a wealthy, cantakerous, elderly woman as she prepares to die. Albee admitted in interviews that the play's main character was directly inspired by his own adoptive mother, Frances Cotter Albee, who expelled a young Albee from his family's home for his homosexuality and later removed him from her will. The play won numerous awards, including Albee's third Pulitzer Prize—his second was for *Seascape*—and the New York Drama Critics Circle Award. Albee won a Tony Award for best play in 2001 for *The Goat: Or, Who Is Sylvia?*

In many of Albee's plays there is little outward action; thus attention is focused on the language. *Seascape* continues this technique. Scholars have generally considered Albee's use of language to be one of his major assets and contributions to American theater. While *Seascape* received considerable negative criticism about both its vitality and its language, especially in the production reviews, some critics commended Albee on these same points. Albee's language, distinct for each play, has continued to be a rich source of material for scholars to examine.

An experimenter with dramatic styles and techniques, Albee has frequently broken out of the realistic mode of traditional theater to become recognized as an avant-garde writer who uses a variety of techniques to explore modern experience. *Seascape* returned to a more traditional structure and a more affirmative view of life than readers and viewers had come to expect; it was criticized by some for lack of profundity.

Albee's plays have been the subject of an enormous amount of critical analysis. Judgments are mixed about such elements as his dialogue, characterization, and view of human existence. Albee's theatrical devices align him with Harold Pinter and Samuel Beckett, and he has publicly acknowledged the influence of Thornton Wilder. Certainly he is one of America's more important playwrights, as well as one of the most controversial.

Sources for Further Study

Amacher, Richard E. *Edward Albee*. Rev. ed. Boston: Twayne, 1982.

Bigsby, C. W. E. "Edward Albee." In *Tennessee Williams, Arthur Miller, Edward Albee*. Vol. 2 in *A Critical Introduction to Twentieth-Century American Drama*. Cambridge, Mass.: Cambridge University Press, 1984.

Bryer, Jackson R., ed. *The Playwright's Art: Conversations with Contemporary American Dramatists*. New Brunswick, N.J.: Rutgers University Press, 1995.

Gabbard, Lucina P. "Albee's *Seascape:* An Adult Fairy Tale." *Modern Drama* 21 (September, 1978): 307-317.

Kolin, Philip C., and J. Madison Davis, eds. *Critical Essays on Edward Albee*. Boston: G. K. Hall, 1986.

Post, Robert M. "Salvation or Damnation, Death in the Plays of Edward Albee." *American Drama* (Spring, 1993): 32-59.

Roudane, Matthew C. *Understanding Edward Albee*. Columbia: University of South Carolina Press, 1987.

Stenz, Anita Maria. *Edward Albee: The Poet of Loss*. New York: Mouton, 1978.

Celia M. Schall

THE SECOND MAN

Author: S. N. Behrman (1893[?]-1973)
Type of plot: Comedy of manners
Time of plot: The 1920's
Locale: New York City
First produced: 1927, at the Guild Theatre, New York City
First published: 1927

Principal characters:
MRS. KENDALL FRAYNE, a wealthy widow, thirty-five years old
CLARK STOREY, a thirty-year-old dilettante writer
AUSTIN LOWE, a rich young chemist
MONICA GREY, a poor and beautiful young woman

The Play

The Second Man opens on the comfortably furnished living room of a suite in a studio apartment building; the baby grand piano, the profusion of books, and the general atmosphere suggest the occupant's interest in the arts. When the curtain rises, Mrs. Kendall Frayne is nervously consulting her watch. She has been trying to reach Clark Storey by telephone, with no success. When it does ring, the caller leaves a message that clearly annoys her. As she turns to leave, Storey enters, late as usual, having been detained by a fellow writer at lunch. Kendall tells him about the message and displays some jealousy because the caller was Monica Grey. Monica is, Kendall believes, in love with Storey although she is engaged to millionaire Austin Lowe, an outstanding scientist. Monica's mother wants her to marry Austin because she is poor. Storey denies any interest in Monica, pointing out that he himself is quite fond of money, of which he has very little, and would never dream of becoming involved with anyone who had none. He invites Kendall to have dinner with him later in his flat, and before she leaves to dress she writes him a check for five hundred dollars. It is clear that the two are lovers and that she has been supporting him while he tries to pursue his literary career. He has already published some short stories, but by his own admission his talent is small.

Austin arrives, disturbed because he is in love with Monica and he is afraid that she loves someone else. Storey promises to persuade her to marry Austin, who thanks Storey for his help and leaves. When Monica enters, Storey announces that he is dining with Kendall and abandons Monica to Austin, who has just returned. As the act ends, Monica and Austin try to make small talk over the meal Storey has ordered.

In the first scene of act 2 a few hours have passed; it is apparent that the dinner has not been a success. Austin mentions that Storey has sold some of his writing to a magazine (this is Storey's explanation of Kendall's check, which he had left carelessly on the table), but when Monica sees the signature, she crushes the check in disgust. Austin, alarmed, smooths it out and only then discovers who the real donor is. He does not disapprove, because he is convinced that Kendall and Storey will eventually marry. When Storey returns, Monica decides that she will win him for herself, aware that he is more fascinated by her than by Kendall, despite the other woman's wealth. She leaves with Austin but comes back alone to persuade Storey of her love. When he hurries her out, her scarf remains behind.

Two hours later, in the second scene, Kendall is again in Storey's flat, waiting for him to dress so that they can go to some late-night spot with Monica and Austin. The latter, catching sight of the scarf, remembers that Monica had been wearing it when they left together a few hours before; he can only conclude that she returned secretly because Storey is the man she really loves. Storey, now in evening dress like the others, joins them in a drink. More depressed than ever, unaccustomed to alcohol, Austin accuses Monica of having visited Storey on the sly. She admits it and, having had too much to drink herself, shocks everyone by announcing that Storey is the father of her unborn child. Austin is devastated, as is Kendall, who shows her contempt for the way Storey has accepted money from her while making love to Monica. When Storey and Monica are alone, she acknowledges her lie; indeed, they have never been lovers. However, her determination to ensnare Storey even if it means destroying her reputation so impresses him that he yields to her wish for marriage—somewhat bitterly, because he sees no happiness in their future without money.

The last act takes place the following afternoon, when Storey, huddled in a chair and trying to write, finally gives up in disgust. Austin breaks into the room, waving a gun. He has walked the streets all night and has now decided to take revenge on Storey for getting Monica pregnant. Storey's insistence that Monica was lying only enrages Austin more; in a highly comic scene, he fires the gun—and misses. Then he faints, from shock, sleeplessness, and hunger. Storey tucks him into his bed and comes back to find Kendall, who has returned to say good-bye. She is sailing for Europe and will never see him again. He tries to clear his name, but she is too disillusioned to listen. Even after Monica admits the truth, Kendall remains unconvinced: It is not the sort of tale a "nice girl" would invent.

After Kendall leaves, Monica informs Storey that she now understands that she never loved him, only her image of him. When she hears that Austin tried to kill Storey for her sake, she realizes that Austin is the right man for her. She begs his forgiveness and says that she will marry him gladly, for she now appreciates the difference between fleeting attraction and enduring devotion. Left alone, the irrepressible Storey telephones Kendall to stop her before she sails. His announcement of the forthcoming marriage between Monica and Austin convinces Kendall of his innocence. As he plans to join her for a trip abroad (and their eventual marriage), the curtain falls.

Themes and Meanings

The Second Man has for its central idea pluralism in personality. There is a word in German that conveys this notion of duality—*Doppelgänger*. This "double" functions as a kind of observer that can stand aside and judge the actions of the other, public self. It is objective, truthful, ironic; it suffers from no illusions. Clark Storey is its epitome:

Though he longs to be a good writer, he admits to having a second-rate talent; though he is fond of Kendall, he acknowledges that her wealth weighs more heavily with him than her charm. When he is tempted briefly by Monica because of her beauty, her youth, and her flattering opinion of him as a man and an artist, even then the "second man" mocks him for aspiring to be more than he is.

Austin Lowe, while far less complicated, also discovers a "second man" within himself. As a scientist, he has always believed in logic, common sense, and self-control; now, made helpless by his first experience with love, he finds himself uncharacteristically humble, jealous, and maddened enough to attempt murder. When the fit passes, he is appalled by this stranger whose presence he had never before suspected.

Dramatic Devices

The Second Man introduces its audience to a group of sophisticated people and scrutinizes their manners and their way of life. All four have a considerable amount of time on their hands—even Austin, whose scientific discoveries do not require him to spend too many hours in the laboratory. On two occasions Storey is seen trying to write, but he expends so little effort on the process that the result cannot be taken very seriously. Although Monica has no money, she always wears elegant clothes, proving that despite her "poverty" she has little in common with those genuinely in want. An actor who once appeared in a Behrman play commented, "Even the bums are fairly affluent."

Music has an important function in the play. At one point, when Kendall has begun to feel that she is losing Storey to the younger woman, she plays excerpts from *Der Rosenkavalier* (1911), Richard Strauss's poignant opera about a mature woman who must surrender her lover to a more youthful rival. Storey plays jazz to illustrate the liveliness of his feeling for Monica, and Austin suggests taking Monica to the opera to hear Richard Wagner's *Götterdämmerung* (1874)—his idea of fun.

Kendall's check is used not only to goad Monica into telling her lie but also to show how cavalier Storey is about money and how ashamed he is subconsciously of his weakness of character. However, when Monica reproaches him for "dawdling away your life on a sofa when you might be standing straight on your own feet," he is angered enough to envision them in five years, "you looking blowsy—with little wrinkles under your eyes—and I in cheap shirts and cracked shoes—brooding in a room over the corpse of my genius."

The abandoned scarf alerts Austin to Monica's obsession with Storey and precipitates the major confrontation with the gun. The telephone is used most skillfully to inform the audience that Storey has finally won Kendall back, but the one-sided conversation, with only Storey visible onstage, keeps the love scene cool and detached, suggesting what their marriage will be like.

Critical Context

The Second Man, S. N. Behrman's first solo play (he had written plays before with collaborators), contains elements that recur repeatedly in his work. Almost all of his comedies deal with the upper classes; all of them, despite the glitter and glamour of their settings, have serious comments to make about the privileged few; and all of them are concerned with conflicts in love. *Serena Blandish: Or, The Difficulty of Getting Married* (pr. 1929, pb. 1934), based on a short story by Enid Bagnold, emphasizes the struggles of a girl with no money contrasted with others who are more fortunately endowed. *Meteor* (pr. 1929) provided a study of a ruthless financier who, although he wins over his competitors, loses his wife because he has sacrificed her happiness to his money-making passion. *Biography* (pr. 1932, pb. 1934) is a return to the more lighthearted mood of *The Second Man* in depicting a successful painter whose easygoing philosophy alienates her lover, a young radical who disapproves of her uninhibited way of life. *Rain from Heaven* (pr., pb. 1934) studies the conflict between a wealthy, sensitive young woman and the man she admires but cannot follow because he has a vision of a better world for which he is willing to sacrifice his life, while she is content to "muddle through." *End of Summer* (pr., pb. 1936), by his own account Behrman's favorite play, is a social comedy which remains one of his best because of the brilliant dialogue and the impressive characterization.

The world outside was beginning to encroach on the world Behrman had created, and so in *No Time for Comedy* (pr., pb. 1939) he studied the dilemma that he himself was facing. In this play, his hero is a writer of light comedies married to a devoted actor who has helped to make his work a success. Now that World War II is about to erupt, the hero asks himself how he can go on composing polite trivialities. He becomes attracted to a young woman who encourages him to write serious pieces, but tragedy is not his métier. In the end he returns to his wife and his former style, realizing that one writes not as one wishes but only as one can.

His later plays were less successful, because he was no longer in tune with his audience; the world had changed too much. He turned to adaptations; among the best was his version of *Amphitryon 38* (pr. 1937, pb. 1938), based on a Jean Giraudoux play depicting an amusing triangle composed of Jupiter, a Greek general, and the woman they both loved. *Jacobowsky and the Colonel* (pr., pb. 1944), a collaboration with Franz Werfel, concerns a Jewish refugee and an anti-Semitic Polish colonel, both fleeing from Adolf Hitler's horrors. *Jane* (pr., pb. 1952) is based on a story by Somerset Maugham about a woman who becomes the darling of society simply because she tells the truth.

In *The Cold Wind and the Warm* (pr. 1958, pb. 1959), Behrman turned to his own work and dramatized a book he had written about his family, *The Worcester Account* (1954). In *Lord Pengo* (pr. 1962, pb. 1963) he dramatized a series of articles he had published in *The New Yorker* based on the life of the famous art merchant Joseph Duveen. In the course of his forty-year writing career, he collaborated on such film classics as *Queen Christina* (1933), which starred Greta Garbo, and *Quo Vadis* (1951). As he grew older, he turned more and more to stories and biographies, producing the year before his death a memoir, *People in a Diary* (1972).

Behrman's gifts as a playwright attracted the talents of some of the theater's most illustrious performers: Ina Claire, Alfred Lunt, Lynn Fontanne, Laurence Olivier, Katharine Cornell, Rex Harrison, and Charles Boyer. His career was at its height in the 1920's and the 1930's, before the Great Depression and World War II transformed the shape and the content of drama forever. His characters are cosseted and protected by social and economic advantages. They are invariably amusing, on the whole well intentioned, and intelligent enough to be aware of the world outside and its perplexities. However, they have no wish to engage in the struggle for moral values, too passive and civilized perhaps to take up the cudgels for an ideal. They seem almost to understand that they are bound to be swept away in the coming storm. As a result, there is something melancholy about even the lightest of Behrman comedies; their characters seem to be dancing on the edge of an abyss. As a mirror of their age, however, they have earned a place, however small, in American theatrical history.

Sources for Further Study

Behrman, S. N. "At 75, S. N. Behrman Speaking as a Survivor, Not a Contemporary, Talks of Many Things." *New York Times Magazine*, June 2, 1968, 28-29.

_______. *People in a Diary: A Memoir.* Boston: Little, Brown, 1972.

Gross, Robert. *S. N. Behrman: A Research and Production Sourcebook.* Westport, Conn.: Greenwood Press, 1992.

Krutch, Joseph Wood. *The American Drama Since 1918: An Informal History.* 1939. Rev. ed. New York: G. Braziller, 1967.

Lewis, Allan. *American Plays and Playwrights of the Contemporary Theater.* New York: Crown, 1965.

Reed, Kenneth T. *S. N. Behrman.* Boston: Twayne, 1975.

Mildred C. Kuner

SERIOUS MONEY
A City Comedy

Author: Caryl Churchill (1938-   )
Type of plot: Satire
Time of plot: The 1980's
Locale: England and New York
First produced: 1987, at the Royal Court Theatre, London
First published: 1987

Principal characters:
SCILLA TODD, a financial trader
JAKE TODD, her brother, a commercial paper dealer
ZACKERMAN, the narrator, an American banker with Klein Merrick
MARYLOU BAINES, an American arbitrageur
JACINTA CONDOR, a Peruvian businesswoman
NIGEL AJIBALA, an importer from Ghana
BILLY CORMAN, a corporate raider
MRS. ETHERINGTON, a stockbroker who works for Corman
GREVILLE TODD, Scilla and Jake's father, a stockbroker

The Play

Serious Money begins with a brief scene from Thomas Shadwell's *The Volunteers: Or, The Stock Jobbers* (pr. 1692), in which the goal of investing is shown to be "turning the penny," regardless of the project or its legality.

On the floor of LIFFE (the London International Financial Futures Exchange), many traders shout their transactions simultaneously, with increasingly furious energy. After work, traders Scilla and Grimes, and Scilla's brother Jake, over drinks, agree that the market is so overcrowded that only those as aggressive as themselves will survive.

The narrator, an American banker named Zackerman, who provides continuity between the rapid scene shifts, also realizes that the money-dealing world has become cutthroat. A flashback to Zackerman's New York employer shows how, in an idle conversation, one executive officer dismisses another. Since there has been deregulation of the exchange in England, Zac (as he is known) observes that such Wall Street scenes will now occur in the City, the trading district of London.

At the country home of Scilla's father, after Scilla, Zac, and others set off on a hunt, Frosby, an old family friend, embittered about losing his trader job, vows to call the Department of Trade and Industry (DTI, the securities investigative unit) about Jake.

Abruptly, Zac telephones Marylou Baines in New York, telling her that Jake is dead, perhaps through a suicide. In various overlapping telephone calls, Zac, investors

Jacinta Condor and Nigel Ajibala, and corporate raider Corman consult on appropriate moves to protect themselves. Zac reports that he went to identify the body with Scilla, who reveals that she thinks Jake was murdered and vows to find the murderer. She begins her investigation with her father, who denies any knowledge of Jake's doings.

Meanwhile, Zac reports to Corman, who is involved in several takeover attempts, including that of Albion. Two flashback scenes show Corman with his associates planning these takeovers. Corman suggests that Marylou Baines might want to buy Albion shares, too, whereupon Zac notifies Jake.

Subsequently, in New York, Marylou and her assistant discuss buying Albion stock. At Albion, the chairman discusses with his white knight (a rescuer of takeover targets) a public relations strategy to fight off the now-obvious takeover attempt. Needing still more shares, Corman orders Etherington and Zac to use any tactic necessary to get them. Corman telephones Marylou, only to learn that she has sold her Albion stock. Furious, Corman threatens her, but, recognizing that the deal cannot be made without her help, calls her back to apologize. Meantime, Scilla has arrived, unnoticed, and has overheard the conversation, including Corman's statement that Jake was "one of mine." Blindly, she accuses Corman of Jake's murder. Intervening, Zac explains to Scilla that Jake gave insider information to Marylou for a percentage of what she made. Realizing that Jake was making "serious money," Scilla decides to track down not the murderer but the money. In the meantime, she will return to work. In the canteen, she and her female coworkers discuss job harassment, then move on the floor, where four groups conduct business as furiously as in the first scene. Out of the fast-paced rhythms of the trading emerges the "Futures Song": "So L.I.F.F.E. is the life for me."

Act 2 opens with a flashback: Jacinta Condor, flying to London, reveals her ruthlessness in acquiring Eurobonds and her cynicism about the poor in Peru. Zac says that Jake introduced Jacinta to him as a possible investor. In flashback, Jake reveals that he has been seen by the DTI and hence Zac might want to call off the deal. Zac retorts that one can go with either greed or fear; Jake settles on greed and introduces the two. Jacinta in turn wants to bring in her friend, the cocoa importer Nigel Ajibala.

In their deal with Corman, he agrees to a complicated arrangement that includes cash donations in return for their investing in Albion and voting Corman's way. Ajibala's liquidity problem is quickly solved; Corman will advance him two million. Immediately, cracks in the deal appear. Aside, Jacinta advises Ajibala to give Jake the two million to invest in something more profitable than Albion. Then she visits Albion itself and wangles a loan from the manager in return for her support for his bid to keep control of the company.

Scilla, sure that her father knows more than he has told her, confronts him about Jake's money. Greville admits that Jake passed on the odd tip but that he told his sister nothing in order to protect her. When Scilla leaves, Frosby confesses to Greville that he alerted the DTI about Jake.

Outside Corman's office, Scilla confronts Zac, who has just learned of Jacinta's double dealing and of Ajibala's disappearance with the two million. Using bribery, Scilla changes places with a model who has just arrived. Inside the office, Corman, desperate to complete his takeover, listens while a public relations expert urges him to acquire a "sexy greedy" image. Creating this image will require being photographed with a beautiful woman—hence the model. Enter Scilla, in place of the model. As the unknowing public relations expert attempts to photograph them in an amorous moment, Corman tries to throw Scilla out, and she grills him about Jake's money. Figuring out enough to blackmail Corman for her silence, Scilla coolly tells the public relations expert that she will deny ever having seen Corman before.

Zac enters, leading Ajibala. As Corman lashes out at them, Etherington enters with an inspector from the DTI, who overhears Corman's incriminating statements. Zac immediately explains the statements away, with the result that Corman must deny ever having given Ajibala two million. Ajibala leaves, pleased, and the inspector goes off with Etherington to inspect the books. Zac tells Scilla that probably only Marylou knows what holding company Jake established for his money. Scilla, determined to get the money, blackmails Zac into forcing Marylou to see her.

A government minister tells Corman that, because of the upcoming election and the need to forgo any appearance of greed, Corman must cease his attempt to take over Albion. If he refuses, the DTI will continue its investigation. If he agrees, it will be halted. Trapped, he agrees.

In New York, Scilla threatens Marylou with going to the authorities if Marylou does not tell her where the money is. Impressed by such aggression, Marylou hires her on the spot. Zac explains that Scilla never returned. He speculates that either British or American intelligence was responsible for Jake's death. However, his death was "incidental," for everyone recognizes that if the system stopped the economy would collapse. Hence, the Conservatives have been reelected in a landslide. The characters return to announce their fates: Scilla has been named Wall Street's "rising star," Zac and Jacinta will marry, Marylou has run for president, and Corman has become a lord. All express their satisfaction with a rousing song, a tribute to the Conservative victory, "Five More Glorious Years."

Themes and Meanings

Serious Money lays bare the greed associated with the money-trading business and in the process bares as well the hypocrisies of both personal conduct and government policy. For an audience of the 1980's, accustomed to being characterized by press and pulpit as rabid materialists, the point was clear: These characters are reflections of those who first watched them.

Greed corrupts all. Scilla may begin her search for her brother's murderer from the decent motive of family ties, but when she discovers that Jake was making enormous sums of money, without a qualm she switches to searching for the money instead. Driven by greed, all can justify their actions: Marylou and Jake can do insider trading because, after all, everyone acts on whatever information happens to come his way;

Jacinta can double-cross even would-be lover Zac because a businesswoman is supposed to make as much money as possible; Jacinta and Marylou can deal in cocaine because the Central Intelligence Agency also benefits.

Personal greed is hardly a new evil, as the opening scene from *The Volunteers* makes clear. Caryl Churchill's point is that the institutionalization of greed has reached alarming proportions. It is relatively harmless when greed lures some traders from BMWs to Lamborghinis. When it invades the boardroom, greed becomes corporate; corporate power is used to enrich the few. Corman's takeovers create no new product or jobs, yet win or lose in the takeover attempts, Corman and his backers will be richer.

Corporate greed corrupts as readily as personal greed. Corman's initial takeover plans are legitimate, but as he becomes desperate to complete the Albion takeover, he demands success by means fair or foul. Though Mrs. Etherington might try to negotiate the fine line between a legal "fan club" of supporters and an illegal "concert party," Corman sneers, "It's a concert party." After mild protests, both she and Zac do just as Corman asks.

Greed and corruption permeate government as well. To win the election, the government schemes to stop Corman's takeover. Worried not about Corman's illegal practices but about how the public's negative perception of the takeover attempt might cost them votes, the government threatens to intensify the DTI investigation if he persists and to call it off if he desists. Hence, keeping the image of respectability and legality becomes more important than being respectable and abiding by the law. The rich, a public relations expert explains, support museums, opera, and the theater not from love of art but from love of a respectable image.

Thus, though greed may begin as a personal evil, it and its accompanying corruption become a part of the fabric of business and government. The connection between personal and governmental greed and corruption is epitomized in the final song, as the traders toast the reelection of Margaret Thatcher with "oysters and champagne" and "mountains of cocaine."

Dramatic Devices

Serious Money, like many of Caryl Churchill's plays, developed from a workshop. Churchill, director Max Stafford-Clark, and the actors researched and observed brokerage firms and trading floors; based on their discussions, Churchill alone wrote the script. The workshop method promotes a unity, a seamlessness between script and performance that leads to impressive productions.

Churchill's allusions to contemporary events add an air of realism to her fictitious ones. Frosby mentions "Big Bang," as deregulation was popularly known. Marylou alludes to Ivan Boesky's "insider" deal with the United States government to unload his billion shares before his arrest was announced—a reference to the Wall Street scandal of 1986. Referring to the scandal in England the previous year, both Zac and Etherington remind Corman of the legal trouble in which the Guinness brewery became mired because of its takeover schemes. Moreover, in Great Britain and the

United States, the Thatcher and Reagan governments were generally considered to favor the rich, while programs for the poor were curtailed. Connecting the adventures of greedy Corman's takeover bid with the election was also topical.

To maintain some distance between the events of the play and the audience, Churchill uses many Brechtian devices: numerous scenes, a narrator, a nonchronological plot, and occasional songs. Moreover, the plot is minimal, the character development nil, so that attention focuses directly on the ideas of the play. To these techniques Churchill adds two of her own, perfected in earlier plays. One is multiple roles for each actor. In *Serious Money*, eight actors play the twenty roles, allowing resonances from one role to the other: the ruthless school dropout, now successfully trading gilts, and the ruthless Corman, who becomes a lord, are played by the same actor. The other device is overlapping dialogue. In the frenzied trading scenes, as many as four conversations take place at the same time, and the energy and confusion created thereby capture the energy and confusion found on trading floors.

Churchill's biggest gamble in *Serious Money* was using rhymed verse. Fittingly for types who have no interest in the arts except for public relations purposes, the verse is doggerel. An example: When Scilla blackmails Zac into enabling her to see Marylou, she says, "I could have my picture in the papers/ With Corman alleging all kinds of capers/ And linking him publicly with bad Jake Todd." Zac responds with the closing rhyme, "Scilla, you wouldn't. God." The verse also helps to distance the audience from the characters and their single-minded concentration on money-making. All the distancing devices free the audience to laugh at them, their double dealings and shady dealings, their schemes and counter-schemes, even while it deplores both their goals and their methods of achieving them.

Critical Context

Although *Serious Money* is unusual among Caryl Churchill's plays in that it is solely about the haves rather than the have-nots, like her other stage plays it addresses contemporary issues from a socialist point of view. Concerned with the uses of power, whether by police, religious leaders, owners, bosses, or husbands, Churchill in *Serious Money* focuses on business and government. Like most of her plays, *Serious Money* draws upon a historical context. The seventeenth century opening of *Serious Money* recalls both *Light Shining in Buckinghamshire* (pr. 1976, pb. 1978) and *Vinegar Tom* (pr. 1976, pb. 1978), which were set in the seventeenth century, although both addressed contemporary problems, particularly the role of women.

Feminist issues are a large part of Churchill's political concern; she dealt with these issues in the two period plays as well as others with contemporary settings: *Cloud Nine* (pr., pb. 1979), *Top Girls* (pr., pb. 1982), and *Fen* (pr., pb. 1983). Gradually, the feminist message has become less overt. In the feminist play *Top Girls*, for example, among the many historical and fictitious female characters who have made their way in the world against overwhelming odds, not one is idealized. *Serious Money* is not a feminist play, yet a feminist subtext exists. In a world that requires ruthlessness to get ahead, women are not left out: Scilla can make it to the top and be a "star." The political point is made explicit: The closing song celebrates Great Britain's star, Margaret Thatcher.

Some critics, though they were caught up in the exuberance and zestful energy of *Serious Money*, found that these elements weakened the seriousness of the political message. Others, familiar with Churchill's daring leaps in dramatic techniques and boldness of theme in previous plays, saw the targets of satire in *Serious Money* as too safe and so found this play less satisfying than earlier ones. Nevertheless, Churchill's ability to write a robust political satire, mostly in rhyme, while making clear such esoteric trading terms as "futures" and "management leveraged buyout"; to interweave a murder plot and a takeover plot with a national election; and to create a fast pace and energy that emulate the pace and energy of the world the play portrays, all with wicked humor, is no small achievement. Little wonder, then, that for 1987 *Serious Money* won not only the *Evening Standard* Drama Award for Best Comedy and the Olivier Award for Best Play, but also an Obie Award in 1988. Churchill's offerings in the last decade of the twentieth century included *Skriker* (pr. 1993), *Blue Heart* (pr., pb. 1997), and *This Is a Chair* (pr. 1997, pb. 1999).

Sources for Further Study

Aston, Elaine. *Caryl Churchill*. Plymouth, England: Northcote House, 1996.

Fitzsimmons, Linda. "'I Won't Turn Back for You or Anyone': Caryl Churchill's Socialist-Feminist Theatre." *Essays in Theater* 6 (Fall, 1987): 19-30.

Itzin, Catherine. "Caryl Churchill." In *Stages in the Revolution: Political Theatre in Britain Since 1968*. London: Eyre Methuen, 1980.

Keyssar, Helene. "The Dramas of Caryl Churchill: The Politics of Possibility." In *Feminist Theatre: An Introduction to Plays of Contemporary British and American Women*. New York: Grove Press, 1985.

Kritzer, Phyllis Howe. *The Plays of Caryl Churchill*. London: Macmillan, 1991.

Nellhaus, Tobin. Review in *Theatre Journal* 42 (March, 1990): 108-110.

Rabillard, Sheila, ed. *Essays on Caryl Churchill: Contemporary Representations*. Winnipeg, Canada: Blizzard, 1997.

Randall, R. Phyllis, ed. *Caryl Churchill: A Casebook*. New York: Garland, 1989.

Phyllis R. Randall

SERJEANT MUSGRAVE'S DANCE
An Unhistorical Parable

Author: John Arden (1930-   )
Type of plot: Social realism
Time of plot: c. 1879
Locale: Northern England
First produced: 1959, at the Royal Court Theatre, London
First published: 1960

Principal characters:
SERJEANT MUSGRAVE, a crazed regular soldier
HURST, a hardened soldier
ATTERCLIFFE, an old soldier
SPARKY, a young soldier
MRS. HITCHCOCK, the manager of a pub
ANNIE, a maid in the pub
WALSH, the spokesman for the colliers
THE MAYOR, the owner of the mine in the town that Musgrave visits

The Play

Most of *Serjeant Musgrave's Dance* is set in a coal-mining town in northern England. The action takes place in the winter; the town is isolated, thus giving Serjeant Musgrave the chance to carry out his plan. In the first scene, though, the sergeant and his three soldier-confederates are about to board a canal barge to take them to the town. A group of soldiers could be going to a mining town either to recruit soldiers—the recruiting sergeant trying to draw unemployed young men into an unpopular trade was a familiar sight in England through much of the eighteenth and nineteenth centuries—or else to assist the authorities in putting down civil disturbance. Since the town to which Serjeant Musgrave and his men are going is a mining town in the middle of a strike (or, the men say, a "lock out" by the employers), the latter would seem to be a likely explanation. The soldiers in act 1, scene 1, however, seem too nervous for such obvious explanations, as if they have some private and irregular purpose. They also have a large amount of baggage with them, including a Gatling gun (an early form of machine gun), which seems out of place for recruiting and too extreme for crowd control. One of their crates further contains, the audience learns later, the skeleton of a former comrade, Billy Hicks, who came from the very town to which they are going.

In scene 2, the soldiers' arrival causes some uncertainty. This scene is set in a neutral place, the bar of a pub, where both the striking colliers and the town authorities could conceivably be found. In this scene, the authorities hold the stage: the parson (a clergyman of the Church of England, the established church, which is closely connected with the upper classes and the government), the constable (a rough equivalent of an American town sheriff), and the mayor (a mine owner and therefore a major employer). These men all assume that Musgrave must have come to their assistance, though they have not sent for him. He can help the constable maintain order, they surmise, or maybe he will recruit some of the striker-troublemakers and take them overseas. All assume that he can be bought.

In scene 3, the audience is shown that this assumption is a desperate mistake. Musgrave sends his men to scout the town, and they meet in a graveyard. As the soldiers begin to squabble, Musgrave asserts his authority, especially on Hurst, whom it is clear that he can dominate because Hurst is a known criminal, on the run for murdering an officer and living in terror of the gallows. Musgrave, however, is in some way or other on the run too; if nothing else, he has embezzled army money and stolen army property. At the end of this scene, and of act 1, Musgrave appears as an Old Testament prophet, dedicated to scourging sin and vice for some reason—and in some way—of his own. He tries to show the colliers (who threaten him in the graveyard) that he is on their side; he calls God to approve his "Deed" and his "Logic."

Act 2 returns to Mrs. Hitchcock's bar, this time occupied by the colliers. One clash in scene 1 is between the colliers and the constable, who tries to close down the bar. Another is between Musgrave and the slatternly Annie. She has had an illegitimate child by Billy Hicks, and she does not know that he is dead. She expects now to sleep with one or all of the soldiers. Musgrave, however, strongly disapproves of this promiscuity, though not exactly of her, seeing her sexuality as a betrayal in some way of God's (and Musgrave's) plan.

Musgrave has meanwhile won over the colliers, to some extent, by lavish supplies of drink. They now think that he has come to recruit them and are not totally against the idea. Their spokesman, Walsh, nevertheless is clever enough to see recruitment as a possible employers' plot, and he tries to intimidate Musgrave into leaving. He rejects Musgrave's assurance that he is really—if in an unexplained way—on the colliers' side.

The final scene in act 2 is the most complex to that point, and it demands careful staging. Briefly, Annie goes in turn to Hurst, to Attercliffe, and to Sparky. Hurst rejects her advances because he is in awe of Musgrave. Attercliffe is mostly sorry for her. Sparky, finally, is afraid of what Musgrave is going to do and tries to get Annie to flee with him. When the others realize what is afoot, there is a scuffle, and Sparky is accidentally killed with a bayonet. In between these events, Musgrave is seen in the grip of a nightmare, and an attempt is made by Walsh to steal the Gatling gun. Musgrave calms the frightened mayor by saying that he will begin recruiting the next day, in the marketplace.

The next day, though, with all assembled at the start of act 3, Musgrave's plan becomes clear at last. The sergeant has been driven mad—or perhaps sane—by remorse. In a far country of the British Empire, terrorists killed one of his men, Billy Hicks. In the ensuing roundup, five innocent civilians, including perhaps a child, were killed. Their deaths are on Musgrave's conscience and he has decided to avenge them. However, he cannot harm his men, for they, too, are victims. Revenge must fall on those who sent them: the British public and the British rulers. In the square, he sets up his Gatling gun and explains that "logic" demands that if five civilians were killed for one soldier, then five times five Britons must die for the civilians. In a macabre gesture, he runs his flag up the flagpole: It is the skeleton of Annie's lover, Billy Hicks.

The massacre is halted by the arrival of other soldiers, the dragoons sent for by the mayor. Hurst is shot and Musgrave overpowered by the bargeman who brought them to the town in the first place. Order is restored in a drink-and-dance scene joined even by Walsh; only Annie sits out—with the skeleton. In a final short scene, Musgrave and Attercliffe moralize, waiting for the gallows.

Themes and Meanings

The play is set in the 1880's but has clear moral significance for the 1950's or 1960's. As its subtitle suggests, it is a parable, and so potentially timeless. For all its careful indications of place and time, it is also unhistorical, even (if one thinks about practicalities) highly implausible and unrealistic. How would four soldiers get home from an imperial colony? How could they conceal a skeleton and a Gatling gun?

Clearly John Arden wishes above all to make a point about guilt. Great Britain has for many years, he says, been making a profit out of imperialism—like most other developed countries, in one way or another. The victims of this exploitation, however, are double. There are the native people of the conquered colonies. There are also the agents of that conquest, the soldiers, sent abroad to do the dirty work of their rulers but receiving no share of the profits—as their rulers take no share in the dangers. The subtlety of the exercise, Serjeant Musgrave realizes, is that the two sets of victims fight and kill each other, when they should turn on those who make them do it. That is what he means to do. He is a sheepdog who has turned on the shepherd.

Another aspect of exploitation is the economic one, and that is why the play is set in a striking mining town. Here, in the strike, conflict has already been started between the rulers and the ruled. By all logic, the colliers should join the rebel soldiers. What stops them? One thing is Musgrave's own lack of clarity, another is the dubious patriotism which the colliers have been taught (which makes them reluctant to identify their own condition with that of nonwhite native peoples in a conquered country). A third is their suspicion that anyone in a red coat is, in almost all cases, an instrument of oppression. The ironies of mixed and mistaken loyalty in the play are very strong. Walsh, the most intelligent of the colliers, fails to understand Musgrave until too late. In the end, even he accepts a drink, which the officer of the dragoons is pouring, to celebrate the return of "normal life." Normal life, for Walsh, means going back down into the coal mine to make profits for the mayor. He has little to celebrate; however, without the Gatling gun, protest will do nothing for him—he might as well take the drink.

A final point is that Musgrave is mad. He is trying to avenge violence by more violence, and his cause is vitiated, if nothing else, by the violent death of Sparky. His remorse may do him credit, but his actions do not. Arden raises a difficult question: Given these facts, what would an acceptable and effective form of protest be?

Dramatic Devices

Perhaps in compensation for its highly abstract theme, *Serjeant Musgrave's Dance* is a play which has strong visual and auditory appeal. The scene is always dominated by the bright scarlet coats and shining metalwork of Queen Victoria's infantry; Musgrave refers several times to the white chevrons on his sleeve (much larger and more clearly marked than in modern armies). In contrast to this striking display stand the grimy colliers. Both groups, at one time or another, perform the rituals of their trade or culture onstage. The colliers do a clog dance in act 2 (a form of tap dance in heavy wooden-soled shoes, local to the North of England). In act 3, Musgrave and his men perform a grisly parody of arms drill. In between, the colliers, half-persuaded to join the army, are found executing what they think is drill: It is a scene for which Arden wrote extremely careful directions, pointing out that all the movements must be made alertly and efficiently but that all the drillers must do different things, and none must obey the word of command—a most difficult effect to achieve. The idea in each case, it seems, is to show men deluded and dehumanized by false jollity or false solidarity.

The suggestion of falseness is further emphasized by several dance scenes. The scene in Mrs. Hitchcock's bar trembles on the edge of violence, as dance turns into brawl. By contrast, at the end of act 3, scene 1 (the play's climax), the fight with the dragoons rapidly turns into a dance. However, joining the dance, as Walsh realizes, is tantamount to betrayal and surrender. Cooperative movements, in this play, tend to mean abandonment of judgment and personal responsibility, not (as they are supposed to) good fellowship or community.

Individual voices are raised in the play, in song. Arden has in several plays been affected by the ballad-poetry of northern England, and in this play there are several traditional songs and several imitations of traditional song, usually expressing sadness, fatalism, or resignation. The songs often come from the play's most oppressed characters: Annie, Sparky, and, at the very end, Attercliffe, waiting for death with his sergeant. There is a suggestion here, perhaps, of a traditional culture older and wiser than the rituals of the British Empire. Arden, who is himself a northerner, may well identify with this sense of antiquity.

Finally, it is clear that Arden sometimes is prepared to strain for shock effects. The raising of a skeleton on a flagpole rises beyond the macabre to the bizarre. Musgrave's nightmare in act 2 recalls the sleepwalking sequence of Lady Macbeth in William Shakespeare's *Macbeth* (pr. 1606); few modern playwrights would risk the comparison. At several points, Arden's own stage directions admit implicitly that his effects will prove hard to stage.

Critical Context

Serjeant Musgrave's Dance can be set firmly within two contexts: the "angry young men" of the 1950's and the "Yorkshire writers" of the same era. The two groups are not quite the same but had considerable similarities. Briefly, the "angry young men" represented a reaction to the end of World War II (1939-1945) and the decline of

British power, even after victory. The feeling they expressed was one of futility, that so much had been suffered for so little result. The "Yorkshire writers" expressed a sense of having been shut out of national wealth and culture after having done so much—in the "rust belt" of northern England—to create it in the past. These two strands, one may say, are combined in the "imperial" and "economic" strands of this play, the returning soldiers and the strike.

The actual incident that gave rise to this play also contains a certain symbolic appropriateness. In 1958, Greek Cypriots attempting to overthrow British rule shot a sergeant's wife in the back while she was shopping. The ensuing roundup was carried out by British troops with obvious rage: Three Cypriots were killed. British public opinion divided between condemning the first murder and condemning the troops' behavior. Arden is clearly trying to mediate between the two knee-jerk reactions.

In that sense, his play has proved a failure. The Cyprus scenario has been repeated many times, with repeated escalation, in Belfast and Jerusalem, Algeria and Vietnam. The removal of British rule from Cyprus ironically prompted only invasion by the Turks. Attercliffe's hope, at the end of the play, that he and Musgrave would plant a seed in people's minds, has proved fruitless. The play, however, after initial hostility, has been repeatedly revived, translated, and produced for television. Its artistic power has outlived its contemporary references.

Sources for Further Study

Anderson, Michael. *Anger and Detachment: A Study of Arden, Osborne, and Pinter.* London: Pitman, 1976.

Brown, John Russell. *Theatre Language: A Study of Arden, Osborne, Pinter, and Wesker.* New York: Taplinger, 1972.

Counts, Michael L. "John Arden." In *British Playwrights, 1956-1995: A Research and Production Sourcebook.* Westport, Conn.: Greenwood Press, 1996.

Hayman, Ronald. *John Arden.* London: Heinemann, 1968.

Hunt, Albert. *Arden: A Study of His Plays.* London: Eyre Methuen, 1974.

Leeming, Glenda. *John Arden.* Harlow, England: Longman, 1974.

Malick, Javed. *Towards a Theatre of the Oppressed: The Dramaturgy of John Arden.* Ann Arbor: University of Michigan Press, 1995.

Taylor, John Russell. *Anger and After: A Guide to the New British Drama.* Rev. ed. London: Methuen, 1969.

Trussler, Simon. *John Arden.* New York: Columbia University Press, 1973.

Wike, Jonathan, ed. *John Arden and Margaretta D'Arcy: A Casebook.* New York: Garland, 1994.

T. A. Shippey